D1094910

Finite Element Solution
of Boundary Value Problems

THEORY AND COMPUTATION

This is a volume in
COMPUTER SCIENCE AND APPLIED MATHEMATICS
A Series of Monographs and Textbooks

Editor: WERNER RHEINBOLDT

A complete list of titles in this series appears at the end of this volume.

Finite Element Solution
of Boundary Value Problems
THEORY AND COMPUTATION

O. AXELSSON
Department of Mathematics
University of Nijmegen
Nijmegen, The Netherlands

V. A. BARKER
Institute for Numerical Analysis
The Technical University of Denmark
Lyngby, Denmark

1984

ACADEMIC PRESS, INC.
(*Harcourt Brace Jovanovich, Publishers*)

Orlando   San Diego   San Francisco   New York   London
Toronto   Montreal   Sydney   Tokyo   São Paulo

COPYRIGHT © 1984, BY ACADEMIC PRESS, INC.
ALL RIGHTS RESERVED.
NO PART OF THIS PUBLICATION MAY BE REPRODUCED OR
TRANSMITTED IN ANY FORM OR BY ANY MEANS, ELECTRONIC
OR MECHANICAL, INCLUDING PHOTOCOPY, RECORDING, OR ANY
INFORMATION STORAGE AND RETRIEVAL SYSTEM, WITHOUT
PERMISSION IN WRITING FROM THE PUBLISHER.

ACADEMIC PRESS, INC.
Orlando, Florida 32887

United Kingdom Edition published by
ACADEMIC PRESS, INC. (LONDON) LTD.
24/28 Oval Road, London NW1 7DX

Library of Congress Cataloging in Publication Data

Axelsson, O.
    Finite element solution of boundary value problems.

    (Computer science and applied mathematics)
    Includes bibliographies and index.
    1. Boundary value problems--Numerical solutions.
2. Finite element method. I. Barker, V. A. (Vincent
Allan). II. Title. III. Series.
QA379.A9 1983   515.3'53   83-7158
ISBN 0-12-068780-1

PRINTED IN THE UNITED STATES OF AMERICA

84 85 86 87   9 8 7 6 5 4 3 2 1

To Anneli and Gunhild

Contents

Preface

The purpose of this book is to provide an introduction to both the theoretical and computational aspects of the finite element method for solving boundary value problems for partial differential equations. It is written for advanced undergraduates and graduates in the areas of numerical analysis, mathematics, and computer science, as well as for theoretically inclined workers in engineering and the physical sciences.

Finite element analysis arose essentially as a discipline for solving problems in structural engineering, and its role in that field is still of fundamental importance today. It soon became clear, however, that the method had implications far beyond those originally considered and that it in fact presented a very general and powerful technique for the numerical solution of differential equations. This newer aspect of finite element analysis has been intensively developed in recent years, with the result that at the present time it is probably as important as the traditional engineering applications.

Because a great deal of material on the finite element method has been published, the task of writing a textbook in this area requires basic decisions regarding the choice of topics and depth of treatment. We have chosen to limit the breadth of material severely, concentrating mainly on boundary value problems of the linear, self-adjoint, second-order type. Even within this framework we have made no attempt to be comprehensive. On the other hand, the detailed treatment of the material presented should give the reader sufficient background for reading much of the current literature. Some of this material appears for the first time in book form.

The application of the finite element method to a boundary value problem of the type described above yields a sparse, symmetric system of linear algebraic equations, usually positive definite and often of very high order. Solving such a system is a major computational task in itself, and an important part of the book is devoted to methods for this purpose. One of the most successful, the conjugate gradient method, is analyzed in Chapter 1. This is an example of a minimization method. More specifically, we can associate with a given $N \times N$ positive definite system

$$H\hat{\mathbf{x}} = \mathbf{b}$$

the quadratic functional

$$f(\mathbf{x}) = \tfrac{1}{2}\mathbf{x}^{\mathrm{T}}H\mathbf{x} - \mathbf{b}^{\mathrm{T}}\mathbf{x}, \qquad \mathbf{x} \in R^{N},$$

and show that

$$\min_{\mathbf{x}\in R^N} f(\mathbf{x}) = f(\hat{\mathbf{x}}).$$

Thus, any numerical procedure that minimizes f is per se a method for solving the above system, and this is the case of the conjugate gradient method. In fact, we have chosen to begin the book with the conjugate gradient method because the analysis of quadratic functionals of the above type helps to prepare the reader for the less simple quadratic functionals introduced in Chapters 2 and 3.

The effectiveness of the conjugate gradient method can be much improved by the technique of preconditioning, a topic of current research. Chapter 1 deals with two important kinds of preconditioning, one based on the symmetric successive overrelaxation (SSOR) iterative method for solving a system of equations and the other on a form of incomplete factorization.

Chapter 2 begins the discussion of boundary value problems. It is essentially a review of the classical use of the calculus of variations to establish that the solution of a boundary value problem often minimizes a quadratic functional defined on an infinite-dimensional space of functions. In the case of the simple problem

$$- [p(x)u']' = r(x), \qquad a < x < b, \quad u(a) = u(b) = 0,$$

for example, such a functional is

$$f(u) = \int_a^b [\tfrac{1}{2}p(u')^2 - ru]\, dx, \qquad u \in V,$$

where V is the space of twice continuously differentiable functions vanishing at the endpoints of the interval.

Chapter 3 is an elementary treatment of an advanced topic, namely, the modern trend in boundary value problems with its emphasis on concepts from functional analysis. In the case of the boundary value problem above, for example, we shall see that V can be enlarged to the Sobolev space $\mathring{H}^1(a, b)$, which includes functions with discontinuous first-order derivatives. This relaxation of the continuity requirement turns out to be of fundamental importance for the finite element method.

Chapter 4 presents the Ritz method (and the closely related Galerkin method), which minimizes the quadratic functional associated with a given boundary value problem over some finite-dimensional subspace of the original space of functions. By this process the problem of solving a linear boundary value problem is replaced by the simpler problem of solving a system of linear algebraic equations.

The Ritz (or Galerkin) method becomes the finite element method when the subspace of functions is taken to be the span of a set of finite element basis functions, and this is the subject of Chapter 5. A finite element basis function is a continuous, piecewise polynomial determined from a chosen discretization (called a finite element mesh) of the boundary value problem's domain of definition. In problems with two space variables the elements are usually triangles or rectangles. The success that the finite element method has enjoyed is due in large part to the fact that there is great flexibility in choosing the mesh, particularly when the elements are triangles. This flexibility can be exploited if the domain has an irregular boundary or if the solution is known to change more rapidly in one part of the domain than in another.

A finite element basis function has local support, i.e., it vanishes everywhere outside of a small region in the domain. Because of this property the Ritz–Galerkin system of equations is sparse and can be solved efficiently by the methods described in Chapters 1, 6, and 7.

Chapter 6 is devoted to direct methods (i.e., Gaussian elimination and related methods) for solving a system of linear algebraic equations. A direct method, in contrast to an iterative method, modifies the coefficient matrix in the course of the computation and, when the matrix is sparse, usually introduces fill-in. In the case of finite element problems, both the details of the computer implementation of a direct method and the amount of fill-in produced are very much related to the ordering of nodes in the mesh. Thus, much of the chapter is concerned with various strategies for ordering the nodes and their corresponding computational features.

Chapter 7 continues the analysis of the preconditioned conjugate gradient method begun in Chapter 1, concentrating on applications to finite element problems. After an examination of SSOR preconditioning in this context, a preconditioning based on a modified form of incomplete factorization that is more robust than the unmodified version of Chapter 1 is presented. The second half of the chapter includes techniques for reducing rounding errors in the iterative solution of finite element equations, a discussion of the relative merits of iterative and direct methods for solving such systems, and an account of some recent multigrid methods. Much of the material of this chapter is rather specialized, reflecting some of the directions of current research.

A reading of the book need not follow the order in which topics are presented. In particular, because Gaussian elimination is central for preconditioning by incomplete factorization, the reader, depending on his background, may prefer to read Sections 6.1 and 6.2 before reading the last part of Chapter 1. He could also delay Chapter 1 until after Chapter 5 or 6.

How the reader chooses to divide his time between the theoretical and computational parts of the book will be very much a matter of taste. Some, for example, may wish to skip over most of the mathematical details of Chapters 2 and 3 and the last half of Chapter 5. In fact, much of the computational material could make independent reading.

Regarding computer implementation of the various methods presented, listings of program code have been by and large avoided. On the other hand, we have not hesitated to describe algorithms in an informal computer-oriented language when convenient. In some cases, details of implementation have been left to the exercises. Considerable effort has been put into providing a broad set of exercises covering most of the topics presented.

The reader's background should include familiarity with linear algebra and basic analysis. In particular, he should be acquainted with matrix and vector norms and with the elementary properties of the eigenvalue problem for symmetric matrices. Naturally, the more he knows about boundary value problems for differential equations, the better.

Acknowledgments

Throughout the writing of this book the authors benefited from the kind assistance of many colleagues, students, and friends. Bruce Kellogg of the University of Maryland supplied material that was useful in Section 5.6. In Holland, Bob Mattheij and Servais Stevens, both of the University of Nijmegen, Ralph Masenge of the University of Dar es Salaam, Tanzania, who was visiting Nijmegen at the time, Jean-François Maitre of the Ecole Centrale de Lyon, and Paul Wolkenfelt of the Technische Hogeschool in Eindhoven energetically read much of the manuscript, finding many errors and making many valuable suggestions.

In Denmark, Peter Kirkegaard of the Atomic Energy Research Establishment at Risø read part of an early version of the manuscript. Søren Christiansen, Leif Mejlbro, Hans Bruun Nielsen, Pauli Pedersen, Per Grove Thomsen, and Ole Tingleff, all of the Technical University of Denmark, read various chapters and supplied the authors with innumerable helpful comments. A similar service was rendered by Per Skafte Hansen and Niels Houbak, both students at the same institution. Another student, Bjørn Eliasen, gave valuable assistance by converting some of the algorithms in the book to program code. Jan Reffstrup and Niels Gerhard Nielsen, both of the Technical University of Denmark, must also be mentioned—the first for sharing his views on the computational aspects of the finite element method and the second for skillfully preparing the illustrations for this book.

Karel Rektorys of the Technical University of Prague visited the Technical University of Denmark when the manuscript was going through its final stages. We are indebted to him for his stimulating remarks and suggestions for last-minute improvements.

It is a pleasure to express our gratitude to the secretarial staffs of the Department of Mathematics, University of Nijmegen, and the Institute for Numerical Analysis, Technical University of Denmark, whose expertise was put to the test time and time again and never found wanting. In particular, Karen Margrethe Hansen of the Institute for Numerical Analysis devoted countless hours to typing and retyping large parts of the manuscript. Her unfailing cheerfulness in performing an often exasperating task is deeply appreciated.

We would like to thank the Vald. Selmer Trane og Hustru Elisa Trane's Fond, Copenhagen, for their generous financial support for the illustrations.

There is no book without a publisher. We are indebted to the staff of Academic Press for their fine work and spirit of cooperation throughout the publication process.

Finally, we owe much to our families, who willingly shared the burden that a project of this type inevitably imposes. This book is dedicated, with gratitude, to our wives.

List of Symbols

Vectors and Matrices

R	field of real numbers
R^N	real N-dimensional vector space
$\mathbf{x} = [x_1, x_2, \ldots, x_N]^T$	typical element of R^N
$\mathbf{x}^T\mathbf{y} = \sum_{i=1}^{N} x_i y_i$	Euclidean inner product of $\mathbf{x}$ and $\mathbf{y}$
$\|\mathbf{x}\| = (\mathbf{x}^T\mathbf{x})^{1/2}$	Euclidean norm of $\mathbf{x}$
$\|\mathbf{x}\|_\infty = \max_i |x_i|$	maximum norm of $\mathbf{x}$
$H = [h_{ij}]$	typical $N \times N$ real matrix
$\lambda_1, \lambda_2, \ldots, \lambda_N$	eigenvalues of H, where $0 \le |\lambda_1| \le |\lambda_2| \le \cdots \le |\lambda_N|$
$\mathbf{v}_1, \mathbf{v}_2, \ldots, \mathbf{v}_N$	eigenvectors of H ($H\mathbf{v}_i = \lambda_i\mathbf{v}_i$)
$\rho(H) = |\lambda_N|$	spectral radius of H
$\|H\| = \rho(H^T H)^{1/2}$	spectral norm of H ($H^T = H \Rightarrow \|H\| = |\lambda_N|$)
$\|H\|_\infty = \max_i \sum_{j=1}^{N} |h_{ij}|$	maximum norm of H
$\kappa(H) = \|H\| \cdot \|H^{-1}\|$	spectral condition number of H $(H^T = H \Rightarrow \kappa(H) = |\lambda_N|/|\lambda_1|)$
$(\mathbf{x}, \mathbf{y})_H = \mathbf{x}^T H\mathbf{y}$	energy inner product of $\mathbf{x}$ and $\mathbf{y}$, where H is symmetric positive definite
$\|\mathbf{x}\|_H = (\mathbf{x}, \mathbf{x})_H^{1/2}$	energy norm of $\mathbf{x}$
$H = LU$	unsymmetric Gaussian factorization of H
$H = LDL^T$	symmetric Gaussian factorization of H, where H is symmetric
$H = \tilde{L}\tilde{L}^T$	Cholesky factorization of H, where H is symmetric positive definite
$H = LU + R, H = LDL^T + R,$ $H = \tilde{L}\tilde{L}^T + R$	incomplete factorizations of H
$m(i)$	column number of the first nonzero entry in the ith row of H

$n(i)$	column number of the last nonzero entry in the ith row of H
$w(H) = \max_{2 \leq i \leq N} \left[i - m(i) \right]$	half-bandwidth of a symmetric matrix H
$e(H) = \sum_{i=2}^{N} \left[i - m(i) \right]$	envelope parameter of a symmetric matrix H
$f(\mathbf{x})$	typical functional defined on $X \subseteq R^N$
$\mathbf{g}(\mathbf{x})$	gradient vector of f with components $g_i = \partial f / \partial x_i$, $i = 1, 2, \ldots, N$
$H(\mathbf{x})$	Hessian matrix of f with entries $h_{ij} = \partial^2 f / \partial x_i \, \partial x_j$, $i, j = 1, 2, \ldots, N$

Functions

(a, b)	$\{x \in R; a < x < b\}$
$[a, b]$	$\{x \in R; a \leq x \leq b\}$
n	number of space dimensions
Ω	open set in R^n
Γ	boundary of Ω
$\bar{\Omega}$	$\Omega \cup \Gamma$
u	typical real function defined on $\bar{\Omega}$
u_ν	outer normal derivative of u on Γ
u_τ	tangential derivative of u on Γ in the counter-clockwise sense
$u^{(\alpha)}$	multi-index notation for the partial derivative $\partial^{|\alpha|} u / \partial x_1^{\alpha_1} \, \partial x_2^{\alpha_2} \, \partial x_n^{\alpha_n}$, where $\alpha = (\alpha_1, \alpha_2, \ldots, \alpha_n)$ and $|\alpha| = \sum_{i=1}^{n} \alpha_i$
Δu	$\sum_{i=1}^{n} \partial^2 u / \partial x_i^2$
$L_2(\Omega)$	space of real square-integrable functions on Ω
$(u, v) = \int_\Omega uv \, d\Omega$	$L_2(\Omega)$ inner product of u and v
$\|u\| = (u, u)^{1/2}$	$L_2(\Omega)$ norm of u
$H^k(\Omega)$	Sobolev space of real functions defined on Ω with square-integrable generalized derivatives of order $\leq k$
$(u, v)_k = \sum_{|\alpha| \leq k} \int_\Omega u^{(\alpha)} v^{(\alpha)} \, d\Omega$	Sobolev [or $H^k(\Omega)$] inner product of u and v
$\|u\|_k = (u, u)_k^{1/2}$	Sobolev [or $H^k(\Omega)$] norm of u

$[u, v]_k = \sum_{\|\alpha\| = k} \int_\Omega u^{(\alpha)} v^{(\alpha)} \, d\Omega$	Sobolev semi-inner product of u and v
$\|u\|_k = [u, u]_k^{1/2}$	Sobolev seminorm of u
$C^k(\Omega), C^k(\bar{\Omega})$	space of real, k times continuously differentiable functions on Ω and $\bar{\Omega}$, respectively; $C(\Omega) = C^0(\Omega)$, $C(\bar{\Omega}) = C^0(\bar{\Omega})$
$\|u\|_\infty = \max_{\mathbf{x} \in \bar{\Omega}} \|u(\mathbf{x})\|$	maximum norm of u, where $u \in C(\bar{\Omega})$
$\mathring{H}^k(\Omega)$	completion with respect to the norm $\|\cdot\|_k$ of the subset of $C^k(\Omega)$ with compact support on Ω
$a(u, v)$	typical bilinear form
$(u, v)_{\mathscr{L}} = a(u, v)$	energy inner product of u and v, where $a(\cdot, \cdot)$ is symmetric and coercive
$\|u\|_{\mathscr{L}} = (u, u)_{\mathscr{L}}^{1/2}$	energy norm of u
$P_k(\bar{\Omega})$	space of polynomials of degree $\leq k$ defined on $\bar{\Omega}$
$T_k(x)$	Chebyshev polynomial of degree k

Finite Elements

L	number of elements in a finite element mesh
M	number of nodes in a finite element mesh
T	number of nodes in a single element
$e_l, l = 1, 2, \ldots, L$	elements
$N_i = (x_i, y_i), i = 1, 2, \ldots, M$	nodes
$i_r^{(l)}, r = 1, 2, \ldots, T$	node numbers of nodes in e_l
$\phi_i(x, y), i = 1, 2, \ldots, M$	global basis functions (defined on $\bar{\Omega}$)
$V_M = \text{SPAN}\{\phi_1, \phi_2, \ldots, \phi_M\}$	finite element space
$u_1 = \sum_{i=1}^M u(N_i)\phi_i$	V_M interpolant of u
$\phi_r^{(l)}(x, y), r = 1, 2, \ldots, T$	local basis functions (defined on e_l)
$\tilde{e}$	standard element
$\tilde{\phi}_r(\tilde{x}, \tilde{y}), r = 1, 2, \ldots, T$	standard local basis functions (defined on $\tilde{e}$)
$(\tilde{x}^{(m)}, \tilde{y}^{(m)}), m = 1, 2, \ldots, Q$	integration points
$w_m, m = 1, 2, \ldots, Q$	integration weights
$K^{(l)}, l = 1, 2, \ldots, L$	element stiffness matrices

$M^{(l)}, l = 1, 2, ..., L$ element mass matrices

$\mathbf{G}^{(l)}, l = 1, 2, ..., L$ element vectors

K global stiffness matrix

M global mass matrix

$\mathbf{G}$ global vector

$\mathbf{G}^*$ global vector modified by a Dirichlet boundary condition

h greatest element edge length in the mesh

CHAPTER 1

Quadratic Functionals on Finite-Dimensional Vector Spaces

Introduction

The application of the finite element method to a linear boundary value problem often leads to the problem of solving a sparse linear system of equations $H\mathbf{x} = \mathbf{b}$, where H is an $N \times N$ symmetric positive definite matrix. Since the latter problem is equivalent to that of minimizing the quadratic functional $f(\mathbf{x}) = \frac{1}{2}\mathbf{x}^T H\mathbf{x} - \mathbf{b}^T\mathbf{x}$, $\mathbf{x} \in R^N$, we are motivated to look at numerical methods for performing this task. In Section 1.1 we develop some basic definitions and theorems for general functionals defined on R^N and then examine the behavior of functionals of the quadratic type. In addition to being important for the numerical methods of the following sections, this material provides insight into the more complex quadratic functionals of Chapter 2.

Section 1.2 is devoted to the method of steepest descent, one of the simplest techniques for minimizing a quadratic functional. We examine first the method in its basic form and show that its rate of convergence (as expressed by the number of iterations required to reduce the initial error by a given factor) is bounded by a constant times $\kappa(H)$, the spectral condition number of H (equal to the ratio of the largest and smallest eigenvalues of H). We then introduce the important concept of preconditioning, a technique for

1

accelerating the rate of convergence. Preconditioning requires one to choose a positive definite matrix C (the so-called preconditioning matrix) with the property that it is easy to solve a system of equations having C as its coefficient matrix. It will be demonstrated that the rate of convergence of the method of steepest descent in its preconditioned version is bounded by a constant times the ratio of the largest and smallest eigenvalues of $C^{-1}H$. Thus, we also want C to have the property that this ratio is significantly smaller than $\kappa(H)$.

Section 1.3 introduces the more sophisticated conjugate gradient method for minimizing a quadratic functional. Unlike the method of steepest descent, it has the property of yielding the exact solution (in the absence of rounding errors) after at most N iterations, where N is the order of H. More important for the case when N is very large, however, is the fact that the rate of convergence of the method is bounded by a constant times $\kappa(H)^{1/2}$, a dramatic improvement over that of the unpreconditioned method of steepest descent if $\kappa(H) \gg 1$.

In Section 1.4 we consider the conjugate gradient method in its preconditioned form and observe that its rate of convergence is bounded by a constant times the square root of the ratio of the largest and smallest eigenvalues of $C^{-1}H$. After some remarks of a general nature on the preconditioning matrix C, we examine two particular choices in detail, one derived from the classical SSOR iterative method and the other from an incomplete factorization of H. The section concludes with a discussion of computer implementation.

Our ultimate concern is the performance of the preconditioned conjugate gradient method when applied to finite element matrices, and to determine this we need to have detailed knowledge of such matrices. For this reason the final analysis is deferred to Chapter 7, where we also describe an important modification of preconditioning by incomplete factorization.

1.1   Quadratic Functionals

Basic Definitions and Theorems

Let S be a set, let X be a subset of S, and let R be the set of real numbers. We define a *functional* f on X to be a mapping $f: X \to R$. The *range* of f, denoted R_f, is the set of values attained by f, i.e.,

$$R_f = \{k \in R; f(x) = k \text{ for some } x \in X\}.$$

In this chapter $S = R^N$, the real N-dimensional vector space. If the typical element of X is written

$$\mathbf{x} = \begin{bmatrix} x_1 \\ x_2 \\ \vdots \\ x_N \end{bmatrix}, \qquad x_i \in R,$$

then f is a real-valued function of the real variables $x_1, x_2, \ldots, x_N$, and we may write either $f(\mathbf{x})$ or $f(x_1, x_2, \ldots, x_N)$. In later chapters we shall consider functionals in which S is some set of functions, usually of infinite dimension.

For $\mathbf{x} \in R^N$ and $\varepsilon > 0$ let $S(\mathbf{x}, \varepsilon)$ denote the *neighborhood* of $\mathbf{x}$ of *radius* ε defined by

$$S(\mathbf{x}, \varepsilon) = \{\mathbf{y} \in R^N; 0 \le \|\mathbf{x} - \mathbf{y}\| < \varepsilon\},$$

where $\|\cdot\|$ denotes the Euclidean vector norm defined for all $\mathbf{x} \in R^N$ by $\|\mathbf{x}\| = [\sum_{i=1}^N x_i^2]^{1/2}$.

Definition 1.1. Let a functional f be defined on $X \subseteq R^N$. Then $\hat{\mathbf{x}} \in X$ is a *local minimizer* of f if there is an $\varepsilon > 0$ such that $f(\hat{\mathbf{x}}) \le f(\mathbf{x}) \ \forall \mathbf{x} \in S(\hat{\mathbf{x}}, \varepsilon) \cap X$. If $f(\hat{\mathbf{x}}) < f(\mathbf{x}) \ \forall \mathbf{x} \in S(\hat{\mathbf{x}}, \varepsilon) \cap X$, $\mathbf{x} \ne \hat{\mathbf{x}}$, then $\hat{\mathbf{x}}$ is a *strong local minimizer* of f.

Definition 1.2. Let a functional f be defined on $X \subseteq R^N$. Then $\hat{\mathbf{x}} \in X$ is a *global minimizer* of f if $f(\hat{\mathbf{x}}) \le f(\mathbf{x}) \ \forall \mathbf{x} \in X$. If $f(\hat{\mathbf{x}}) < f(\mathbf{x}) \ \forall \mathbf{x} \in X, \mathbf{x} \ne \hat{\mathbf{x}}$, then $\hat{\mathbf{x}}$ is a *strong global minimizer* of f.

Local, strong local, global, and strong global maximizers are defined analogously. Note that a maximizer (in any of these four senses) of a functional f is a minimizer (in the same sense) of the functional $-f$.

We now want to examine the behavior of a functional in the neighborhood of a local minimizer $\hat{\mathbf{x}}$, and the principal tool for this is a Taylor expansion about $\hat{\mathbf{x}}$. First, however, we must introduce the gradient vector and Hessian matrix. In the following, X will always denote an *open* subset of R^N; i.e., every $\mathbf{x} \in X$ has the property that $S(\mathbf{x}, \varepsilon) \subset X$ for sufficiently small values of ε. We define $C^m(X)$, where m is a nonnegative integer, to be the set of functionals for which all partial derivatives of order $\le m$ exist and are continuous on X.

Definition 1.3. Let $f \in C^1(X)$. The *gradient* of f at $\mathbf{x} \in X$ is the vector

$$\mathbf{g}(\mathbf{x}) = \begin{bmatrix} \partial f / \partial x_1 \\ \partial f / \partial x_2 \\ \vdots \\ \partial f / \partial x_N \end{bmatrix}.$$

Let $f \in C^2(X)$. The *Hessian* of f at $\mathbf{x} \in X$ is the symmetric matrix

$$H(\mathbf{x}) = [h_{ij}]_{i,j=1}^N, \qquad h_{ij} = \partial^2 f/\partial x_i \, \partial x_j.$$

The Taylor expansion of f about a point $\mathbf{x}$ is conveniently expressed in terms of the gradient and Hessian. More specifically, if $f \in C^1(X)$, then for any $\mathbf{x} \in X$ we have

$$f(\mathbf{x} + \mathbf{h}) = f(\mathbf{x}) + \mathbf{g}^T(\mathbf{x})\mathbf{h} + o(\|\mathbf{h}\|), \qquad (1.1)$$

and if $f \in C^2(X)$, then

$$f(\mathbf{x} + \mathbf{h}) = f(\mathbf{x}) + \mathbf{g}^T(\mathbf{x})\mathbf{h} + \tfrac{1}{2}\mathbf{h}^T H(\mathbf{x})\mathbf{h} + o(\|\mathbf{h}\|^2). \qquad (1.2)$$

(See Exercise 1.3.) We recall that a statement of the type "$\phi(h) = o(h^p)$" means that $\lim_{h \to 0} h^{-p}\phi(h) = 0$.

Definition 1.4. Let $f \in C^1(X)$. f is *stationary* at $\hat{\mathbf{x}} \in X$ (or, equivalently, $\hat{\mathbf{x}} \in X$ is a *stationary point* of f) if $\mathbf{g}(\hat{\mathbf{x}}) = \mathbf{0}$.

Theorem 1.1. Let $f \in C^1(X)$. If $\hat{\mathbf{x}} \in X$ is a local minimizer of f, then f is stationary at $\hat{\mathbf{x}}$.

PROOF: In (1.1) put $\mathbf{x} = \hat{\mathbf{x}}$ and $\mathbf{h} = -h\mathbf{g}(\hat{\mathbf{x}})$, where h is a real variable in some interval $[0, h_0]$. Then,

$$f(\hat{\mathbf{x}} + \mathbf{h}) = f(\hat{\mathbf{x}}) - h\|\mathbf{g}(\hat{\mathbf{x}})\|^2 + o(h).$$

Assume that f is not stationary at $\hat{\mathbf{x}}$. Then $\mathbf{g}(\hat{\mathbf{x}}) \neq \mathbf{0}$ and for sufficiently small h we find that

$$-h\|\mathbf{g}(\hat{\mathbf{x}})\|^2 + o(h) < 0,$$

or $f(\hat{\mathbf{x}} + \mathbf{h}) < f(\hat{\mathbf{x}})$, in which case $\hat{\mathbf{x}}$ cannot be a local minimizer. ∎

The condition that f is stationary at $\hat{\mathbf{x}}$ is a necessary but not sufficient condition for $\hat{\mathbf{x}}$ to be a local minimizer. Sufficient conditions are given by the following theorem.

Theorem 1.2. Let $f \in C^2(X)$ and let f be stationary at $\hat{\mathbf{x}} \in X$. Then $\hat{\mathbf{x}}$ is a strong local minimizer of f if the Hessian matrix $H(\hat{\mathbf{x}})$ is positive definite.

PROOF: From (1.2) and the assumption $\mathbf{g}(\hat{\mathbf{x}}) = \mathbf{0}$ we have

$$f(\hat{\mathbf{x}} + \mathbf{h}) = f(\hat{\mathbf{x}}) + \tfrac{1}{2}\mathbf{h}^T H(\hat{\mathbf{x}})\mathbf{h} + o(\|\mathbf{h}\|^2).$$

If $H(\hat{\mathbf{x}})$ is positive definite, then there exists a positive number λ_1 [which may be taken to be the smallest eigenvalue of $H(\hat{\mathbf{x}})$] such that

$$\mathbf{h}^T H(\hat{\mathbf{x}})\mathbf{h} \geq \lambda_1 \|\mathbf{h}\|^2 \qquad \forall \mathbf{h} \in R^N.$$

[See, e.g., Strang (1976).] Thus,

$$f(\hat{\mathbf{x}} + \mathbf{h}) - f(\hat{\mathbf{x}}) \geq \tfrac{1}{2}\lambda_1\|\mathbf{h}\|^2 + o(\|\mathbf{h}\|^2),$$

and since the expression on the right must be positive for sufficiently small values of $\|\mathbf{h}\|$, it follows that $f(\hat{\mathbf{x}} + \mathbf{h}) > f(\hat{\mathbf{x}})$ in some neighborhood of $\hat{\mathbf{x}}$; i.e., $\hat{\mathbf{x}}$ is a strong local minimizer of f.   ∎

The situation in the case of a local maximizer of f is entirely analogous. If $\hat{\mathbf{x}}$ is a local maximizer, then $\hat{\mathbf{x}}$ must be a stationary point, and if $H(\hat{\mathbf{x}})$ is negative definite, then $\hat{\mathbf{x}}$ is a strong local maximizer. Further, it is easy to show that if $\hat{\mathbf{x}}$ is a stationary point, then

(1)   it is neither a local minimizer nor a local maximizer if $H(\hat{\mathbf{x}})$ has both positive and negative eigenvalues;

(2)   it may or may not be a local minimizer (maximizer) if $H(\hat{\mathbf{x}})$ is positive (negative) semidefinite.

Definition 1.5. Let $f \in C^m(X)$, $\mathbf{x} \in X \subseteq R^N$, and $\mathbf{y} \in R^N$, where $\|\mathbf{y}\| = 1$. The mth-order *directional derivative* of f at $\mathbf{x}$ in the direction $\mathbf{y}$ is

$$f^{(m)}(\mathbf{x}; \mathbf{y}) \equiv \left.\frac{d^m f(\mathbf{x} + \tau\mathbf{y})}{d\tau^m}\right|_{\tau = 0}.$$

The directional derivatives of f can be computed by use of the familiar "chain rule" of differentiation. Thus, assuming $f \in C^1(X)$, we have

$$f^{(1)}(\mathbf{x}; \mathbf{y}) = \left.\frac{df}{d\tau}(x_1 + \tau y_1, \ldots, x_N + \tau y_N)\right|_{\tau = 0}$$

$$= \sum_{i=1}^{N} \frac{\partial f}{\partial x_i}(x_1, \ldots, x_N)y_i = \mathbf{g}^{\mathrm{T}}(\mathbf{x})\mathbf{y}. \tag{1.3}$$

By further differentiation we find that for any $f \in C^2(X)$,

$$f^{(2)}(\mathbf{x}; \mathbf{y}) = \mathbf{y}^{\mathrm{T}}H(\mathbf{x})\mathbf{y}. \tag{1.4}$$

From the Cauchy–Schwarz inequality $|\mathbf{x}^{\mathrm{T}}\mathbf{y}| \leq \|\mathbf{x}\| \cdot \|\mathbf{y}\|\ \forall \mathbf{x}, \mathbf{y} \in R^N$ and (1.3), we note that

$$\max_{\mathbf{y},\|\mathbf{y}\|=1} |f^{(1)}(\mathbf{x}; \mathbf{y})| = |f^{(1)}(\mathbf{x}; \hat{\mathbf{y}})|$$

$$= \|\mathbf{g}(\mathbf{x})\|, \qquad \hat{\mathbf{y}} \equiv \mathbf{g}(\mathbf{x})/\|\mathbf{g}(\mathbf{x})\|.$$

This and (1.3) prove that $f^{(1)}(\mathbf{x}; \mathbf{y}) = 0$ for all directions $\mathbf{y}$ if and only if $\mathbf{g}(\mathbf{x}) = \mathbf{0}$, i.e., if and only if $\mathbf{x}$ is a stationary point of f. Further, it is clear from (1.4) that $f^{(2)}(\mathbf{x}; \mathbf{y}) > 0$ for all directions $\mathbf{y}$ if and only if $H(\mathbf{x})$ is positive definite. On the basis of these observations we can reformulate the preceding theorems as follows.

Theorem 1.3. Let $f \in C^1(X)$. If $\hat{\mathbf{x}} \in X$ is a local minimizer of f, then $f^{(1)}(\hat{\mathbf{x}}; \mathbf{y}) = 0$ for all directions $\mathbf{y}$.

Theorem 1.4. Let $f \in C^2(X)$ and suppose that for some $\hat{\mathbf{x}} \in X$ we have $f^{(1)}(\hat{\mathbf{x}}; \mathbf{y}) = 0$ for all directions $\mathbf{y}$. Then $\hat{\mathbf{x}}$ is a strong local minimizer of f if $f^{(2)}(\hat{\mathbf{x}}; \mathbf{y}) > 0$ for all directions $\mathbf{y}$.

The significance of Theorems 1.3 and 1.4 will be appreciated in the following chapter when we consider functionals defined on sets of functions. For such functionals it is far from obvious how to define an appropriate "gradient" and "Hessian." On the other hand, the concept of the directional derivative is obviously extendable to any functional since, regardless of the domain of definition X, it involves only the derivative of a scalar function of a scalar variable.

Definition 1.6. Let f be defined on $X \subseteq R^N$ and let $k \in R_f$, where R_f is the range of f. Then the set

$$L_k = \{\mathbf{x} \in X; \ f(\mathbf{x}) = k\}$$

defines the *level surface* of f for the value k.

Suppose $\hat{\mathbf{x}} \in X$ is a strong local minimizer of f and $f(\hat{\mathbf{x}}) = \hat{k}$. Then the intersection of $L_{\hat{k}}$ and the neighborhood $S(\hat{\mathbf{x}}; \varepsilon)$ consists of the single point $\hat{\mathbf{x}}$ if ε is sufficiently small. For values of k that are slightly greater than $\hat{k}$, the level surfaces usually surround $\hat{\mathbf{x}}$ and assume the form of ellipsoids as $k \to \hat{k}$. (We shall see shortly why this is the case.) This behavior is sketched in Fig. 1.1.

A well-known fact is that if $\mathbf{x}$ belongs to the level surface L_k, then the

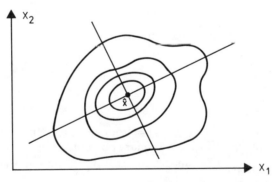

Fig. 1.1. Level surfaces ($N = 2$) in the neighborhood of a local minimizer.

gradient vector $\mathbf{g}(\mathbf{x})$ is perpendicular to L_k at $\mathbf{x}$ and points in the direction in which the functional increases most rapidly. Thus gradients near a strong local minimizer point "outward," whereas those near a strong local maximizer point "inward."

Generally speaking, numerical methods for finding a strong local minimizer of a functional perform best when the level surfaces in the neighborhood of the minimizer are spheres and poorly when they show a pronounced distortion from spheres. The quantity

$$D_k = \inf_{\mathbf{y} \in S_k} \{ \sup_{\mathbf{x} \in L_k} \|\mathbf{x} - \mathbf{y}\| / \inf_{\mathbf{x} \in L_k} \|\mathbf{x} - \mathbf{y}\| \} \geq 1,$$

where S_k is the set of all points interior to L_k, is a measure of the distortion of L_k from spherical form. For a sphere, $D_k = 1$.

Quadratic Functionals

Definition 1.7. A *quadratic functional* is a functional of the form

$$f(\mathbf{x}) = \tfrac{1}{2}\mathbf{x}^T H\mathbf{x} - \mathbf{b}^T\mathbf{x} + c, \qquad \mathbf{x} \in R^N, \tag{1.5}$$

where H is an $N \times N$ symmetric matrix, $\mathbf{b} \in R^N$, and $c \in R$.

The gradient and Hessian of (1.5) are easily found to be $\mathbf{g}(\mathbf{x}) = H\mathbf{x} - \mathbf{b}$ and $H(\mathbf{x}) = H$, respectively. Thus a quadratic functional has the property that its Hessian is constant. Quadratic functionals provide the simplest examples of functionals that possess a strong local minimizer or maximizer. It will be seen in Chapter 4 that the application of the Ritz method to linear boundary value problems often leads to the problem of minimizing a functional of this type.

We shall now examine (1.5) more closely. A point $\hat{\mathbf{x}}$ is a stationary point of f if the gradient vanishes at $\hat{\mathbf{x}}$, i.e., if $H\hat{\mathbf{x}} - \mathbf{b} = \mathbf{0}$. If H is nonsingular, which we henceforth assume, then $\hat{\mathbf{x}}$ is uniquely determined by $\hat{\mathbf{x}} = H^{-1}\mathbf{b}$. A simple calculation shows that (1.5) may be rewritten as

$$f(\mathbf{x}) = \tfrac{1}{2}(\mathbf{x} - \hat{\mathbf{x}})^T H(\mathbf{x} - \hat{\mathbf{x}}) + \hat{c}, \qquad \mathbf{x} \in R^N,$$

where

$$\hat{c} = -\tfrac{1}{2}\mathbf{b}^T\hat{\mathbf{x}} + c.$$

Let $\{\lambda_i, \mathbf{v}_i\}_{i=1}^N$ denote the eigensolutions of H, i.e., $H\mathbf{v}_i = \lambda_i\mathbf{v}_i$, $i = 1, 2, ..., N$. Since H is symmetric, the eigenvalues are real and can be ordered by $\lambda_1 \leq \lambda_2 \leq \cdots \leq \lambda_N$ and the eigenvectors can be assumed to satisfy the orthonormality condition $\mathbf{v}_i^T\mathbf{v}_j = \delta_{ij}$, $i, j = 1, 2, ..., N$. Defining $\Lambda = \text{diag}(\lambda_1, \lambda_2, ..., \lambda_N)$ and $V = [\mathbf{v}_1, \mathbf{v}_2, ..., \mathbf{v}_N]$, we see that V is an orthogonal matrix (i.e., $V^{-1} = V^T$) and $HV = V\Lambda$. Introducing the new variable $\mathbf{z} = V^T(\mathbf{x} - \hat{\mathbf{x}})$, we now have

$$\tilde{f}(\mathbf{z}) \equiv f(V\mathbf{z} + \hat{\mathbf{x}}) = \tfrac{1}{2}\mathbf{z}^T V^T H V \mathbf{z} + \hat{c} = \tfrac{1}{2}\mathbf{z}^T \Lambda \mathbf{z} + \hat{c}$$

or

$$\tilde{f}(\mathbf{z}) = \tfrac{1}{2} \sum_{i=1}^{N} \lambda_i z_i^2 + \hat{c}, \qquad \mathbf{z} \in R^N.$$

Since $\tilde{f}(\mathbf{z}) = f(\mathbf{x})$ under the transformation $\mathbf{z} = V^T(\mathbf{x} - \hat{\mathbf{x}})$, we can turn our attention from f to $\tilde{f}$. If H is positive definite, then all of its eigenvalues are positive and the range of $\tilde{f}$ is $[\hat{c}, \infty)$. Clearly, $\mathbf{z} = \mathbf{0}$ is the strong global minimizer of $\tilde{f}$. If H is negative definite, then the range of $\tilde{f}$ is $(-\infty, \hat{c}]$ and $\mathbf{z} = \mathbf{0}$ is the strong global maximizer. If H has both positive and negative eigenvalues, then the range of $\tilde{f}$ is $(-\infty, \infty)$. $\tilde{f}$ is still stationary at $\mathbf{z} = \mathbf{0}$ but possesses no minimizer or maximizer there.

We consider again the case in which H is positive definite. For $k > \hat{c}$ the level surface L_k is the ellipsoid

$$\sum_{i=1}^{N} \lambda_i z_i^2 = \hat{k},$$

where $\hat{k} = 2(k - \hat{c}) > 0$, as sketched in Fig. 1.2. The distortion measure D_k, defined previously, is found to have the value

$$\kappa(H) \equiv \lambda_N/\lambda_1,$$

the so-called *spectral condition number* of H. As we mentioned earlier, numerical methods for minimizing a functional tend to behave badly if the level surfaces are much distorted from spherical form, and in the analysis of the methods of steepest descent and conjugate gradients in the following sections we shall find that the spectral condition number of the Hessian plays a critical role.

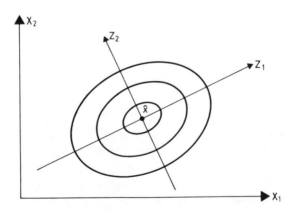

Fig. 1.2.   Level surfaces ($N = 2$) of a quadratic functional with a positive definite Hessian.

Clearly, the level curves of f are also ellipsoids when H is negative definite. Assume now that H is indefinite with eigenvalues $\lambda_1 \leq \lambda_2 \leq \cdots \leq \lambda_p < 0 < \lambda_{p+1} \leq \cdots \leq \lambda_N$. For any $k \in R$, the level surface L_k is the set

$$\left\{ \mathbf{z} \in R^N; \ -\sum_{i=1}^{p} |\lambda_i| z_i^2 + \sum_{i=p+1}^{N} |\lambda_i| z_i^2 = \hat{k} \right\},$$

where $\hat{k} = 2(k - c)$. We observe that L_k is unbounded.

The properties of quadratic functionals are relevant to any nonquadratic functional in $C^2(X)$. To see this we need only compare the Taylor expansion for (1.5),

$$f(\mathbf{x} + \mathbf{h}) = f(\mathbf{x}) + \mathbf{g}^T(\mathbf{x})\mathbf{h} + \tfrac{1}{2}\mathbf{h}^T H \mathbf{h},$$

with the Taylor expansion (1.2) for an arbitrary functional in $C^2(X)$,

$$f(\mathbf{x} + \mathbf{h}) = f(\mathbf{x}) + \mathbf{g}^T(\mathbf{x})\mathbf{h} + \tfrac{1}{2}\mathbf{h}^T H(\mathbf{x})\mathbf{h} + o(\|\mathbf{h}\|^2).$$

In a sufficiently small neighborhood of $\mathbf{x}$, the arbitrary functional behaves like a quadratic functional. In particular, if $\mathbf{x}$ is a stationary point and $H(\mathbf{x})$ is positive definite, then the level surfaces assume ellipsoidal form as $\mathbf{h} \to \mathbf{0}$.

Putting $\mathbf{h} = \tau\mathbf{y}$, where $\|\mathbf{y}\| = 1$, and recalling (1.3) and (1.4), we have for any quadratic functional f the identity

$$f(\mathbf{x} + \tau\mathbf{y}) = f(\mathbf{x}) + \tau f^{(1)}(\mathbf{x}; \mathbf{y}) + \tfrac{1}{2}\tau^2 f^{(2)}(\mathbf{x}; \mathbf{y}), \qquad -\infty < \tau < \infty. \quad (1.6)$$

As will be made clear, (1.6) establishes a connection between the quadratic functionals on R^N discussed in this chapter and those defined on sets of functions in the following chapters.

A valuable source of background information on functionals defined on R^N are texts on optimization methods. [See, e.g., Gill, Murray, and Wright (1981), Hestenes (1975), Wismer and Chattergy (1978), and Wolfe (1978).]

1.2 The Method of Steepest Descent

In this section we shall present and analyze a simple iterative method for finding a strong local minimizer of a functional, concentrating on the case in which the functional is quadratic with a positive definite Hessian. It will be shown that the number of iterations required to make the error in the so-called "energy norm" less than some number ε times the initial error is roughly bounded by $\tfrac{1}{2}\kappa(H) \ln(1/\varepsilon)$, where $\kappa(H)$ is the spectral condition number of H. Motivated by the desire to reduce this bound, we shall then introduce the concept of preconditioning.

Preliminaries

Most iterative methods for finding a local minimizer of a functional f defined on R^N are of the form

$$\mathbf{x}^{k+1} = \mathbf{x}^k + \tau_k \mathbf{d}^k, \tag{1.7}$$

where the direction of $\mathbf{d}^k$ is a "search direction" (for convenience we shall call $\mathbf{d}^k$ itself a search direction) and where τ_k is chosen to minimize, or at least reduce, $f(\mathbf{x})$ on some interval of the line that passes through $\mathbf{x}^k$ in the direction of $\mathbf{d}^k$. Thus there are two distinct problems associated with (1.7): the choice of $\mathbf{d}^k$ and the inspection of $f(\mathbf{x})$ on the line $\mathbf{x} = \mathbf{x}^k + \tau \mathbf{d}^k$, $-\infty < \tau < \infty$.

Definition 1.8. Suppose that for some functional f and vectors $\mathbf{x}$ and $\mathbf{d}$ there exists $\tau_0 > 0$ such that

$$f(\mathbf{x} + \tau \mathbf{d}) < f(\mathbf{x}), \qquad 0 < \tau \leq \tau_0.$$

Then $\mathbf{d}$ is a *descent direction* for f at $\mathbf{x}$.

Theorem 1.5. Let $f \in C^1(R^N)$ and let $\mathbf{g}(\mathbf{x})$ denote (as usual) the gradient of f at $\mathbf{x}$. If a vector $\mathbf{d}$ satisfies $\mathbf{g}^T(\mathbf{x})\mathbf{d} < 0$, then $\mathbf{d}$ is a descent direction for f at $\mathbf{x}$.

PROOF: From (1.1) we have

$$f(\mathbf{x} + \tau \mathbf{d}) = f(\mathbf{x}) + \tau \mathbf{g}^T(\mathbf{x})\mathbf{d} + o(\tau),$$

and since by the assumption $\mathbf{g}^T(\mathbf{x})\mathbf{d} < 0$ we must have $\tau \mathbf{g}^T(\mathbf{x})\mathbf{d} + o(\tau) < 0$ for sufficiently small values of τ.   ∎

If $\mathbf{g}^T(\mathbf{x})\mathbf{d} = 0$ we cannot determine whether $\mathbf{d}$ is a descent direction without further information.

Theorem 1.6. Let $f \in C^2(R^N)$ and suppose that $\mathbf{g}^T(\mathbf{x})\mathbf{d} = 0$ and $\mathbf{d}^T H(\mathbf{x})\mathbf{d} < 0$ for some $\mathbf{x}$ and $\mathbf{d}$. Then $\mathbf{d}$ is a descent direction for f at $\mathbf{x}$.
The proof follows from (1.2).   ∎

Theorem 1.7. Let $f \in C^1(R^N)$. Then among all search directions $\mathbf{d}$ at some point $\mathbf{x}$, that direction in which f descends most rapidly in a neighborhood of $\mathbf{x}$ is $\mathbf{d} = -\mathbf{g}(\mathbf{x})$.

PROOF: We want to minimize the directional derivative of f at $\mathbf{x}$ over all search directions. It follows from (1.3) that this is the same problem as that of minimizing $\mathbf{g}^T(\mathbf{x})\mathbf{y}$ for all $\mathbf{y}$ such that $\|\mathbf{y}\| = 1$. Since $|\mathbf{g}^T(\mathbf{x})\mathbf{y}| \leq \|\mathbf{g}(\mathbf{x})\|$, the minimum is obviously attained for $\mathbf{y} = -\mathbf{g}(\mathbf{x})/\|\mathbf{g}(\mathbf{x})\|$.   ∎

We now consider the problem of determining τ_k, given $\mathbf{x}^k$ and $\mathbf{d}^k$, so that

$f(\mathbf{x})$ is minimized on the line $\mathbf{x} = \mathbf{x}^k + \tau\mathbf{d}^k$, $-\infty < \tau < \infty$ for $\tau = \tau_k$. Any procedure for finding τ_k is called a *line search*. For general functionals, line searches are often quite complicated and involve some iterative process. In the case of a quadratic functional with a positive definite Hessian, however, we can derive a simple formula for τ_k. If

$$f(\mathbf{x}) = \tfrac{1}{2}\mathbf{x}^\mathrm{T}H\mathbf{x} - \mathbf{b}^\mathrm{T}\mathbf{x} + c, \tag{1.8}$$

then a straightforward calculation shows that

$$f(\mathbf{x} + \tau\mathbf{d}) = \tfrac{1}{2}\tau^2\mathbf{d}^\mathrm{T}H\mathbf{d} + \tau\mathbf{d}^\mathrm{T}\mathbf{g}(\mathbf{x}) + \tilde{c},$$

where $\tilde{c}$ is independent of τ. If H is positive definite and $\mathbf{d} \neq \mathbf{0}$, then $\mathbf{d}^\mathrm{T}H\mathbf{d} > 0$, and $f(\mathbf{x} + \tau\mathbf{d})$ is a parabola in the variable τ and opens upwards. $f(\mathbf{x} + \tau\mathbf{d})$ is uniquely minimized by

$$\tau = -\mathbf{d}^\mathrm{T}\mathbf{g}(\mathbf{x})/\mathbf{d}^\mathrm{T}H\mathbf{d}.$$

Thus, regardless of the choice of $\mathbf{d}^k$ in (1.7), a natural choice of τ_k, when $f(\mathbf{x})$ is a quadratic functional,* is

$$\tau_k = -\mathbf{d}^{k\mathrm{T}}\mathbf{g}(\mathbf{x}^k)/\mathbf{d}^{k\mathrm{T}}H\mathbf{d}^k. \tag{1.9}$$

The Method of Steepest Descent

On the basis of Theorem 1.7 it is natural to put $\mathbf{d}^k = -\mathbf{g}(\mathbf{x}^k)$ in (1.7):

$$\mathbf{x}^{k+1} = \mathbf{x}^k - \tau_k\mathbf{g}(\mathbf{x}^k). \tag{1.10}$$

This relation, together with some chosen line search strategy, defines a *method of steepest descent* for minimizing a general functional $f(\mathbf{x})$. When the functional has the quadratic form of (1.8), then (1.9) is the obvious way to determine τ_k. Hence the method of steepest descent for (1.8) is

$$\mathbf{g}^k = H\mathbf{x}^k - \mathbf{b}, \tag{1.11a}$$

$$\tau_k = \mathbf{g}^{k\mathrm{T}}\mathbf{g}^k/\mathbf{g}^{k\mathrm{T}}H\mathbf{g}^k, \tag{1.11b}$$

$$\mathbf{x}^{k+1} = \mathbf{x}^k - \tau_k\mathbf{g}^k, \tag{1.11c}$$

where $k = 0, 1, \ldots$, and $\mathbf{g}^k = \mathbf{g}(\mathbf{x}^k)$. The kth iteration of (1.11) is sketched in Fig. 1.3. The line through $\mathbf{x}^k$ and $\mathbf{x}^{k+1}$ is tangent at the point $\mathbf{x}^{k+1}$ to the ellipsoidal level surface $\{\mathbf{x} \in R^N; f(\mathbf{x}) = f(\mathbf{x}^{k+1})\}$.

---

* The notation $\mathbf{d}^{k\mathrm{T}}$ should be read as $(\mathbf{d}^k)^\mathrm{T}$.

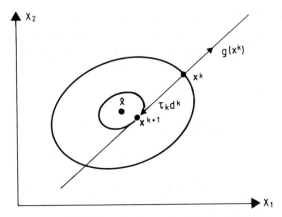

Fig. 1.3.   The kth step in the method of steepest descent.

Since (1.10) implies the relation

$$\mathbf{g}^{k+1} = \mathbf{g}^k - \tau_k H \mathbf{g}^k, \qquad (1.12)$$

we have the option of computing the gradients in (1.11) recursively. The iterations can thus be formulated as follows:

$$\tau_k = \mathbf{g}^{k^T} \mathbf{g}^k / \mathbf{g}^{k^T} H \mathbf{g}^k, \qquad (1.13a)$$

$$\mathbf{x}^{k+1} = \mathbf{x}^k - \tau_k \mathbf{g}^k, \qquad (1.13b)$$

$$\mathbf{g}^{k+1} = \mathbf{g}^k - \tau_k H \mathbf{g}^k, \qquad (1.13c)$$

where $k = 0, 1, \dots$. Initially we compute $\mathbf{g}^0 = H\mathbf{x}^0 - \mathbf{b}$.

Note that (1.13) can be implemented with only one multiplication by H per iteration. Two multiplications are required if $\mathbf{g}^k$ is computed directly.

Convergence Analysis

We shall now show that the sequence $\mathbf{x}^0, \mathbf{x}^1, \dots$ produced by (1.13) converges to $\hat{\mathbf{x}} \equiv H^{-1}\mathbf{b}$, the minimizer of (1.8), and we shall estimate the rate of convergence.

To describe convergence quantitatively it is necessary to measure the error in any vector $\mathbf{x}$ that is to be considered as an approximation to $\hat{\mathbf{x}}$. The most obvious choice is perhaps $\|\mathbf{x} - \hat{\mathbf{x}}\|$, the Euclidean norm of the error vector $\mathbf{x} - \hat{\mathbf{x}}$ and the classical distance from $\mathbf{x}$ to $\hat{\mathbf{x}}$. However, in view of the fact that the purpose of the computation is to minimize $f(\mathbf{x})$, an alternative idea is to use the quantity $f(\mathbf{x}) - f(\hat{\mathbf{x}})$ as a measure of error. When (1.10) arises from a physical problem, $f(\mathbf{x})$ is often the energy of a system. Indeed, making the energy difference $f(\mathbf{x}) - f(\hat{\mathbf{x}})$ small may be more important than making $\|\mathbf{x} - \hat{\mathbf{x}}\|$ small, and faced with two approximations, $\mathbf{x}_1$ and $\mathbf{x}_2$, where $\|\mathbf{x}_1 - \hat{\mathbf{x}}\| < \|\mathbf{x}_2 - \hat{\mathbf{x}}\|$ but $f(\mathbf{x}_2) - f(\hat{\mathbf{x}}) < f(\mathbf{x}_1) - f(\hat{\mathbf{x}})$, the approximation $\mathbf{x}_2$ might be preferred. Our reason for introducing the so-called "energy norm" at this point, however, is not its possible physical relevance, but the fact that it simplifies the analysis of convergence.

Definition 1.9. The *energy inner product* and *energy norm* corresponding to a positive definite matrix H are

$$(\mathbf{x}, \mathbf{y})_H = \mathbf{x}^T H \mathbf{y}$$

and

$$\|\mathbf{x}\|_H = (\mathbf{x}, \mathbf{x})_H^{1/2} = (\mathbf{x}^T H \mathbf{x})^{1/2},$$

respectively.

$(\mathbf{x}, \mathbf{y})_H$ and $\|\mathbf{x}\|_H$ satisfy all of the standard requirements of an inner product and norm, i.e., for all $\mathbf{x}, \mathbf{y}, \mathbf{z} \in R^N$ and $\alpha, \beta \in R$, we have

$$(\mathbf{x}, \mathbf{y})_H = (\mathbf{y}, \mathbf{x})_H,$$

$$(\alpha\mathbf{x} + \beta\mathbf{y}, \mathbf{z})_H = \alpha(\mathbf{x}, \mathbf{z})_H + \beta(\mathbf{y}, \mathbf{z})_H,$$

$$(\mathbf{x}, \mathbf{x})_H \geq 0,$$

$$(\mathbf{x}, \mathbf{x})_H = 0 \quad \Leftrightarrow \quad \mathbf{x} = \mathbf{0},$$

and

$$\|\alpha\mathbf{x}\|_H = |\alpha| \cdot \|\mathbf{x}\|_H,$$

$$\|\mathbf{x} + \mathbf{y}\|_H \leq \|\mathbf{x}\|_H + \|\mathbf{y}\|_H,$$

$$\|\mathbf{x}\|_H \geq 0,$$

$$\|\mathbf{x}\|_H = 0 \quad \Leftrightarrow \quad \mathbf{x} = \mathbf{0}.$$

Note that when H is the identity matrix, the energy inner product and norm reduce to the Euclidean inner product and norm, respectively. It is also convenient to have a simple designation for the square of the energy norm, and we accordingly define

$$E(\mathbf{x}) = \mathbf{x}^T H \mathbf{x}, \qquad \mathbf{x} \in R^N.$$

To show the connection between the energy norm and the "energy" $f(\mathbf{x})$, we rewrite (1.8) in the form

$$f(\mathbf{x}) = \tfrac{1}{2}(\mathbf{x} - \hat{\mathbf{x}})^T H (\mathbf{x} - \hat{\mathbf{x}}) + f(\hat{\mathbf{x}}) \tag{1.14}$$

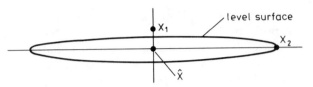

Fig. 1.4.   An illustration of the concept of size: $(x_2 - \hat{x})$ is smaller than $(x_1 - \hat{x})$ in the energy norm.

and note that

$$E(x - \hat{x}) = 2[f(x) - f(\hat{x})], \tag{1.15}$$

$$\|x - \hat{x}\|_H = \sqrt{2[f(x) - f(\hat{x})]}. \tag{1.16}$$

$\|x - \hat{x}\|_H$ and $E(x - \hat{x})$ are constant on every level surface of f. The difference between measuring errors in the Euclidean and energy norms becomes more pronounced as the ellipsoids become more eccentric. This is illustrated in Fig. 1.4, where $\|x_2 - \hat{x}\|_H < \|x_1 - \hat{x}\|_H$ even though $\|x_1 - \hat{x}\| < \|x_2 - \hat{x}\|$.

It is appropriate to mention here that the technique of preconditioning, which will be introduced later in this section, has the effect of replacing H by a matrix whose level surfaces are significantly less eccentric than those of H. This reduces the disparity between the Euclidean and energy norms.

We shall now derive the rate of convergence of the method of steepest descent in the energy norm.

Theorem 1.8. We have

$$\|x^k - \hat{x}\|_H \le \left(\frac{\kappa(H) - 1}{\kappa(H) + 1}\right)^k \|x^0 - \hat{x}\|_H, \tag{1.17}$$

where $\kappa(H)$ is the spectral condition number of H. Further, if $p(\varepsilon)$ is defined for any $\varepsilon > 0$ to be the smallest integer k such that

$$\|x^k - \hat{x}\|_H \le \varepsilon\|x^0 - \hat{x}\|_H \qquad \forall x^0 \in R^N,$$

then

$$p(\varepsilon) \le \tfrac{1}{2}\kappa(H) \ln(1/\varepsilon) + 1. \tag{1.18}$$

PROOF: We need the relation

$$E(x - \hat{x}) = g(x)^T H^{-1} g(x), \tag{1.19}$$

which follows from (1.14), (1.15), and the relation $x - \hat{x} = H^{-1}g(x)$. We also need a classical inequality for positive definite matrices. If H is an $N \times N$ positive definite matrix with eigenvalues $0 < \lambda_1 \le \lambda_2 \le \cdots \le \lambda_N$, then

$$1 \le \frac{(x^T H x)(x^T H^{-1} x)}{(x^T x)^2} \le \frac{(\lambda_1 + \lambda_N)^2}{4\lambda_1\lambda_N} \qquad \forall x \in R^N, \tag{1.20}$$

and equality is attainable on each side. [See Beckenbach and Bellman (1971) and Exercise 1.13.] Using (1.19), (1.12), and (1.9) we obtain

$$E(\mathbf{x}^{k+1} - \hat{\mathbf{x}}) = \mathbf{g}^{k+1^\mathsf{T}} H^{-1}\mathbf{g}^{k+1} = \mathbf{g}^{k^\mathsf{T}}(I - \tau_k H)H^{-1}(I - \tau_k H)\mathbf{g}^k$$

$$= \mathbf{g}^{k^\mathsf{T}} H^{-1}(I - \tau_k H)^2\mathbf{g}^k = \mathbf{g}^{k^\mathsf{T}} H^{-1}\mathbf{g}^k - (\mathbf{g}^{k^\mathsf{T}}\mathbf{g}^k)^2/\mathbf{g}^{k^\mathsf{T}} H\mathbf{g}^k,$$

and it follows from (1.19) and (1.20) that

$$E(\mathbf{x}^{k+1} - \hat{\mathbf{x}}) = \{1 - (\mathbf{g}^{k^\mathsf{T}}\mathbf{g}^k)^2/[(\mathbf{g}^{k^\mathsf{T}} H\mathbf{g}^k)(\mathbf{g}^{k^\mathsf{T}} H^{-1}\mathbf{g}^k)]\}E(\mathbf{x}^k - \hat{\mathbf{x}})$$

$$\leq [1 - 4\lambda_1\lambda_N/(\lambda_1 + \lambda_N)^2]E(\mathbf{x}^k - \hat{\mathbf{x}}),$$

or, in terms of the spectral condition number $\kappa(H) \equiv \lambda_N/\lambda_1 \geq 1$,

$$E(\mathbf{x}^{k+1} - \hat{\mathbf{x}}) \leq \left(\frac{\kappa(H) - 1}{\kappa(H) + 1}\right)^2 E(\mathbf{x}^k - \hat{\mathbf{x}}).$$

Thus the convergence of the method of steepest descent is described in the energy norm by

$$\|\mathbf{x}^{k+1} - \hat{\mathbf{x}}\|_H \leq \left(\frac{\kappa(H) - 1}{\kappa(H) + 1}\right)\|\mathbf{x}^k - \hat{\mathbf{x}}\|_H,$$

and (1.17) follows. The proof of (1.18) is left as an exercise (see Exercise 1.14). ∎

Preconditioning

Let C be a positive definite matrix factored in the form $C = EE^\mathsf{T}$, and let

$$f(\mathbf{x}) = \tfrac{1}{2}\mathbf{x}^\mathsf{T} H\mathbf{x} - \mathbf{b}^\mathsf{T}\mathbf{x} + c, \qquad \mathbf{x} \in R^N, \tag{1.21}$$

where H is positive definite. We define a second quadratic functional $\tilde{f}(\mathbf{y})$ by the transformation $\mathbf{y} = E^\mathsf{T}\mathbf{x}$, i.e.,

$$\tilde{f}(\mathbf{y}) = f(E^{-\mathsf{T}}\mathbf{y}) = \tfrac{1}{2}\mathbf{y}^\mathsf{T}\tilde{H}\mathbf{y} - \tilde{\mathbf{b}}^\mathsf{T}\mathbf{y} + \tilde{c}, \tag{1.22}$$

where

$$\tilde{H} = E^{-1}HE^{-\mathsf{T}}, \qquad \tilde{\mathbf{b}} = E^{-1}\mathbf{b}, \qquad \tilde{c} = c. \tag{1.23}$$

$\tilde{H}$ is obviously symmetric. Moreover, since $\mathbf{y}^\mathsf{T}\tilde{H}\mathbf{y} = \mathbf{x}^\mathsf{T} H\mathbf{x}$ and $\mathbf{x}^\mathsf{T} H\mathbf{x} > 0$ $\forall\mathbf{x} \neq \mathbf{0}$ (H is positive definite), then $\mathbf{y}^\mathsf{T}\tilde{H}\mathbf{y} > 0$ $\forall\mathbf{y} \neq \mathbf{0}$, showing that $\tilde{H}$ is also positive definite. The similarity transformation

$$E^{-\mathsf{T}}\tilde{H}E^\mathsf{T} = E^{-\mathsf{T}}E^{-1}H = C^{-1}H$$

reveals that $\tilde{H}$ and $C^{-1}H$ have the same eigenvalues, which we denote $0 < \tilde{\lambda}_1 \leq \cdots \leq \tilde{\lambda}_N$. Obviously, the spectral condition number

$$\kappa(\tilde{H}) = \tilde{\lambda}_N/\tilde{\lambda}_1 \tag{1.24}$$

is completely determined by C and H, even though $\tilde{H}$ depends on the particular factorization of C.

Consider the application of the method of steepest descent to (1.22). For the time being it is convenient for our analysis to use the direct computation of the gradient, and the iterations are described by

$$\tilde{\mathbf{g}}^k = \tilde{H}\mathbf{y}^k - \tilde{\mathbf{b}}, \tag{1.25a}$$

$$\tilde{\tau}_k = \tilde{\mathbf{g}}^{k^T}\tilde{\mathbf{g}}^k/\tilde{\mathbf{g}}^{k^T}\tilde{H}\tilde{\mathbf{g}}^k, \tag{1.25b}$$

$$\mathbf{y}^{k+1} = \mathbf{y}^k - \tilde{\tau}_k\tilde{\mathbf{g}}^k, \tag{1.25c}$$

where $k = 0, 1, \ldots$ and $\mathbf{y}^0$ is arbitrarily chosen. It follows from the preceding convergence analysis that

$$\lim_{k \to \infty} \mathbf{y}^k = \hat{\mathbf{y}} \equiv \tilde{H}^{-1}\tilde{\mathbf{b}}$$

and that the rate of convergence depends on $\kappa(\tilde{H})$.

Let $\mathbf{x}^k = E^{-T}\mathbf{y}^k$ and $\mathbf{g}^k = H\mathbf{x}^k - \mathbf{b}$ for $k = 0, 1, \ldots$. Simple calculations based on (1.23) and (1.25) show that

$$\tilde{\mathbf{g}}^k = E^{-1}\mathbf{g}^k, \qquad \tilde{\tau}_k = \mathbf{g}^{k^T}\mathbf{h}^k/\mathbf{h}^{k^T}H\mathbf{h}^k, \qquad \mathbf{y}^{k+1} = E^T(\mathbf{x}^k - \tilde{\tau}_k\mathbf{h}^k),$$

where we have introduced the vector $\mathbf{h}^k = C^{-1}\mathbf{g}^k$. But since $\mathbf{y}^{k+1} = E^T\mathbf{x}^{k+1}$, this establishes that the sequence $\mathbf{x}^1, \mathbf{x}^2, \ldots$ is produced directly by the recursion

$$\mathbf{g}^k = H\mathbf{x}^k - \mathbf{b}, \tag{1.26a}$$

$$\mathbf{h}^k = C^{-1}\mathbf{g}^k, \tag{1.26b}$$

$$\tau_k = \mathbf{g}^{k^T}\mathbf{h}^k/\mathbf{h}^{k^T}H\mathbf{h}^k, \tag{1.26c}$$

$$\mathbf{x}^{k+1} = \mathbf{x}^k - \tau_k\mathbf{h}^k, \tag{1.26d}$$

where $k = 0, 1, \ldots$.

The minimizers of $f(\mathbf{x})$ and $\tilde{f}(\mathbf{y})$ are $\hat{\mathbf{x}} \equiv H^{-1}\mathbf{b}$ and $\hat{\mathbf{y}} \equiv \tilde{H}^{-1}\tilde{\mathbf{b}}$, respectively, and it is easily shown that $\hat{\mathbf{y}} = E^T\hat{\mathbf{x}}$. Further,

$$\mathbf{y}^k - \hat{\mathbf{y}} = E^T\mathbf{x}^k - E^T\hat{\mathbf{x}} = E^T(\mathbf{x}^k - \hat{\mathbf{x}})$$

and

$$\|\mathbf{y}^k - \hat{\mathbf{y}}\|_{\tilde{H}}^2 = [E^T(\mathbf{x}^k - \hat{\mathbf{x}})]^T E^{-1}HE^{-T}[E^T(\mathbf{x}^k - \hat{\mathbf{x}})]$$

$$= (\mathbf{x}^k - \hat{\mathbf{x}})H(\mathbf{x}^k - \hat{\mathbf{x}}) = \|\mathbf{x}^k - \hat{\mathbf{x}}\|_H^2.$$

But since by Theorem 1.8

$$\|\mathbf{y}^k - \hat{\mathbf{y}}\|_{\tilde{H}} \leq \left(\frac{\kappa(\tilde{H}) - 1}{\kappa(\tilde{H}) + 1}\right)^k \|\mathbf{y}^0 - \hat{\mathbf{y}}\|_{\tilde{H}},$$

it must be true that

$$\|\mathbf{x}^k - \hat{\mathbf{x}}\|_H \leq \left(\frac{\kappa(\tilde{H}) - 1}{\kappa(\tilde{H}) + 1}\right)^k \|\mathbf{x}^0 - \hat{\mathbf{x}}\|_H.$$

Thus the sequence $\mathbf{x}^0$, $\mathbf{x}^1$, ..., where $\mathbf{x}^0$ is arbitrary and $\mathbf{x}^1$, $\mathbf{x}^2$, ... are found from (1.26), converges to $\hat{\mathbf{x}}$ and the rate of convergence is determined by $\kappa(\tilde{H})$. If C can be found such that $\kappa(\tilde{H}) < \kappa(H)$, then estimate (1.18) indicates that the rate of convergence of (1.26) is better than that of (1.13).

We call C the *preconditioning matrix*, $\tilde{H}$ the *preconditioned matrix*, (1.25) the *transformed preconditioned steepest descent method*, and (1.26) the *untransformed preconditioned steepest descent method*. We call (1.25) "transformed" because the sequence $\mathbf{y}^0$, $\mathbf{y}^1$, ... converges to $\hat{\mathbf{y}} = E^T\hat{\mathbf{x}}$, a transformation of $\hat{\mathbf{x}}$, rather than to $\hat{\mathbf{x}}$ itself. We can obtain a sequence that converges to $\hat{\mathbf{x}}$ by making the inverse transformation $\mathbf{x}^k = E^{-T}\mathbf{y}^k$. Naturally, this need not be done in every iteration.

Regarding the computational work for the two preconditioned methods, it should first be pointed out that the gradients can be determined economically by recursion. Thus step (1.25a) and (1.26a) can be replaced by

$$\tilde{\mathbf{g}}^k = \tilde{\mathbf{g}}^{k-1} - \tilde{\tau}_{k-1}\tilde{H}\tilde{\mathbf{g}}^{k-1}$$

and

$$\mathbf{g}^k = \mathbf{g}^{k-1} - \tau_{k-1}H\mathbf{h}^{k-1},$$

respectively. The vectors $\tilde{H}\tilde{\mathbf{g}}^{k-1}$ and $H\mathbf{h}^{k-1}$ will be available from the preceding iteration.

In the problems we are interested in, H is large and sparse and E is often a sparse lower triangular matrix. In performing the transformed method, $\tilde{H}$ is not computed explicitly because this matrix is usually not sparse. Thus, the computation of the vector $\tilde{H}\tilde{\mathbf{g}}^k$ in step (1.25b), which dominates the total computational work per iteration, is performed indirectly:

$$E^T\mathbf{z} = \tilde{\mathbf{g}}^k \qquad \text{is solved for } \mathbf{z},$$

$$\mathbf{z}^* = H\mathbf{z},$$

$$E\mathbf{z}^{**} = \mathbf{z}^* \qquad \text{is solved for } \mathbf{z}^{**},$$

and we see that $\mathbf{z}^{**} = E^{-1}HE^{-T}\tilde{\mathbf{g}}^k = \tilde{H}\tilde{\mathbf{g}}^k$. To find this vector, then, we must solve two triangular systems and multiply by H. Further, the transformation

$\mathbf{x}^k = E^{-T}\mathbf{y}^k$, which must be performed at least once, requires the solution of a triangular system.

Most of the computational work of the untransformed method (1.26) takes place in step (1.26b) where $C^{-1}\mathbf{g}^k$ is computed and in step (1.26c) where $H\mathbf{h}^k$ is computed. The vector $C^{-1}\mathbf{g}^k$ is computed as follows:

$$E\mathbf{z} = \mathbf{g}^k \qquad \text{is solved for } \mathbf{z},$$

$$E^T\mathbf{h}^k = \mathbf{z} \qquad \text{is solved for } \mathbf{h}^k,$$

and clearly $\mathbf{h}^k = C^{-1}\mathbf{g}^k$. Thus, the solution of two triangular systems and a multiplication by H is required for the untransformed method also.

The convenience of producing in each iteration an approximation to the desired minimizer $\hat{\mathbf{x}}$ would appear to make the untransformed method preferable. Certain preconditioning matrices are so special, however, as to allow a more efficient implementation of the transformed method than that described previously. Since our real interest in preconditioning matrices is their application to the conjugate gradient method, we defer further discussion of them to Section 1.4. (The remarks there are equally relevant to the method of steepest descent.)

1.3 The Conjugate Gradient Method

Introduction

We shall describe in this section the conjugate gradient method for finding the minimizer of a quadratic functional with a positive definite Hessian. It will be shown that the conjugate gradient method—unlike the method of steepest descent—produces the minimizer after at most N iterations, where N is the order of the Hessian. Although this property is welcome, it is not particularly relevant when N is very large, since the computing time for that number of iterations is usually prohibitive and the property does not hold in the presence of rounding errors anyway. We therefore derive a bound on the error in the energy norm after any given number of iterations and show that the number of iterations necessary to make the error less than ε times the initial error is roughly bounded by $\frac{1}{2}\sqrt{\kappa(H)}\ln(2/\varepsilon)$. If the spectral condition number $\kappa(H)$ is large, then this result is much superior to (1.18) for the method of steepest descent. We then show that for certain eigenvalue distributions of H this bound can be reduced.

Derivation of the Method

As in the preceding section, we are concerned here with finding the minimizer $\hat{\mathbf{x}} = H^{-1}\mathbf{b}$ of the quadratic functional

$$f(\mathbf{x}) = \tfrac{1}{2}\mathbf{x}^{\mathsf{T}}H\mathbf{x} - \mathbf{b}^{\mathsf{T}}\mathbf{x} + c, \qquad \mathbf{x} \in R^N,$$

where H is an $N \times N$ positive definite matrix, by performing iterations of the type

$$\mathbf{x}^{k+1} = \mathbf{x}^k + \tau_k\mathbf{d}^k, \qquad k = 0, 1, 2, \dots. \tag{1.27}$$

We shall take as τ_k the value

$$\tau_k = -\mathbf{d}^{k^{\mathsf{T}}}\mathbf{g}^k / \mathbf{d}^{k^{\mathsf{T}}}H\mathbf{d}^k, \tag{1.28}$$

where $\mathbf{g}^k = \mathbf{g}(\mathbf{x}^k) = H\mathbf{x}^k - \mathbf{b}$. We have seen that this choice of τ_k has the property of minimizing the function $f(\mathbf{x}^k + \tau\mathbf{d}^k)$, $-\infty < \tau < \infty$. It also makes the gradient at $\mathbf{x}^{k+1}$ orthogonal to search direction $\mathbf{d}^k$. To see this, we multiply both sides of (1.27) by H and subtract $\mathbf{b}$ to obtain

$$\mathbf{g}^{k+1} = \mathbf{g}^k + \tau_k H\mathbf{d}^k. \tag{1.29}$$

Then,

$$\mathbf{d}^{k^{\mathsf{T}}}\mathbf{g}^{k+1} = \mathbf{d}^{k^{\mathsf{T}}}\mathbf{g}^k + \tau_k\mathbf{d}^{k^{\mathsf{T}}}H\mathbf{d}^k = 0. \tag{1.30}$$

(See Fig. 1.3.)

We suppose now that the search directions are determined by an iteration of the form

$$\mathbf{d}^{k+1} = -\mathbf{g}^{k+1} + \beta_k\mathbf{d}^k, \qquad k = 0, 1, 2, \dots, \tag{1.31}$$

where $\mathbf{d}^0 = -\mathbf{g}^0$ and $\beta_0, \beta_1, \dots$ remain to be determined. It will be observed that the method of steepest descent is obtained by putting $\beta_k = 0$ and that in (1.31) we find the new search direction in the plane spanned by the gradient at the most recent point and the previous search direction.

Since τ_k is not defined by (1.28) if $\mathbf{d}^k = \mathbf{0}$, it is important to investigate the situation that arises when (1.31) produces a zero search vector. Replacing $(k + 1)$ by k in (1.31) and taking the scalar product with $\mathbf{g}^k$, we obtain

$$\mathbf{g}^{k^{\mathsf{T}}}\mathbf{d}^k = -\|\mathbf{g}^k\|^2 + \beta_{k-1}\mathbf{g}^{k^{\mathsf{T}}}\mathbf{d}^{k-1}. \tag{1.32}$$

But $\mathbf{g}^{k^{\mathsf{T}}}\mathbf{d}^{k-1} = 0$ by (1.30), and if $\mathbf{d}^k = \mathbf{0}$ then $\|\mathbf{g}^k\| = 0$, implying $\mathbf{g}^k = H\mathbf{x}^k - \mathbf{b} = \mathbf{0}$ and $\mathbf{x}^k = \hat{\mathbf{x}}$. Thus a zero search direction can be produced only after the minimizer has been found, and there is no problem in computing τ_k by (1.28). Furthermore, if $\mathbf{x}^k \neq \hat{\mathbf{x}}$ then $\tau_k \neq 0$; for $\mathbf{x}^k \neq \hat{\mathbf{x}}$ implies $\|\mathbf{g}^k\| \neq 0$, and it follows from (1.32) and the relation $\mathbf{g}^{k^{\mathsf{T}}}\mathbf{d}^{k-1} = 0$ that $\mathbf{g}^{k^{\mathsf{T}}}\mathbf{d}^k \neq 0$, and hence

$\tau_k \neq 0$. These remarks make it clear that regardless of the choice of β_0, β_1, ..., the iterative process defined by (1.27), (1.28), and (1.31) will either be nonterminating, with $\mathbf{x}^k \neq \hat{\mathbf{x}}$, $\mathbf{d}^k \neq \mathbf{0}$ and $\tau_k \neq 0$ for all values of k, or there will be some integer m such that $\mathbf{x}^k \neq \hat{\mathbf{x}}$, $\mathbf{d}^k \neq \mathbf{0}$ and $\tau_k \neq 0$ for $k = 0, 1, ...,$ $m - 1$, and $\mathbf{x}^m = \hat{\mathbf{x}}$.

Our strategy in determining β_0, β_1, ... is to minimize in each iteration the error $\|\mathbf{x} - \hat{\mathbf{x}}\|_H$ over a certain subset of R^N. The following analysis requires use of the inner product

$$(\mathbf{x}, \mathbf{y})_{H^{-1}} = \mathbf{x}^T H^{-1} \mathbf{y}, \qquad \mathbf{x}, \mathbf{y} \in R^N \tag{1.33}$$

and the associated norm

$$\|\mathbf{x}\|_{H^{-1}} = (\mathbf{x}, \mathbf{x})_{H^{-1}}^{1/2} = (\mathbf{x}^T H^{-1} \mathbf{x})^{1/2}, \qquad \mathbf{x} \in R^N. \tag{1.34}$$

H^{-1} is positive definite since H has this property, and (1.33) is a well-defined inner product on R^N. (See Definition 1.9.)

It turns out to be convenient to work with the gradient $\mathbf{g} = H\mathbf{x} - \mathbf{b}$ rather than directly with $\mathbf{x}$. From the relation $\mathbf{x} - \hat{\mathbf{x}} = H^{-1}\mathbf{g}$ we obtain

$$\|\mathbf{x} - \hat{\mathbf{x}}\|_H = \|\mathbf{g}\|_{H^{-1}}. \tag{1.35}$$

Using (1.29) and (1.31) recursively, one finds easily that for any choice of β_0, β_1, ..., the gradient $\mathbf{g}^k$ has the form

$$\mathbf{g}^k = \mathbf{g}^0 + \sum_{l=1}^{k} \alpha_l^{(k)} H^l \mathbf{g}^0, \tag{1.36}$$

where $\alpha_k^{(k)} = (-1)^k \prod_{i=1}^{k-1} \tau_i \neq 0$. Let

$$S_k = \mathrm{SPAN}\{H\mathbf{g}^0, H^2\mathbf{g}^0, ..., H^k\mathbf{g}^0\},$$

$$T_k = \{\mathbf{g} \in R^N; \mathbf{g} = \mathbf{g}^0 + \mathbf{h}, \mathbf{h} \in S_k\}.$$

S_k is a subspace of R^N with dimension equal to the number of linearly independent vectors in the set $H\mathbf{g}^0, ..., H^k\mathbf{g}^0$. T_k is a subset of R^N but generally not a subspace. Clearly, $\mathbf{g}^k \in T_k$.

Theorem 1.9. The parameter β_k in the iterative process (1.27), (1.28), and (1.31) is given by

$$\beta_k = \mathbf{g}^{k+1^T} H \mathbf{d}^k / \mathbf{d}^{k^T} H \mathbf{d}^k \tag{1.37}$$

if we impose the condition

$$\|\mathbf{g}^k\|_{H^{-1}} = \min_{\mathbf{g} \in T_k} \|\mathbf{g}\|_{H^{-1}}. \tag{1.38}$$

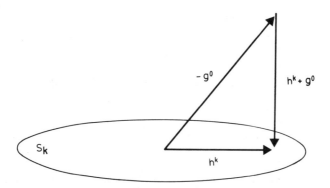

Fig. 1.5.   A geometrical interpretation of the best approximation to $-\mathbf{g}^0$ in the subspace S_k.

Further, this condition also implies the relations

$$\mathbf{g}^{k^\mathrm{T}}\mathbf{g}^l = 0, \qquad l \neq k \tag{1.39}$$

and

$$\mathbf{d}^{k^\mathrm{T}} H\mathbf{d}^l = 0, \qquad l \neq k. \tag{1.40}$$

PROOF: Property (1.38) is equivalent to

$$\|\mathbf{g}^0 + \mathbf{h}^k\|_{H^{-1}} = \min_{\mathbf{h} \in S_k} \|\mathbf{g}^0 + \mathbf{h}\|_{H^{-1}}, \tag{1.41}$$

where $\mathbf{h}^k = \mathbf{g}^k - \mathbf{g}^0$. Now if we view any $\mathbf{h} \in S_k$ as an approximation to the vector $-\mathbf{g}^0$, then the corresponding error in the approximation is $\mathbf{h} - (-\mathbf{g}^0) = \mathbf{h} + \mathbf{g}^0$. Thus we have the problem of finding in the subspace S_k the vector $\mathbf{h}^k$ that most closely approximates $-\mathbf{g}^0$, the error being measured in the H^{-1} norm. According to a well-known theorem of linear algebra, $\mathbf{h}^k$ exists, is unique, and has the property of making the error $\mathbf{g}^0 + \mathbf{h}^k$ orthogonal [with respect to inner product (1.33)] to every $\mathbf{h}$ in S_k, i.e.,

$$(\mathbf{g}^0 + \mathbf{h}^k)^\mathrm{T} H^{-1}\mathbf{h} = 0 \qquad \forall \mathbf{h} \in S_k.$$

See Fig. 1.5 for a geometrical interpretation.

Obviously, the solution of (1.38) is $\mathbf{g}^k \equiv \mathbf{g}^0 + \mathbf{h}^k$, and this vector satisfies

$$\mathbf{g}^{k^\mathrm{T}} H^{-1}\mathbf{h} = 0 \qquad \forall \mathbf{h} \in S_k.$$

For any $\mathbf{g} \in T_{k-1}$, the vector $\mathbf{h} = H\mathbf{g}$ belongs to S_k. Thus $\mathbf{g}^k$ has the property that

$$\mathbf{g}^{k^\mathrm{T}}\mathbf{g} = 0 \qquad \forall \mathbf{g} \in T_{k-1}, \tag{1.42}$$

and the orthogonality relation (1.39) follows since we have $\mathbf{g}^l \in T_l \subseteq T_{k-1}$ for $l < k$.

To establish (1.40) we assume $l < k$ and use (1.29), (1.31), and (1.39) to obtain

$$\mathbf{d}^{k^{\mathrm{T}}} H\mathbf{d}^l = (H\mathbf{d}^k)^{\mathrm{T}}\mathbf{d}^l = \tau_k^{-1}(\mathbf{g}^{k+1} - \mathbf{g}^k)^{\mathrm{T}}\mathbf{d}^l$$

$$= \tau_k^{-1}(\mathbf{g}^{k+1} - \mathbf{g}^k)^{\mathrm{T}}(-\mathbf{g}^l + \beta_{l-1}\mathbf{d}^{l-1}) = (\beta_{l-1}/\tau_k)(\mathbf{g}^{k+1} - \mathbf{g}^k)^{\mathrm{T}}\mathbf{d}^{l-1}.$$

Hence, by induction,

$$\mathbf{d}^{k^{\mathrm{T}}} H\mathbf{d}^l = \tau_k^{-1}\left(\prod_{i=0}^{l-1} \beta_i\right)(\mathbf{g}^{k+1} - \mathbf{g}^k)^{\mathrm{T}}\mathbf{d}^0 = 0,$$

since $\mathbf{d}^0 = -\mathbf{g}^0$ and we can apply (1.39). The search directions are said to be *conjugately orthogonal* by virtue of (1.40).

It remains to show that β_k is given by (1.37). This follows easily from (1.40) and (1.31) since

$$0 = \mathbf{d}^{k+1^{\mathrm{T}}} H\mathbf{d}^k = (-\mathbf{g}^{k+1} + \beta_k\mathbf{d}^k)^{\mathrm{T}} H\mathbf{d}^k,$$

yielding (1.37).   ∎

The iterative process of Theorem 1.9 is called the *conjugate gradient method* (Hestenes and Stiefel, 1952). Various identities allow a number of formulations of this method. For example, the gradient can be computed directly by the formula $\mathbf{g}^k = H\mathbf{x}^k - \mathbf{b}$ or recursively by (1.29). There are also alternative expressions for β_k and τ_k. If we expand $\mathbf{d}^k$ as

$$\mathbf{d}^k = -\mathbf{g}^k + \beta_{k-1}\mathbf{d}^{k-1} = -\mathbf{g}^k + \beta_{k-1}(-\mathbf{g}^{k-1} + \beta_{k-2}\mathbf{d}^{k-2})$$

$$= -\mathbf{g}^k - \beta_{k-1}\mathbf{g}^{k-1} + \beta_{k-1}\beta_{k-2}(-\mathbf{g}^{k-2} + \beta_{k-3}\mathbf{d}^{k-3}) = \cdots$$

and rewrite (1.29) as

$$H\mathbf{d}^k = \tau_k^{-1}(\mathbf{g}^{k+1} - \mathbf{g}^k),$$

then substituting in (1.37) and applying the orthogonality relations (1.39), we obtain

$$\beta_k = \mathbf{g}^{k+1^{\mathrm{T}}}\mathbf{g}^{k+1}/\mathbf{g}^{k^{\mathrm{T}}}\mathbf{g}^k. \tag{1.43}$$

We observe that in this expression for β_k the Hessian is not needed. This property is important when the conjugate gradient method is extended to nonquadratic functionals. [See, e.g., Gill *et al.* (1981).]

Using the same expansion of $\mathbf{d}^k$ we find that $\mathbf{d}^k \mathbf{g}^k = -\mathbf{g}^{k^{\mathrm{T}}}\mathbf{g}^k$, and it then follows from (1.28) that

$$\tau_k = \mathbf{g}^{k^{\mathrm{T}}}\mathbf{g}^k/\mathbf{d}^{k^{\mathrm{T}}} H\mathbf{d}^k. \tag{1.44}$$

Computer Implementation

Although all of the versions of the conjugate gradient method obtained by combining the formulas for $\mathbf{g}^k$, β_k, and τ_k in various ways are mathematically equivalent, their computer implementation is not. In Reid (1971) the versions are compared with respect to computational labor, storage requirement, and accuracy, and the results tend to favor the following:

$$\tau_k = \mathbf{g}^{k^T}\mathbf{g}^k / \mathbf{d}^{k^T} H \mathbf{d}^k \tag{1.45a}$$

$$\mathbf{x}^{k+1} = \mathbf{x}^k + \tau_k \mathbf{d}^k \tag{1.45b}$$

$$\mathbf{g}^{k+1} = \mathbf{g}^k + \tau_k H \mathbf{d}^k \tag{1.45c}$$

$$\beta_k = \mathbf{g}^{k+1^T}\mathbf{g}^{k+1} / \mathbf{g}^{k^T}\mathbf{g}^k \tag{1.45d}$$

$$\mathbf{d}^{k+1} = -\mathbf{g}^{k+1} + \beta_k \mathbf{d}^k \tag{1.45e}$$

where $k = 0, 1, \ldots$. Initially we choose $\mathbf{x}^0$, calculate $\mathbf{g}^0 = H\mathbf{x}^0 - \mathbf{b}$, and put $\mathbf{d}^0 = -\mathbf{g}^0$.

The computer implementation of this algorithm is clarified as follows:

$$\begin{aligned}
&\mathbf{x} := \mathbf{x}^0; \quad \mathbf{g} := \mathbf{b}; \\
&\mathbf{g} := H\mathbf{x} - \mathbf{g}; \quad \delta 0 := \mathbf{g}^T\mathbf{g}; \\
&\text{IF } \delta 0 \le \varepsilon \text{ THEN STOP}; \\
&\mathbf{d} := -\mathbf{g}; \\
R: \quad &\mathbf{h} := H\mathbf{d}; \\
&\tau := \delta 0 / \mathbf{d}^T\mathbf{h}; \\
&\mathbf{x} := \mathbf{x} + \tau \mathbf{d}; \\
&\mathbf{g} := \mathbf{g} + \tau \mathbf{h}; \quad \delta 1 := \mathbf{g}^T\mathbf{g}; \\
&\text{IF } \delta 1 \le \varepsilon \text{ THEN STOP}; \\
&\beta := \delta 1 / \delta 0; \quad \delta 0 := \delta 1; \\
&\mathbf{d} := -\mathbf{g} + \beta \mathbf{d}; \\
&\text{GOTO } R;
\end{aligned} \tag{1.46}$$

$\mathbf{x}_0$ and $\mathbf{b}$ in the first line of the code are input vectors.

Regarding the storage requirement, single-indexed arrays are needed for $\mathbf{h}$, $\mathbf{x}$, $\mathbf{g}$, and $\mathbf{d}$. The storage requirement for H depends on the number of nonzero entries and the chosen data structure. In our problems H is usually large and sparse, and the simplest data structure—an $N \times N$ array—is much too wasteful of storage. See Fig. 1.8 at the end of Section 1.4 for a storage scheme suitable for a general sparse symmetric matrix.

Most of the computational labor per iteration is usually expended in the computation of $H\mathbf{d}$. There are in addition two inner products and three recursion formulas per iterative step requiring about $5N$ multiplications and $5N$ additions.

For remarks on the significance of ε in the termination criterion used in this code, see the end of Section 1.4.

Convergence Analysis

Theorem 1.10. The conjugate gradient method has the property that $\mathbf{x}^m = \hat{\mathbf{x}}$ for some $m \leq N$, where N is the order of H.

PROOF: Suppose the contrary is true. Then, $\mathbf{g}^k \neq \mathbf{0}$ for $k = 0, 1, \ldots, N$, and (1.39) implies that these $N + 1$ N-dimensional nonzero vectors are mutually orthogonal. Since this is impossible, the theorem is proved. ∎

Thus, in contrast to the method of steepest descent (see Exercise 1.15), the conjugate gradient method has the property of finite termination. The value m in Theorem 1.10 does not exceed, and is usually equal to, the number of distinct eigenvalues of H (Exercise 1.18). There are two remarks to be made concerning the finite termination property in the context of practical computation. The first is that rounding errors prevent our obtaining $\hat{\mathbf{x}}$ exactly and thus permit the iterations to continue for $k > m$. The second is that m may be so great that the computing time required for m iterations is unacceptable. Since the matrices we deal with in this book are generally of large order, the latter difficulty usually outweighs the problem of rounding errors, particularly in the preconditioned version of the algorithm, and we want to know how much accuracy we obtain after relatively few iterations.

We have seen that the gradient vector $\mathbf{g}^k$ produced by the conjugate gradient method has the property that

$$\|\mathbf{g}^k\|_{H^{-1}} = \min_{\mathbf{g} \in \tilde{T}_k} \|\mathbf{g}\|_{H^{-1}},$$

where the typical element of T_k has the form

$$\mathbf{g} = \mathbf{g}^0 + \sum_{l=1}^{k} \alpha_l H^l \mathbf{g}^0.$$

Let Π_k^1 denote the set of polynomals P_k of degree k such that $P_k(0) = 1$. The independent variable of P_k will be, at our convenience, a scalar or an $N \times N$ matrix. Consider the set

$$\tilde{T}_k = \{\mathbf{g} \in R^N; \mathbf{g} = P_k(H)\mathbf{g}^0, P_k \in \Pi_k^1\}.$$

$\tilde{T}_k$ is a subset of T_k and contains $\mathbf{g}^k$ [since $\alpha_k^{(k)} \neq 0$ in (1.36)]. Then,

$$\|\mathbf{g}^k\|_{H^{-1}} = \min_{\mathbf{g} \in \tilde{T}_k} \|\mathbf{g}\|_{H^{-1}} = \min_{P_k \in \Pi_k^1} \|P_k(H)\mathbf{g}^0\|_{H^{-1}}$$
$$= \min_{P_k \in \Pi_k^1} [\mathbf{g}^{0^{\mathrm{T}}} H^{-1} P_k(H)^2 \mathbf{g}^0]^{1/2}. \tag{1.47}$$

Here we have used (1.34) and the identity $P_k(H)^{\mathrm{T}} H^{-1} P_k(H) = H^{-1} P_k(H)^2$.

With this result we can prove a fundamental theorem on the convergence of the conjugate gradient method.

Theorem 1.11. Suppose that for some set S containing all of the eigenvalues of H and for some $M \geq 0$ and for some $\tilde{P}_k(\lambda) \in \Pi_k^1$ the following is true:

$$\max_{\lambda \in S} |\tilde{P}_k(\lambda)| \leq M.$$

Then,

$$\|\mathbf{x}^k - \hat{\mathbf{x}}\|_H \leq M \|\mathbf{x}^0 - \hat{\mathbf{x}}\|_H. \tag{1.48}$$

PROOF: Let the eigensolutions of H be $\{\lambda_i, \mathbf{v}_i\}_{i=1}^N$ with the ordering $0 < \lambda_1 \leq \lambda_2 \leq \cdots \leq \lambda_N$. We may assume the eigenvectors to be orthonormal, i.e., $\mathbf{v}_i^{\mathrm{T}} \mathbf{v}_j = \delta_{ij}$. The initial gradient has the expansion

$$\mathbf{g}^0 = \sum_{i=1}^N a_i \mathbf{v}_i, \qquad a_i = \mathbf{v}_i^{\mathrm{T}} \mathbf{g}^0,$$

and a straightforward calculation shows that

$$\mathbf{g}^{0^{\mathrm{T}}} H^{-1} P_k(H)^2 \mathbf{g}^0 = \sum_{i=1}^N a_i^2 \lambda_i^{-1} P_k(\lambda_i)^2.$$

Hence, by (1.47),

$$\|\mathbf{g}^k\|_{H^{-1}}^2 = \min_{P_k \in \Pi_k^1} \sum_{i=1}^N a_i^2 \lambda_i^{-1} P_k(\lambda_i)^2.$$

Since the assumption of the theorem implies $|\tilde{P}_k(\lambda_i)| \leq M$, we have

$$\|\mathbf{g}^k\|_{H^{-1}}^2 \leq M^2 \sum_{i=1}^N a_i^2 \lambda_i^{-1} = M^2 \|\mathbf{g}^0\|_{H^{-1}}^2,$$

and (1.48) follows from the identity $\|\mathbf{x}^k - \hat{\mathbf{x}}\|_H = \|\mathbf{g}^k\|_{H^{-1}}$. ∎

The remaining part of the convergence analysis may be described as follows. On the basis of some assumption regarding the eigenvalue distribution of H, we select a set S containing all of the eigenvalues. Then we seek a polynomial $\tilde{P}_k \in \Pi_k^1$ such that $M \equiv \max_{\lambda \in S} |\tilde{P}_k(\lambda)|$ is small. This value of M may then be used in (1.48).

Let us suppose first that we assume nothing about the eigenvalue distribution beyond the fact that all the eigenvalues are real and positive. Then it is natural to take $S = [\lambda_1, \lambda_N]$ and to seek the polynomial $\tilde{P}_k \in \Pi_k^1$ with the property that

$$\max_{\lambda_1 \le \lambda \le \lambda_N} |\tilde{P}_k(\lambda)| = \min_{P_k \in \Pi_k^1} \max_{\lambda_1 \le \lambda \le \lambda_N} |P_k(\lambda)|.$$

The solution of this problem is known to be

$$\tilde{P}_k(\lambda) = \frac{T_k[(\lambda_N + \lambda_1 - 2\lambda)/(\lambda_N - \lambda_1)]}{T_k[(\lambda_N + \lambda_1)/(\lambda_N - \lambda_1)]},$$

where T_k is the Chebyshev polynomial of degree k. (See Theorem A.1 in Appendix 1.) Moreover, the property

$$\max_{\lambda_1 \le \lambda \le \lambda_N} |\tilde{P}_k(\lambda)| = T_k[(\lambda_N + \lambda_1)/(\lambda_N - \lambda_1)]^{-1} \qquad (1.49)$$

together with Theorem 1.11 and (A.5) in Appendix 1 leads to the following theorem.

Theorem 1.12. For the conjugate gradient method we have the error estimate

$$\|x^k - \hat{x}\|_H \le T_k[(\lambda_N + \lambda_1)/(\lambda_N - \lambda_1)]^{-1} \cdot \|x^0 - \hat{x}\|_H.$$

Further, if $p(\varepsilon)$ is defined for any $\varepsilon > 0$ to be the smallest integer k such that

$$\|x^k - \hat{x}\|_H \le \varepsilon \|x^0 - \hat{x}\|_H \qquad \forall x^0 \in R^N,$$

then

$$p(\varepsilon) \le \tfrac{1}{2}\sqrt{\kappa(H)} \ln(2/\varepsilon) + 1. \qquad (1.50)$$

If $\kappa(H)$ is large, then this bound is much smaller than the corresponding bound (1.18) for the method of steepest descent. For example, if $\kappa(H) = 10^4$ and $\varepsilon = 10^{-4}$, then $p(\varepsilon) \le 496$ for the conjugate gradient method, whereas $p(\varepsilon) \le 46,052$ for the method of steepest descent.

We shall now show by two examples that the bound in (1.50) can be reduced for certain distributions of the eigenvalues.

Example 1.1. Assume that the eigenvalues are distributed in

$$S = [\lambda_1, b] \cup [c, \lambda_N],$$

where $0 < \lambda_1 < b < c < \lambda_N$, $b - \lambda_1 = \lambda_N - c$, and $4b < \lambda_N$. Thus S consists of two well-separated intervals of equal length.

For any $\gamma \ne 0$ the parabola

$$P_2(\lambda) = 1 - \gamma\lambda(\lambda_1 + \lambda_N - \lambda)$$

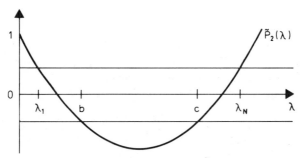

Fig. 1.6.   The polynomial $\tilde{P}_2(\lambda)$.

belongs to Π_2^1, and its axis is the line $\lambda = (\lambda_1 + \lambda_N)/2$, making $P_2(\lambda_1) = P_2(\lambda_N)$ and $P_2(b) = P_2(c)$. Let $\tilde{P}_2(\lambda)$ be the polynomial of this type uniquely determined by the additional requirement that $P_2(c) = -P_2(\lambda_N)$. One finds easily that

$$\tilde{P}_2(\lambda) = 1 - 2[\lambda_N(c + \lambda_1) - c(c - \lambda_1)]^{-1}\lambda(\lambda_1 + \lambda_N - \lambda). \quad (1.51)$$

(See Fig. 1.6.)

Now let

$$\tilde{P}_{2k}(\lambda) = \frac{T_k\{[\beta + \alpha - 2(1 - \tilde{P}_2(\lambda))]/[\beta - \alpha]\}}{T_k[(\beta + \alpha)/(\beta - \alpha)]}, \qquad k = 1, 2, \ldots, \quad (1.52)$$

where $\alpha = 1 - \tilde{P}_2(\lambda_1)$ and $\beta = 1 - \tilde{P}_2(b)$. It can be shown that

$$\max_{\lambda \in S} |\tilde{P}_{2k}(\lambda)| = \min_{P_{2k} \in \Pi_{2k}^1} \max_{\lambda \in S} |P_{2k}(\lambda)|,$$

making $\tilde{P}_{2k}(\lambda)$ the best polynomial in Π_{2k}^1 we can find on the basis of the given set S. Since

$$\max_{\lambda \in S} |\tilde{P}_{2k}(\lambda)| = T_k[(\beta + \alpha)/(\beta - \alpha)]^{-1}, \qquad k = 1, 2, 3, \ldots,$$

we obtain from (1.48) the estimate

$$\|\mathbf{x}^k - \hat{\mathbf{x}}\|_H \le T_{k/2}[(\beta + \alpha)/(\beta - \alpha)]^{-1}\|\mathbf{x}^0 - \hat{\mathbf{x}}\|_H, \qquad k = 2, 4, 6, \ldots.$$

Using (A.5) again we find that $p(\varepsilon)$, the smallest number of iterations that makes $\|\mathbf{x}^k - \hat{\mathbf{x}}\|_H \le \varepsilon\|\mathbf{x}^0 - \hat{\mathbf{x}}\|_H$, satisfies

$$p(\varepsilon) \le \tfrac{1}{2}\sqrt{4\beta/\alpha}\,\ln(2/\varepsilon) + 1. \quad (1.53)$$

By analogy with (1.50) we call the quantity $4\beta/\alpha$ the *effective spectral condition number* of H. A simple computation shows that

$$4\beta/\alpha = r\kappa(H), \qquad r = 4bc/\lambda_N^2 \le 4b/\lambda_N.$$

Since $r < 1$ by assumption, we see that (1.53) is a better bound than (1.50).

Example 1.2. For some m and b satisfying $1 < m < N$ and $\lambda_{N-m} \le b < \lambda_{N-m+1}$, let $S = S_1 \cup S_2$, where $S_1 = [\lambda_1, b]$ and $S_2 = \bigcup_{i=N-m+1}^{N} \lambda_i$. Clearly, all of the eigenvalues are in S. We assume that m and b are "small," so that S describes a distribution in which a few of the highest eigenvalues are well separated from the remaining eigenvalues.

The polynomial

$$\tilde{P}_k(\lambda) = \left[\prod_{i=N-m+1}^{N} \left(1 - \frac{\lambda}{\lambda_i}\right) \right] \frac{T_{k-m}[(b + \lambda_1 - 2\lambda)/(b - \lambda_1)]}{T_{k-m}[(b + \lambda_1)/(b - \lambda_1)]} \quad (1.54)$$

belongs to Π_k^1, and since

$$\max_{\lambda \in S} |\tilde{P}_k(\lambda)| = \max_{\lambda \in S_1} |\tilde{P}_k(\lambda)|$$

$$\le \max_{\lambda \in S_1} \frac{T_{k-m}[(b + \lambda_1 - 2\lambda)/(b - \lambda_1)]}{T_{k-m}[(b + \lambda_1)/(b - \lambda_1)]} = T_{k-m}\left(\frac{b + \lambda_1}{b - \lambda_1}\right)^{-1},$$

we may take this as the value of M in (1.48). This leads to the bound

$$p(\varepsilon) \le \tfrac{1}{2}\sqrt{b/\lambda_1} \, \ln(2/\varepsilon) + m + 1. \quad (1.55)$$

If m and b are sufficiently small, then (1.55) is a better bound than (1.50).

The foregoing examples illustrate the fact that the "clustering" of eigenvalues tends to increase the rate of convergence of the conjugate gradient method. This is related to the property, mentioned earlier, that the value of m in Theorem 1.10 never exceeds the number of distinct eigenvalues.

Because of its generality and simplicity, the bound given by (1.50) is very useful and motivates our use of the spectral condition number $\kappa(H)$ to assess the rate of convergence. It should be kept in mind, however, that depending on the distribution of the interior eigenvalues (1.50) may be quite pessimistic, hiding the true rate of convergence. For further reading on this topic see Stewart (1975), Axelsson (1976), Jennings (1977), Greenbaum (1979), and also van der Vorst and van der Sluis (1984), where it is shown that the distribution of the smallest eigenvalues plays a particularly important role.

1.4   The Preconditioned Conjugate Gradient Method

The technique of preconditioning was introduced in Section 1.2 in the context of the method of steepest descent. It was seen that the basic idea is to reduce the problem of minimizing the functional

$$f(\mathbf{x}) = \tfrac{1}{2}\mathbf{x}^{\mathsf{T}}H\mathbf{x} - \mathbf{b}^{\mathsf{T}}\mathbf{x} + c, \qquad \mathbf{x} \in R^N$$

to that of minimizing the related functional

$$\tilde{f}(\mathbf{y}) = \tfrac{1}{2}\mathbf{y}^{\mathsf{T}}\tilde{H}\mathbf{y} - \tilde{\mathbf{b}}^{\mathsf{T}}\mathbf{y} + \tilde{c}, \qquad \mathbf{y} \in R^N,$$

where

$$\tilde{H} = E^{-1}HE^{-\mathsf{T}}, \qquad \tilde{\mathbf{b}} = E^{-1}\mathbf{b}, \qquad \tilde{c} = c,$$

E being some nonsingular matrix. The motivation given for minimizing $\tilde{f}(\mathbf{y})$ instead of $f(\mathbf{x})$ was the observation that if E makes $\kappa(\tilde{H}) < \kappa(H)$, then the rate of convergence of the method of steepest descent is greater for $\tilde{f}(\mathbf{y})$ than for $f(\mathbf{x})$. Since the rate of convergence of the conjugate gradient method also depends on the spectral condition number of the Hessian, preconditioning is just as relevant for this method. We shall begin this section with some general remarks concerning preconditioning matrices and show that the class of so-called stationary iterative methods for solving the system $H\hat{\mathbf{x}} = \mathbf{b}$ is a source of such matrices. Then we shall look at two important examples in detail, the preconditioning matrix derived from the SSOR stationary iterative method and that based on an incomplete factorization of H. Finally, we shall discuss the computer implementation of the preconditioned conjugate gradient method.

Formulation of the Method

As before, the preconditioned method can be formulated in two versions, one "transformed" and one "untransformed." The untransformed method directly produces vectors that approximate the desired minimizer $\hat{\mathbf{x}} \equiv H^{-1}\mathbf{b}$, whereas the transformed method produces approximations to $\hat{\mathbf{y}} \equiv \tilde{H}^{-1}\tilde{\mathbf{b}}$ that must be transformed to obtain approximations to $\hat{\mathbf{x}}$. Because of this advantage of the untransformed method, we will confine our attention to it for the time being and call it the *preconditioned conjugate gradient method*. It is defined as follows:

$$\tau_k = \mathbf{g}^{k\mathsf{T}}\mathbf{h}^k / \mathbf{d}^{k\mathsf{T}}H\mathbf{d}^k, \tag{1.56a}$$

$$\mathbf{x}^{k+1} = \mathbf{x}^k + \tau_k\mathbf{d}^k, \tag{1.56b}$$

$$\mathbf{g}^{k+1} = \mathbf{g}^k + \tau_k H\mathbf{d}^k, \tag{1.56c}$$

$$\mathbf{h}^{k+1} = C^{-1}\mathbf{g}^{k+1} \tag{1.56d}$$

$$\beta_k = \mathbf{g}^{k+1\mathsf{T}}\mathbf{h}^{k+1} / \mathbf{g}^{k\mathsf{T}}\mathbf{h}^k, \tag{1.56e}$$

$$\mathbf{d}^{k+1} = -\mathbf{h}^{k+1} + \beta_k\mathbf{d}^k, \tag{1.56f}$$

where $k = 0, 1, \ldots$. Initially we choose $\mathbf{x}^0$ and put $\mathbf{g}^0 = H\mathbf{x}^0 - \mathbf{b}$, $\mathbf{h}^0 = C^{-1}\mathbf{g}^0$, and $\mathbf{d}^0 = -\mathbf{h}^0$. The multiplication by C^{-1} in (1.56d) is to be interpreted as solving a system of equations with coefficient matrix C.

The derivation of (1.56) is analogous to that of (1.26). The details are left to Exercise 1.20.

The Preconditioning Matrix C

The matrix C is given by

$$C = EE^{\mathrm{T}}$$

and is positive definite, since E is nonsingular by assumption. An analysis of (1.56) shows that the sequence $\mathbf{y}^0, \mathbf{y}^1, \ldots$, where $\mathbf{y}^k = E^{\mathrm{T}}\mathbf{x}^k$, can be obtained by applying the ordinary conjugate gradient method to the quadratic functional $\tilde{f}(\mathbf{y})$. Thus $\lim_{k \to \infty} \mathbf{y}^k = \hat{\mathbf{y}}$, and the rate of convergence (in the $\tilde{H}$-norm) depends on $\kappa(\tilde{H})$ [See (1.50)]. Since the relations $\mathbf{y}^k = E^{\mathrm{T}}\mathbf{x}^k$, $k = 0, 1, \ldots$ and $\hat{\mathbf{y}} = E^{\mathrm{T}}\hat{\mathbf{x}}$ imply

$$\|\mathbf{y}^k - \hat{\mathbf{y}}\|_{\tilde{H}} = \|\mathbf{x}^k - \hat{\mathbf{x}}\|_H,$$

we conclude that $\lim_{k \to \infty} \mathbf{x}^k = \hat{\mathbf{x}}$ and that the rate of convergence (in the H-norm) also depends on $\kappa(\tilde{H})$. More specifically, the smallest number of iterations $p(\varepsilon)$ required to make

$$\|\mathbf{x}^k - \hat{\mathbf{x}}\|_H \leq \varepsilon \|\mathbf{x}^0 - \hat{\mathbf{x}}\|_H \qquad \forall \mathbf{x}^0 \in R^N$$

satisfies

$$p(\varepsilon) \leq \tfrac{1}{2}\sqrt{\kappa(\tilde{H})} \ln(2/\varepsilon) + 1. \tag{1.57}$$

Thus, if C has the property that $\kappa(\tilde{H}) < \kappa(H)$, then the preconditioned conjugate gradient method has a faster rate of convergence that the nonpreconditioned method.

It is important to observe that it is the preconditioning matrix C and not E that appears in algorithm (1.56). Since any positive definite matrix C has many factorizations of the form $C = EE^{\mathrm{t}}$, we may search for preconditioning matrices among the entire class of positive definite matrices. Further, we are not required to use C factored in the form $C = EE^{\mathrm{T}}$, and in fact we shall have use for the more general form $C = FG^{-1}F^{\mathrm{T}}$. Finally, let us recall that the spectral condition number $\kappa(\tilde{H})$ is given by

$$\kappa(\tilde{H}) = \tilde{\lambda}_N/\tilde{\lambda}_1,$$

where $\tilde{\lambda}_1$ and $\tilde{\lambda}_N$ are the smallest and largest eigenvalues, respectively, of $C^{-1}H$, and hence is entirely independent of the way we choose to factorize C.

In general, a good preconditioning matrix has the following properties:

(1) $\kappa(\tilde{H})$ is significantly less than $\kappa(H)$;

(2) the factors of C can be determined quickly and do not require excessive storage in relation to H;

(3) the system $C\mathbf{h}^k = \mathbf{g}^k$ can be solved much more efficiently than $H\mathbf{x} = \mathbf{b}$.

Consider the requirement

$$1 \leq \kappa(\tilde{H}) < \kappa(H). \tag{1.58}$$

If and only if C is a scalar multiple of H is it true that $\kappa(\tilde{H}) = 1$ (Exercise 1.22), and hence we would like C to be a good approximation to H. On the other hand, the fact that $\kappa(\tilde{H}) = \kappa(H)$ when C is the identity matrix indicates that C need not be a particularly good approximation to H for (1.58) to hold.

The preconditioning matrices to be presented shortly are of the form

$$C = FG^{-1}F^{\mathrm{T}}, \tag{1.59}$$

where F is sparse and lower triangular and G is diagonal. The system $C\mathbf{h}^k = \mathbf{g}^k$ in the kth iteration of the preconditioned conjugate gradient method is solved in the following steps:

$$F\tilde{\mathbf{h}}^k = \mathbf{g}^k \qquad \text{is solved for } \tilde{\mathbf{h}}^k;$$

$$F^{\mathrm{T}}\mathbf{h}^k = G\tilde{\mathbf{h}}^k \qquad \text{is solved for } \mathbf{h}^k.$$

Requirement (3) for a good preconditioning matrix is satisfied, since it is easy to solve triangular systems of equations. Regarding requirement (2), two situations can arise:

(1) the entries of F and G are also entries of H and hence are immediately available;

(2) F and G are obtained from H by some computational process and require storage beyond that needed for H.

Stationary Iterative Methods

A source of preconditioning matrices is the class of stationary iterative methods for solving the system $H\hat{\mathbf{x}} = \mathbf{b}$ (Hageman and Young, 1981; Varga, 1962; Young, 1971). Let

$$H = M + R \tag{1.60}$$

be any decomposition of H such that M is nonsingular. Let $\mathbf{x}^0$ be an arbitrary vector and consider the vector sequence $\mathbf{x}^0, \mathbf{x}^1, \mathbf{x}^2, \ldots$ generated by solving the systems

$$Mx^{k+1} = -Rx^k + b, \qquad k = 0, 1, 2, \dots . \tag{1.61}$$

To determine when this sequence converges to $\hat{x}$ we combine the relation

$$M\hat{x} = -R\hat{x} + b$$

with (1.61) to obtain

$$M(x^{k+1} - \hat{x}) = -R(x^k - \hat{x}).$$

After multiplying by M^{-1} we find by recursion that

$$x^k - \hat{x} = B^k(x^0 - \hat{x}), \qquad B \equiv -M^{-1}R. \tag{1.62}$$

Let $\{\xi_i, w_i\}_{i=1}^N$ denote the eigensolutions of B and assume that the eigenvectors are linearly independent. Then for any x^0 we can express $x^0 - \hat{x}$ in the form

$$x^0 - \hat{x} = c_1 w_1 + c_2 w_2 + \cdots + c_N w_N,$$

and it follows from (1.62) that

$$x^k - \hat{x} = c_1 \xi_1^k w_1 + c_2 \xi_2^k w_2 + \cdots + c_N \xi_N^k w_N.$$

This relation establishes that

$$\lim_{k \to \infty} x^k = \hat{x} \qquad \forall x^0 \in R^N \quad \Leftrightarrow \quad \rho(B) < 1, \tag{1.63}$$

where $\rho(B)$ is the spectral radius of B defined by

$$\rho(B) = \max_{1 \le i \le N} |\xi_i|.$$

The inequality $\rho(B) < 1$ is thus the necessary and sufficient condition for the convergence of the sequence $x^0, x^1, x^2, \dots$ to $\hat{x}$ for any initial vector x^0. Further, the rate of convergence increases as $\rho(B)$ decreases. Although this analysis has assumed the linear independence of the eigenvectors of B, (1.63) can in fact be proved for any matrix B [see Varga (1962)].

We call (1.60) a *splitting* of H and (1.61) the corresponding *stationary iterative method* for solving the system $H\hat{x} = b$. A good stationary iterative method has the properties that it is relatively easy to solve a system of equations having coefficient matrix M and that $\rho(B) < 1$ (the smaller, the better).

Suppose now that H and M are positive definite and consider M as the preconditioning matrix C for the conjugate gradient method. Since we are assuming that the stationary iterative method is a good one, the requirement that it be easy to solve the system $Ch^k = g^k$ in (1.56) is satisfied. To investigate the size of the spectral condition number $\kappa(\tilde{H})$, we note that the relation

$$C^{-1}H = M^{-1}H = I - B$$

implies that the eigenvalues of $C^{-1}H$ are

$$\tilde{\lambda}_i = 1 - \xi_i, \qquad i = 1, 2, \ldots, N.$$

If the eigenvalues of B are ordered by

$$-1 < \xi_N \le \cdots \le \xi_2 \le \xi_1 < 1,$$

then we have the usual ordering for the eigenvalues of $C^{-1}H$,

$$0 < \tilde{\lambda}_1 \le \tilde{\lambda}_2 \le \cdots \le \tilde{\lambda}_N,$$

and the spectral condition number is

$$\kappa(\tilde{H}) = \tilde{\lambda}_N/\tilde{\lambda}_1 = (1 - \xi_N)/(1 - \xi_1) \le [1 + \rho(B)]/[1 - \rho(B)]. \quad (1.64)$$

Using this inequality one can compare the rates of convergence of the stationary iterative method and the corresponding preconditioned conjugate gradient method. Thus, let k_1 and k_2 denote the number of iterations required by the two methods, respectively, to make

$$\|\mathbf{x}^k - \hat{\mathbf{x}}\|_H < \varepsilon\gamma,$$

where ε is any positive value and

$$\mathbf{x}^0 - \hat{\mathbf{x}} = \sum_{i=1}^N c_i \mathbf{w}_i, \qquad \gamma = \sum_{i=1}^N |c_i| \, \|\mathbf{w}_i\|_H.$$

It is straightforward to derive bounds $\hat{k}_1$ and $\hat{k}_2$ on k_1 and k_2, respectively, such that

$$\hat{k}_2/\hat{k}_1 \le \tfrac{1}{2} f[\rho(B)][\ln(2/\varepsilon)/\ln(1/\varepsilon)], \qquad (1.65)$$

where we have introduced the function

$$f(\xi) = \ln(1/\xi)\sqrt{(1 + \xi)/(1 - \xi)}, \qquad 0 < \xi < 1.$$

(See Exercise 1.23 for details.) This function is monotonic decreasing, and

$$f(\xi) = \left(\sqrt{2(1 - \xi)}\right)^{-1} + O[(1 - \xi)^{3/2}], \qquad \xi \to 1. \quad (1.66)$$

Since $\lim_{\xi \to 1} f(\xi) = 0$, (1.65) indicates that the preconditioned conjugate gradient method is very much faster than the stationary iterative method when $\rho(B)$ is close to unity, which is the case when the given problem is difficult.

Note that if B has the property that $\xi_N < -1$, then it may still be useful as a preconditioning matrix even though the corresponding stationary iterative method diverges.

SSOR Preconditioning

The symmetric successive overrelaxation method (SSOR) for solving the system $H\hat{x} = b$ is the two-step iterative procedure defined by the following algorithm (Sheldon, 1955):

$$x_i^{(k+1/2)} = (1 - \omega)x_i^{(k)} - \frac{\omega}{h_{ii}}\left(\sum_{j=1}^{i-1} h_{ij}x_j^{(k+1/2)} + \sum_{j=i+1}^{N} h_{ij}x_j^{(k)} - b_i\right),$$

$$i = 1, 2, ..., N, \qquad (1.67a)$$

$$x_i^{(k+1)} = (1 - \omega)x_i^{(k+1/2)} - \frac{\omega}{h_{ii}}\left(\sum_{j=1}^{i-1} h_{ij}x_j^{(k+1/2)} + \sum_{j=i+1}^{N} h_{ij}x_j^{(k+1)} - b_i\right),$$

$$i = N, N - 1, ..., 1. \quad (1.67b)$$

Let H (which, as usual, we assume to be positive definite) be decomposed as

$$H = D + L + L^{\mathrm{T}},$$

where

$$d_{ij} = \begin{cases} h_{ij} & \text{for} \quad i = j, \\ 0 & \text{for} \quad i \neq j, \end{cases} \qquad l_{ij} = \begin{cases} h_{ij} & \text{for} \quad i > j, \\ 0 & \text{for} \quad i \leq j; \end{cases}$$

D and L are the diagonal and lower triangular parts of H, respectively. Equation (1.67) can be formulated as

$$x^{k+1/2} = (1 - \omega)x^k - \omega D^{-1}(Lx^{k+1/2} + L^{\mathrm{T}}x^k - b),$$

$$x^{k+1} = (1 - \omega)x^{k+1/2} - \omega D^{-1}(Lx^{k+1/2} + L^{\mathrm{T}}x^{k+1} - b)$$

or, after the elimination of $x^{k+1/2}$,

$$x^{k+1} = Bx^k + M^{-1}b, \qquad (1.68)$$

where

$$B = \left(\frac{1}{\omega}D + L^{\mathrm{T}}\right)^{-1}\left[\left(\frac{1}{\omega} - 1\right)D - L\right]\left(\frac{1}{\omega}D + L\right)^{-1}\left[\left(\frac{1}{\omega} - 1\right)D - L^{\mathrm{T}}\right],$$

$$M = \frac{1}{2 - \omega}\left(\frac{1}{\omega}D + L\right)\left(\frac{1}{\omega}D\right)^{-1}\left(\frac{1}{\omega}D + L\right)^{\mathrm{T}}.$$

Equation (1.68) assumes the form of (1.61) when we multiply by M and introduce $R \equiv -MB$. We leave it to the reader to verify that M and R constitute a splitting of H.

We now consider the use of the *SSOR preconditioning matrix*

$$C = \frac{1}{2 - \omega}\left(\frac{1}{\omega}D + L\right)\left(\frac{1}{\omega}D\right)^{-1}\left(\frac{1}{\omega}D + L\right)^{\mathrm{T}} \qquad (1.69)$$

in the preconditioned conjugate gradient algorithm (1.56). The matrix C is positive definite if and only if $0 < \omega < 2$, and we henceforth restrict ω to this interval. Note that apart from the scalar factor (which will be dropped later) C has the factorized form of (1.59).

Theorem 1.13. The spectral condition number $\kappa(\tilde{H})$ associated with the preconditioned conjugate gradient method, with C given by (1.69), satisfies

$$\kappa(\tilde{H}) \leq F(\omega),$$

where

$$F(\omega) = \frac{1 + [(2 - \omega)^2/4\omega]\mu + \omega\,\delta}{2 - \omega}, \qquad 0 < \omega < 2, \qquad (1.70)$$

$$\mu = \max_{x \neq 0} x^T D x / x^T H x > 0,$$

$$\delta = \max_{x \neq 0} \frac{x^T(LD^{-1}L^T - \frac{1}{4}D)x}{x^T H x} \geq -\frac{1}{4}.$$

Further, if

$$\left\| D^{-1/2}LD^{-1/2} \right\|_\infty \leq \tfrac{1}{2}, \ \left\| D^{-1/2}L^T D^{-1/2} \right\|_\infty \leq \tfrac{1}{2}, \qquad (1.71)$$

then

$$-\tfrac{1}{4} \leq \delta \leq 0.$$

PROOF: $\kappa(\tilde{H}) = \tilde{\lambda}_N/\tilde{\lambda}_1$, where $\tilde{\lambda}_1$ and $\tilde{\lambda}_N$ are the smallest and largest eigenvalues of $C^{-1}H$, respectively. These eigenvalues have the property that

$$\tilde{\lambda}_1 = \min_{x \neq 0} R(x), \qquad \tilde{\lambda}_N = \max_{x \neq 0} R(x), \qquad (1.72)$$

where $R(x)$ is the Rayleigh quotient defined by

$$R(x) = x^T H x / x^T C x, \qquad x \neq 0.$$

We shall show first that $\tilde{\lambda}_N \leq 1$. Let

$$A = (2/\omega - 1)D, \qquad V = (1 - 1/\omega)D + L,$$

and note that A is positive definite for $0 < \omega < 2$. The matrix C in (1.69) can be written as

$$C = (A + V)A^{-1}(A + V)^T = A + V + V^T + VA^{-1}V^T = H + VA^{-1}V^T,$$

and for any x and $y \equiv V^T x$ we have

$$x^T C x = x^T H x + y^T A^{-1} y.$$

The positive definiteness of C, H, and A^{-1} makes all of these terms non-negative, and it follows from (1.72) that $\tilde{\lambda}_N \leq 1$.

The matrix C can also be expressed as

$$C = (2 - \omega)^{-1}\left[H + \frac{1}{4\omega}(2 - \omega)^2 D + \omega\left(LD^{-1}L^{\text{T}} - \frac{1}{4}D\right)\right].$$

By forming $\mathbf{x}^{\text{T}}C\mathbf{x}$ and using the inequalities

$$\mathbf{x}^{\text{T}}D\mathbf{x} \leq \mu\mathbf{x}^{\text{T}}H\mathbf{x},$$

$$\mathbf{x}^{\text{T}}(LD^{-1}L^{\text{T}} - \tfrac{1}{4}D)\mathbf{x} \leq \delta\mathbf{x}^{\text{T}}H\mathbf{x},$$

we find that $R(\mathbf{x}) \geq 1/F(\omega) \; \forall \mathbf{x} \neq \mathbf{0}$, where $F(\omega)$ is given by (1.70). Then, by virtue of (1.72), $\tilde{\lambda}_1 \geq 1/F(\omega)$, and this result together with the inequality $\tilde{\lambda}_N \leq 1$ implies that $\kappa(\tilde{H}) \leq F(\omega)$.

The positive definiteness of H and D makes $\mu > 0$ and it remains only to estimate δ. Let $\mathbf{x}$ be a nonzero vector such that $L^{\text{T}}\mathbf{x} = \mathbf{0}$. (There must be such a vector since L^{T} is singular.) Then, since $D = H - L - L^{\text{T}}$,

$$\mathbf{x}^{\text{T}}(LD^{-1}L^{\text{T}} - \tfrac{1}{4}D)\mathbf{x} = -\tfrac{1}{4}\mathbf{x}^{\text{T}}H\mathbf{x}$$

implying $\delta \geq -\tfrac{1}{4}$.

Assume now that (1.71) is satisfied. (It is usually easy to determine whether these properties are present.) Simple calculations show that

$$\mathbf{x}^{\text{T}}LD^{-1}L^{\text{T}}\mathbf{x} = \mathbf{y}^{\text{T}}\tilde{L}\tilde{L}^{\text{T}}\mathbf{y}, \qquad \mathbf{x}^{\text{T}}D\mathbf{x} = \mathbf{y}^{\text{T}}\mathbf{y},$$

where $\mathbf{y} = D^{1/2}\mathbf{x}$ and $\tilde{L} = D^{-1/2}LD^{-1/2}$. Using basic inequalities we find that

$$\mathbf{y}^{\text{T}}\tilde{L}\tilde{L}^{\text{T}}\mathbf{y}/\mathbf{y}^{\text{T}}\mathbf{y} \leq \rho(\tilde{L}\tilde{L}^{\text{T}}) \leq \|\tilde{L}\tilde{L}^{\text{T}}\|_\infty \leq \|\tilde{L}\|_\infty \cdot \|\tilde{L}^{\text{T}}\|_\infty \leq \tfrac{1}{4},$$

where, for any matrix B, $\rho(B)$ and $\|B\|_\infty$ denote the spectral radius and maximum norm of B, respectively. (See the list of symbols at the beginning of this book.) Then,

$$\mathbf{x}^{\text{T}}LD^{-1}L^{\text{T}}\mathbf{x} - \tfrac{1}{4}\mathbf{x}^{\text{T}}D\mathbf{x} = \mathbf{y}^{\text{T}}\tilde{L}\tilde{L}^{\text{T}}\mathbf{y} - \tfrac{1}{4}\mathbf{y}^{\text{T}}\mathbf{y} \leq 0,$$

and hence $\delta \leq 0$. ∎

Rate of Convergence with Optimal SSOR Preconditioning

An analysis of $F(\omega)$, which we omit here, shows that

$$\min_{0 < \omega < 2} F(\omega) = F(\omega^*) = \sqrt{(\tfrac{1}{2} + \delta)\mu} + \tfrac{1}{2}, \tag{1.73a}$$

where

$$\omega^* = 2/[1 + (2/\sqrt{\mu})\sqrt{\tfrac{1}{2} + \delta}]. \tag{1.73b}$$

We shall now establish that $\mu \leq \kappa(H)$. For this purpose we introduce the Rayleigh quotient for H

$$\tilde{R}(\mathbf{x}) = \mathbf{x}^T H \mathbf{x} / \mathbf{x}^T \mathbf{x}, \qquad \mathbf{x} \neq \mathbf{0},$$

which has the properties

$$\lambda_1 = \min_{\mathbf{x} \neq \mathbf{0}} \tilde{R}(\mathbf{x}), \qquad \lambda_N = \max_{\mathbf{x} \neq \mathbf{0}} \tilde{R}(\mathbf{x}).$$

Further, because

$$\tilde{R}(\mathbf{e}_i) = h_{ii}, \qquad \mathbf{e}_i = [0, ..., 0, \overset{i}{1}, 0, ..., 0]^T,$$

we have

$$\max_{1 \leq i \leq N} h_{ii} \leq \lambda_N.$$

Now,

$$\mu = \max_{\mathbf{x} \neq \mathbf{0}} \frac{\mathbf{x}^T D \mathbf{x}}{\mathbf{x}^T H \mathbf{x}} \leq \frac{\max_{\mathbf{x} \neq \mathbf{0}} (\mathbf{x}^T D \mathbf{x} / \mathbf{x}^T \mathbf{x})}{\min_{\mathbf{x} \neq \mathbf{0}} (\mathbf{x}^T H \mathbf{x} / \mathbf{x}^T \mathbf{x})} = \frac{d}{\lambda_1},$$

where $d = \max_{1 \leq i \leq N} d_{ii}$. (Because D is diagonal, d is its largest eigenvalue and hence the largest value attained by the Rayleigh quotient for D.) But $d_{ii} = h_{ii}$ and it follows that $d \leq \lambda_N$ and $\mu \leq \kappa(H)$.

We thus arrive at the bound

$$\min_{0 < \omega < 2} \kappa(\tilde{H})(\omega) \leq \sqrt{(\tfrac{1}{2} + \delta)\kappa(H)} + \tfrac{1}{2}, \tag{1.73c}$$

and this is our major result for SSOR preconditioning. Whenever the right-hand side of (1.73c) is less than $\kappa(H)$, the SSOR-preconditioned conjugate gradient method (with the optimal value of ω) in general has a greater rate of convergence than the simple conjugate gradient method. Further, if $\kappa(H) \gg 1$ and if H satisfies (1.71), then SSOR preconditioning yields a *much* greater rate of convergence. As we shall see later, some of the matrices that arise in the finite element method are precisely of this type. In Section 7.1 we shall examine (1.73c) more closely in the context of finite element matrices.

Sensitivity of Rate of Convergence with Respect to ω

Normally, only rough estimates of μ and δ are available, and inserting these in the right-hand side of (1.73b) yields a value ω that differs from ω^*. One wants to know then whether the rate of convergence of the preconditioned conjugate gradient method is appreciably decreased. Let $\tilde{\mu}$ and $\tilde{\delta}$ denote the estimates, and let

$$\alpha = [\tilde{\mu}/(\tfrac{1}{2} + \tilde{\delta})]/[\mu/(\tfrac{1}{2} + \delta)].$$

It is not difficult to show that

$$\sqrt{F(\omega)/F(\omega^*)} \le \phi(\alpha) \equiv \sqrt{\tfrac{1}{2}[\sqrt{\alpha} + 1/\sqrt{\alpha}]}.$$

The left-hand side of this inequality is seen from (1.57) and Theorem 1.13 to be the ratio between bounds on the number of iterations required by ω and ω^*. $\phi(\alpha)$ is a very slowly increasing function of α for $\alpha > 1$:

α:	1	2	3	4	5
$\phi(\alpha)$:	1	1.03	1.07	1.12	1.16

Thus the rate of convergence of the conjugate gradient method with SSOR preconditioning is remarkably insensitive to the estimates of μ and δ.

Preconditioning by Incomplete Factorization

The relation $H = M + R$ allows us to eliminate R in the stationary iterative method (1.61). Using the identity

$$-Rx^k + b = Mx^k + b - Hx^k$$

we see that (1.61) is equivalent to

$$\text{Solve} \quad M\delta^k = b - Hx^k,$$
$$x^{k+1} = x^k + \delta^k, \tag{1.74}$$

for $k = 0, 1, 2, \dots$.

Sometimes (1.74) is the more advantageous formulation for computation. This is the case, for example, when $M = LU$, where L and U are computed approximations to the Gaussian factors of H (Chapter 6). The procedure defined by (1.74) is then commonly known as *iterative refinement*. The error $(H - LU)$ may be due exclusively to rounding errors (see Section 6.4) or it may be due to an "incomplete" factorization of H. It is the latter case we shall discuss here. As mentioned earlier, a splitting of H gives rise to a preconditioning matrix for (1.56) as well as to a stationary iterative method. Our interest in M above is its use as a preconditioning matrix. Readers not familiar with Gaussian elimination should read the relevant parts of Sections 6.1 and 6.2.

In Gaussian elimination, without pivoting, for an $(N \times N)$ matrix H, there arise the operations: for $r = 1, 2, \dots, N - 1$,

$$l_{ir} = h_{ir}^{(r)}/h_{rr}^{(r)},$$
$$h_{ij}^{(r+1)} = h_{ij}^{(r)} - l_{ir}h_{rj}^{(r)}, \qquad j = r + 1, r + 2, \dots, N, \tag{1.75}$$

where $i = r + 1, r + 2, ..., N$ and $h_{ij}^{(1)} = h_{ij}$ [see (6.1)]. L and $H^{(r+1)}$, $r = 1$, $2, ..., N - 1$ are completely defined $N \times N$ matrices when we add

$$l_{ij} = \begin{cases} 0 & \text{for} \quad j > i, \\ 1 & \text{for} \quad j = i, \end{cases} \tag{1.76}$$

$$h_{ij}^{(r+1)} = \begin{cases} 0 & \text{for} \quad j = 1, ..., r; \quad i = j + 1, ..., N, \\ h_{ij}^{(i)} & \text{for} \quad i = 1, ..., r; \quad j = i, ..., N. \end{cases} \tag{1.77}$$

$[H^{(r+1)}$ is illustrated by $K^{(3)}$ after algorithm (6.1).] Let

$$u_{ij} = \begin{cases} 0 & \text{for} \quad j < i, \\ h_{ij}^{(i)} & \text{for} \quad i = 1, 2, ..., N; \quad j = i, i + 1, ..., N; \end{cases} \tag{1.78}$$

L and U are lower and upper triangular matrices, respectively, and we recall the fundamental relation $H = LU$.

Provided that the whole of H were stored in the computer at the outset of the computation, every matrix entry generated by (1.75) could be written into the position in memory originally occupied by the entry of H with the same row and column indices. We are interested in the case in which H is large and sparse, however, and in which the storage of all of H is not tenable. The amount of storage required for the nonzero matrix entries in (1.75) is almost always greater than the number of nonzero entries of H, because of fill-in, but never greater than the size of the envelope. For any matrix H with symmetric structure $(h_{ij} \neq 0 \Rightarrow h_{ji} \neq 0)$ and no zeros on the main diagonal, let

$$m(i) = \min\{j; (1 \leq j \leq i) \wedge (h_{ij} \neq 0)\}, \qquad i = 1, 2, ..., N.$$

(i.e., $h_{i,m(i)}$ is the first nonzero entry in the ith row.) Then, the envelope of H is the set of index pairs

$$S = \{(i, j) \cup (j, i); m(i) \leq j \leq i, 1 \leq i \leq N\}.$$

See Fig. 6.1 for an illustration.

It is a common feature of the matrices that arise in finite element problems that the envelope is large but only sparsely populated by nonzero entries. (See Table 6.1.) Unfortunately, it is typical that most of the envelope is filled in during the elimination, a fact that can make the computer implementation of (1.75) expensive with regard to storage and computational labor. If we are willing to settle for an *incomplete factorization* of H, however, then we can reduce both substantially. The error, or *defect*,

$$R = H - LU \tag{1.79}$$

is acceptable, if not too large, because our purpose is to use LU as the pre-conditioning matrix C in (1.56).

The basic idea of incomplete factorization is to choose a symmetric subset J of S, always including the diagonal index pairs $(1, 1), (2, 2), ..., (N, N)$, and to modify (1.75) so that the nonzero entries of $H^{(2)}, H^{(3)}, ..., H^{(N)}$ are restricted to J. There are various ways this modification can be made. Ours is the following: if $(i, j) \notin J$ then we put $h_{ij}^{(r+1)} = 0$ and add $(h_{ij}^{(r)} - l_{ir}h_{rj}^{(r)})$ to the "current value" of $h_{ii}^{(r+1)}$. That is, for $r = 1, 2, ..., N - 1$ we perform the operations

$$l_{ir} = h_{ir}^{(r)}/h_{rr}^{(r)},$$

$$h_{ij}^{(r+1)} = \begin{cases} h_{ij}^{(r)} - l_{ir}h_{rj}^{(r)}, & (r + 1 \leq j \leq N) \wedge [(i, j) \in J] \wedge (j \neq i), \\ 0, & (r + 1 \leq j \leq N) \wedge [(i, j) \notin J], \\ h_{ii}^{(r)} - l_{ir}h_{ri}^{(r)} + \displaystyle\sum_{\substack{k=r+1 \\ (i,k) \notin J}}^{N} (h_{ik}^{(r)} - l_{ir}h_{rk}^{(r)}), & j = i, \end{cases} \tag{1.80}$$

where $i = r + 1, r + 2, ..., N$. When $r > 1$, $h_{ij}^{(r)} = 0$ for $(i, j) \notin J$ and the last line of (1.80) can be rewritten

$$h_{ii}^{(r+1)} = h_{ii}^{(r)} - l_{ir}h_{ri}^{(r)} - \sum_{\substack{k=r+1 \\ (i,k) \notin J}}^{N} l_{ir}h_{rk}^{(r)}. \tag{1.81}$$

We shall henceforth assume that J is large enough to include the index pairs of all nonzero entries in H, i.e., $S_H \subseteq J$, where

$$S_H = \{(i, j); h_{ij} \neq 0\}. \tag{1.82}$$

This implies that $h_{ij} = 0$, $(i, j) \notin J$, and (1.81) holds even for $r = 1$.

A computer implementation of this incomplete factorization method is shown in Fig. 1.7.

Remarks

1. The $(N \times N)$ matrices L, U, $H^{(r+1)}$, $r = 1, 2, ..., N - 1$ are completely defined when (1.80) is supplemented by (1.76)–(1.78). We call LU the *incomplete factorization* of H.

2. The code in Fig. 1.7 has the virtues of clarifying the calculations and of demonstrating that only matrix entries with index pairs in J need be referenced. If H is sparse, however, then the $N \times N$ array h would of course be much too wasteful of storage to be used in practice.

3. In the case when H is symmetric, storage and computing time can be roughly halved with appropriate programming. Note that the necessity of adding off-diagonal fill-in to the diagonal elements restricts the freedom with which the sequence of operations in (1.80) can be rearranged. For example, the row-wise algorithm of Fig. 6.9 for complete symmetric factorization, which uses only the lower left triangle of the matrix, cannot be immediately

extended to incomplete factorization. For details on computer implementation, see the end of this section and Exercise 1.27.

4. For any given H, the incomplete factors L and U depend only on the choice of J. If $J \supseteq S$ then L and U are the complete factors of H. Since the complete factors tend to occupy most of the envelope, L and U are usually incomplete when $J \subset S$. A reduction of J implies a reduction of computer storage, factorization time, and the time required to perform one iteration of (1.56) with $C = LU$. It also implies, however, an increase in the defect R that tends to decrease the rate of convergence of (1.56). These conflicting tendencies make it difficult to determine the optimal choice of J. Perhaps the most common choice is $J = S_H$, which allows no fill-in at all.

5. Early papers on incomplete factorization presented a method that differs from (1.80) in that, for $(i, j) \notin J$, one put $h_{ij}^{(r+1)} = 0$ without making any corresponding change in the diagonal entry $h_{ii}^{(r+1)}$. See, e.g., Varga (1960), Meijerink and van der Vorst (1977), and, more recently, Meijerink and van der Vorst (1981). (In some cases an incomplete Cholesky factorization is used instead of the Gaussian, but this difference is trivial.) Algorithm (1.80) was examined in Gustafsson (1978) and Axelsson and Munksgaard (1979) and often found to be superior for systems of equations arising in the finite element method. More precisely, it tended to reduce the spectral condition number $\kappa(\tilde{H})$, the ratio of the extreme eigenvalues of $(LU)^{-1}H$, which is important for the rate of convergence of (1.56) when incomplete factorization is used for preconditioning.

Since (1.80) is a modification of the earlier version of incomplete factorization, it is sometimes referred to in the literature as "modified incomplete factorization." The reader is hereby advised that in this book the latter phrase is reserved exclusively for a modification of (1.80) to be introduced in Chapter 7.

```
for r := 1 step 1 until (N − 1) do
begin d:= h[r, r];
    for i := (r + 1) step 1 until N do
    begin if (i, r) ∈ J and h[i, r] ≠ 0 then
        begin e := h[i, r]/d; h[i, r] := e;
            for j := (r + 1) step 1 until N do
            if (r, j) ∈ J and h[r, j] ≠ 0 then
            begin if (i, j) ∈ J then
                h[i, j] := h[i, j] − e × h[r, j]
                else
                h[i, i] := h[i, i] − e × h[r, j]
            end
        end
    end
end;
```

Fig. 1.7. An algorithm for incomplete factorization.

Stability of Incomplete Factorization

Our first task in the analysis of (1.80) is to determine whether the process is stable in the sense that the size of the entries of $H^{(r)}$ does not increase rapidly as r increases. In particular, we would like the "growth factor"

$$q \equiv \max_{i,j,r} |h_{ij}^{(r)}| / \max_{ij} |h_{ij}| \geq 1 \qquad (1.83)$$

to be reasonably bounded. (For a discussion of the stability concept see Section 6.4.) We shall now proceed to establish stability for an important class of matrices.

Definition 1.10. An $N \times N$ matrix H is *diagonally dominant* if

$$|h_{ii}| \geq \sum_{\substack{j=1, \\ j \neq i}}^{N} |h_{ij}|, \qquad i = 1, 2, ..., N.$$

For any matrix H such that $h_{ii} \neq 0$, $i = 1, 2, ..., N - 1$, let

$$n(i) = \max\{j; (i \leq j \leq N) \wedge (h_{ij} \neq 0)\}, \qquad i = 1, 2, ..., N - 1.$$

That is, $h_{i,n(i)}$ is the last nonzero entry in the ith row.

Definition 1.11. An $N \times N$ matrix H is an $\hat{M}$ *matrix* if

(1) $h_{ii} > 0$, $i = 1, 2, ..., N - 1$; $h_{NN} \geq 0$.
(2) $h_{ij} \leq 0$, $i, j = 1, 2, ..., N, i \neq j$.
(3) $n(i) > i$, $i = 1, 2, ..., N - 1$.

The definition of an $\hat{M}$ matrix is our own, introduced here for the convenience of the following analysis. The concept is closely related to that of an M matrix, which often appears in the literature on incomplete factorization and elsewhere. (H is an M matrix if all of its off-diagonal entries are nonpositive, it is nonsingular, and all entries of H^{-1} are nonnegative.)
Let

$$s_i^{(r)} = \sum_{j=1}^{N} h_{ij}^{(r)}, \qquad i = 1, 2, ..., N, \quad r = 1, 2, ..., N.$$

We call $s_i^{(r)}$ a *row sum* of $H^{(r)}$. If $H^{(r)}$ is an $\hat{M}$ matrix, then obviously $H^{(r)}$ is diagonally dominant if and only if all of its row sums are nonnegative.

Theorem 1.14. Let H be a diagonally dominant $\hat{M}$ matrix. Then, $H^{(2)}$, $H^{(3)}$, ..., $H^{(N)}$ defined by (1.80) and (1.77) are diagonally dominant $\hat{M}$ matrices.

Further,

$$h_{ij}^{(r+1)} \leq h_{ij}^{(r)} \leq 0, \qquad\qquad i, j = r+1, r+2, ..., N, \quad i \neq j, \quad (1.84a)$$

$$s_i^{(r+1)} \geq s_i^{(r)} \geq 0, \qquad\qquad i = r+1, r+2, ..., N, \qquad\qquad (1.84b)$$

$$0 < h_{ii}^{(r+1)} \leq h_{ii}^{(r)}, \qquad\quad i = r+1, r+2, ..., N-1, \qquad (1.84c)$$

$$0 \leq h_{NN}^{(r+1)} \leq h_{NN}^{(r)}. \qquad\qquad\qquad\qquad\qquad\qquad\qquad (1.84d)$$

PROOF: The proof is by induction. Thus, suppose that $H^{(r)}$ is a diagonally dominant $\hat{M}$ matrix. $H^{(r+1)}$ is identical to $H^{(r)}$ in the first r rows and contains zeros in the first r columns of the last $(N-r)$ rows. Hence, $H^{(r+1)}$ is a diagonally dominant $\hat{M}$ matrix if and only if the lower right $(N-r) \times (N-r)$ submatrix of $H^{(r+1)}$ is a diagonally dominant $\hat{M}$ matrix.

Consider an off-diagonal entry $h_{ij}^{(r+1)}$ in this submatrix. If $(i, j) \in J$, then, by (1.80),

$$h_{ij}^{(r+1)} = h_{ij}^{(r)} - l_{ir}h_{rj}^{(r)} = h_{ij}^{(r)} - \frac{h_{ir}^{(r)}h_{rj}^{(r)}}{h_{rr}^{(r)}} \leq h_{ij}^{(r)},$$

the inequality following from the fact that $H^{(r)}$ is assumed to be an $\hat{M}$ matrix. On the other hand, if $(i, j) \notin J$, then

$$h_{ij}^{(r+1)} = 0 = h_{ij}^{(r)}.$$

(Note that this would not necessarily be true for $r = 1$ without our earlier assumption that $S_H \subseteq J$.) Hence (1.84a) is established.

To prove (1.84b) we observe that

$$s_i^{(r+1)} = \sum_{j=r+1}^{N} h_{ij}^{(r+1)}$$

$$= \sum_{j=r+1}^{N} (h_{ij}^{(r)} - l_{ir}h_{rj}^{(r)}) \qquad \text{[from (1.80)]}$$

$$= \sum_{j=r+1}^{N} h_{ij}^{(r)} - (h_{ir}^{(r)}/h_{rr}^{(r)}) \sum_{j=r+1}^{N} h_{rj}^{(r)}$$

$$= (s_i^{(r)} - h_{ir}^{(r)}) - (h_{ir}^{(r)}/h_{rr}^{(r)})(s_r^{(r)} - h_{rr}^{(r)})$$

$$= s_i^{(r)} - (h_{ir}^{(r)}/h_{rr}^{(r)})s_r^{(r)}. \qquad\qquad (1.85)$$

Inequality (1.84b) follows, since $H^{(r)}$ is a diagonally dominant $\hat{M}$ matrix.

For a diagonal entry $h_{ii}^{(r+1)}$, we see from (1.81) and a consideration of signs that $h_{ii}^{(r+1)} \leq h_{ii}^{(r)}$, and it remains only to establish the sign of $h_{ii}^{(r+1)}$. By (1.84b),

$$s_i^{(r+1)} = h_{ii}^{(r+1)} - \sum_{\substack{j=r+1 \\ j \neq i}}^{N} |h_{ij}^{(r+1)}| \geq 0$$

and hence

$$h_{ii}^{(r+1)} \geq \sum_{\substack{j=r+1 \\ j \neq i}}^{N} \left| h_{ij}^{(r+1)} \right| \geq 0, \qquad i = r+1, r+2, \ldots, N.$$

Then

$$h_{ii}^{(r+1)} \geq \left| h_{i,n(i)}^{(r+1)} \right| \geq \left| h_{i,n(i)} \right| > 0, \qquad i = r+1, r+2, \ldots, N-1,$$

and the proof is complete. ■

Theorem 1.15. Incomplete factorization, as defined by (1.80), is a stable numerical process if H is a diagonally dominant $\hat{M}$ matrix.

PROOF: The entry of greatest absolute value of any diagonally dominant $\hat{M}$ matrix must be on the main diagonal. Further, the preceding theorem establishes that

$$0 \leq h_{ii}^{(r)} \leq h_{ii}.$$

Hence,

$$\max_{j,r} \left| h_{ij}^{(r)} \right| = h_{ii},$$

and the growth factor defined in (1.83) is equal to one, the optimal value. ■

Analysis of the Defect

Our next objective is to examine the defect $R = H - LU$. Let $S^{(r)}$ denote the matrix obtained from $H^{(r)}$ by replacing all entries outside the lower right $(N - r + 1) \times (N - r + 1)$ submatrix by zero. For example, if $N = 6$ and $r = 3$, we have matrices (I) and (II).

$$H^{(3)} = \begin{bmatrix} h_{11}^{(1)} & h_{12}^{(1)} & h_{13}^{(1)} & h_{14}^{(1)} & h_{15}^{(1)} & h_{16}^{(1)} \\ 0 & h_{22}^{(2)} & h_{23}^{(2)} & h_{24}^{(2)} & h_{25}^{(2)} & h_{26}^{(2)} \\ 0 & 0 & h_{33}^{(3)} & h_{34}^{(3)} & h_{35}^{(3)} & h_{36}^{(3)} \\ 0 & 0 & h_{43}^{(3)} & h_{44}^{(3)} & h_{45}^{(3)} & h_{46}^{(3)} \\ 0 & 0 & h_{53}^{(3)} & h_{54}^{(3)} & h_{55}^{(3)} & h_{56}^{(3)} \\ 0 & 0 & h_{63}^{(3)} & h_{64}^{(3)} & h_{65}^{(3)} & h_{66}^{(3)} \end{bmatrix}, \qquad \text{(I)}$$

$$S^{(3)} = \begin{bmatrix} 0 & 0 & 0 & 0 & 0 & 0 \\ 0 & 0 & 0 & 0 & 0 & 0 \\ 0 & 0 & h_{33}^{(3)} & h_{34}^{(3)} & h_{35}^{(3)} & h_{36}^{(3)} \\ 0 & 0 & h_{43}^{(3)} & h_{44}^{(3)} & h_{45}^{(3)} & h_{46}^{(3)} \\ 0 & 0 & h_{53}^{(3)} & h_{54}^{(3)} & h_{55}^{(3)} & h_{56}^{(3)} \\ 0 & 0 & h_{63}^{(3)} & h_{64}^{(3)} & h_{65}^{(3)} & h_{66}^{(3)} \end{bmatrix}. \qquad \text{(II)}$$

It is convenient to decompose the typical step $H^{(r)} \to H^{(r+1)}$ of (1.80) into the two steps $H^{(r)} \to \tilde{H}^{(r+1)}$ and $\tilde{H}^{(r+1)} \to H^{(r+1)}$, where $\tilde{H}^{(r+1)}$ is the result of a step of ordinary Gaussian elimination applied to $H^{(r)}$. Let $\tilde{S}^{(r+1)}$ denote the matrix obtained from $\tilde{H}^{(r+1)}$ by replacing all entries outside the lower right $(N - r) \times (N - r)$ submatrix by zero. We leave it to the reader to verify that

$$\tilde{S}^{(r+1)} = S^{(r)} - \mathbf{l}^{(r)}\mathbf{u}^{(r)}, \qquad r = 1, 2, \ldots, N - 1, \tag{1.86}$$

where

$$\mathbf{l}^{(r)} = \begin{bmatrix} 0 \\ \vdots \\ 0 \\ 1 \\ l_{r+1,r} \\ l_{r+2,r} \\ \vdots \\ l_{N,r} \end{bmatrix} = \frac{1}{h_{rr}^{(r)}} \begin{bmatrix} 0 \\ \vdots \\ 0 \\ h_{rr}^{(r)} \\ h_{r+1,r}^{(r)} \\ h_{r+2,r}^{(r)} \\ \vdots \\ h_{N,r}^{(r)} \end{bmatrix} \begin{matrix} \updownarrow \ r-1 \\ \\ \\ \\ \updownarrow \ N-r+1 \\ \\ \\ \end{matrix}$$

and

$$\mathbf{u}^{(r)} = \overset{\xleftarrow{\quad r-1 \quad}\,\xleftarrow{\quad N-r+1 \quad}}{[0, \ldots, 0, u_{rr}, u_{r,r+1}, \ldots, u_{rN}]}$$
$$= [0, \ldots, 0, h_{rr}^{(r)}, h_{r,r+1}^{(r)}, \ldots, h_{rN}^{(r)}].$$

(Note that in defining $\mathbf{u}^{(r)}$ as a *row* vector we are departing from our usual vector notation.) $\mathbf{l}^{(r)}$ and $\mathbf{u}^{(r)}$ are the rth column and row of L and U, respectively, where LU is the incomplete factorization of H.

Let

$$R^{(r+1)} = \tilde{H}^{(r+1)} - H^{(r+1)}.$$

Since $\tilde{H}^{(r+1)}$ and $H^{(r+1)}$ are identical outside the lower right $(N - r) \times (N - r)$ corner, the nonzero entries of $R^{(r+1)}$ are restricted to this corner. An examination of the incomplete factorization process establishes that

$$r_{ij}^{(r+1)} = \begin{cases} 0 & \text{for } (i, j) \in J \wedge i \neq j, \\ -l_{ir}h_{rj}^{(r)} & \text{for } (i, j) \notin J, \\ \displaystyle\sum_{\substack{k=r+1 \\ (i,k)\notin J}}^{N} l_{ir}h_{rk}^{(r)} & \text{for } i = j, \end{cases} \tag{1.87}$$

for $i, j = r + 1, r + 2, \ldots, N$. Obviously,

$$R^{(r+1)} = \tilde{S}^{(r+1)} - S^{(r+1)},$$

and combining this relation with (1.86) we obtain

$$S^{(r+1)} = S^{(r)} - \mathbf{l}^{(r)}\mathbf{u}^{(r)} - R^{(r+1)}, \qquad r = 1, 2, ..., N - 1.$$

Then, by recursion,

$$S^{(N)} = S^{(1)} - \sum_{r=1}^{N-1} \mathbf{l}^{(r)}\mathbf{u}^{(r)} - R, \qquad (1.88)$$

where

$$R = \sum_{r=1}^{N-1} R^{(r+1)}. \qquad (1.89)$$

[We shall see shortly that (1.89) is consistent with (1.79).]

Now, $S^{(1)} = H^{(1)} = H$ and

$$s_{ij}^{(N)} = \begin{cases} 0 & \text{for} \quad (i, j) \neq (N, N) \\ u_{NN} = h_{NN}^{(N)} & \text{for} \quad i = j = N \end{cases}$$

or, equivalently, $S^{(N)} = \mathbf{l}^{(N)}\mathbf{u}^{(N)}$, where

$$\mathbf{l}^{(N)} = \begin{bmatrix} 0 \\ \vdots \\ 0 \\ 1 \end{bmatrix}, \qquad \mathbf{u}^{(N)} = [0, \cdot, 0, u_{NN}].$$

These relations allow us to rewrite (1.88) as

$$H = \sum_{r=1}^{N} \mathbf{l}^{(r)}\mathbf{u}^{(r)} + R.$$

But since $\mathbf{l}^{(1)}, \mathbf{l}^{(2)}, ..., \mathbf{l}^{(N)}$ and $\mathbf{u}^{(1)}, \mathbf{u}^{(2)}, ..., \mathbf{u}^{(N)}$ are the columns and rows of L and U, respectively, a standard matrix identity tells us that

$$\sum_{r=1}^{N} \mathbf{l}^{(r)}\mathbf{u}^{(r)} = LU.$$

Thus, we have proved the following theorem.

Theorem 1.16. Let L and U denote the incomplete factors of H determined by (1.80). Then,

$$H = LU + R,$$

where R is given by (1.89) and (1.87).

Note that the only assumption in Theorem 1.16 is the implicit one that (1.80) must not break down, i.e., we require $h_{rr}^{(r)} \neq 0$ for $r = 1, 2, ..., N - 1$. The proof of Theorem 1.14 shows that this requirement is satisfied if H is a diagonally dominant $\hat{M}$ matrix.

Singularity

A diagonally dominant $\hat{M}$ matrix may be singular, a simple example being

$$H = \begin{bmatrix} 1 & -1 \\ -1 & 1 \end{bmatrix}.$$

Even if a diagonally dominant $\hat{M}$ matrix is nonsingular, however, it may happen that $H^{(N)}$ is singular, singularity always being revealed by the property $h_{NN}^{(N)} = 0$. An example is

$$H = \begin{bmatrix} 3 & -1 & 0 & -2 \\ -2 & 4 & -1 & 0 \\ 0 & 0 & 1 & -1 \\ -1 & 0 & -1 & 2 \end{bmatrix}$$

with $J = S_H$. Incomplete factorization produces the matrices

$$\tilde{H}^{(2)} = \begin{bmatrix} 3 & -1 & 0 & -2 \\ 0 & \frac{10}{3} & -1 & -\frac{4}{3} \\ 0 & 0 & 1 & -1 \\ 0 & -\frac{1}{3} & -1 & \frac{4}{3} \end{bmatrix}, \qquad H^{(2)} = \tilde{H}^{(3)} = H^{(3)} = \begin{bmatrix} 3 & -1 & 0 & -2 \\ 0 & 2 & -1 & 0 \\ 0 & 0 & 1 & -1 \\ 0 & 0 & -1 & 1 \end{bmatrix},$$

$$\tilde{H}^{(4)} = H^{(4)} = \begin{bmatrix} 3 & -1 & 0 & 2 \\ 0 & 2 & -1 & 0 \\ 0 & 0 & 1 & -1 \\ 0 & 0 & 0 & 0 \end{bmatrix},$$

and we observe that $h_{NN}^{(N)} = 0$.

The following theorem gives conditions that guarantee that $h_{NN}^{(N)} > 0$ and hence that $H^{(N)}$ is nonsingular.

Theorem 1.17. Let H be a diagonally dominant $\hat{M}$ matrix with symmetric structure, and suppose that at least one row sum is positive. Then,

(1) the matrix $H^{(r)}$, for $r = 1, 2, ..., N$, has at least one positive row sum in rows $r, r + 1, ..., N$;
(2) $h_{NN}^{(N)} > 0$.

PROOF: Let the ith row sum of H be positive. It then follows from (1.84b) that the ith row sums of $H^{(r)}$, $r = 1, 2, ..., N$ are all positive. This establishes assertion (1) for the cases $r = 1, 2, ..., i$.

If $i < N$ then we put $r = i$ and $i = n(i)$ in (1.85) to obtain

$$s_{n(i)}^{(i+1)} = s_{n(i)}^{(i)} - (h_{n(i),i}^{(i)}/h_{ii}^{(i)})s_i^{(i)}.$$

The assumptions on H imply that $h_{n(i),i}^{(1)} < 0$ and $s_i^{(1)} > 0$, and it follows from (1.84) that $h_{n(i),i}^{(i)} < 0$ and $s_i^{(i)} > 0$. Further, $h_{ii}^{(i)} > 0$ since Theorem 1.14 states that $H^{(i)}$ is an $\hat{M}$ matrix. Then, since $s_{n(i)}^{(i)} \geq 0$,

$$s_{n(i)}^{(i+1)} \geq -(h_{n(i),i}^{(i)}/h_{ii}^{(i)})s_i^{(i)} > 0.$$

Thus the $n(i)$th row sum of $H^{(i+1)}$ and hence those of $H^{(i+2)}, \ldots, H^{(N)}$ are all positive, and assertion (1) is now established for $r = 1, 2, \ldots, n(i)$.

The proof of (1) is completed by repetition of the above arguments. To prove (2) we note from (1) that the Nth row sum of $H^{(N)}$ is positive, so that $h_{NN}^{(N)} = s_N^{(N)} > 0$. ∎

Preconditioning

We assume now that H is a symmetric, positive definite, diagonally dominant $\hat{M}$ matrix with at least one positive row sum, and we consider the incomplete factors L and U obtained from (1.80). Symmetry considerations allow us to write $LU = LDL^{\mathrm{T}}$, where

$$D = \mathrm{diag}(u_{11}, u_{22}, \ldots, u_{NN}) = \mathrm{diag}(h_{11}^{(1)}, h_{22}^{(2)}, \ldots, h_{NN}^{(N)}).$$

Theorem 1.16 then tells us that

$$H = C + R, \tag{1.90}$$

where C is the symmetric matrix

$$C = LDL^{\mathrm{T}} \tag{1.91}$$

and R is given by (1.89) and (1.87). Under the stated assumptions we have $d_{ii} > 0$, $i = 1, 2, \ldots, N$ and

$$\mathbf{x}^{\mathrm{T}}C\mathbf{x} = (D^{1/2}L^{\mathrm{T}}\mathbf{x})^{\mathrm{T}}(D^{1/2}L^{\mathrm{T}}\mathbf{x}) > 0 \qquad \forall \mathbf{x} \neq \mathbf{0},$$

where

$$D^{1/2} = \mathrm{diag}(d_{11}^{1/2}, d_{22}^{1/2}, \ldots, d_{NN}^{1/2}).$$

The matrix C is therefore symmetric positive definite and can be used as the preconditioning matrix in (1.56).

The spectral condition number $\kappa(\tilde{H}) = \tilde{\lambda}_N/\tilde{\lambda}_1$, where $0 < \tilde{\lambda}_1 \leq \tilde{\lambda}_2 \leq \cdots \leq \tilde{\lambda}_N$ are the eigenvalues of $C^{-1}H$, determines the rate of convergence of (1.56). To examine this quantity more closely we note that the matrix $R^{(r+1)}$ in (1.87), and therefore R itself, can be expressed as the sum of matrices of the form

$$l_{ir}h_{rj}^{(r)} \begin{bmatrix} & | & & | & \\ \underline{} & 1 & \underline{} & -1 & \underline{} \\ & | & & | & \\ \underline{} & -1 & \underline{} & 1 & \underline{} \\ & | & & | & \end{bmatrix},$$

all entries other than the four shown being zeros. Recalling that $l_{ir}h_{rj}^{(r)} \geq 0$, it is easy to see that R is symmetric positive semidefinite with $Rx = 0$ for $x = [1, 1, ..., 1]^T$.

Combining the inequality

$$x^T Rx \geq 0 \qquad \forall x \neq 0$$

with (1.90), we find that

$$x^T Hx/x^T Cx = 1 + x^T Rx/x^T Cx \geq 1 \qquad \forall x \neq 0.$$

Since equality is obtained when x is the vector shown above, it follows from (1.72) that $\tilde{\lambda}_1 = 1$ and $\kappa(\tilde{H}) = \tilde{\lambda}_N$.

We shall not pursue the analysis of $\kappa(\tilde{H})$ further, since our ultimate interest is the preconditioning matrix obtained by the modification of (1.80) given by (7.18) in Section 7.2. Despite the fact that the modified process generally yields a better preconditioning matrix, the one obtained from (1.80) is often quite satisfactory and (1.80) has the advantage of being somewhat easier to implement. Thus, in addition to providing us with the necessary background for the analysis of the modified process, (1.80) is an important numerical tool in its own right.

Computer Implementation of (1.56)

The following pseudocode gives a partial description of the computer implementation of (1.56):

$$
\begin{aligned}
& x := x^0; \quad g := b; \\
& g := Hx - g; \quad h := C^{-1}g; \\
& d := -h; \quad \delta 0 := g^T h; \\
& \text{IF } \delta 0 \leq \varepsilon \text{ THEN STOP}; \\
R: \quad & h := Hd; \\
& \tau := \delta 0/d^T h; \\
& x := x + \tau d; \\
& g := g + \tau h; \\
& h := C^{-1}g; \quad \delta 1 := g^T h; \\
& \text{IF } \delta 1 \leq \varepsilon \text{ THEN STOP}; \\
& \beta := \delta 1/\delta 0; \quad \delta 0 := \delta 1; \\
& d := -h + \beta d; \\
& \text{GOTO } R;
\end{aligned}
\qquad (1.92)
$$

The statement $h := C^{-1}g$ is to be interpreted as solving the system $Ch = g$. The vectors x^0 and b are input, or, alternatively, b is input and $x^0 = C^{-1}b$. Note that array h is used to store both Hd^k and h^{k+1}.

We consider first the termination criterion $\mathbf{g}^{k^T} C^{-1} \mathbf{g}^k \leq \varepsilon$. Since $\mathbf{g}^k = H(\mathbf{x}^k - \hat{\mathbf{x}})$, this immediately gives the error bound

$$\left\| \mathbf{x}^k - \hat{\mathbf{x}} \right\|_{HC^{-1}H} = \left[(\mathbf{x}^k - \hat{\mathbf{x}})^T HC^{-1}H(\mathbf{x}^k - \hat{\mathbf{x}}) \right]^{1/2} \leq \varepsilon^{1/2}.$$

On the other hand, we recall that the quantity that is minimized at each step of the conjugate gradient method and that decreases monotonically is the error $\left\| \mathbf{x}^k - \hat{\mathbf{x}} \right\|_H = \left\| \mathbf{g}^k \right\|_{H^{-1}}$. This is not available during the calculation, however, and even if it were one might want a bound on some other norm of the error, for example $\left\| \mathbf{x}^k - \hat{\mathbf{x}} \right\|$. Unfortunately, there is no simple relation between the norms $\left\| \mathbf{x}^k - \hat{\mathbf{x}} \right\|_H$, $\left\| \mathbf{x}^k - \hat{\mathbf{x}} \right\|$ and $\left\| \mathbf{x}^k - \hat{\mathbf{x}} \right\|_{HC^{-1}H}$. Expanding $\mathbf{x}^k - \hat{\mathbf{x}}$ in terms of the orthonormal eigenvectors of H, however, one can easily derive the inequalities

$$\lambda_N^{-1/2} \left\| \mathbf{x}^k - \hat{\mathbf{x}} \right\|_{HC^{-1}H} \leq \left\| \mathbf{x}^k - \hat{\mathbf{x}} \right\|_H \leq \lambda_1^{-1/2} \left\| \mathbf{x}^k - \hat{\mathbf{x}} \right\|_{HC^{-1}H},$$

$$\lambda_N^{-1} \left\| \mathbf{x}^k - \hat{\mathbf{x}} \right\|_{HC^{-1}H} \leq \left\| \mathbf{x}^k - \hat{\mathbf{x}} \right\| \leq \lambda_1^{-1} \left\| \mathbf{x}^k - \hat{\mathbf{x}} \right\|_{HC^{-1}H}$$

in the case $C = I$ (the simple conjugate gradient method). The termination criterion then implies

$$\left\| \mathbf{x}^k - \hat{\mathbf{x}} \right\|_H \leq \lambda_1^{-1/2} \varepsilon^{1/2}, \qquad \left\| \mathbf{x}^k - \hat{\mathbf{x}} \right\| \leq \lambda_1^{-1} \varepsilon^{1/2}.$$

The size of λ_1 (and of λ_N) depends of course on any scaling of H.

We shall now consider the question of storage. Single-indexed arrays of length N are required for $\mathbf{x}$, $\mathbf{g}$, $\mathbf{h}$, and $\mathbf{d}$. Regarding the storage of H, the schemes for band matrices described in Section 6.1 are efficient if the band (or envelope) has relatively few nonzero entries. This point is rather academic, however, since if H has such a structure, then the system $H\hat{\mathbf{x}} = \mathbf{b}$ is probably best solved by the direct methods of Chapter 6.

Let us suppose then that H is a general sparse matrix having the properties of symmetry and positive definiteness. It is often expedient to store the lower left triangle of H, including the main diagonal, as a *row-ordered list* as illustrated in Fig. 1.8.

The values of the nonzero matrix entries on and below the main diagonal are stored by rows in array H in floating-point representation. CN (column number) is an integer array containing the column numbers of the corresponding matrix entries. RS (row start) is an integer array of length $(N + 1)$ whose ith element $(1 \leq i \leq N)$ "points" to the beginning of the ith row of the matrix. It is convenient to put RS$(N + 1) = Z + 1$, where Z is the number of matrix entries stored in the list, since this permits the end of the ith row to be addressed by RS$(i + 1) - 1$ even when $i = N$.

In the case of SSOR preconditioning, this data structure is efficient for the implementation of both

$$\mathbf{h} := H\mathbf{d} \tag{1.93a}$$

and

$$\mathbf{h} := C^{-1}\mathbf{g} \tag{1.93b}$$

in (1.92). We recall that

$$C = \left(\frac{1}{\omega}D + L\right)\left(\frac{1}{\omega}D\right)^{-1}\left(\frac{1}{\omega}D + L\right)^{\mathrm{T}},$$

where the nonzero entries of L and D are the nonzero entries of H below and on, respectively, the main diagonal. [We have dropped the scalar factor $(2 - \omega)^{-1}$ which has no influence on $\kappa(\tilde{H})$.] L and D are therefore available in the data structure for H. The implementation of (1.93b) requires the solution of two triangular systems of equations; see Exercise 1.24 for details.

In the case of preconditioning by incomplete factorization, we have

$$C = LDL^{\mathrm{T}},$$

where now L and D must be computed from H and stored in a second data structure. We take this to be a row-ordered list also, initially containing all entries of H whose index pairs belong to J. To simplify the discussion we assume that the data structure ignores symmetry in H, i.e., entries of H

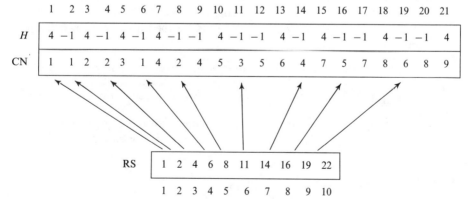

Fig. 1.8.   An example of a row-ordered list for the storage of the lower left triangle of a general sparse symmetric matrix.

from above as well as from below (and on) the main diagonal are stored. It is not difficult to translate the pseudocode for incomplete factorization in Fig. 1.7 to real code based on this row-ordered list. The only operation not organized by rows is the search for nonzero entries in the rth column, but since we are now assuming symmetry, we can change this to a search in the rth row. At the end of the factorization, the entries l_{ij} $(i > j)$ and d_{ii} occupy the positions in the list originally occupied by h_{ij} $(i \geq j)$.

With appropriate programming one can dispense with the storage of matrix entries above the main diagonal and also halve the computational labor. See Exercise 1.27 for details. Once L and D have been computed, the implementation of (1.93b) is very similar to that in the case of SSOR preconditioning.

Finally, we consider the *computational labor* required by (1.92). In almost all algorithms of numerical linear algebra, most of the floating-point operations occur in pairs, a pair consisting of an addition or subtraction together with a multiplication. It is therefore natural to take as the unit of computational labor the *flop*, which we define to be a combined floating-point addition (or subtraction) and a floating-point multiplication. Although the total time used by a computer in executing program code can greatly exceed the time spent in executing the floating-point operations alone, it is often roughly proportional to the number of flops for "in-core" computations.

Inspecting the code in (1.92) we see that the computational labor per iteration is about $5N$ flops plus that required by (1.93). If H has an average of r_H nonzero entries per row, then (1.93a) costs about $r_H N$ flops. The work required by (1.93b) depends on the type of preconditioning. With SSOR preconditioning it is roughly $(r_H + 1)N$ flops. In the case of preconditioning by incomplete factorization, it is about $r_H^{(J)}N$ flops, where $r_H^{(J)}$ is the average number of nonzero entries per row of $(D + L + L^T)$. If $J = S_H$ then $r_H^{(J)} = r_H$, whereas if $J \supset S_H$ then $r_H^{(J)} \geq r_H$. Combining these results with (1.50) and (1.57) we find that the work required to reduce the initial error by a factor ε is bounded as follows:

$$\tfrac{1}{2}(r_H + 5)N\sqrt{\kappa(H)}\,\ln(2/\varepsilon) \text{ flops} \qquad \text{(no preconditioning),} \qquad (1.94a)$$

$$\tfrac{1}{2}(2r_H + 6)N\sqrt{\kappa(\widetilde{H})}\,\ln(2/\varepsilon) \text{ flops} \qquad \text{(SSOR preconditioning),} \quad (1.94b)$$

$$\tfrac{1}{2}(r_H + r_H^{(J)} + 5)N\sqrt{\kappa(\widetilde{H})}\,\ln(2/\varepsilon) \text{ flops} \qquad \text{(preconditioning by incomplete factorization).} \qquad (1.94c)$$

Alternative Computational Procedures

We recall that (1.56) describes the *untransformed* variant of the preconditioned conjugate gradient method for solving the system $H\hat{x} = \mathbf{b}$. If C is factored in the form $C = EE^T$, then the *transformed* variant arises when we apply the simple conjugate gradient method to the system

$$\tilde{H}\hat{y} = \tilde{b}, \tag{1.95}$$

where

$$\tilde{H} = E^{-1}HE^{-T}, \quad \tilde{b} = E^{-1}b, \quad \hat{y} = E^T\hat{x}.$$

If, as in the case of preconditioning by both SSOR and incomplete factorization, the matrix C is in the factored form

$$C = FG^{-1}F^T,$$

then we put $E = FG^{-1/2}$ in (1.95).

Because of the diagonal form of G in our problems, however, it turns out that yet a third variant deserves consideration; namely, the application of the preconditioned conjugate gradient method, with preconditioning matrix $C = G^{-1}$, to the system

$$\overset{*}{H}\hat{z} = \overset{*}{b}, \tag{1.96}$$

where

$$\overset{*}{H} = F^{-1}HF^{-T}, \quad \overset{*}{b} = F^{-1}b, \quad \hat{z} = F^T\hat{x}.$$

All three variants are equivalent in the sense that if

$$y^0 = G^{-1/2}z^0 = (FG^{-1/2})^T x^0, \tag{1.97a}$$

then

$$y^k = G^{-1/2}z^k = (FG^{-1/2})^T x^k, \quad k = 1, 2, 3, \ldots, \tag{1.97b}$$

and

$$\|y^k - \hat{y}\|_{\tilde{H}} = \|z^k - \hat{z}\|_{\overset{*}{H}} = \|x^k - \hat{x}\|_H.$$

Since given any of the initial vectors x^0, y^0, and z^0, we can determine the other two so as to satisfy (1.97a), it follows that all three processes have the rate of convergence given in (1.57).

The third variant may be formulated as follows:

$$\overset{*}{\tau}_k = \overset{*}{g}{}^{k^T}\overset{*}{h}{}^k / \overset{*}{d}{}^{k^T}\overset{*}{H}\overset{*}{d}{}^k, \tag{1.98a}$$

$$z^{k+1} = z^k + \overset{*}{\tau}_k\overset{*}{d}{}^k, \tag{1.98b}$$

$$\overset{*}{g}{}^{k+1} = \overset{*}{g}{}^k + \overset{*}{\tau}_k\overset{*}{H}\overset{*}{d}{}^k, \tag{1.98c}$$

$$\overset{*}{h}{}^{k+1} = G\overset{*}{g}{}^{k+1}, \tag{1.98d}$$

$$\overset{*}{\beta}_k = \overset{*}{g}{}^{k+1^T}\overset{*}{h}{}^{k+1} / \overset{*}{g}{}^{k^T}\overset{*}{h}{}^k, \tag{1.98e}$$

$$\overset{*}{d}{}^{k+1} = -\overset{*}{h}{}^{k+1} + \overset{*}{\beta}_k\overset{*}{d}{}^k, \tag{1.98f}$$

where $k = 0, 1, \ldots$. Initially we choose $\mathbf{x}^0$ and compute $\mathbf{z}^0 = F^T\mathbf{x}^0$, $\overset{*}{\mathbf{g}}{}^0 = F^{-1}(H\mathbf{x}^0 - \mathbf{b})$, $\overset{*}{\mathbf{h}}{}^0 = G\overset{*}{\mathbf{g}}{}^0$, and $\overset{*}{\mathbf{d}}{}^0 = -\overset{*}{\mathbf{h}}{}^0$. Note that $\overset{*}{\mathbf{g}}{}^0 = \overset{*}{H}\mathbf{z}^0 - \overset{*}{\mathbf{b}}$, as required. Instead of choosing $\mathbf{x}^0$ we can compute

$$\mathbf{x}^0 = (FG^{-1}F^T)^{-1}\mathbf{b} = F^{-T}GF^{-1}\mathbf{b},$$

since $(FG^{-1}F^T)$ is an approximation of H.

The procedure given by (1.98) is incomplete in so far as the vector sequence $\mathbf{z}^0, \mathbf{z}^1, \mathbf{z}^2, \ldots$ converges to $\hat{\mathbf{z}}$ rather than to the desired vector $\hat{\mathbf{x}}$. We note from (1.97b), however, that the sequence

$$\mathbf{x}^k = F^{-T}\mathbf{z}^k, \qquad k = 0, 1, 2, \ldots$$

converges to $\hat{\mathbf{x}}$. Naturally, $\mathbf{x}^k$ need not be computed in every iteration.

The superiority of (1.98) over (1.56) in certain cases lies in the details of the computation of $\overset{*}{H}\overset{*}{\mathbf{d}}{}^k$. Let us consider SSOR preconditioning first, where

$$F = (1/\omega)D + L, \qquad G = (1/\omega)D,$$

$$H = D + L + L^T = E + F + F^T, \qquad E = [1 - (2/\omega)]D.$$

Then, following Eisenstat (1981) we have

$$\overset{*}{H}\overset{*}{\mathbf{d}}{}^k = F^{-1}HF^{-T}\overset{*}{\mathbf{d}}{}^k = F^{-1}(E + F + F^T)F^{-T}\overset{*}{\mathbf{d}}{}^k = F^{-1}(E\overset{*}{\mathbf{e}}{}^k + \overset{*}{\mathbf{d}}{}^k) + \overset{*}{\mathbf{e}}{}^k,$$

where we have introduced

$$\overset{*}{\mathbf{e}}{}^k = F^{-T}\overset{*}{\mathbf{d}}{}^k.$$

Restricting attention to operations involving nondiagonal matrices, we see that (1.98) can be implemented by solving two triangular systems of equations per iteration. On the other hand, (1.56) requires the solution of two triangular systems plus a multiplication by H, or about twice as much work. For not-so-sparse matrices, then, (1.98) is much more efficient. [An analogous trick is employed in Niethammer (1964) to halve the work for the SSOR stationary iterative method.]

In the case of preconditioning by incomplete factorization, we have

$$F - L, \qquad G = D^{-1}, \qquad H - LDL^T + R = FG^{-1}F^T + R,$$

so that

$$\overset{*}{H}\overset{*}{\mathbf{d}}{}^k = F^{-1}HF^{-T}\overset{*}{\mathbf{d}}{}^k = G^{-1}\overset{*}{\mathbf{d}}{}^k + F^{-1}RF^{-T}\overset{*}{\mathbf{d}}{}^k. \qquad (1.99)$$

Comparing with (1.56), we see that from the point of view of computational labor we are essentially replacing a multiplication by H with a multiplication by R. Although our treatment of incomplete factorization has not advocated the explicit storage of R, (1.99) motivates such a step if R is significantly sparser than H. We shall see an example of this situation in Section

7.4. It is clear from (1.89) and (1.87) that the nonzero entries of R can be "assembled" from data generated by the incomplete factorization process. However, the choice of a data structure for R is complicated by the fact that the sparsity pattern of R may not be known a priori.

The code shown in (1.100) indicates the computer implementation of (1.98) for both types of preconditioning.

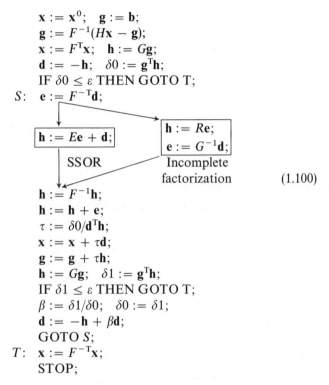

$$\begin{aligned}
&\mathbf{x} := \mathbf{x}^0; \quad \mathbf{g} := \mathbf{b}; \\
&\mathbf{g} := F^{-1}(H\mathbf{x} - \mathbf{g}); \\
&\mathbf{x} := F^T\mathbf{x}; \quad \mathbf{h} := G\mathbf{g}; \\
&\mathbf{d} := -\mathbf{h}; \quad \delta 0 := \mathbf{g}^T\mathbf{h}; \\
&\text{IF } \delta 0 \le \varepsilon \text{ THEN GOTO } T; \\
S:\quad &\mathbf{e} := F^{-T}\mathbf{d};
\end{aligned}$$

$$\boxed{\mathbf{h} := Ee + \mathbf{d};}$$
SSOR

$$\boxed{\begin{aligned}&\mathbf{h} := Re; \\ &\mathbf{e} := G^{-1}\mathbf{d};\end{aligned}}$$
Incomplete factorization   (1.100)

$$\begin{aligned}
&\mathbf{h} := F^{-1}\mathbf{h}; \\
&\mathbf{h} := \mathbf{h} + \mathbf{e}; \\
&\tau := \delta 0/\mathbf{d}^T\mathbf{h}; \\
&\mathbf{x} := \mathbf{x} + \tau\mathbf{d}; \\
&\mathbf{g} := \mathbf{g} + \tau\mathbf{h}; \\
&\mathbf{h} := G\mathbf{g}; \quad \delta 1 := \mathbf{g}^T\mathbf{h}; \\
&\text{IF } \delta 1 \le \varepsilon \text{ THEN GOTO } T; \\
&\beta := \delta 1/\delta 0; \quad \delta 0 := \delta 1; \\
&\mathbf{d} := -\mathbf{h} + \beta\mathbf{d}; \\
&\text{GOTO } S; \\
T:\quad &\mathbf{x} := F^{-T}\mathbf{x}; \\
&\text{STOP};
\end{aligned}$$

$\mathbf{x}^0$ and $\mathbf{b}$ are input, or $\mathbf{b}$ is input and $\mathbf{x}^0 = F^{-T}GF^{-1}\mathbf{b}$.

We observe that H appears only once in the algorithm, and using the identities

$$H = E + F + F^T \qquad \text{(SSOR)},$$

$$H = FG^{-1}F^T + R \qquad \text{(Incomplete factorization)},$$

we can in fact easily eliminate it altogether. This has no significance for the SSOR case, but it is important for incomplete factorization since it means we need arrays only for L and D (which can be written over the lower triangle of H during the factorization process) and the lower triangle of R. This should be compared to (1.92), where we need to store simultaneously L, D, and the lower triangle of H. Hence, when R is sparser than H, (1.100) is not only faster than (1.92) but also potentially more economical with respect to storage.

An examination of (1.100) yields the following rough estimates of computational labor:

$$\tfrac{1}{2}(r_H + 7)N\sqrt{\kappa(\widetilde{H})}\ln(2/\varepsilon) \qquad \text{flops} \quad \text{(SSOR)} \qquad\qquad (1.101a)$$

$$\tfrac{1}{2}(r_H^{(J)} + r_R + 6)N\sqrt{\kappa(\widetilde{H})}\ln(2/\varepsilon) \text{ flops} \quad \text{(Incomplete factorization) (1.101b)}$$

The parameters r_H and $r_H^{(J)}$ are defined above (1.94). With r_R we denote the average number of nonzero entries per row of R.

The computational labor required by (1.100) can be reduced slightly in the case of SSOR preconditioning by first transforming the system $H\hat{\mathbf{x}} = \mathbf{b}$ to

$$(\tilde{D}H\tilde{D})(\tilde{D}^{-1}\hat{\mathbf{x}}) = (\tilde{D}\mathbf{b}),$$

where

$$\tilde{D} = \omega^{1/2}\,\text{diag}(h_{11}^{-1/2}, \dots, h_{NN}^{-1/2}),$$

an example of *diagonal scaling*. This makes

$$\tilde{D}H\tilde{D} = \omega I + (\tilde{D}L\tilde{D}) + (\tilde{D}L\tilde{D})^{\mathsf{T}},$$

and for the new system we have $G = \text{diag}(F) = I$. Hence, we can remove the statement $\mathbf{h} := G\mathbf{g}$ and also avoid division by diagonal entries f_{ii} in solving the triangular systems of equations. Naturally, the output vector is an approximation to $\tilde{D}^{-1}\hat{\mathbf{x}}$ and must be multiplied by $\tilde{D}$.

In the case of preconditioning by incomplete factorization, one could make the computation implied by

$$LDL^{\mathsf{T}} = (LD^{1/2})(LD^{1/2})^{\mathsf{T}}$$

to achieve $G = I$. (This arises naturally if the factorization process is based on the Cholesky method rather than that of Gauss.) This would allow us to remove the statements $\mathbf{e} := G^{-1}\mathbf{d}$ and $\mathbf{h} := G\mathbf{g}$, but since there are now "non-ones" on the main diagonal of F, a corresponding amount of extra work would be required to solve the triangular systems.

Exercises

1.1. Prove (1.4).

1.2. Show that the directional derivative $f^{(m)}(\mathbf{x}; \mathbf{y})$ satisfies

$$f^{(m)}(\mathbf{x}; \mathbf{y}) = \left(y_1\frac{\partial}{\partial x_1} + y_2\frac{\partial}{\partial x_2} + \cdots + y_N\frac{\partial}{\partial x_N}\right)^m f(\mathbf{x}).$$

1.3. Let $f \in C^m(X)$, and for any $\mathbf{x} \in X, \mathbf{y} \in R^N, \|\mathbf{y}\| = 1$ consider the function $f(\mathbf{x} + \tau\mathbf{y})$, $0 \leq \tau \leq \varepsilon$. By Taylor's theorem there exists $\theta \in (0, 1)$ such that

$$f(\mathbf{x} + \tau\mathbf{y}) = \sum_{k=0}^{m-1} \frac{\tau^k}{k!} f^{(k)}(\mathbf{x}; \mathbf{y}) + \frac{\tau^m}{m!} f^{(m)}(\mathbf{x} + \theta\tau\mathbf{y}; \mathbf{y}).$$

Putting $m = 2$, using (1.3) and (1.4) (or the preceding exercise), and introducing $\mathbf{h} = \tau\mathbf{y}$, we have

$$f(\mathbf{x} + \mathbf{h}) = f(\mathbf{x}) + \mathbf{g}^T(\mathbf{x})\mathbf{h} + \tfrac{1}{2}\mathbf{h}^T H(\mathbf{x} + \theta\mathbf{h})\mathbf{h}$$
$$= f(\mathbf{x}) + \mathbf{g}^T(\mathbf{x})\mathbf{h} + \tfrac{1}{2}\mathbf{h}^T H(\mathbf{x})\mathbf{h} + R(\mathbf{x}; \mathbf{h}),$$

where

$$R(\mathbf{x}; \mathbf{h}) = \tfrac{1}{2}\mathbf{h}^T[H(\mathbf{x} + \theta\mathbf{h}) - H(\mathbf{x})]\mathbf{h}$$
$$= \tfrac{1}{2}\sum_{i,j=1}^N h_i h_j\left[\frac{\partial^2 f}{\partial x_i\, \partial x_j}(\mathbf{x} + \theta\mathbf{h}) - \frac{\partial^2 f}{\partial x_i\, \partial x_j}(\mathbf{x})\right].$$

Use the continuity of the second-order derivatives to show that there exists a function $M(h; \mathbf{x}), 0 \leq h \leq \varepsilon$, such that

$$|R(\mathbf{x}; \mathbf{h})| \leq M(h; \mathbf{x}) \cdot h^2 \quad \forall \mathbf{h} \ni \|\mathbf{h}\| = h, \qquad \lim_{h \to 0} M(h; \mathbf{x}) = 0.$$

1.4. Describe the behavior of the following functionals, giving particular attention to stationary points:

(i) $f(x, y) = x^2$,   (ii) $f(x, y) = x^2 + y^2$,
(iii) $f(x, y) = x^2 + y$,   (iv) $f(x, y) = x^2 - y^4$,
(v) $f(x, y) = \tfrac{1}{2}x^2 - x^4 + y^4$,   (vi) $f(x, y) = (2x^2 + y^2)/(x^2 + y^2)$.

1.5. Sketch some of the level curves of the quadratic functional

$$f(\mathbf{x}) = \frac{1}{50}\mathbf{x}^T\begin{bmatrix} 93 & 24 \\ 24 & 107 \end{bmatrix}\mathbf{x} - \frac{1}{5}\begin{bmatrix} 42 \\ 31 \end{bmatrix}^T\mathbf{x} - \frac{23}{2}, \qquad \mathbf{x} \in R^2.$$

1.6. An $(N \times N)$ symmetrix matrix H is positive definite if and only if $\det(H_k) > 0$ for $k = 1, 2, \ldots, N$, where

$$H_k = \begin{bmatrix} h_{11} & h_{12} & \cdots & \cdots & h_{1k} \\ h_{21} & h_{22} & \cdots & \cdots & h_{2k} \\ \vdots & \vdots & \vdots & \ddots & \vdots \\ h_{k1} & h_{k2} & \cdots & \cdots & h_{kk} \end{bmatrix}.$$

Use this property to show that the quadratic functional

$$f(x, y, z) = 10x^2 + 2y^2 + 2z^2 + 6xy + 4xz + 2yz, \qquad (x, y, z) \in R^3$$

has a global minimum at the origin.

1.7. Describe the behavior of a quadratic functional having a positive semidefinite Hessian.

1.8. A subset $X \subseteq R^N$ is said to be *convex* if for any $\mathbf{x}, \mathbf{y} \in X$,

$$\lambda\mathbf{x} + (1 - \lambda)\mathbf{y} \in X, \qquad 0 \leq \lambda \leq 1.$$

A functional f defined on $X \subseteq R^N$ is said to be *convex* if X is convex and if for any $\mathbf{x}, \mathbf{y} \in X$,

$$f[\lambda\mathbf{x} + (1 - \lambda)\mathbf{y}] \leq \lambda f(\mathbf{x}) + (1 - \lambda)f(\mathbf{y}), \qquad 0 \leq \lambda \leq 1.$$

If strict inequality holds $\forall \lambda \in (0, 1)$ and $\forall \mathbf{x}, \mathbf{y} \in X, \mathbf{x} \neq \mathbf{y}$, then f is *strongly convex*.

Prove that a quadratic functional defined on R^N is convex (strongly convex) if its Hessian is positive semidefinite (positive definite).

1.9. Let f be a functional defined on a convex set $X \subseteq R^N$. Show that f is convex if and only if

$$f\left(\sum_{i=1}^{m} \xi_i \mathbf{x}_i\right) \leq \sum_{i=1}^{m} \xi_i f(\mathbf{x}_i)$$

for any vectors $\mathbf{x}_1, \ldots, \mathbf{x}_m \in X$ and any numbers $\xi_1, \ldots, \xi_m$ such that $\xi_i \geq 0, i = 1, \ldots, m$, and $\sum_{i=1}^{m} \xi_i = 1$.

1.10. Prove the inequality between the arithmetic and geometric means

$$\frac{1}{m} \sum_{i=1}^{m} x_i \geq (x_1 x_2 \cdots x_m)^{1/m},$$

where $x_1, \ldots, x_m$ are positive numbers.

HINT: Use the inequality of the preceding exercise with $N = 1, X = \{x \in R; x > 0\}$, $f(x) = -\ln(x)$ and $\xi_i = 1/m, i = 1, \ldots, m$.

1.11. Consider the functional

$$f(\mathbf{x}) = \tfrac{1}{2}(H\mathbf{x} - \mathbf{b})^{\mathrm{T}}(H\mathbf{x} - \mathbf{b}), \qquad \mathbf{x} \in R^N,$$

where H is an $(M \times N)$ real matrix, $M \geq N$, of rank N and $\mathbf{b} \in R^N$.

(i)   Write $f(\mathbf{x})$ in the quadratic form

$$f(\mathbf{x}) = \tfrac{1}{2}\mathbf{x}^{\mathrm{T}}F\mathbf{x} - \mathbf{d}^{\mathrm{T}}\mathbf{x} + e.$$

(ii) Show that F is positive definite.

(iii) Show that when H is symmetric then $\kappa(F) = \kappa(H)^2$.

1.12. Consider the functional

$$f(\mathbf{x}) = \mathbf{x}^{\mathrm{T}}A\mathbf{x}/\mathbf{x}^{\mathrm{T}}B\mathbf{x}, \qquad \mathbf{x} \in R^N, \quad \mathbf{x} \neq \mathbf{0},$$

where A and B are $N \times N$ real symmetric matrices and B is positive definite.

(i)   Show that $f(\mathbf{x})$ has the gradient

$$\mathbf{g}(\mathbf{x}) = (2/\mathbf{x}^{\mathrm{T}}B\mathbf{x})(A\mathbf{x} - f(\mathbf{x})B\mathbf{x})$$

and the Hessian

$$H(\mathbf{x}) = (2/\mathbf{x}^{\mathrm{T}}B\mathbf{x})[A - f(\mathbf{x})B - \mathbf{g}(\mathbf{x})(B\mathbf{x})^{\mathrm{T}} - B\mathbf{x}\,\mathbf{g}(\mathbf{x})^{\mathrm{T}}].$$

(ii) The eigenvalue problem $A\mathbf{x} = \lambda B\mathbf{x}$ is known to possess real eigensolutions $(\lambda, \mathbf{x}) = (\lambda_s, \mathbf{x}_s), s = 1, 2, \ldots, N$. Show that the eigenvectors are the stationary values of $f(\mathbf{x})$.

1.13. The object of this exercise is to establish (1.20). Without loss of generality we consider only vectors $\mathbf{x}$ such that $\|\mathbf{x}\| = 1$.

For any $\mathbf{x} \in R^N$, $\|\mathbf{x}\| = 1$ let $\xi_i = (\mathbf{x}^T \mathbf{v}_i)^2$, $\phi(\mathbf{x}) = \sum_{i=1}^N \xi_i \lambda_i$ and $\psi(\mathbf{x}) = \sum_{i=1}^N \xi_i \lambda_i^{-1}$, where $\mathbf{v}_1, \mathbf{v}_2, \ldots, \mathbf{v}_N$ are the orthonormal eigenvectors of H and $\lambda_1, \lambda_2, \ldots, \lambda_N$ are the corresponding eigenvalues. Show that

(i) $\sum_{i=1}^N \xi_i = 1$, $\phi(\mathbf{x}) = \mathbf{x}^T H \mathbf{x}$, $\psi(\mathbf{x}) = \mathbf{x}^T H^{-1} \mathbf{x}$;
(ii) $1 \le \phi(\mathbf{x}) \psi(\mathbf{x})$ (*Hint:* first consider the case $N = 2$);
(iii) $\phi(\mathbf{x}) + \lambda_1 \lambda_N \psi(\mathbf{x}) \le \lambda_1 + \lambda_N$;
(iv) $\phi(\mathbf{x}) = \lambda$ for some $\lambda \in [\lambda_1, \lambda_N]$;
(v) $\phi(\mathbf{x}) \psi(\mathbf{x}) \le \phi(\mathbf{x})[\lambda_1 + \lambda_N - \phi(\mathbf{x})]/(\lambda_1 \lambda_N) \le (\lambda_1 + \lambda_N)^2/(4\lambda_1 \lambda_N)$.

1.14. Derive the rate of convergence estimate (1.18).

HINT: $\ln[(1 + s)/(1 - s)] = 2(s + \tfrac{1}{3}s^3 + \tfrac{1}{5}s^5 + \cdots)$, $0 \le s < 1$.

1.15. Show geometrically, by considering level curves, that the method of steepest descent applied to a two-dimensional quadratic functional does not usually converge in a finite number of iterations when the spectral condition number of the Hessian is greater than one.

1.16. The transformation $\tilde{H} = E^{-1} H E^{-T}$ becomes a *diagonal scaling* of H when E is a diagonal matrix. Compute $\kappa(H)$, $\tilde{H}$, and $\kappa(\tilde{H})$ for the case

$$H = \begin{bmatrix} 100 & -8 & 0 \\ -8 & 9 & 0 \\ 0 & 0 & 1 \end{bmatrix}, \qquad E = \mathrm{diag}(h_{11}^{1/2}, h_{22}^{1/2}, h_{33}^{1/2}).$$

1.17. Show that the iterative method

$$\mathbf{g}^k = H\mathbf{x}^k - \mathbf{b},$$

$$\mathbf{d}^k = -\mathbf{g}^k + \beta_{k-1} \mathbf{d}^{k-1},$$

$$\mathbf{x}^{k+1} = \mathbf{x}^k + \tau_k \mathbf{d}^k,$$

for $k = 0, 1, 2, \ldots$, where $\beta_{-1} = 0$, τ_0 is defined by

$$f(\mathbf{x}^0 - \tau_0 \mathbf{g}^0) = \min_{-\infty < \tau < \infty} f(\mathbf{x}^0 - \tau \mathbf{g}^0),$$

and where, for $k \ge 1$, τ_k and β_{k-1} are defined by

$$f[\mathbf{x}^k + \tau_k(-\mathbf{g}^k + \beta_{k-1} \mathbf{d}^{k-1})] = \min_{-\infty < \tau, \beta < \infty} f[\mathbf{x}^k + \tau(-\mathbf{g}^k + \beta \mathbf{d}^{k-1})],$$

is identical to the conjugate gradient method.

1.18. Consider the quadratic functional

$$f(\mathbf{x}) = \tfrac{1}{2}\mathbf{x}^T H \mathbf{x} - \mathbf{b}^T \mathbf{x} + c, \qquad \mathbf{x} \in R^N,$$

where H is positive definite with p *distinct* eigenvalues, $p \le N$. Let $\hat{\mathbf{x}}$ be the minimizer of $f(\mathbf{x})$ and $\mathbf{x}^0$ an arbitrary vector in R^N. The initial error $(\mathbf{x}^0 - \hat{\mathbf{x}})$ has an expansion of the form

$$\mathbf{x}^0 - \hat{\mathbf{x}} = \sum_{i=1}^p c_i \mathbf{v}_i,$$

where $\mathbf{v}_1, \ldots, \mathbf{v}_p$ are eigenvectors of H. Let m denote the number of nonzero coefficients in the set $c_1, \ldots, c_p$. Prove that the conjugate gradient method applied to $f(\mathbf{x})$, with initial vector $\mathbf{x}^0$, converges in m iterations.

HINT: Determine the eigenvector expansion of the initial gradient $\mathbf{g}^0$ and use the proof of Theorem 1.11.

1.19. Consider the conjugate gradient method applied to a quadratic functional with Hessian

$$H = \begin{bmatrix} 4 & -2 & -1 & 0 \\ -2 & 4 & 0 & -2 \\ -1 & 0 & 4 & -1 \\ 0 & -2 & -1 & 4 \end{bmatrix}.$$

(i) Show that convergence takes place in at most 3 iterations for any initial vector $\mathbf{x}^0$.

HINT: Investigate the eigenvalues of H.

(ii) Show that if $\mathbf{x}^0$ has the property of making $\mathbf{g}^0 = [1, 1, -2, -1]^T$, then convergence takes place in only one iteration.

1.20. Consider the quadratic functionals

$$f(\mathbf{x}) = \tfrac{1}{2}\mathbf{x}^T H \mathbf{x} - \mathbf{b}^T \mathbf{x} + c, \qquad\qquad \mathbf{x} \in R^N,$$
$$\tilde{f}(\mathbf{y}) \equiv f(E^{-T}\mathbf{y}) = \tfrac{1}{2}\mathbf{y}^T \tilde{H}\mathbf{y} - \tilde{\mathbf{b}}^T \mathbf{y} + \tilde{c}, \qquad \mathbf{y} \in R^N,$$

where H is positive definite, E is nonsingular, $\tilde{H} = E^{-1}HE^{-T}$, $\tilde{\mathbf{b}} = E^{-1}\mathbf{b}$, and $\tilde{c} = c$. Let $\mathbf{x}^k$, $\mathbf{g}^k$, $\mathbf{d}^k$, and $\mathbf{h}^k$ be the typical vectors produced by the application of the preconditioned conjugate gradient method (1.56) to $f(\mathbf{x})$, and let $\mathbf{y}^k$, $\tilde{\mathbf{g}}^k$, and $\tilde{\mathbf{d}}^k$ be the typical vectors produced by applying the simple conjugate gradient method to $\tilde{f}(\mathbf{y})$. Show that if $\mathbf{y}^0 = E^T\mathbf{x}^0$, then $\forall k$

$$\mathbf{y}^k = E^T\mathbf{x}^k,$$
$$\tilde{\mathbf{g}}^k = E^{-1}\mathbf{g}^k = E^T\mathbf{h}^k,$$
$$\tilde{\mathbf{d}}^k = E^T\mathbf{d}^k.$$

1.21. A common matrix in finite difference and finite element analyses of one-dimensional boundary value problems is

$$H = \begin{bmatrix} 2 & -1 & & & \\ -1 & 2 & -1 & & \\ & \cdot & \cdot & \cdot & \\ & & \cdot & \cdot & \cdot \\ & & -1 & 2 & -1 \\ & & & -1 & 2 \end{bmatrix}.$$

Let

$$E = \tfrac{1}{2}D + L = \begin{bmatrix} 1 & & & & \\ -1 & 1 & & & \\ & \cdot & \cdot & & \\ & & \cdot & \cdot & \\ & & -1 & 1 & \\ & & & -1 & 1 \end{bmatrix}$$

and $\tilde{H} = E^{-1}HE^{-T}$.

(i) Show that $\tilde{H} = I + R$, where $r_{ij} = 1$ for $i, j = 1, 2, \ldots, N$.

(ii) Show that the eigenvalues of $\tilde{H}$ are 1 (multiplicity $N - 1$) and $N + 1$ (multiplicity 1).

(iii) Deduce from Exercise 1.18 that the preconditioned conjugate gradient method applied to $f(\mathbf{x}) = \frac{1}{2}\mathbf{x}^T H \mathbf{x} - \mathbf{b}^T \mathbf{x} + c, \mathbf{x} \in R^N$, with the preconditioning matrix $C \equiv EE^T$, converges in at most two iterations.

1.22. Let H, E, C, and $\tilde{H}$ be real $N \times N$ matrices such that H is positive definite, E is nonsingular, $C = EE^T$, and $\tilde{H} = E^{-1}HE^{-T}$. Prove that

$$\kappa(\tilde{H}) = 1 \quad \Leftrightarrow \quad C = \alpha H,$$

where α is a scalar.

1.23.

(i) Given an initial vector $\mathbf{x}^0$ for the stationary iterative method (1.61), we can expand $(\mathbf{x}^0 - \hat{\mathbf{x}})$ in terms of the eigenvectors of B:

$$\mathbf{x}^0 - \hat{\mathbf{x}} = \sum_{i=1}^{N} c_i \mathbf{w}_i.$$

Show that

$$\|\mathbf{x}^k - \hat{\mathbf{x}}\|_H \le \varepsilon\gamma, \qquad k > \hat{k}_1 \equiv [\ln(1/\varepsilon)/\ln(1/\rho(B))],$$

where

$$\gamma = \sum_{i=1}^{N} |c_i| \cdot \|\mathbf{w}_i\|_H.$$

(ii) Show that for the preconditioned conjugate gradient method (1.56) with the preconditioning matrix M of (1.60) and with the same initial vector we have

$$\|\mathbf{x}^k - \hat{\mathbf{x}}\|_H \le \varepsilon\gamma, \qquad k \ge \hat{k}_2 \equiv \frac{1}{2}\sqrt{\kappa(\tilde{H})}\,\ln(2/\varepsilon),$$

where γ is defined as before.

(iii) Hence, derive (1.65) and (1.66).

1.24. We consider here the programming aspect of the conjugate gradient method with SSOR preconditioning, assuming the lower left triangle of H to be stored in a row-ordered list as illustrated in Fig. 1.8.

(i) Write a piece of program code for the implementation of (1.93a).

HINT: Rather than compute the components of $\mathbf{h}$ sequentially, base the computation on a simple pass through the list.

(ii) The implementation of (1.93b) can be performed in the steps

$$\mathbf{h} := [(1/\omega)D + L]^{-1}\mathbf{g},$$

$$\mathbf{h} := (1/\omega)D\mathbf{h},$$

$$\mathbf{h} := [(1/\omega)D + L^T]^{-1}\mathbf{h}.$$

The first step requires the solution of a lower triangular system of equations by the familiar process of forward substitution [see (6.8a)]. Write a piece of program code that does this.

(iii)   The third step requires the solution of an upper triangular system of equations by back substitution [see (6.8b)]. The usual sequence of operations would go through the entries of L^T by rows and hence through the entries of L by columns. This is inconvenient here, since L is stored as a row-ordered list. Find a sequence of operations for back substitution that goes through the entries of L^T by columns, and write a piece of program code that implements the third step.

1.25. Some matrices are of such a regular nature that no arrays are needed for their storage for the purpose of applying the SSOR preconditioned conjugate gradient method. Write program code for the implementation of (1.93) given the matrices

$$
H = \begin{bmatrix} B & -I & & & \\ -I & B & -1 & & \\ & \cdot & \cdot & \cdot & \\ & & \cdot & \cdot & \cdot \\ & & & -I & B \end{bmatrix} \begin{matrix} (1) \\ (2) \\ \\ \\ (N_1) \end{matrix} , \qquad
B = \begin{bmatrix} 4 & -1 & & & \\ -1 & 4 & -1 & & \\ & \cdot & \cdot & \cdot & \\ & & \cdot & \cdot & \cdot \\ & & & -1 & 4 \end{bmatrix} \begin{matrix} (1) \\ (2) \\ \\ \\ (N_2) \end{matrix}
$$

of order $N_1 N_2$ and N_2, respectively, assuming that H and B are not stored.

1.26. Write a complete subroutine for the implementation of (1.100) in the case of SSOR preconditioning, assuming the nonzero entries of the lower left triangle of H to be stored in a row-ordered list. With this data structure for H, an effective implementation of the statement "$\mathbf{x} := F^T\mathbf{x}$" requires a vector array in addition to $\mathbf{x}$ (Why?). Array $\mathbf{h}$ can be used for this purpose.

1.27. We consider the problem of computing the incomplete factorization $H = LU + R = LDL^T + R$ of a sparse, positive definite matrix H.

(i)   Assume that all entries (zeros as well as nonzeros) in the part of H belonging to J are stored in a row-ordered list. Write a piece of program code based on the algorithm in Fig. 1.7 that overwrites H with L and U.

(ii)   Assume that all entries in the lower triangle of H belonging to J are stored in a *column-ordered* list. Write a piece of program code that overwrites the lower triangle of H with L and D.

(iii)   Assuming a priori knowledge of the location of the nonzero entries in R, analyze the problem of computing R.

1.28. The conjugate gradient method with preconditioning by incomplete factorization can be implemented by either (1.92) or (1.100). Discuss the computational details of each version.

References

Axelsson, O. (1976). A class of iterative methods for finite element equations. *Comput. Methods Appl. Mech. Engrg.* **9**, 123–137.

Axelsson, O., and Munksgaard, N. (1979). A class of preconditioned conjugate gradient methods for the solution of a mixed finite element discretization of the biharmonic operator. *Internat. J. Numer. Methods Engrg.* **14**, 1001–1019.

Beckenbach, E. F., and Bellman, R. (1971). "Inequalities," vol. 30. *In* Ergebnisse der Mathematik und Ihrer Grenzgebiete. Springer-Verlag, Berlin and New York.

Eisenstat, S. C. (1981). Efficient implementation of a class of preconditioned conjugate gradient methods. *SIAM J. Sci. Stat. Comput.* **2,** 1–4.

Gill, P. E., Murray, W., and Wright, M. H. (1981). "Practical Optimization." Academic Press, New York.

Greenbaum, A. (1979). Comparison of splittings used with the conjugate gradient algorithm. *Numer. Math.* **33,** 181–194.

Gustafsson, I. (1978). A class of first order factorization methods. *BIT* **18,** 142–156.

Hageman, L. A., and Young, D. M. (1981). "Applied Iterative Methods." Academic Press, New York.

Hestenes, M. R. (1975). "Optimization Theory: The Finite Dimensional Case." Wiley, New York.

Hestenes, M. R., and Stiefel, E. (1952). Methods of conjugate gradients for solving linear systems. *J. Res. Nat. Bur. Standards Sect. B* **49,** 409–436.

Jennings, A. (1977). Influence of the eigenvalue spectrum on the convergence rate of the conjugate gradient method. *J. Inst. Math. Appl.* **20,** 61–72.

Meijerink, J. A., and van der Vorst, H. A. (1977). An iterative solution method for linear systems of which the coefficient matrix is a symmetric M-matrix. *Math. Comp.* **31,** 148–162.

Meijerink, J. A., and van der Vorst, H. A. (1981). Guidelines for the usage of incomplete decompositions in solving sets of linear equations as they occur in practical problems. *J. Comput. Phys.* **44,** 134–155.

Niethammer, W. (1964). Relaxation bei komplexen Matrizen. *Math. Z.* **86,** 34–40.

Reid, J. K. (1971). On the method of conjugate gradients for the solution of large sparse systems of equations. *In* "Large Sparse Sets of Linear Equations" (J. K. Reid, ed.), pp. 231–254. Academic Press, New York.

Sheldon, J. (1955). On the numerical solution of elliptic difference equations. *Math. Tables Aids Comput.* **9,** 101–112.

Stewart, G. W. (1975). The convergence of the method of conjugate gradients at isolated extreme points of the spectrum. *Numer. Math.* **24,** 85–93.

Strang, G. (1976). "Linear Algebra and Its Applications." Academic Press, New York.

van der Vorst, H. A., and van der Sluis, A. (1984). An expression and upper bounds for the residual in the conjugate gradient method. *SIAM J. Sci. Stat. Comput.* (forthcoming).

Varga, R. S. (1960). Factorization and normalized iterative methods. *In* "Boundary Value Problems in Differential Equations" (R. E. Langer, ed.), pp. 121–142. Univ. of Wisconsin Press, Madison, Wisconsin.

Varga, R. S. (1962). "Matrix Iterative Analysis." Prentice-Hall, Englewood Cliffs, New Jersey.

Wismer, D. A., and Chattergy, R. (1978). "Introduction to Nonlinear Optimization." North-Holland Publ., Amsterdam.

Wolfe, M. A. (1978). "Numerical Methods for Unconstrained Optimization." Van Nostrand-Reinhold, Princeton, New Jersey.

Young, D. M. (1971). "Iterative Solution of Large Linear Systems." Academic Press, New York.

CHAPTER 2

Variational Formulation of Boundary Value Problems: Part I

Introduction

One of the most important problems of mathematical physics is the boundary value problem in which one seeks a function that satisfies some differential equation in a region Ω and satisfies specified conditions on the boundary of Ω. Many problems of this type have the property that the solution minimizes a certain functional f defined on some set of functions V, or, more generally, is a stationary point of such a functional. Thus the task of solving a boundary value problem is equivalent to that of finding a function in V that makes f stationary, and we call this latter problem the variational formulation of the boundary value problem. This chapter is devoted to the analysis of functionals of the above type and their associated boundary value problems. Our approach here is basically that of the classical calculus of variations. [See, e.g., Courant and Hilbert (1953), Gelfand and Fomin (1963), and Sagan (1969).]

Section 2.1 develops some fundamental definitions and theorems for functionals in one space dimension and then proceeds to a number of examples. Special attention is given to *quadratic* functionals, since they are the source of *linear* boundary value problems. Section 2.2 discusses the important distinction between essential boundary conditions, which must be imposed on the functions in V, and natural boundary conditions, which need not be imposed. In Section 2.3 the analysis of the previous sections is extended to problems in two and three space dimensions. The final section presents a number of physical problems that give rise to the mathematical problem of minimizing a quadratic functional.

2.1 The Euler–Lagrange Equation for One-Dimensional Problems

Basic Definitions and Theorems

In Chapter 1 we considered functionals of the type $f: X \to R$, where X is a subset of R^N, the real N-dimensional vector space. In this section we are concerned with functionals $f: V \to R$, where V is some set of continuous, real functions defined on a closed interval $[a, b]$. The typical element of V may be written $u = u(x)$, $a \le x \le b$. We call V the *set of admissible functions of* f. For $u \in V$ and $\varepsilon > 0$ let $S(u; \varepsilon)$ denote the *neighborhood of* u *of radius* ε defined by

$$S(u; \varepsilon) = \{v \in V; 0 \le \|u - v\| < \varepsilon\},$$

where $\|\cdot\|$ denotes the norm defined for any square-integrable function u by $\|u\| = [\int_a^b u(x)^2 \, dx]^{1/2}$.

There follow some basic definitions and theorems, all of which are obvious extensions of the analysis of Section 1.1. Because the proofs are short, we include them for the sake of completeness.

Definition 2.1. Let f be defined on V. Then $\hat{u} \in V$ is a *local minimizer* of f if there is an $\varepsilon > 0$ such that $f(\hat{u}) \le f(u) \ \forall u \in S(\hat{u}; \varepsilon)$. If $f(\hat{u}) < f(u)$ $\forall u \in S(\hat{u}; \varepsilon)$, $u \ne \hat{u}$, then $\hat{u}$ is a *strong local minimizer* of f.

Definition 2.2. Let f be defined on V. Then $\hat{u} \in V$ is a *global minimizer* of f if $f(\hat{u}) \le f(u) \ \forall u \in V$. If $f(\hat{u}) < f(u) \ \forall u \in V$, $u \ne \hat{u}$, then $\hat{u}$ is a *strong global minimizer* of f.

In some of the examples in this chapter, V is a *linear space*, i.e., it has the property

$$u, v \in V, \quad \alpha, \beta \in R \quad \Rightarrow \quad \alpha u + \beta v \in V.$$

In other examples V is not a linear space. In all cases, however, we shall find that the set $\tilde{V}$ defined by

$$\tilde{V} = \{\eta; \eta = u - v, u, v \in V\} \tag{2.1}$$

is a linear space. We call $\tilde{V}$ the space of *test* (or *perturbation*) *functions*. The set V may be written as

$$V = \{v; v = u^* + \eta, \eta \in \tilde{V}\},$$

where u^* is an arbitrary but fixed element of V. Note that the neighborhood $S(u; \varepsilon)$ defined above is equivalently defined by

$$S(u; \varepsilon) = \{v \in V; v = u + \tau\eta, \eta \in \tilde{V}, \|\eta\| = 1, \tau \in [0, \varepsilon)\}.$$

Definition 2.3. Let f be defined on V. Let $u \in V$ and $\eta \in \tilde{V}$ be given, where $\|\eta\| = 1$, and suppose that for some $\tau_0 > 0$ the function $f(u + \tau\eta)$, $|\tau| < \tau_0$, has a continuous mth-order derivative with respect to τ. Then the mth-order *directional derivative* of f at u in the direction η is

$$f^{(m)}(u; \eta) \equiv \left. \frac{d^m f(u + \tau\eta)}{d\tau^m} \right|_{\tau = 0}.$$

Definition 2.4. Let f be defined on V and suppose that for some $\hat{u} \in V$,

$$f^{(1)}(\hat{u}; \eta) = 0 \qquad \forall \eta \in \tilde{V}, \quad \|\eta\| = 1.$$

Then f is *stationary* at $\hat{u}$ (or, equivalently, $\hat{u}$ is a *stationary point* of f).

Theorem 2.1. Let f be defined on V and suppose that for some $\hat{u} \in V$ the first-order directional derivative $f^{(1)}(\hat{u}; \eta)$ exists for all directions η. If $\hat{u}$ is a local minimizer of f, then f is stationary at $\hat{u}$.

PROOF: Under the assumptions of the theorem we have the Taylor expansion

$$f(\hat{u} + \tau\eta) = f(\hat{u}) + \tau f^{(1)}(\hat{u}; \eta) + o(\tau)$$

for any $\eta \in \tilde{V}$, $\|\eta\| = 1$. Suppose $\hat{u}$ is not a stationary point, so that $f^{(1)}(\hat{u}; \eta) \neq 0$ for some η. Then there exists $\tau_0 > 0$ such that $\tau f^{(1)}(\hat{u}; \eta) + o(\tau) < 0$ for either $0 < \tau < \tau_0$ or $-\tau_0 < \tau < 0$, depending on the sign of $f^{(1)}(\hat{u}; \eta)$. Hence in every neighborhood $S(\hat{u}; \varepsilon)$ of $\hat{u}$ there is a point $u = \hat{u} + \tau\eta$ such that $f(u) < f(\hat{u})$, and $\hat{u}$ cannot be a local minimizer. ∎

In general, for any $u \in V$ and $\eta \in \tilde{V}$, $\|\eta\| = 1$, there is the Taylor expansion

$$f(u + \tau\eta) = f(u) + \tau f^{(1)}(u; \eta) + \tfrac{1}{2}\tau^2 f^{(2)}(u; \eta) + \cdots$$

$$+ \frac{1}{m!} \tau^m f^{(m)}(u; \eta) + o(\tau^m),$$

provided that $f^{(m)}(u; \eta)$ exists. For a stationary point $\hat{u}$, we then have

$$f(\hat{u} + \tau\eta) = f(\hat{u}) + \tfrac{1}{2}\tau^2 f^{(2)}(\hat{u}; \eta) + \cdots + \frac{1}{m!} \tau^m f^{(m)}(\hat{u}; \eta) + o(\tau^m), \quad (2.2)$$

and the behavior of f in a neighborhood of $\hat{u}$ is determined primarily by $f^{(2)}(\hat{u}; \eta)$.

Theorem 2.2. Let f be defined on V. Let $\hat{u} \in V$ be a stationary point of f and suppose that $f^{(2)}(\hat{u}; \eta)$ exists for all directions η. If $\hat{u}$ is a local minimizer of f, then $f^{(2)}(\hat{u}; \eta) \geq 0$ for all directions η.

PROOF: If $f^{(2)}(\hat{u}; \eta) < 0$ for some η, then (2.2), with $m = 2$, shows that $\hat{u}$ cannot be a local minimizer.   ∎

Theorems 2.1 and 2.2 give only necessary conditions for $\hat{u}$ to be a local minimizer of f, and the derivation of sufficient conditions requires further analysis. This is easy, however, in the simple but important case when f is a quadratic functional.

Definition 2.5. A functional $f: V \to R$ is a *quadratic functional* if it satisfies the identity

$$f(u + \tau\eta) = f(u) + \tau f^{(1)}(u; \eta) + \tfrac{1}{2}\tau^2 f^{(2)}(u; \eta) \tag{2.3}$$

$\forall u \in V, \forall \eta \in \tilde{V}, \|\eta\| = 1$, and $\forall \tau \in R$.

Suppose that f is any functional with the property that $f(u + \tau\eta)$ is a second-degree polynomial with respect to τ. Then the direct computation of $f^{(1)}(u; \eta)$ and $f^{(2)}(u; \eta)$ shows that (2.3) must hold, i.e., f is quadratic.

Theorem 2.3. Let f be a quadratic functional defined on V. Then $\hat{u} \in V$ is the unique strong local and strong global minimizer of f if

$$f^{(1)}(\hat{u}; \eta) = 0 \qquad \forall \eta \in \tilde{V}, \quad \|\eta\| = 1, \tag{2.4}$$

$$f^{(2)}(\hat{u}; \eta) > 0 \qquad \forall \eta \in \tilde{V}, \quad \|\eta\| = 1. \tag{2.5}$$

PROOF: The proof is evident from (2.3).   ∎

The Euler–Lagrange Equation

We shall now proceed to examine some particular functionals. Let $F(x, r, s)$ be a real function defined on $a \leq x \leq b, -\infty < r, s < \infty$. We assume that F has continuous partial derivatives of order ≤ 2. Let

$$V = \{v \in C^2[a, b]; v(a) = \alpha, v(b) = \beta\},$$

$$f(u) = \int_a^b F[x, u(x), u'(x)]\, dx, \qquad u \in V. \tag{2.6}$$

Note that if $\alpha \neq 0$ or $\beta \neq 0$, then the set V of admissible functions is not a linear space. If, for example, $\alpha \neq 0$, then

$$u, v \in V \quad \Rightarrow \quad u(a) + v(a) = 2\alpha \quad \Rightarrow \quad u + v \notin V.$$

On the other hand, the set $\tilde{V}$ of test functions defined by (2.1) is the linear space

$$\tilde{V} = \{v \in C^2[a, b]; v(a) = v(b) = 0\}.$$

In the case of homogeneous boundary conditions (i.e., $\alpha = \beta = 0$), we have $\tilde{V} = V$.

According to Definition 2.3, the directional derivatives of f are obtained by differentiating the function

$$f(u + \tau\eta) = \int_a^b F(x, u + \tau\eta, u' + \tau\eta') \, dx$$

with respect to τ and then setting $\tau = 0$. Differentiating once under the integral sign and using the familiar chain rule we find that

$$f^{(1)}(u; \eta) = \int_a^b \left(\frac{\partial F}{\partial u} \eta + \frac{\partial F}{\partial u'} \eta' \right) dx. \tag{2.7}$$

Hence, by Definition 2.4, f is stationary at some $u \in V$ if and only if

$$\int_a^b \left(\frac{\partial F}{\partial u} \eta + \frac{\partial F}{\partial u'} \eta' \right) dx = 0 \qquad \forall \eta \in \tilde{V}. \tag{2.8}$$

(Note that it makes no difference here that we have dropped the requirement $\|\eta\| = 1$.)

The functions u and F are smooth enough to permit the second term of the integrand to be integrated by parts:

$$\int_a^b \frac{\partial F}{\partial u'} \eta' \, dx = \left[\frac{\partial F}{\partial u'} \eta \right]_a^b - \int_a^b \frac{d}{dx} \left(\frac{\partial F}{\partial u'} \right) \eta \, dx$$

$$= - \int_a^b \frac{d}{dx} \left(\frac{\partial F}{\partial u'} \right) \eta \, dx.$$

We have used here the boundary conditions $\eta(a) = \eta(b) = 0$, which hold for every $\eta \in \tilde{V}$. Combining this result with (2.8) yields

$$\int_a^b \left[\frac{\partial F}{\partial u} - \frac{d}{dx} \left(\frac{\partial F}{\partial u'} \right) \right] \eta \, dx = 0 \qquad \forall \eta \in \tilde{V}. \tag{2.9}$$

The function in brackets, which we denote $\theta(x)$, is necessarily continuous. We shall now show that it is identically zero. Thus, suppose that $\theta(x_0) \neq 0$ for some $x_0 \in (a, b)$. Then, because $\theta(x)$ is continuous at x_0, there is some interval $I = (x_0 - \varepsilon, x_0 + \varepsilon)$, $\varepsilon > 0$, such that $\theta(x)$ is nonzero and has constant sign everywhere in I. Now one can easily find a function $\eta \in \tilde{V}$ that vanishes everywhere outside I and is positive everywhere in I. Obviously, $\int_a^b \theta \eta \, dx \neq 0$ for this η. We conclude, then, that $u \in V$ is a stationary point of f if and only if u satisfies

$$\frac{\partial F}{\partial u} - \frac{d}{dx}\left(\frac{\partial F}{\partial u'}\right) = 0, \qquad a < x < b. \tag{2.10}$$

This is the famous *Euler–Lagrange differential equation* for (2.6). It is usually a second-order ordinary differential equation for u, and the problem of finding a function u that satisfies (2.10) and the boundary conditions $u(a) = \alpha$, $u(b) = \beta$ is a classical *two-point boundary value problem*. What we have established is that this two-point boundary value problem is equivalent to finding a stationary point of (2.6), i.e., a function $u \in V$ that satisfies (2.8). We call the latter problem the *variational formulation* of the two-point boundary value problem.

Example 2.1. Let

$$V = \{v \in C^2[0, 1]; v(0) = 0, v(1) = 1\},$$

$$f(u) = \int_0^1 \left[\tfrac{1}{2}(u')^2 - r(x)u\right] dx, \qquad u \in V,$$

where $r \in C[0, 1]$. Then,

$$\frac{\partial F}{\partial u} = -r, \qquad \frac{\partial F}{\partial u'} = u', \qquad \frac{d}{dx}\left(\frac{\partial F}{\partial u'}\right) = u''.$$

The problem of finding a $u \in V$ that satisfies (2.8),

$$\int_0^1 (u'\eta' - r\eta) \, dx = 0 \qquad \forall \eta \in \tilde{V},$$

is the variational formulation of the two-point boundary value problem consisting of the Euler–Lagrange equation (2.10),

$$-u'' = r(x), \qquad 0 < x < 1,$$

and the boundary conditions $u(0) = 0$, $u(1) = 1$. The theory of differential equations tells us [see, e.g., Birkhoff and Rota (1978)] that this problem has a unique solution in $C^2[0, 1]$ (and therefore in V), which we denote $\hat{u}$.

For any $u \in V$ and $\eta \in \tilde{V}$,

$$f(u + \tau\eta) = \int_0^1 \left[\tfrac{1}{2}(u' + \tau\eta')^2 - r(u + \tau\eta)\right] dx$$

$$= \int_0^1 \left[\tfrac{1}{2}(u')^2 - ru\right] dx + \tau \int_0^1 (u'\eta' - r\eta) \, dx + \tfrac{1}{2}\tau^2 \int_0^1 (\eta')^2 \, dx,$$

showing that f is a quadratic functional. The directional derivatives are

$$f^{(1)}(u; \eta) = \int_0^1 (u'\eta' - r\eta) \, dx, \qquad f^{(2)}(u; \eta) = \int_0^1 (\eta')^2 \, dx,$$

$$f^{(m)}(u; \eta) = 0, \qquad m \geq 3,$$

for any η with $\|\eta\| = 1$. Clearly, $f^{(2)}(u; \eta) > 0$ for all directions η. Since the function $\hat{u}$ mentioned previously makes $f^{(1)}(\hat{u}; \eta) = 0$ for all directions η, we conclude from Theorem 2.3 that $\hat{u}$ is the unique strong global minimizer of f.

Example 2.2. Let

$$V = \{v \in C^2[0, 1]; v(0) = 0, v(1) = 1\},$$

$$f(u) = \int_0^1 \tfrac{1}{2}u^2 \, dx, \qquad u \in V.$$

Then,

$$\frac{\partial F}{\partial u} = u, \qquad \frac{\partial F}{\partial u'} = 0, \qquad \frac{d}{dx}\left(\frac{\partial F}{\partial u'}\right) = 0,$$

and the Euler–Lagrange equation (2.10) becomes

$$u(x) = 0, \qquad 0 < x < 1.$$

This is not a standard equation for a two-point boundary value problem, since no derivative of u appears. Further, it is obviously not satisfied by any function in V. It follows that f has no stationary point and hence, by Theorem 2.1, no local minimizer. Further, since a global minimizer is necessarily also a local minimizer, f has no global minimizer.

On the other hand, we see directly from the definition of f that $f(u) \geq 0$ $\forall u \in V$, so f possesses a nonnegative infimum (greatest lower bound). Consider the sequence of functions $u_i(x) = x^i$, $0 \leq x \leq 1$, $i = 1, 2, \ldots$, which belong to V. Since $f(u_i) = (2i + 1)^{-1}$ and $\lim_{i \to \infty} f(u_i) = 0$, it is established that $\inf_{u \in V} f(u) = 0$.

Fourth-Order Boundary Value Problems

We shall now consider a functional that is relevant to two-point boundary value problems of fourth order. Let $F(x, r, s, t)$ be a real function defined on $a \leq x \leq b$, $-\infty < r, s, t < \infty$. We assume that F has continuous partial derivatives of order ≤ 3. Let

$$V = \{v \in C^4[a, b]; v(a) = \alpha_0, v'(a) = \alpha_1, v(b) = \beta_0, v'(b) = \beta_1\},$$

$$f(u) = \int_a^b F(x, u, u', u'') \, dx, \qquad u \in V. \tag{2.11}$$

The space $\tilde{V}$ of test functions associated with V is seen from (2.1) to be

$$\tilde{V} = \{v \in C^4[a, b]; v(a) = v'(a) = v(b) = v'(b) = 0\}.$$

Differentiating the function

$$f(u + \tau\eta) = \int_a^b F(x, u + \tau\eta, u' + \tau\eta', u'' + \tau\eta'') \, dx$$

with respect to τ and then setting $\tau = 0$, we obtain the first-order directional derivative

$$f^{(1)}(u; \eta) = \int_a^b \left(\frac{\partial F}{\partial u} \eta + \frac{\partial F}{\partial u'} \eta' + \frac{\partial F}{\partial u''} \eta'' \right) dx,$$

and the condition for a stationary point of f is thus

$$\int_a^b \left(\frac{\partial F}{\partial u} \eta + \frac{\partial F}{\partial u'} \eta' + \frac{\partial F}{\partial u''} \eta'' \right) dx = 0 \qquad \forall \eta \in \tilde{V}. \tag{2.12}$$

Integrating twice by parts we find that

$$\int_a^b \left[\frac{\partial F}{\partial u} - \frac{d}{dx}\left(\frac{\partial F}{\partial u'} \right) + \frac{d^2}{dx^2}\left(\frac{\partial F}{\partial u''} \right) \right] \eta \, dx + \left[\frac{\partial F}{\partial u''} \eta' \right]_a^b$$

$$- \left[\left(\frac{d}{dx}\left(\frac{\partial F}{\partial u''} \right) - \frac{\partial F}{\partial u'} \right) \eta \right]_a^b = 0 \qquad \forall \eta \in \tilde{V},$$

and the boundary conditions on the test functions then imply

$$\int_a^b \left[\frac{\partial F}{\partial u} - \frac{d}{dx}\left(\frac{\partial F}{\partial u'} \right) + \frac{d^2}{dx^2}\left(\frac{\partial F}{\partial u''} \right) \right] \eta \, dx = 0 \qquad \forall \eta \in \tilde{V}.$$

The function in brackets is continuous for any $u \in V$, and using the argument following (2.9), we conclude that (2.12) is equivalent to the condition

$$\frac{\partial F}{\partial u} - \frac{d}{dx}\left(\frac{\partial F}{\partial u'}\right) + \frac{d^2}{dx^2}\left(\frac{\partial F}{\partial u''}\right) = 0, \qquad a < x < b. \qquad (2.13)$$

This is the Euler–Lagrange equation for the functional (2.11). The problem of finding a function u which satisfies (2.13) and the boundary conditions $v(a) = \alpha_0, v'(a) = \alpha_1, v(b) = \beta_0, v'(b) = \beta_1$ is another example of a two-point boundary value problem, the equation now usually being of fourth order. The variational formulation of this problem is finding a function $u \in V$ that satisfies (2.12).

Example 2.3. Let

$$V = \{v \in C^4[a, b]; v(a) = \alpha_0, v'(a) = \alpha_1, v(b) = \beta_0, v'(b) = \beta_1\},$$

$$f(u) = \int_a^b \left[\tfrac{1}{2}s(x)(u'')^2 + \tfrac{1}{2}p(x)(u')^2 + \tfrac{1}{2}q(x)u^2 - r(x)u\right] dx, \qquad u \in V,$$

where $s \in C^2[a, b]$, $p \in C^1[a, b]$, $q, r \in C[a, b]$. Then,

$$\partial F/\partial u = qu - r, \qquad \partial F/\partial u' = pu', \qquad \partial F/\partial u'' = su'',$$

and the Euler–Lagrange equation (2.13) is

$$[s(x)u'']'' - [p(x)u']' + q(x)u = r(x), \qquad a < x < b.$$

This equation together with the four boundary conditions defines a two-point boundary value problem, and its variational formulation is the problem of finding $u \in V$ such that (2.12) holds, or

$$\int_a^b \left[su''\eta'' + pu'\eta' + (qu - r)\eta\right] dx = 0 \qquad \forall \eta \in \tilde{V}.$$

f is a quadratic functional since

$$f(u + \tau\eta) = \int_a^b \left[\tfrac{1}{2}s(u'')^2 + \tfrac{1}{2}p(u')^2 + \tfrac{1}{2}qu^2 - ru\right] dx$$

$$+ \tau \int_a^b \left[su''\eta'' + pu'\eta' + (qu - r)\eta\right] dx$$

$$+ \tfrac{1}{2}\tau^2 \int_a^b \left[s(\eta'')^2 + p(\eta')^2 + q\eta^2\right] dx$$

$$= f(u) + \tau f^{(1)}(u; \eta) + \tfrac{1}{2}\tau^2 f^{(2)}(u; \eta), \qquad \|\eta\| = 1.$$

If $s(x) > 0$ and $p(x)$, $q(x) \geq 0$ for $x \in [a, b]$, then the two-point boundary value problem is known to have a solution $\hat{u}$, and the variational formulation of the problem asserts that $\hat{u}$ is a stationary point of f. Further, $f^{(2)}(\hat{u}; \eta)$ is positive for all directions η (why can't it vanish?) and Theorem 2.3 states that $\hat{u}$ is the unique minimizer of f.

We have seen that a quadratic functional f is recognized by the property that $f(u + \tau\eta)$ is a second-degree polynomial with respect to τ. Consider a functional f of the form

$$f(u) = \int_a^b F(x, u, u', \ldots, u^{(k)}) \, dx, \qquad u \in V,$$

where F is a second-degree polynomial with respect to $u, u', \ldots, u^{(k)}$. We leave it to the reader to verify that

(1) f is quadratic;
(2) the associated Euler–Lagrange equation is linear;
(3) if F is written in the form $F = \frac{1}{2}F_2 + F_1 + F_0$, where F_i contains terms of degree i only, then

$$f^{(2)}(u; \eta) = \int_a^b F_2(\eta, \eta', \ldots, \eta^{(k)}) \, dx.$$

For example, the functional

$$f(u) = \int_a^b \left[\tfrac{1}{2}(u'')^2 - \tfrac{1}{2} \sin(x)uu' + xu + u' - 2x^2 \right] dx, \qquad u \in V$$

is quadratic with

$$F_2 = (u'')^2 - \sin(x)uu', \qquad F_1 = xu + u', \qquad F_0 = -2x^2,$$

and

$$f^{(2)}(u; \eta) = \int_a^b \left[(\eta'')^2 - \sin(x)\eta\eta' \right] dx.$$

The Euler–Lagrange equation is readily found to be

$$u^{iv} + \tfrac{1}{2} \cos(x)u + x = 0.$$

2.2 Natural and Essential Boundary Conditions

From our choice of admissible functions for f in (2.6), we have required every $u \in V$ to satisfy the boundary conditions $u(a) = \alpha$, $u(b) = \beta$. This naturally implies that every stationary point of f satisfies these conditions. The question then arises, If we impose no boundary conditions on the admissible functions, then what boundary conditions will a stationary point satisfy?

To answer this question we must examine the functional

$$f(u) = \int_a^b F[x, u(x), u'(x)] \, dx, \qquad u \in V = C^2[a, b].$$

We observe from (2.1) that the space of test functions is now $\tilde{V} = C^2[a, b]$, and it may no longer be assumed that $\eta(a) = \eta(b) = 0 \; \forall \eta \in \tilde{V}$. Returning to (2.8) and integrating by parts, we find that the condition for a stationary point of f is

$$\int_a^b \left[\frac{\partial F}{\partial u} - \frac{d}{dx} \left(\frac{\partial F}{\partial u'} \right) \right] \eta \, dx + \left[\frac{\partial F}{\partial u'} \eta \right]_a^b = 0 \qquad \forall \eta \in \tilde{V}. \tag{2.14}$$

Suppose that (2.14) is satisfied by some admissible function $\hat{u}$. Since (2.14) holds for all $\eta \in C^2[a, b]$, it must hold in particular for that subset of $C^2[a, b]$ for which $\eta(a) = \eta(b) = 0$. But as we have seen, this implies that

$$\frac{\partial F}{\partial u} - \frac{d}{dx} \left(\frac{\partial F}{\partial u'} \right) = 0, \qquad a < x < b, \tag{2.15}$$

and (2.14) is thus reduced to

$$\left[\frac{\partial F}{\partial u'} \eta \right]_a^b = 0 \qquad \forall \eta \in \tilde{V}. \tag{2.16}$$

Since there are no restrictions on the values $\eta(a)$ and $\eta(b)$ when η is permitted to be any function in $\tilde{V}$, we must have

$$\frac{\partial F}{\partial u'} = 0 \qquad \text{for} \quad x = a, b. \tag{2.17}$$

Thus, in addition to satisfying the Euler–Lagrange differential equation (2.15), every stationary point of f must satisfy the boundary conditions given by (2.17). Because these boundary conditions were not imposed on the admissible functions, they are called the *natural boundary conditions* for $f(u) = \int_a^b F(x, u, u') \, dx$. In contrast, the conditions $u(a) = \alpha, u(b) = \beta$, where α and β are given real numbers, are called the *essential boundary conditions* for $f(u)$. It is convenient to arrange the various boundary conditions as shown in Table 2.1.

If an essential boundary condition is imposed on the admissible functions, then the test functions must satisfy the corresponding boundary condition

Table 2.1

The Essential and Natural Boundary Conditions Associated with
$f(u) = \int_a^b F(x, u, u') \, dx$

Essential boundary condition	Boundary condition on η	Natural boundary condition
$u(a) = \alpha$	$\eta(a) = 0$	$\left[\dfrac{\partial F}{\partial u'}\right]_{x=a} = 0$
$u(b) = \beta$	$\eta(b) = 0$	$\left[\dfrac{\partial F}{\partial u'}\right]_{x=b} = 0$

shown in the second column of the table. An inspection of (2.16) shows that if any of the essential boundary conditions is not imposed on the admissible functions, then a stationary point must satisfy the corresponding natural boundary condition. For example, if only the first essential boundary condition is imposed, then

$$V = \{v \in C^2[a, b]; \, v(a) = \alpha\},$$
$$\tilde{V} = \{\eta \in C^2[a, b]; \, \eta(a) = 0\}, \tag{2.18}$$

and

$$\left[\frac{\partial F}{\partial u'} \eta\right]_a^b = 0 \quad \forall \eta \in \tilde{V} \quad \Rightarrow \quad \eta(b) \left[\frac{\partial F}{\partial u'}\right]_{x=b} = 0 \quad \forall \eta \in \tilde{V}$$

$$\Rightarrow \quad \left[\frac{\partial F}{\partial u'}\right]_{x=b} = 0,$$

since there is no restriction on the value of $\eta(b)$. This is the natural boundary condition corresponding to the omitted essential boundary condition.

We shall now seek the natural boundary conditions for the functional

$$f(u) = \int_a^b F(x, u, u', u'') \, dx.$$

Taking $V = \tilde{V} = C^4[a, b]$, it is straightforward to show that every stationary point must satisfy the Euler–Lagrange equation (2.13) and, moreover, the condition

$$\left[\frac{\partial F}{\partial u''} \eta'\right]_a^b - \left[\left(\frac{d}{dx}\left(\frac{\partial F}{\partial u''}\right) - \frac{\partial F}{\partial u'}\right) \eta\right]_a^b = 0 \quad \forall \eta \in \tilde{V}. \tag{2.19}$$

Table 2.2

The Essential and Natural Boundary Conditions Associated with
$$f(u) = \int_a^b F(x, u, u', u'') \, dx$$

Essential boundary condition	Boundary condition on η	Natural boundary condition
$u(a) = \alpha_0$	$\eta(a) = 0$	$\left[\dfrac{d}{dx}\left(\dfrac{\partial F}{\partial u''}\right) - \dfrac{\partial F}{\partial u'} \right]_{x=a} = 0$
$u'(a) = \alpha_1$	$\eta'(a) = 0$	$\left[\dfrac{\partial F}{\partial u''} \right]_{x=a} = 0$
$u(b) = \beta_0$	$\eta(b) = 0$	$\left[\dfrac{d}{dx}\left(\dfrac{\partial F}{\partial u''}\right) - \dfrac{\partial F}{\partial u'} \right]_{x=b} = 0$
$u'(b) = \beta_1$	$\eta'(b) = 0$	$\left[\dfrac{\partial F}{\partial u''} \right]_{x=b} = 0$

Since there are no restrictions on the values of η and η' at the endpoints of the interval, we conclude that a stationary point must satisfy

$$\frac{d}{dx}\left(\frac{\partial F}{\partial u''}\right) - \frac{\partial F}{\partial u'} = 0 \qquad \text{for} \quad x = a, b, \tag{2.20a}$$

$$\frac{\partial F}{\partial u''} = 0 \qquad \text{for} \quad x = a, b. \tag{2.20b}$$

These are therefore the natural boundary conditions for f. The essential boundary conditions are those we imposed on V in Section 2.1: $u(a) = \alpha_0$, $u'(a) = \alpha_1$, $u(b) = \beta_0$, and $u'(b) = \beta_1$. The correspondence between the various boundary conditions is given in Table 2.2. If any of the essential boundary conditions is not imposed on the admissible functions, then it is seen from (2.19) that a stationary point must satisfy the corresponding natural boundary condition.

Generally speaking, removing essential boundary conditions expands the set of admissible functions and therefore tends to lower the minimum value of a functional. The "least" minimum value is attained when all essential boundary conditions are removed, and then the minimizer, being a stationary point, satisfies the natural boundary conditions.

Example 2.4. Let

$$f(u) = \int_a^b \left[\tfrac{1}{2}p(x)(u')^2 + \tfrac{1}{2}q(x)u^2 - r(x)u \right] dx, \qquad u \in C^2[a, b],$$

where $p \in C^1[a, b]$, $p(x) > 0$ for $a \leq x \leq b$, $q, r \in C[a, b]$, and $q(x) \geq 0$ for $a \leq x \leq b$. The Euler–Lagrange equation is (2.15), or

$$-[p(x)u']' + q(x)u = r(x), \qquad a < x < b.$$

We find from (2.17) that the natural boundary conditions for f are $u'(a) = u'(b) = 0$.

Example 2.5. We shall now consider a uniform linearly elastic beam of unit length that is clamped at one end and either clamped, supported, or free at the other. The beam is subjected to a load $r(x)$ that causes a vertical deflection $u(x)$. The three cases are sketched in Fig. 2.1. In each case the mathematical boundary conditions at the left end, which is clamped, are $u(0) = u'(0) = 0$.

The simplest mathematical model for this system states that the deflection $u(x)$, which we assume to be small, is the global minimizer of

$$f(u) = \int_0^1 \left[\tfrac{1}{2}\alpha(u'')^2 - r(x)u\right] dx, \qquad u \in V, \tag{2.21}$$

where $\alpha > 0$ is a material constant and V is appropriately chosen for each case. The natural boundary conditions are given by (2.20):

$$\frac{\partial F}{\partial u''} = \alpha u'' = 0 \qquad \text{or} \qquad u'' = 0,$$

$$\frac{d}{dx}\left[\frac{\partial F}{\partial u''}\right] - \frac{\partial F}{\partial u'} = \alpha u''' = 0 \qquad \text{or} \qquad u''' = 0.$$

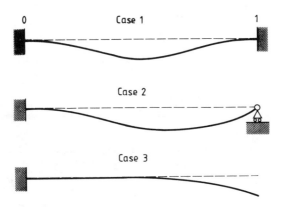

Fig. 2.1. A loaded beam subjected to various boundary conditions. Case 1, clamped, $u(1) = u'(1) = 0$; Case 2, supported, $u(1) = u''(1) = 0$; Case 3, free, $u''(1) = u'''(1) = 0$.

All of the boundary conditions in the three cases are either essential or natural, and only the essential boundary conditions need be imposed on the admissible functions. Thus V is chosen as follows:

(1) $V = \{v \in C^4[0, 1]; v(0) = v'(0) = v(1) = v'(1) = 0\}$,
(2) $V = \{v \in C^4[0, 1]; v(0) = v'(0) = v(1) = 0\}$,
(3) $V = \{v \in C^4[0, 1]; v(0) = v'(0) = 0\}$.

Note that the natural boundary conditions replace essential boundary conditions as indicated by Table 2.2. For example, in Case 2 the essential boundary condition $u'(1) = \beta_1$ is missing, but we have the natural boundary condition $u''(1) = 0$. This is the natural boundary condition associated with $u'(1) = \beta_1$ in Table 2.2. The minimum value of f is least for Case 3, since we then have the fewest restrictions on the admissible functions. The greater "mathematical freedom" in Case 3 reflects the physical freedom of the right end of the beam.

The Euler–Lagrange equation for this problem is (2.13), or

$$\alpha u^{iv} = r(x), \qquad 0 < x < 1,$$

for all three cases. A two-point boundary value problem for a fourth-order equation requires four boundary conditions. The total number of essential and natural boundary conditions in each of the three cases is precisely four.

Other Boundary Conditions

One frequently seeks a solution of the Euler–Lagrange equation

$$\frac{\partial F}{\partial u} - \frac{d}{dx}\left(\frac{\partial F}{\partial u'}\right) = 0, \qquad a < x < b,$$

with boundary conditions that are neither essential nor natural for the corresponding functional

$$f(u) = \int_a^b F(x, u, u')\,dx.$$

It is thus relevant to point out that one can sometimes modify f, without at the same time modifying the Euler–Lagrange equation, so that the given boundary conditions appear as the natural boundary conditions.

Thus, consider

$$V = C^2[a, b],$$

$$f(u) = \int_a^b F(x, u, u')\,dx + [G(x, u)]_{x=a} + [H(x, u)]_{x=b}, \qquad u \in V, \qquad (2.22)$$

where G and H have continuous first-order partial derivatives. Then $\tilde{V} = V$, and it is readily seen that the condition for a stationary point of f is

$$\int_a^b \left[\frac{\partial F}{\partial u} - \frac{d}{dx}\left(\frac{\partial F}{\partial u'}\right)\right] \eta \, dx + \left[\left(\frac{\partial F}{\partial u'} + \frac{\partial H}{\partial u}\right)\eta\right]_{x=b}$$

$$- \left[\left(\frac{\partial F}{\partial u'} - \frac{\partial G}{\partial u}\right)\eta\right]_{x=a} = 0 \qquad \forall \eta \in \tilde{V}.$$

The Euler–Lagrange equation is the same as before, but now the natural boundary conditions are

$$\frac{\partial F}{\partial u'} - \frac{\partial G}{\partial u} = 0 \qquad \text{for} \quad x = a, \tag{2.23a}$$

$$\frac{\partial F}{\partial u'} + \frac{\partial H}{\partial u} = 0 \qquad \text{for} \quad x = b. \tag{2.23b}$$

Sometimes $G(x, u)$ and $H(x, u)$ can be chosen so that (2.23a,b) are the desired boundary conditions.

Example 2.6. We seek a functional f whose Euler–Lagrange equation is the same as in Example 2.4 and whose natural boundary conditions are $u'(a) - \alpha u(a) = 0$ and $u'(b) + \beta u(b) = 0$, where $\alpha, \beta > 0$.

Thus let

$$f(u) = \int_a^b \left[\tfrac{1}{2}p(x)(u')^2 + \tfrac{1}{2}q(x)u^2 - r(x)u\right] dx$$

$$+ \left[G(x, u)\right]_{x=a} + \left[H(x, u)\right]_{x=b}, \qquad u \in C^2[a, b],$$

where G and H are to be determined. Boundary conditions (2.23) can be written as

$$u' - \frac{1}{p}\frac{\partial G}{\partial u} = 0 \qquad \text{for} \quad x = a,$$

$$u' + \frac{1}{p}\frac{\partial H}{\partial u} = 0 \qquad \text{for} \quad x = b.$$

These are the desired boundary conditions if we choose

$$G(x, u) = \tfrac{1}{2}\alpha p(a)u^2, \qquad H(x, u) = \tfrac{1}{2}\beta p(b)u^2.$$

The distinction between essential and natural boundary conditions will be seen to be of considerable importance in the numerical methods for boundary value problems to be discussed later. In choosing approximating functions, one is required to impose only the essential conditions.

It is easy to see that the Euler–Lagrange equation associated with a functional of the type

$$f(u) = \int_a^b F(x, u, u', u'', \ldots, u^{(k)}) \, dx$$

contains derivatives of u of order up to $2k$. The essential boundary conditions contain derivatives of order less than k, whereas the natural boundary conditions can contain derivatives of order up to $(2k - 1)$.

2.3   Problems in Two and Three Dimensions

Preliminaries

We shall now extend the analysis of Sections 2.1 and 2.2 to problems in two and three space variables, considering first the two-dimensional case. Our notation is

x, y	the space variables
Ω	the problem's domain of definition in R^2
Γ	the boundary of Ω
u_ν	the outer normal derivative of $u(x, y)$ on Γ
ν_1, ν_2	the direction cosines with respect to the x and y axes, respectively, of the outer normal to Γ
u_τ	the tangential derivative of $u(x, y)$ in the counterclockwise sense
$\int_\Gamma u \, ds$	the line integral of $u(x, y)$ over Γ in the counterclockwise sense

The domain of definition Ω is assumed to be open, bounded, and simply connected, and its boundary Γ is assumed to be smooth except possibly at a finite number of "corners." We define $\bar{\Omega} = \Omega \cup \Gamma$ and denote by $C^k(\bar{\Omega})$ the set of all functions with continuous partial derivatives on $\bar{\Omega}$ of order up to and including k.

The direction cosine ν_i is a function of (x, y) on Γ. The following identities hold:

$$u_\nu = \nu_1 u_x + \nu_2 u_y, \tag{2.24a}$$

$$u_\tau = -\nu_2 u_x + \nu_1 u_y, \tag{2.24b}$$

$$u_{\nu\nu} = \nu_1^2 u_{xx} + 2\nu_1 \nu_2 u_{xy} + \nu_2^2 u_{yy}, \tag{2.25a}$$

$$u_{v\tau} = -v_1 v_2 u_{xx} + (v_1^2 - v_2^2)u_{xy} + v_1 v_2 u_{yy}, \qquad (2.25b)$$

$$u_{\tau\tau} = v_2^2 u_{xx} - 2v_1 v_2 u_{xy} + v_1^2 u_{yy}, \qquad (2.25c)$$

where $u_x = \partial u/\partial x$, etc.

We shall frequently make use of the Gauss integral identities

$$\iint_\Omega uv_x \, dx \, dy = \int_\Gamma v_1 uv \, ds - \iint_\Omega u_x v \, dx \, dy, \qquad (2.26a)$$

$$\iint_\Omega uv_y \, dx \, dy = \int_\Gamma v_2 uv \, ds - \iint_\Omega u_y v \, dx \, dy, \qquad (2.26b)$$

which express integration by parts of functions of x and y.

It is occasionally convenient to employ the operators ∇ (or grad), div, and Δ of vector analysis. These are defined by

$$\nabla u = \text{grad}(u) = [u_x, u_y]^\text{T}, \qquad \text{where T means transpose,}$$

$$\text{div}(\mathbf{u}) = u_x^{(1)} + u_y^{(2)}, \qquad \text{where} \quad \mathbf{u} = [u^{(1)}, u^{(2)}]^\text{T},$$

$$\Delta u = \text{div grad}(u) = u_{xx} + u_{yy}.$$

Further,

$$|\nabla u| = [(\nabla u)^\text{T} \nabla u]^{1/2} = (u_x^2 + u_y^2)^{1/2},$$

$$\nabla^2 u = \nabla^\text{T}(\nabla u) = u_{xx} + u_{yy} = \Delta u,$$

$$\Delta^2 u = \Delta(\Delta u) = u_{xxxx} + 2u_{xxyy} + u_{yyyy}.$$

For background information on vector analysis see, e.g., Kaplan (1952) and Marsden and Tromba (1976).

Second-Order Boundary Value Problems

We now want to examine functionals of the type $f: V \to R$, where V is some set of real functions defined on Ω. The definitions and theorems of Section 2.1 carry over immediately to the case of two space variables, the norm $\|\cdot\|$ now being defined by

$$\|u\| = \left[\iint_\Omega u(x, y)^2 \, dx \, dy \right]^{1/2}.$$

We begin with the two-dimensional analog of (2.6):

$$V = \{v \in C^2(\bar\Omega); v = \alpha \text{ on } \Gamma\},$$

$$f(u) = \iint_\Omega F(x, y, u, u_x, u_y) \, dx \, dy, \qquad u \in V, \qquad (2.27)$$

where $\alpha = \alpha(x, y)$ is a continuous function on Γ and $F(x, y, r, s, t)$ has continuous partial derivatives of order ≤ 2 for $(x, y) \in \bar{\Omega}$, $-\infty < r, s, t < \infty$. We see from (2.1) that the test functions are $\tilde{V} = \mathring{V}$, where

$$\mathring{V} = \{v \in C^2(\bar{\Omega}); v = 0 \text{ on } \Gamma\}. \tag{2.28}$$

The first-order directional derivative is

$$f^{(1)}(u; \eta) = \int\int_\Omega \left(\frac{\partial F}{\partial u} \eta + \frac{\partial F}{\partial u_x} \eta_x + \frac{\partial F}{\partial u_y} \eta_y \right) dx \, dy.$$

Hence the condition for a stationary point of f is

$$\int\int_\Omega \left(\frac{\partial F}{\partial u} \eta + \frac{\partial F}{\partial u_x} \eta_x + \frac{\partial F}{\partial u_y} \eta_y \right) dx \, dy = 0 \qquad \forall \eta \in \mathring{V}. \tag{2.29}$$

We can integrate by parts with the help of (2.26) to remove η_x and η_y. Putting $u = \partial F/\partial u_x$, $v = \eta$ in (2.26a), and $u = \partial F/\partial u_y$, $v = \eta$ in (2.26b), we obtain relations which enable us to rewrite (2.29) as

$$\int\int_\Omega \left[\frac{\partial F}{\partial u} - \frac{\partial}{\partial x}\left(\frac{\partial F}{\partial u_x} \right) - \frac{\partial}{\partial y}\left(\frac{\partial F}{\partial u_y} \right) \right] \eta \, dx \, dy$$

$$+ \int_\Gamma \left(v_1 \frac{\partial F}{\partial u_x} + v_2 \frac{\partial F}{\partial u_y} \right) \eta \, ds = 0 \qquad \forall \eta \in \mathring{V}. \tag{2.30}$$

Since $\eta = 0$ on Γ, the line integral vanishes. Then the first integral must vanish for all test functions, and it is easy to show that this implies the Euler–Lagrange equation

$$\frac{\partial F}{\partial u} - \frac{\partial}{\partial x}\left(\frac{\partial F}{\partial u_x} \right) - \frac{\partial}{\partial y}\left(\frac{\partial F}{\partial u_y} \right) = 0 \qquad \text{in } \Omega. \tag{2.31}$$

The boundary condition $u = \alpha$ on Γ is the essential boundary condition for f. To find the natural boundary condition, we remove the essential boundary condition by putting $V = \tilde{V} = C^2(\bar{\Omega})$. A stationary point must satisfy (2.30) for the new choice of $\tilde{V}$, but since $\mathring{V} \subset \tilde{V}$, where $\mathring{V}$ is given by (2.28), it follows from the above that the Euler–Lagrange equation (2.31) is still valid. Thus,

$$\int_\Gamma \left(v_1 \frac{\partial F}{\partial u_x} + v_2 \frac{\partial F}{\partial u_y} \right) \eta \, ds = 0 \qquad \forall \eta \in C^2(\bar{\Omega}),$$

yielding the natural boundary condition

$$v_1 \frac{\partial F}{\partial u_x} + v_2 \frac{\partial F}{\partial u_y} = 0 \qquad \text{on } \Gamma. \tag{2.32}$$

Example 2.7. A frequently occurring functional is

$$f(u) = \int\int_\Omega \left[\tfrac{1}{2}p(x, y)(u_x^2 + u_y^2) + \tfrac{1}{2}q(x, y)u^2 - r(x, y)u\right] dx\, dy, \qquad u \in V,$$

where

$$V = \{v \in C^2(\bar{\Omega}); v = \alpha \text{ on } \Gamma\} \qquad \text{or} \qquad V = C^2(\bar{\Omega}).$$

It is assumed that $p \in C^1(\bar{\Omega})$, q, $r \in C(\bar{\Omega})$ and that $p > 0$, $q \geq 0$ everywhere in $\bar{\Omega}$.

We find from (2.31) that the Euler–Lagrange equation is

$$-(pu_x)_x - (pu_y)_y + qu = r \qquad \text{in } \Omega, \tag{2.33}$$

and the natural boundary condition, determined from (2.32), is

$$v_1 pu_x + v_2 pu_y = 0 \qquad \text{on } \Gamma.$$

Dividing by p and using (2.24a) we obtain

$$u_v = 0 \qquad \text{on } \Gamma.$$

We leave it to the reader to establish that f is a quadratic functional with

$$f^{(2)}(u; \eta) = \int\int_\Omega \left[p(\eta_x^2 + \eta_y^2) + q\eta^2\right] dx\, dy.$$

Regardless of whether $\tilde{V} = \mathring{V}$ or $C^2(\bar{\Omega})$ (corresponding to the two choices of V above), it is clear that $f^{(2)}(u; \eta) \geq 0 \;\forall \eta \in \tilde{V}$, $\|\eta\| = 1$. Hence a stationary point of f is a global minimizer.

A boundary condition where u is prescribed on Γ is called a *Dirichlet boundary condition*; if u_v is prescribed on Γ then we speak of a *Neumann boundary condition*. Thus the essential and natural boundary conditions for this example are of the Dirichlet and Neumann types, respectively.

In some problems the essential boundary condition applies only to a part of the boundary Γ, i.e., there is given a function $\alpha(x, y)$ defined on some $\Gamma_1 \subset \Gamma$, and the admissible functions are

$$V = \{v \in C^2(\bar{\Omega}); v = \alpha \text{ on } \Gamma_1\}.$$

The space of test functions is then

$$\tilde{V} = \{v \in C^2(\bar{\Omega}); v = 0 \text{ on } \Gamma_1\}.$$

A stationary point makes the line integral in (2.30) vanish for all $\eta \in \tilde{V}$, and it therefore satisfies

$$v_1 \frac{\partial F}{\partial u_x} + v_2 \frac{\partial F}{\partial u_y} = 0 \qquad \text{on } \Gamma - \Gamma_1.$$

Boundary conditions of different types on different portions of the boundary are called *mixed boundary conditions*.

In Section 2.2 we presented a technique for modifying the natural boundary condition of the functional $f(u) = \int_a^b F(x, u, u') \, dx$ without at the same time modifying the Euler–Lagrange equation. To do the same for (2.27) consider

$$f(u) = \int\int_\Omega F(x, y, u, u_x, u_y) \, dx \, dy + \int_\Gamma G(x, y, u) \, ds, \qquad u \in C^2(\bar{\Omega}), \quad (2.34)$$

where G is a differentiable function. It is easily seen that the condition for a stationary point is

$$\int\int_\Omega \left[\frac{\partial F}{\partial u} - \frac{\partial}{\partial x}\left(\frac{\partial F}{\partial u_x}\right) - \frac{\partial}{\partial y}\left(\frac{\partial F}{\partial u_y}\right) \right] \eta \, dx \, dy$$

$$+ \int_\Gamma \left(v_1 \frac{\partial F}{\partial u_x} + v_2 \frac{\partial F}{\partial u_y} + \frac{\partial G}{\partial u} \right) \eta \, ds = 0 \qquad \forall \eta \in C^2(\bar{\Omega}).$$

Thus (2.31) is still the Euler–Lagrange equation, but now the natural boundary condition is

$$v_1 \frac{\partial F}{\partial u_x} + v_2 \frac{\partial F}{\partial u_y} + \frac{\partial G}{\partial u} = 0 \qquad \text{on } \Gamma. \qquad (2.35)$$

Example 2.8. Let $F(x, y, u, u_x, u_y)$ be as in Example 2.7, and let

$$G(x, y, u) = \tfrac{1}{2}\sigma(x, y)u^2.$$

The natural boundary condition is

$$v_1 p u_x + v_2 p u_y + \sigma u = 0 \qquad \text{on } \Gamma,$$

or

$$u_v + (\sigma/p)u = 0 \qquad \text{on } \Gamma.$$

Thus, if we wish the stationary point to satisfy $u_v + \alpha(x, y)u = 0$ on Γ, for some given $\alpha(x, y)$, we should put $\sigma = p\alpha$.

A boundary condition of the form $u_v + \alpha(x, y)u = \beta(x, y)$ is called a *boundary condition of the third* (or *Robin*) *type*.

Fourth-Order Boundary Value Problems

We now consider the functional

$$f(u) = \int\int_\Omega F(x, y, u, u_x, u_y, u_{xx}, u_{xy}, u_{yy}) \, dx \, dy, \qquad u \in V, \quad (2.36)$$

where V is some set of admissible functions. Suitable choices of V will be mentioned later; for any given V, the test functions $\tilde{V}$ are determined by (2.1). The condition for a stationary point of f is readily found to be

$$\int\int_\Omega \left(\frac{\partial F}{\partial u} \eta + \frac{\partial F}{\partial u_x} \eta_x + \frac{\partial F}{\partial u_y} \eta_y + \frac{\partial F}{\partial u_{xx}} \eta_{xx} + \frac{\partial F}{\partial u_{xy}} \eta_{xy} \right.$$

$$\left. + \frac{\partial F}{\partial u_{yy}} \eta_{yy} \right) dx \, dy = 0 \qquad \forall \eta \in \tilde{V}. \quad (2.37)$$

We have already seen how the second and third terms can be handled with the help of (2.26). Each of the last three terms requires two applications of (2.26). For example,

$$\int\int_\Omega \frac{\partial F}{\partial u_{xx}} \eta_{xx} \, dx \, dy = \int_\Gamma v_1 \frac{\partial F}{\partial u_{xx}} \eta_x \, ds - \int\int_\Omega \frac{\partial}{\partial x}\left(\frac{\partial F}{\partial u_{xx}} \right) \eta_x \, dx \, dy$$

$$= \int_\Gamma v_1 \frac{\partial F}{\partial u_{xx}} \eta_x \, ds - \int_\Gamma v_1 \frac{\partial}{\partial x}\left(\frac{\partial F}{\partial u_{xx}} \right) \eta \, ds + \int\int_\Omega \frac{\partial^2}{\partial x^2}\left(\frac{\partial F}{\partial u_{xx}} \right) \eta \, dx \, dy,$$

and a similar expression holds for $\int\int_\Omega (\partial F/\partial u_{yy}) \eta_{yy} \, dx \, dy$. The result obtained for $\int\int_\Omega (\partial F/\partial u_{xy}) \eta_{xy} \, dx \, dy$ depends upon the order in which we apply (2.26a) and (2.26b). To obtain a "symmetric" expression we perform the integration in both orders and then "average" the two identities. This gives

$$\int\int_\Omega \frac{\partial F}{\partial u_{xy}} \eta_{xy} \, dx \, dy = \int_\Gamma \frac{1}{2} \frac{\partial F}{\partial u_{xy}} (v_2 \eta_x + v_1 \eta_y) \, ds$$

$$- \int_\Gamma \frac{1}{2}\left[v_2 \frac{\partial}{\partial x}\left(\frac{\partial F}{\partial u_{xy}} \right) + v_1 \frac{\partial}{\partial y}\left(\frac{\partial F}{\partial u_{xy}} \right) \right] \eta \, ds$$

$$+ \int\int_\Omega \frac{\partial^2}{\partial x \, \partial y}\left(\frac{\partial F}{\partial u_{xy}} \right) \eta \, dx \, dy.$$

Using these identities we can rewrite (2.37) as

$$\int\int_\Omega E_1 \eta \, dx \, dy + \int_\Gamma E_2 \eta \, ds + \int_\Gamma (E_3 \eta_x + E_4 \eta_y) \, ds = 0 \qquad \forall \eta \in \tilde{V},$$

where

$$
E_1 = \frac{\partial F}{\partial u} - \frac{\partial}{\partial x}\left(\frac{\partial F}{\partial u_x}\right) - \frac{\partial}{\partial y}\left(\frac{\partial F}{\partial u_y}\right) + \frac{\partial^2}{\partial x^2}\left(\frac{\partial F}{\partial u_{xx}}\right)
$$
$$
+ \frac{\partial^2}{\partial xy}\left(\frac{\partial F}{\partial u_{xy}}\right) + \frac{\partial^2}{\partial y^2}\left(\frac{\partial F}{\partial u_{yy}}\right),
$$

$$
E_2 = v_1 \frac{\partial F}{\partial u_x} + v_2 \frac{\partial F}{\partial u_y} - v_1 \frac{\partial}{\partial x}\left(\frac{\partial F}{\partial u_{xx}}\right)
$$
$$
- \frac{1}{2}\left[v_2 \frac{\partial}{\partial x}\left(\frac{\partial F}{\partial u_{xy}}\right) + v_1 \frac{\partial}{\partial y}\left(\frac{\partial F}{\partial u_{xy}}\right)\right] - v_2 \frac{\partial}{\partial y}\left(\frac{\partial F}{\partial u_{yy}}\right),
$$

$$
E_3 = v_1 \frac{\partial F}{\partial u_{xx}} + \frac{1}{2}v_2 \frac{\partial F}{\partial u_{xy}},
$$

$$
E_4 = \frac{1}{2}v_1 \frac{\partial F}{\partial u_{xy}} + v_2 \frac{\partial F}{\partial u_{yy}}.
$$

It is expedient to express the third integral in terms of η_v and η_τ. From (2.24) one easily obtains the relations

$$
\eta_x = v_1\eta_v - v_2\eta_\tau, \qquad \eta_y = v_2\eta_v + v_1\eta_\tau,
$$

and hence

$$
\int_\Gamma (E_3\eta_x + E_4\eta_y)\, ds = \int_\Gamma (E_5\eta_v + E_6\eta_\tau)\, ds,
$$

where

$$
E_5 = v_1^2 \frac{\partial F}{\partial u_{xx}} + v_1 v_2 \frac{\partial F}{\partial u_{xy}} + v_2^2 \frac{\partial F}{\partial u_{yy}},
$$

$$
E_6 = -v_1 v_2 \frac{\partial F}{\partial u_{xx}} + \frac{1}{2}(v_1^2 - v_2^2) \frac{\partial F}{\partial u_{xy}} + v_1 v_2 \frac{\partial F}{\partial u_{yy}}.
$$

The point of this transformation is that the tangential derivative η_τ can be removed by integrating by parts on Γ:

$$
\int_\Gamma E_6\eta_\tau\, ds = -\int_\Gamma (E_6)_\tau\eta\, ds.
$$

Thus the condition for a stationary point is

$$
\iint_\Omega E_1\eta\, dx\, dy + \int_\Gamma [E_2 - (E_6)_\tau]\eta\, ds + \int_\Gamma E_5\eta_v\, ds = 0 \qquad \forall \eta \in \tilde{V}. \quad (2.38)
$$

From this we deduce that the Euler–Lagrange equation for f is

$$E_1 = 0 \quad \text{in } \Omega \tag{2.39a}$$

and that the natural boundary conditions are

$$E_2 - (E_6)_\tau = 0 \quad \text{on } \Gamma, \tag{2.39b}$$

$$E_5 = 0 \quad \text{on } \Gamma. \tag{2.39c}$$

The essential boundary conditions are evidently $u = \alpha$, $u_\nu = \beta$ on Γ, where α and β are given functions, since these conditions make the test functions satisfy $\eta = \eta_\nu = 0$ on Γ, forcing the two line integrals in (2.38) to vanish.

Example 2.9. The functional

$$f(u) = \iint_\Omega \left[\tfrac{1}{2}(u_{xx} + u_{yy})^2 + (1 - \tilde{v})(u_{xy}^2 - u_{xx}u_{yy}) - g(x, y)u \right] dx\, dy, \quad u \in V,$$

expresses the energy of a thin plate subjected to a load (Fig. 2.2). Here $u(x, y)$ is the deflection of the plate, $\tilde{v}$ is Poisson's ratio, and $g(x, y)$ determines the load $r(x, y)$ through the relation

$$r(x, y) = \frac{Ee^3}{12(1 - \tilde{v}^2)} g(x, y), \qquad E \equiv \frac{\mu(3\lambda + 2\mu)}{\lambda + \mu},$$

where E is Young's modulus, e is the thickness of the plate, λ and μ are the Lamé constants for the material, and $\tilde{v} = \lambda/2(\lambda + \mu)$. Further, we have $\lambda \geq 0$, $\mu > 0$ and therefore $0 \leq \tilde{v} \leq \tfrac{1}{2}$. Among all "possible" deflections (i.e., among all admissible functions), the true deflection is that which minimizes f. [See Courant and Hilbert (1953) and Exercise 2.15.]

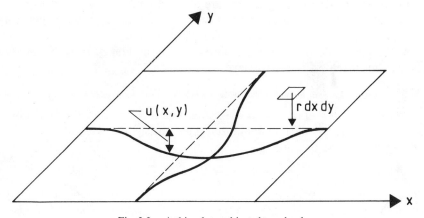

Fig. 2.2.   A thin plate subjected to a load.

In deriving this mathematical model of the plate, it must be assumed that the true deflection is small. The one-dimensional analog of this problem was discussed in Example 2.5.

Denoting the preceding integrand by F, we find that

$$\frac{\partial F}{\partial u} = -g, \qquad \frac{\partial F}{\partial u_x} = \frac{\partial F}{\partial u_y} = 0,$$

$$\frac{\partial F}{\partial u_{xx}} = u_{xx} + \tilde{v}u_{yy}, \qquad \frac{\partial F}{\partial u_{xy}} = 2(1 - \tilde{v})u_{xy}, \qquad \frac{\partial F}{\partial u_{yy}} = u_{yy} + \tilde{v}u_{xx},$$

$$E_1 = u_{xxxx} + 2u_{xxyy} + u_{yyyy} - g = \Delta^2 u - g,$$

$$E_2 = -v_1(u_{xx} + u_{yy})_x - v_2(u_{xx} + u_{yy})_y = -(\Delta u)_v,$$

$$E_5 = (v_1^2 u_{xx} + 2v_1 v_2 u_{xy} + v_2^2 u_{yy}) + \tilde{v}(v_2^2 u_{xx} - 2v_1 v_2 u_{xy} + v_1^2 u_{yy}) = u_{vv} + \tilde{v}u_{\tau\tau},$$

$$E_6 = (1 - \tilde{v})(-v_1 v_2 u_{xx} + (v_1^2 - v_2^2)u_{xy} + v_1 v_2 u_{yy}) = (1 - \tilde{v})u_{v\tau}.$$

We have made use of (2.25) in these calculations. The Euler–Lagrange equation is $E_1 = 0$, or

$$\Delta^2 u = g \qquad \text{in } \Omega.$$

If $g = 0$, this is the so-called *biharmonic equation*.

The choice of V, the set of admissible functions, is determined by the physical conditions imposed at the boundary of the plate. If the plate is "clamped," then

$$V = \{v \in C^4(\overline{\Omega}); v = v_v = 0 \text{ on } \Gamma\},$$

and the corresponding set of test functions is $\tilde{V} = V$. Both boundary conditions on the admissible functions are of the essential type. The deflection of the plate is the unique solution of the boundary value problem $\Delta^2 u = g$ in Ω, $u = u_v = 0$ on Γ, and hence is independent of $\tilde{v}$.

If the plate is "simply supported" then only the first of these boundary conditions is imposed, and we have

$$V = \tilde{V} = \{v \in C^4(\overline{\Omega}); v = 0 \text{ on } \Gamma\}.$$

The condition $\eta = 0$ on Γ makes the first line integral in (2.38) vanish but not the second. Thus the minimizer must satisfy the natural boundary condition $E_5 = 0$, or

$$u_{vv} + \tilde{v}u_{\tau\tau} = 0 \qquad \text{on } \Gamma.$$

The fact that u is constant on Γ implies $u_\tau = 0$ on Γ, but it does not imply that the tangential derivatives of higher order vanish. They do vanish, however, on any section of Γ that is a straight line. Thus, if Γ is a polygon, then the deflection is the solution of the boundary value problem $\Delta^2 u = g$ in Ω, $u = u_{vv} = 0$ on Γ. It is worth mentioning that this fourth-order problem can be reduced to two problems of second order, namely

$$\Delta m = g \quad \text{in} \quad \Omega, \quad m = 0 \quad \text{on } \Gamma,$$

which determines m, and

$$\Delta u = m \quad \text{in} \quad \Omega, \quad u = 0 \quad \text{on } \Gamma,$$

which then determines u.

A third example of boundary conditions is the case in which the plate is clamped on a part of the boundary, Γ_0, for example, and free on the remaining part $\Gamma_1 \equiv \Gamma - \Gamma_0$. Then,

$$V = \tilde{V} = \{v \in C^4(\bar{\Omega}); v = v_v = 0 \text{ on } \Gamma_0\}.$$

The minimizer satisfies these two essential boundary conditions on Γ_0 and the natural boundary conditions (2.39b) and (2.39c) on Γ_1. Thus,

$$(\Delta u)_v + (1 - \tilde{v})u_{v\tau\tau} = 0 \quad \text{on } \Gamma_1,$$

$$u_{vv} + \tilde{v}u_{\tau\tau} = 0 \quad \text{on } \Gamma_1.$$

Problems in Three Dimensions

The analysis of three-dimensional problems is little different from that of two. The domain of definition Ω is now an open subset of $\mathbb{R}^3$ and its boundary Γ is a surface. Let x, y, and z denote the space variables, and v_1, v_2, and v_3 the direction cosines of the outer normal to Γ. For arbitrary smooth functions $u(x, y, z)$ and $v(x, y, z)$ we have

$$\iiint_\Omega uv_x \, dx \, dy \, dz = \iint_\Gamma v_1 uv \, dS - \iiint_\Omega u_x v \, dx \, dy \, dz. \quad (2.40)$$

Similar identities hold with respect to y and z.

The condition for a stationary point of the functional

$$f(u) = \iiint_\Omega F(x, y, z, u, u_x, u_y, u_z) \, dx \, dy \, dz, \quad u \in V,$$

is readily found to be

$$\iiint_\Omega \left(\frac{\partial F}{\partial u} \eta + \frac{\partial F}{\partial u_x} \eta_x + \frac{\partial F}{\partial u_y} \eta_y + \frac{\partial F}{\partial u_z} \eta_z \right) dx \, dy \, dz = 0 \quad \forall \eta \in \tilde{V}.$$

Using (2.40) and the corresponding identities for y and z we can rewrite this condition as

$$\iiint_\Omega \left[\frac{\partial F}{\partial u} - \frac{\partial}{\partial x}\left(\frac{\partial F}{\partial u_x}\right) - \frac{\partial}{\partial y}\left(\frac{\partial F}{\partial u_y}\right) - \frac{\partial}{\partial z}\left(\frac{\partial F}{\partial u_z}\right) \right] \eta \, dx \, dy \, dz$$

$$+ \iint_\Gamma \left(v_1 \frac{\partial F}{\partial u_x} + v_2 \frac{\partial F}{\partial u_y} + v_3 \frac{\partial F}{\partial u_z} \right) \eta \, dS = 0 \qquad \forall \eta \in \tilde{V}.$$

Thus the Euler–Lagrange equation, essential boundary condition, and natural boundary condition are

$$\frac{\partial F}{\partial u} - \frac{\partial}{\partial x}\left(\frac{\partial F}{\partial u_x}\right) - \frac{\partial}{\partial y}\left(\frac{\partial F}{\partial u_y}\right) - \frac{\partial}{\partial z}\left(\frac{\partial F}{\partial u_z}\right) = 0 \qquad \text{in } \Omega, \quad (2.41)$$

$$u = \alpha(x, y, z) \qquad \text{on } \Gamma, \quad (2.42)$$

$$v_1 \frac{\partial F}{\partial u_x} + v_2 \frac{\partial F}{\partial u_y} + v_3 \frac{\partial F}{\partial u_z} = 0 \qquad \text{on } \Gamma, \quad (2.43)$$

respectively, where α is some prescribed function on Γ.

Problems with Several Dependent Variables

We have until now considered functionals having a single independent variable u. Some important problems, however, lead to functionals of several variables, $u^{(1)}$, $u^{(2)}$, ..., $u^{(n)}$, each variable belonging to a specified set of admissible functions. Typically, a stationary point is then a set of n functions simultaneously satisfying a system of n Euler–Lagrange equations.

As an example we consider

$$f(u, v) = \iint_\Omega F(x, y, u, u_x, u_y, v, v_x, v_y) \, dx \, dy, \qquad u \in V_1, \quad v \in V_2,$$

where V_1 and V_2 are chosen sets of admissible functions in $C^2(\bar{\Omega})$. The corresponding spaces of test functions $\tilde{V}_1$ and $\tilde{V}_2$ are given by (2.1). The condition for a function pair (u, v) to be a stationary point of f is

$$\frac{\partial}{\partial \tau} f(u + \tau\eta, v + \rho\zeta)\bigg|_{\tau = \rho = 0} = \frac{\partial}{\partial \rho} f(u + \tau\eta, v + \rho\zeta)\bigg|_{\tau = \rho = 0} = 0$$

$$\forall \eta \in \tilde{V}_1, \qquad \forall \zeta \in \tilde{V}_2,$$

where τ and ρ are scalar variables, or

$$\int\int_\Omega \left(\frac{\partial F}{\partial u}\eta + \frac{\partial F}{\partial u_x}\eta_x + \frac{\partial F}{\partial u_y}\eta_y\right)dx\,dy = 0 \qquad \forall \eta \in \tilde{V}_1,$$

$$\int\int_\Omega \left(\frac{\partial F}{\partial v}\zeta + \frac{\partial F}{\partial v_x}\zeta_x + \frac{\partial F}{\partial v_y}\zeta_y\right)dx\,dy = 0 \qquad \forall \zeta \in \tilde{V}_2.$$

Using the integral identities (2.26) we obtain

$$\int\int_\Omega \left[\frac{\partial F}{\partial u} - \frac{\partial}{\partial x}\left(\frac{\partial F}{\partial u_x}\right) - \frac{\partial}{\partial y}\left(\frac{\partial F}{\partial u_y}\right)\right]\eta\,dx\,dy$$

$$+ \int_\Gamma \left(v_1\frac{\partial F}{\partial u_x} + v_2\frac{\partial F}{\partial u_y}\right)\eta\,ds = 0 \qquad \forall \eta \in \tilde{V}_1,$$

$$\int\int_\Omega \left[\frac{\partial F}{\partial v} - \frac{\partial}{\partial x}\left(\frac{\partial F}{\partial v_x}\right) - \frac{\partial}{\partial y}\left(\frac{\partial F}{\partial v_y}\right)\right]\zeta\,dx\,dy$$

$$+ \int_\Gamma \left(v_1\frac{\partial F}{\partial v_x} + v_2\frac{\partial F}{\partial v_y}\right)\zeta\,ds = 0 \qquad \forall \zeta \in \tilde{V}_2.$$

Thus, a stationary point of f is a solution of the system

$$\frac{\partial F}{\partial u} - \frac{\partial}{\partial x}\left(\frac{\partial F}{\partial u_x}\right) - \frac{\partial}{\partial y}\left(\frac{\partial F}{\partial u_y}\right) = 0 \qquad \text{in } \Omega, \qquad (2.44a)$$

$$\frac{\partial F}{\partial v} - \frac{\partial}{\partial x}\left(\frac{\partial F}{\partial v_x}\right) - \frac{\partial}{\partial y}\left(\frac{\partial F}{\partial v_y}\right) = 0 \qquad \text{in } \Omega. \qquad (2.44b)$$

Further, we see from the line integrals that the essential boundary conditions are of the type

$$u = \alpha(x, y) \qquad \text{on } \Gamma, \qquad (2.45a)$$

$$v = \beta(x, y) \qquad \text{on } \Gamma, \qquad (2.45b)$$

and that the natural boundary conditions are

$$v_1\frac{\partial F}{\partial u_x} + v_2\frac{\partial F}{\partial u_y} = 0 \qquad \text{on } \Gamma, \qquad (2.46a)$$

$$v_1\frac{\partial F}{\partial v_x} + v_2\frac{\partial F}{\partial v_y} = 0 \qquad \text{on } \Gamma. \qquad (2.46b)$$

An example of an appropriate choice of admissible functions is

$$V_1 = \{w \in C^2(\bar{\Omega}); u = \alpha \text{ on } \Gamma\},$$

$$V_2 = \{w \in C^2(\bar{\Omega}); u = \beta \text{ on } \Gamma\}.$$

A local minimizer of $f(u, v)$ must then be a function pair that satisfies system (2.44) and boundary conditions (2.45a) and (2.45b).

Example 2.10. Introducing the notation $x_1 = x$, $x_2 = y$, $u^{(1)} = u$, $u^{(2)} = v$, $\mathbf{u} = [u^{(1)}, u^{(2)}]^T$ and

$$\varepsilon_{ij}(\mathbf{u}) = \tfrac{1}{2}(u_{x_j}^{(i)} + u_{x_i}^{(j)}), \qquad 1 \le i, j \le 2,$$

we define

$$f(\mathbf{u}) = \int\!\!\int_\Omega \left[(\lambda/2) \operatorname{div} \mathbf{u}\right]^2 + \mu \sum_{i,j=1}^{2} (\varepsilon_{ij}(\mathbf{u}))^2 - \mathbf{g}^T\mathbf{u}\right] dx_1 \, dx_2,$$

$$u^{(1)} \in V_1, \qquad u^{(2)} \in V_2,$$

where $V_i \subseteq C^2(\bar{\Omega})$, $i = 1, 2$. The corresponding Euler–Lagrange equations (2.44) are readily found to be

$$-\mu \, \Delta u^{(i)} - (\lambda + \mu) \frac{\partial}{\partial x_i} \operatorname{div} \mathbf{u} = g^{(i)}, \qquad i = 1, 2.$$

These equations arise in linear elasticity theory and are known as *Navier's equations*.

It is obvious how the preceding analysis can be extended to the more general functional $f(u^{(1)}, \ldots, u^{(n)})$ in two or three space variables. As with earlier problems, we can modify the natural boundary conditions by adding a line (or surface) integral to the functional.

2.4   Boundary Value Problems in Physics and Engineering

The Field Equation

Much of this book is devoted to the numerical solution of the so-called *field equation*

$$\sum_{i=1}^{n} \frac{\partial}{\partial x_i} \left[p_i(\mathbf{x}) \frac{\partial u}{\partial x_i} \right] = g(\mathbf{x}), \qquad \mathbf{x} \in \Omega \subset R^n, \tag{2.47}$$

special cases of which are Poisson's equation $p_i(\mathbf{x}) \equiv 1$ $\forall i$ and Laplace's equation $p_i(\mathbf{x}) \equiv 1$ $\forall i$ and $g(\mathbf{x}) \equiv 0$. In this section we shall briefly describe a few of the numerous physical phenomena that are governed by the field equation.

We consider first the flow of electric current in a purely resistive two-dimensional conductor. Figure 2.3 shows the current flow in a small square element of the conductor; i_1 and i_2 are the current densities (i.e., current per unit length) in the x and y directions, respectively.

A current density (current per unit area) $I(x, y)$ is introduced by means of a "source" at (x, y). The total current entering the element is

$$i_1 \, \Delta y + i_2 \, \Delta x + I(x, y) \, \Delta x \, \Delta y$$

and that leaving the element is

$$\left(i_1 + \frac{\partial i_1}{\partial x} \Delta x \right) \Delta y + \left(i_2 + \frac{\partial i_2}{\partial y} \Delta y \right) \Delta x,$$

the difference in these amounts being

$$\left[-\frac{\partial i_1}{\partial x} - \frac{\partial i_2}{\partial y} + I(x, y) \right] \Delta x \, \Delta y.$$

Now a conductor is not able to accumulate electric current in any portion of its body, and it follows that this expression equals zero at every point (x, y), i.e.,

$$\frac{\partial i_1}{\partial x} + \frac{\partial i_2}{\partial y} = I(x, y). \tag{2.48}$$

This equation, known as the *continuity condition*, ensures the continuity of current flow within the conductor.

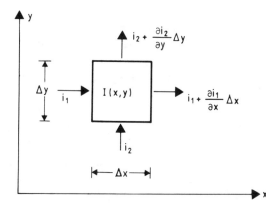

Fig. 2.3.   Current flow in a small element of a two-dimensional conductor.

Ohm's law states that the current intensities are related to the potential (voltage) function u through the equations

$$i_1 = -\frac{1}{r_1}\frac{\partial u}{\partial x}, \qquad i_2 = -\frac{1}{r_2}\frac{\partial u}{\partial y}, \qquad (2.49)$$

where r_1 and r_2 denote the electrical resistances of the conductor in the x and y directions, respectively. Combining (2.48) and (2.49) we obtain

$$-\frac{\partial}{\partial x}\left(\frac{1}{r_1}\frac{\partial u}{\partial x}\right) - \frac{\partial}{\partial y}\left(\frac{1}{r_2}\frac{\partial u}{\partial y}\right) = I(x, y),$$

which is the field equation.

Examples of other physical phenomena governed by the field equation are the torsion of elastic prismatic bars, the transverse deflection of thin loaded membranes, and processes that involve some form of *diffusion*, such as the stationary conduction of heat in solid or fluid media, electromagnetic field distribution, electrostatic potential distribution in insulating media, fluid flow in porous media, and neutron diffusion in a nuclear reactor. All of these phenomena have the following properties in common.

(1)   There exists a scalar function $u(\mathbf{x})$ (we retain the notation of the above example) defined at every point in the body.

(2)   "Gradient variables" i_1 and i_2 are related to u by equations similar to (2.49).

(3)   In these equations the parameters r_1 and r_2 represent some physical property of the body in the x and y directions, respectively. If $r_1(x, y) = r_2(x, y) \; \forall (x, y)$, then the property is independent of direction and the body is said to be *isotropic*. If r_1 and r_2 are constants then the body is said to be *homogeneous*. A body that is not isotropic (homogeneous) is said to be *anisotropic* (*inhomogeneous*).

The energy functional corresponding to the field equation (2.47) in three space dimensions, with a general boundary condition of the third type, is

$$\mathscr{f}(u) = \iiint_\Omega \frac{1}{2}\sum_{i=1}^{3} p_i\left(\frac{\partial u}{\partial x_i}\right)^2 dx_1\, dx_2\, dx_3 + \iint_\Gamma \frac{1}{2}\sigma(u - u_0)^2\, dS$$

$$- \iiint_\Omega gu\, dx_1\, dx_2\, dx_3 - \iint_\Gamma \gamma u\, dS - \sum_{j=1}^{J} q_j u(\mathbf{x}_j).$$

In the case of a heat conduction problem u is the temperature, p_1, p_2, and p_3 the heat conductivity coefficients, σ the heat transfer coefficient, u_0 the temperature of the surrounding medium, g the rate of heat generated per unit volume, γ the rate of heat transfer per unit surface area of the body, and q_j a concentrated heat flow source at a point $x_j \in \Omega$.

A function u is a stationary point of f if

$$
\iiint_\Omega \sum_{i=1}^{3} p_i \frac{\partial u}{\partial x_i} \frac{\partial \eta}{\partial x_i}\, dx_1\, dx_2\, dx_3 + \iint_\Gamma \sigma(u - u_0)\eta\, dS
$$

$$
= \iiint_\Omega g\eta\, dx_1\, dx_2\, dx_3 + \iint_\Gamma \gamma\eta\, dS + \sum_{j=1}^{J} q_j\eta(x_j)
$$

for all η in the space of perturbation functions. The corresponding Euler–Lagrange equation is known as the *equilibrium equation of heat flow*; the rate of heat transfer by conduction is equal to the rate of heat generation.

The natural boundary condition associated with f is

$$
-\partial u/\partial v = \sigma(u - u_0) - \gamma \qquad \text{on } \Gamma.
$$

The first term on the right-hand side expresses the rate at which heat conducted to the boundary is convected away (we have $\sigma > 0$) in the surrounding medium. Note that this boundary condition includes the Neumann- and Dirichlet-type boundary conditions as limiting cases:

$$
\sigma = 0 \quad \Rightarrow \quad \partial u/\partial v = \gamma \qquad \text{(perfect insulation if } \gamma = 0\text{)},
$$

$$
\sigma = +\infty \quad \Rightarrow \quad u = u_0 \qquad \text{(no insulation).}
$$

Fourth-Order Problems

As Example 2.9 shows, fourth-order problems appear in connection with the displacement of a plate. They also arise in certain fluid flow problems. Regretably, limitation of space prevents us from dealing in detail with the numerical solution of fourth-order problems in this book. It is relevant to point out, however, that there exist so-called "mixed variational formulations" that essentially decompose a fourth-order problem into two second-order problems, and the finite element method (Chapter 5) can be applied to these formulations rather than directly to the fourth-order problem.

Two important advantages of this approach are the following.

(1) The regularity requirement of the approximating functions is lower.
(2) The condition number of the associated stiffness matrix is of the order of the square root of that of the original fourth-order problem. This implies less rounding error in solving the system of algebraic equations and, in the case of an iterative solver, a greater rate of convergence.

Exercises

2.1. The first-order directional derivative of the functional

$$f(u) = \int_a^b F(x, u, u')\, dx, \qquad u \in V,$$

is given by

$$f^{(1)}(u; \eta) = \int_a^b \left(\frac{\partial F}{\partial u}\eta + \frac{\partial F}{\partial u'}\eta' \right) dx.$$

What is the corresponding expression for $f^{(2)}(u; \eta)$?

2.2. Find the simplest functional of type (2.6) such that the associated Euler–Lagrange equation is

$$-u'' + u^2 = r(x), \qquad a < x < b.$$

Does f have a global minimizer or maximizer?

2.3. Show that if $F = F(u, u')$, then a solution of the Euler–Lagrange equation

(i) $$\frac{\partial F}{\partial u} - \frac{d}{dx}\left(\frac{\partial F}{\partial u'} \right) = 0, \qquad a < x < b,$$

is also a solution of

(ii) $$\frac{d}{dx}\left[F - u' \frac{\partial F}{\partial u'} \right] = 0, \qquad a < x < b.$$

Show that a solution of (ii) is also a solution of (i) if $u' \neq 0$.

2.4. A classical problem treated by the calculus of variations is the *brachistochrone problem*. We consider a particle falling under the influence of gravity from point $(0, h)$,

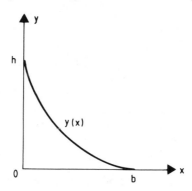

where it is initially at rest, to point $(b, 0)$ along a path $[x, y(x)]$, $0 \le x \le b$ (see the accompanying illustration). The time of descent is given by

$$f(y) = \frac{1}{\sqrt{2g}} \int_0^b \sqrt{\frac{1 + (y')^2}{h - y}}\, dx,$$

where g is the gravitational constant. The problem is to find the function y that minimizes $f(y)$. For the set V of admissible functions we choose all $y \in C[0, b]$ that satisfy

(a) $y(0) = h,$ $-\infty \le y'(0) < 0,$ $y(b) = 0,$
(b) $y(x) < h,$ $0 < x \le b,$
(c) $y \in C^2(0, b].$

(i) Discuss conditions (a) and (b) from a physical point of view. Is the set of test functions $\tilde{V}$ defined by (2.1) a linear space?

(ii) Deduce from Exercise 2.3 that y is a stationary point of f if

$$(h - y)[1 + (y')^2] = k, \qquad 0 < x < b,$$

where k is a constant, and verify that the solution of this equation is given in parametric representation by

$$x = (k/2)(2\theta - \sin 2\theta), \qquad 0 \le \theta \le \theta_0,$$

$$y = h - (k/2)(1 - \cos 2\theta), \qquad 0 \le \theta \le \theta_0.$$

k and θ_0 are determined by the conditions $x(\theta_0) = b$, $y(\theta_0) = 0$.

This path, which can be shown to be the global minimizer of f, describes a cycloid. It is the locus of a point on the perimeter of a circle of radius $k/2$ that rolls on the underside of the horizontal line $y = h$.

2.5. Investigate the functional

$$f(u) = \frac{1}{2} \int_0^b [(u')^2 - u^2] \, dx, \qquad u \in V,$$

$$V = \{v \in C^2[0, b]; v(0) = v(b) = 0\}, \qquad 0 < b \le \pi,$$

distinguishing between the cases $0 < b < \pi$ and $b = \pi$.

HINT: $\int_0^b (u')^2 \, dx \ge (\pi/b)^2 \int_0^b u^2 \, dx \qquad \forall u \in V.$

2.6. Investigate the functional

$$f(u) = \int_0^\pi u^2[1 - (u')^2] \, dx, \qquad u \in V,$$

$$V = \{v \in C^2[0, \pi]; v(0) = v(\pi) = 0\}.$$

2.7. Consider the functional

$$f(u) = \int_a^b F(x, u, u') \, dx, \qquad u \in V \subseteq C^2[a, b],$$

and let $\tilde{V}$ be the set of test functions determined from V by (2.1). It is clear from (2.14) that a stationary point of f must satisfy

$$R \equiv \frac{\partial F}{\partial u'} \eta \bigg|_b - \frac{\partial F}{\partial u'} \eta \bigg|_a = 0 \qquad \forall \eta \in \tilde{V}.$$

Essential and natural boundary conditions make each of the two terms of R vanish (see Table 2.1). What boundary conditions imposed on the admissible functions V make R vanish without necessarily making each term of R vanish? Consider as a special case the function

$$F = \tfrac{1}{2}p(x)(u')^2 + \tfrac{1}{2}q(x)u^2 - r(x)u.$$

Boundary conditions of this type are called *periodic*.

2.8. In the brachistochrone problem (Exercise 2.4), let the essential boundary condition $y(b) = 0$ be removed as a requirement for the admissible functions. What is the natural boundary condition at $x = b$? Discuss the physical significance of this new brachistochrone problem.

2.9. The purpose of this exercise is to illustrate how a quadratic functional $f: V \to R$ can be formulated to resemble a quadratic functional of the type discussed in Chapter 1. Let

$$f(u) = \int_0^\pi \left[\tfrac{1}{2}(u')^2 - r(x)u\right] dx, \qquad u \in V,$$

$$V = \{v \in C^2[0, \pi]; v(0) = v(\pi) = 0\},$$

where $r \in C^1[0, \pi]$. The Fourier sine expansions for any $u \in V$ and for r are given by

$$u(x) = \sum_{i=1}^\infty \alpha_i \phi_i(x), \qquad \alpha_i = \int_0^\pi u(x)\phi_i(x)\, dx,$$

$$r(x) = \sum_{i=1}^\infty \beta_i \phi_i(x), \qquad \beta_i = \int_0^\pi r(x)\phi_i(x)\, dx,$$

respectively, where $\phi_i(x) = \sqrt{2/\pi}\, \sin(ix)$.

(i) Show by formal manipulations (i.e., without regard to convergence) of these expansions that

$$f(u) = \hat{f}(\boldsymbol{\alpha}) \equiv \tfrac{1}{2}\boldsymbol{\alpha}^T H \boldsymbol{\alpha} - \boldsymbol{\beta}^T \boldsymbol{\alpha},$$

where

$$\boldsymbol{\alpha} = \begin{bmatrix} \alpha_1 \\ \alpha_2 \\ \alpha_3 \\ \vdots \end{bmatrix}, \qquad \boldsymbol{\beta} = \begin{bmatrix} \beta_1 \\ \beta_2 \\ \beta_3 \\ \vdots \end{bmatrix}, \qquad H = \begin{bmatrix} 1^2 & & & \\ & 2^2 & & \\ & & 3^2 & \\ & & & \ddots \end{bmatrix}.$$

(ii) By analogy with the quadratic functionals of Chapter 1, we expect $\hat{f}$ to be minimized by the solution of $H\boldsymbol{\alpha} = \boldsymbol{\beta}$. Find this $\boldsymbol{\alpha}$.

(iii) Substitute the above sine expansions directly in the Euler–Lagrange equation $-u'' = r(x)$ and determine $\alpha_1, \alpha_2, \ldots$.

2.10. In Chapter 1 we defined a gradient vector $\mathbf{g}(\mathbf{x})$ for a functional of the type $f: X \to R$, $X \subseteq R^N$ and observed that it satisfies the identity

$$f^{(1)}(\mathbf{x}; \mathbf{y}) = \mathbf{g}^T(\mathbf{x})\mathbf{y} \qquad \forall \mathbf{y} \in R^N, \qquad \|\mathbf{y}\| = 1.$$

This suggests that we call $g(u)$ the *gradient function* of a functional $f: V \to R$ in one space dimension if $g(u)$ is a function satisfying

$$f^{(1)}(u; \eta) = \int_a^b g(u)\eta \, dx \qquad \forall \eta \in \tilde{V}, \quad \|\eta\| = 1.$$

Determine $g(u)$ for the functional (2.6) and interpret the Euler–Lagrange equation in terms of $g(u)$.

2.11. Using the Gauss integral identities (2.26), establish that

(i) $$\iint_\Omega (u \, \Delta v - v \, \Delta u) \, dx \, dy = \int_\Gamma (uv_v - vu_v) \, ds,$$

(ii) $$\iint_\Omega \Delta u \, \Delta v \, dx \, dy = \iint_\Omega v \, \Delta^2 u \, dx \, dy + \int_\Gamma \left[v_v \, \Delta u - v(\Delta u)_v \right] ds,$$

for all $u \in C^4(\bar{\Omega})$ and $v \in C^2(\bar{\Omega})$.

2.12. Determine the Euler–Lagrange equation and the natural boundary condition associated with a functional of the form

$$f(u) = \iint_\Omega \left[\tfrac{1}{2}p(x, y)u_x^2 + \tfrac{1}{2}q(x, y)u_y^2 - r(x, y)u \right] dx \, dy, \qquad u \in V.$$

2.13. We consider the functional

$$f(u) = \iint_\Omega \left[\tfrac{1}{2}au_x^2 + bu_x u_y + \tfrac{1}{2}cu_y^2 - r(x, y)u \right] dx \, dy, \qquad u \in V,$$

where a, b, and c are constants, $r \in C(\bar{\Omega})$, and $V = \{v \in C^2(\bar{\Omega}); v = 0 \text{ on } \Gamma\}$.

(i) Derive the Euler–Lagrange equation

$$-(au_{xx} + 2bu_{xy} + cu_{yy}) = r, \qquad (x, y) \in \Omega.$$

(ii) Show by examining $f^{(2)}(u; \eta)$ that a stationary point of f minimizes f if $a, c > 0$ and $b^2 < ac$.

2.14. We consider the functional of Example 2.7 with $V = C^2(\bar{\Omega})$. What further conditions on the coefficients q and r imply that f has an infinite number of local and global minimizers?

2.15. Let f be a functional of the form

$$f(u) = \iint_\Omega \left[\tfrac{1}{2}F_2 + F_1 + F_0 \right] dx \, dy, \qquad u \in V,$$

where

$$F_2 = \sum_{i,j,k,l=0}^{p} c_{ijkl} \frac{\partial^{i+j}u}{\partial x^i \, \partial y^j} \frac{\partial^{k+l}u}{\partial x^k \, \partial y^l},$$

$$F_1 = \sum_{i,j=0}^{q} d_{ij} \frac{\partial^{i+j}u}{\partial x^i \, \partial y^j},$$

$$F_0 = e,$$

where c_{ijkl}, d_{ij}, and e are constants or functions of x and y.

(i) Show that f is quadratic and find its directional derivatives.

(ii) Verify that the functional of Example 2.9 is quadratic, and show that $f^{(2)}(u; \eta) > 0$ $\forall \eta \in \tilde{V}$, $\|\eta\| = 1$, where $\tilde{V}$ is any of the three sets of test functions discussed in the example. It follows that a stationary point of f is a strong local and global minimizer.

2.16. Show that the functional in Example 2.9 reduces to

$$f(u) = \int \int_{\Omega} \left[\tfrac{1}{2}(u_{xx} + u_{yy})^2 - g(x, y)u \right] dx \, dy, \qquad u \in V$$

if Poisson's ratio $\tilde{v}$ is constant and the plate is clamped.

HINT: Use the Gauss integral identities (2.26) to show that

$$\int \int_{\Omega} u_{xy}^2 \, dx \, dy = \int \int_{\Omega} u_{xx} u_{yy} \, dx \, dy, \qquad u \in V.$$

Note that $f(u)$ is independent of $\tilde{v}$.

References

Birkhoff, G., and Rota, G.-C. (1978). "Ordinary Differential Equations." Wiley, New York.

Courant, R., and Hilbert, D. (1953). "Methods of Mathematical Physics," vol. 1. Wiley (Interscience), New York.

Gelfand, I. M., and Fomin, S. V. (1963). "Calculus of Variations." Prentice-Hall, Englewood Cliffs, New Jersey.

Kaplan, W. (1952). "Advanced Calculus." Addison-Wesley, Reading, Massachusetts.

Marsden, J. E., and Tromba, A. J. (1976). "Vector Calculus." Freeman, San Francisco, California.

Sagan, H. (1969). "Introduction to the Calculus of Variations." McGraw-Hill, New York.

CHAPTER 3

Variational Formulation of Boundary Value Problems: Part II

Introduction

The analysis of the preceding chapter establishes that the problem of finding a stationary point of a functional $f: V \to R$ is equivalent to that of solving a boundary value problem consisting of the associated Euler–Lagrange equation and certain boundary conditions. If the functional contains derivatives of order up to m, then the order of the Euler–Lagrange equation is in general $2m$, and for this reason we required the functions in V to be a subset of $C^{2m}[a, b]$ or $C^{2m}(\bar{\Omega})$.

In Section 3.1 we introduce the idea of "completion," whereby the set of admissible functions V is enlarged to a so-called Sobolev space that contains, in addition to V, functions with less smoothness than C^{2m} continuity. The mathematics involved here is that of Hilbert spaces, and we accordingly begin the section with a review of Hilbert space properties, using $L_2[a, b]$ as a model. It should be stressed that the process of completion is not a purely academic exercise, but a step of fundamental importance for the finite element method, in which one approximates the solution of a boundary value problem (however smooth it may be) by one of the new "rough" admissible functions obtained by completion. Our presentation of this material owes much to Mikhlin (1970). See also Rektorys (1975) for an excellent discussion.

A second advantage of completion is that it makes possible the use of the Lax–Milgram lemma to assert the existence of a unique solution $\hat{u}$ of the variational formulation of a boundary value problem satisfying certain conditions. Section 3.2 is devoted to the Lax–Milgram lemma and its applications. We shall see that if the boundary value problem has a "classical" solution, then this solution must coincide with $\hat{u}$. If it has no such solution, due to a lack of smoothness in the data (e.g., the function on the right-hand side of the equation may be discontinuous), then we call $\hat{u}$ the "generalized" solution of the boundary value problem.

Sometimes the variational problem is of such a nature that the corresponding differential equation lacks a right-hand side in the conventional sense. This situation, by no means irrelevant to physical problems, leads to entities called symbolic functions, and these are the main topic of Section 3.3.

In contrast to Chapter 2, this chapter reflects (in a very simplified way) the modern treatment of partial differential equations, characterized by the use of functional analysis in general and Hilbert spaces in particular. Texts devoted to this advanced subject include Friedman (1969), Gilbarg and Trudinger (1977), Gustafson (1980), Lions and Magenes (1972), Nečas (1967), and Showalter (1977).

3.1 The Concept of Completion

The Hilbert Space $L_2[a, b]$

Let $L_2[a, b]$ denote the set of all integrable real functions $u(x)$, $-\infty < a \le x \le b < \infty$, such that $\int_a^b u^2\, dx < \infty$. We will always associate with $L_2[a, b]$ the inner product and norm defined by (3.2) and (3.3), respectively. Here and subsequently, the integration sign will be understood to denote the Lebesgue integral rather than the more familar, but less general, Riemann integral. [For a discussion of the Lebesgue integral see, e.g., Titchmarsh (1939) and Goffman and Pedrick (1965).] We recall that if a function is Riemann integrable then it is also Lebesgue integrable, and the two integrals have the same value. If u and v belong to $L_2[a, b]$, then so does their difference $(u - v)$. If, further, u and v are such that $\int_a^b (u - v)^2\, dx = 0$, then we think of u and v as being one and the same element in $L_2[a, b]$. In other words, an element of $L_2[a, b]$ is actually an *equivalence class* of functions with the property that if u and v are any pair of functions in the class, then $\int_a^b (u - v)^2\, dx = 0$.

In the theory of the Lebesgue integral, the concept of the length of an interval is generalized to the concept of the *measure* of an arbitrary point set. Certain point sets are so "sparse" that they have *measure zero*. For example, any denumerable set of points has measure zero. (Certain nondenumerable sets also have measure zero.) If a function in $L_2[a, b]$ possesses a certain property at all points in $[a, b]$, except possibly on a set of measure zero, then it is said to possess that property *almost everywhere* (hereafter abbreviated "AE") in $[a, b]$.

An important property of the Lebesgue integral is that if $\int_a^b u^2 \, dx = 0$ then $u(x) = 0$ AE. Thus two functions in the same equivalence class are equal AE. If, given any $u \in L_2[a, b]$, we determine a new function v by changing the values of u on a set of measure zero, then v belongs to the same equivalence class as u. Thus, for example, if Q and T are the sets of rational and irrational numbers, respectively, in $[a, b]$, then the functions

$$u(x) = 1, \quad a \leq x \leq b, \quad v(x) = \begin{cases} x^2 & \text{for } x \in Q, \\ 1 & \text{for } x \in T, \end{cases}$$

belong to the same equivalence class, because Q is denumerable and has measure zero. Clearly, every equivalence class contains functions that are discontinuous at an infinite number of points.

To avoid the repeated use of "AE" in describing equivalence classes (as in "$u(x) = 0$ AE"), we shall adopt the convention of representing an equivalence class by a particular function from the class, selecting for this purpose one having the fewest number of points of discontinuity. If an equivalence class contains a function from $C[a, b]$, then this function is the unique representative of the class. (Confirm this.)

The set $L_2[a, b]$ has the property

$$u, v \in L_2[a, b], \quad \alpha, \beta \in R \quad \Rightarrow \quad (\alpha u + \beta v) \in L_2[a, b] \tag{3.1}$$

and is therefore a *linear space*.

If u and v are arbitrary functions in $L_2[a, b]$, then the product uv is Lebesgue integrable. Let

$$(u, v) = \int_a^b uv \, dx, \quad u, v \in L_2[a, b], \tag{3.2}$$

$$\|u\| = \sqrt{(u, u)}, \quad u \in L_2[a, b]. \tag{3.3}$$

The following properties hold for all $u, v, w \in L_2[a, b]$, $\alpha, \beta \in R$:

$$(u, v) = (v, u), \tag{3.4a}$$

$$(\alpha u + \beta v, w) = \alpha(u, w) + \beta(v, w), \tag{3.4b}$$

$$(u, u) \geq 0, \tag{3.4c}$$

$$(u, u) = 0 \quad \Leftrightarrow \quad u = 0. \tag{3.4d}$$

Further,

$$\|\alpha u\| = |\alpha| \, \|u\|, \tag{3.5a}$$

$$\|u + v\| \leq \|u\| + \|v\|, \tag{3.5b}$$

$$\|u\| \geq 0, \tag{3.5c}$$

$$\|u\| = 0 \quad \Leftrightarrow \quad u = 0. \tag{3.5d}$$

By virtue of these properties, $(\cdot, \cdot)$ and $\|\cdot\|$ are called an *inner product* and *norm*, respectively. (More generally, for any continuous positive function $H(x)$, $a \leq x \leq b$, we can define an inner product and norm by $(u, v)_H = \int_a^b Huv \, dx$ and $\|u\|_H = (u, u)_H^{1/2}$, respectively. Compare with the inner product and norm for vectors given by Definition 1.9 in Section 1.2.) It is not difficult to show that (3.5) is implied by (3.3) and (3.4). The proof of (3.5b) is based on the fundamental Cauchy–Schwarz inequality

$$|(u, v)| \leq \|u\| \, \|v\|, \qquad u, v \in L_2[a, b]. \tag{3.6}$$

(See Exercise 3.2.)

A sequence $\{u_n\}_{n=1}^\infty \subset L_2[a, b]$ is said to *converge in the mean* to $u \in L_2[a, b]$ if

$$\lim_{n \to \infty} \|u - u_n\| = 0.$$

This property is not identical to *pointwise convergence*,

$$\lim_{n \to \infty} u_n(x) = u(x), \qquad a \leq x \leq b.$$

A sequence $\{u_n\}_{n=1}^\infty \subset L_2[a, b]$ is said to be a *Cauchy sequence* if

$$\lim_{m, n \to \infty} \|u_m - u_n\| = 0.$$

Suppose that some sequence $\{u_n\}_{n=1}^\infty \subset L_2[a, b]$ converges in the mean to $u \in L_2[a, b]$. Then, using (3.5b) we can write

$$\|u_m - u_n\| = \|(u_m - u) + (u - u_n)\| \leq \|u_m - u\| + \|u - u_n\|,$$

and $\{u_n\}_{n=1}^\infty$ is clearly a Cauchy sequence. A fundamental property of $L_2[a, b]$ is that the converse is also true, i.e., if $\{u_n\}_{n=1}^\infty \subset L_2[a, b]$ is a Cauchy sequence, then there exists a unique $u \in L_2[a, b]$ such that $\{u_n\}_{n=1}^\infty$ converges in the mean to u. The space $L_2[a, b]$ is said to be *complete* by virtue of this property.

A linear space equipped with an inner product and norm related by (3.3) is a *Hilbert space*, provided that the completeness property is present. Thus $L_2[a, b]$ is a Hilbert space. We shall meet other examples of Hilbert spaces later.

A *linear functional* on $L_2[a, b]$ is a mapping $\phi: L_2[a, b] \to R$ such that

$$u, v \in L_2[a, b], \quad \alpha, \beta \in R \quad \Rightarrow \quad \phi(\alpha u + \beta v) = \alpha\phi(u) + \beta\phi(v). \quad (3.7)$$

The functional is said to be *bounded* if there exists $\alpha > 0$ such that

$$|\phi(u)| \leq \alpha\|u\| \qquad \forall u \in L_2[a, b].$$

A simple example of a bounded linear functional is

$$\phi(u) = (u, u_0), \qquad u \in L_2[a, b], \qquad (3.8)$$

where u_0 is some fixed element in $L_2[a, b]$. The functional ϕ is linear because of (3.4b), and its boundedness follows from (3.6). An interesting fact is that every bounded linear functional can be expressed in the form of (3.8). For later reference we shall state this as a theorem.

Theorem 3.1. (Riesz Representation Theorem) Let ϕ be a bounded linear functional on $L_2[a, b]$. Then there exists a unique $u_0 \in L_2[a, b]$ such that

$$\phi(u) = (u, u_0) \qquad \forall u \in L_2[a, b].$$

This important theorem extends to bounded linear functionals on any Hilbert space. For a proof see Goffman and Pedrick (1965, p. 170).

An Example of Completion: Preliminaries

The ideas of this section are perhaps most easily explained with the help of a simple example, and we accordingly introduce the functional

$$f(u) = \int_a^b \left[\tfrac{1}{2}p(x)(u')^2 + \tfrac{1}{2}q(x)u^2 - g(x)u \right] dx, \qquad u \in V, \qquad (3.9)$$

$$V = \{v \in C^2[a, b]; v(a) = v(b) = 0\},$$

where $p \in C^1[a, b]$, $q, g \in C[a, b]$, and $0 < p_0 \leq p(x) \leq p_1$ and $0 \leq q(x) \leq q_1$ for $a \leq x \leq b$, p_0, p_1, and q_1 being constants. The corresponding set of test functions is seen from (2.1) to be $\tilde{V} = V$. From the point of view of the discussion to follow, this example is representative of almost all of the functionals in Chapter 2.

Introducing

$$a(u, v) = \int_a^b \left[p(x)u'v' + q(x)uv \right] dx, \qquad u, v \in V, \qquad (3.10a)$$

$$G(u) = \int_a^b g(x)u \, dx, \qquad\qquad u \in V, \qquad (3.10b)$$

we can express f as

$$f(u) = \tfrac{1}{2}a(u, u) - G(u), \qquad u \in V.$$

The mapping $G: V \to R$ given by (3.10b) is a functional on V and has the linear property

$$G(\alpha u + \beta v) = \alpha G(u) + \beta G(v), \qquad u, v \in V, \quad \alpha, \beta \in R.$$

The mapping $a: V \times V \to R$, which has the properties

$$a(\alpha u + \beta v, w) = \alpha a(u, w) + \beta a(v, w),$$

$$a(w, \alpha u + \beta v) = \alpha a(w, u) + \beta a(w, v),$$

where $u, v, w \in V$, $\alpha, \beta \in R$, is commonly called a *bilinear form*. It is in fact a *symmetric* bilinear form, since

$$a(u, v) = a(v, u), \qquad u, v \in V.$$

Using these properties we can write

$$a(u + \eta, u + \eta) = a(u, u) + 2a(u, \eta) + a(\eta, \eta),$$

$$G(u + \eta) = G(u) + G(\eta),$$

and hence derive the identity

$$f(u + \eta) = f(u) + \left[a(u, \eta) - G(\eta)\right] + \tfrac{1}{2}a(\eta, \eta), \qquad u, \eta \in V. \quad (3.11)$$

To compute the directional derivatives of f we replace η by $\tau\eta$, where $\|\eta\| = 1$ and $\tau \in R$, obtaining

$$f(u + \tau\eta) = f(u) + \tau\left[a(u, \eta) - G(\eta)\right] + (\tau^2/2)a(\eta, \eta),$$

and by Definition 2.3,

$$f^{(1)}(u; \eta) = a(u, \eta) - G(\eta), \qquad f^{(2)}(u; \eta) = a(\eta, \eta),$$

$$f^{(m)}(u; \eta) = 0, \qquad m = 3, 4, \dots.$$

A function $u \in V$ is a stationary point of f if $f^{(1)}(u; \eta) = 0 \ \forall \eta \in V, \|\eta\| = 1$, or equivalently, if

$$a(u, \eta) = G(\eta) \qquad \forall \eta \in V. \qquad (3.12)$$

Integrating $a(u, \eta)$ by parts we obtain the identity

$$a(u, \eta) = \int_a^b (\mathcal{L}u)\eta \, dx, \qquad u, \eta \in V,$$

where we have introduced the mapping $\mathcal{L}: V \to C[a, b]$ defined by

$$\mathcal{L}u = -[p(x)u']' + q(x)u, \qquad u \in V.$$

A mapping of one set of functions into another is called an *operator*. The operator $\mathscr{L}$ is *linear*, since it has the property

$$\mathscr{L}(\alpha u + \beta v) = \alpha \mathscr{L} u + \beta \mathscr{L} v, \qquad u, v \in V, \quad \alpha, \beta \in R.$$

Making use of the $L_2[a, b]$ inner product notation (3.2) we can write

$$a(u, n) = (\mathscr{L}u, \eta), \qquad G(\eta) = (g, \eta).$$

Then,

$$a(u, \eta) = G(\eta) \qquad \forall \eta \in V \quad \Leftrightarrow \quad (\mathscr{L}u - g, \eta) = 0 \qquad \forall \eta \in V$$
$$\Leftrightarrow \quad \mathscr{L}u = g,$$

the last step following from a continuity argument explained in Section 2.1.

Thus the Euler–Lagrange equation for (3.9) is $\mathscr{L}u = g$, and (3.12) is the variational formulation of the two-point boundary value problem $\mathscr{L}u = g$, $u(a) = u(b) = 0$. The theory of differential equations tells us that this problem has a unique solution $\hat{u}$ in V. Hence, (3.12) holds for $u = \hat{u}$. Further, a simple rewriting of (3.11) yields the identity

$$f(u) = f(\hat{u}) + \tfrac{1}{2} a(u - \hat{u}, u - \hat{u}), \tag{3.13}$$

and, since $a(\eta, \eta) > 0 \ \forall \eta \in V, \eta \neq 0$, (show this) it follows that

$$\min_{u \in V} f(u) = f(\hat{u}).$$

Enlargement of the Set of Admissible Functions

Up to this point we have done nothing more than apply the analysis of Section 2.1 to (3.9), expressing it in terms of some general notation. Our next step is to describe the process of completion. This is essentially an expansion of the domain of definition of f from the set V of (3.9) to a larger set $\overline{V}$ such that

(1) every function in $\overline{V}$ can be approximated arbitrarily closely (in a sense to be defined shortly) by functions in V;

(2) the solution $\hat{u}$ of the two-point boundary value problem $\mathscr{L}u = g$, $u(a) = u(b) = 0$ is the unique solution of the variational problem of finding $u \in \overline{V}$ such that $a(u, \eta) = G(\eta) \ \forall \eta \in \overline{V}$;

(3) $\min_{u \in V} f(u) = \min_{u \in \overline{V}} f(u) = f(\hat{u})$.

We shall see that $\overline{V}$, in contrast to V, contains functions that do not have a continuous second-order derivative or even a continuous first-order derivative. The introduction of these "rough" functions into the domain of definition of f is fundamental for the application of the finite element method (see Chapter 5).

The following theorem will be needed.

Theorem 3.2.

$$(u', u') \geq \frac{2(u, u)}{(b - a)^2} \qquad \forall u \in \{v \in C^1[a, b]; v(a) = 0\}.$$

PROOF: Consider the identity

$$u(x) = u(a) + \int_a^x u'(t) \, dt = \int_a^x u'(t) \, dt.$$

We can apply the Cauchy–Schwarz inequality (3.6) over any subinterval of $[a, b]$, and in particular over $[a, x]$:

$$u(x)^2 = \left[\int_a^x 1 \cdot u'(t) \, dt \right]^2 \leq \int_a^x 1^2 \, dt \int_a^x [u'(t)]^2 \, dt$$

$$\leq (x - a) \int_a^b [u'(t)]^2 \, dt.$$

Then,

$$\int_a^b u(x)^2 \, dx \leq \int_a^b (x - a) \, dx \int_a^b [u'(t)]^2 \, dt$$

$$\leq \tfrac{1}{2}(b - a)^2 \int_a^b [u'(t)]^2 \, dt,$$

which proves the theorem.   ∎

We recall that $L_2[a, b]$ is complete with respect to the norm $\|\cdot\|$ in the sense that if $\{u_n\}_{n=1}^\infty \subset L_2[a, b]$ is a Cauchy sequence in this norm (i.e., if $\lim_{m,n \to \infty} \|u_m - u_n\| = 0$), then there exists $u \in L_2[a, b]$ such that $\lim_{n \to \infty} \|u - u_n\| = 0$. Let

$$(u, v)_\mathscr{L} = a(u, v), \qquad\qquad u, v \in V,$$

$$\|u\|_\mathscr{L} = (u, u)_\mathscr{L}^{1/2} = a(u, u)^{1/2}, \qquad u \in V,$$

where $a(u, v)$ is given by (3.10). It can be verified that $(\cdot, \cdot)_\mathscr{L}$ and $\|\cdot\|_\mathscr{L}$ are a well-defined inner product and norm, respectively, on V; i.e., they have properties (3.4) and (3.5). We call $(\cdot, \cdot)_\mathscr{L}$ the *energy inner product* and $\|\cdot\|_\mathscr{L}$ the *energy norm*. These names stem from the identity

$$\|u - \hat{u}\|_\mathscr{L} = \sqrt{2[f(u) - f(\hat{u})]}$$

[see (3.13)] and the fact that in many applications f expresses the energy of some physical system. The space V is not complete in the energy norm, however, because (as we shall see) there are sequences $\{u_n\}_{n=1}^\infty \subset V$ such that $\lim_{m,n\to\infty} \|u_m - u_n\|_{\mathscr{L}} = 0$, but for which no element $u \in V$ satisfies $\lim_{n\to\infty} \|u - u_n\|_{\mathscr{L}} = 0$.

Let $\{u_n\}_{n=1}^\infty \subset V$ be any sequence in V with the Cauchy sequence property $\lim_{m,n\to\infty} \|u_n - u_m\|_{\mathscr{L}} = 0$. From Theorem 3.2 and the assumptions on p and q in (3.9) we have the inequality

$$\|u\|_{\mathscr{L}}^2 = (pu', u') + (qu, u) \geq p_0(u', u')$$

$$= \frac{p_0}{2}\left[(u', u') + (u', u')\right]$$

$$\geq \frac{p_0}{2}(u', u') + \frac{p_0}{(b-a)^2}(u, u)$$

$$\geq \rho(\|u'\|^2 + \|u\|^2) \qquad \forall u \in V, \tag{3.14}$$

where

$$\rho = p_0 \min\{\tfrac{1}{2}, (b-a)^{-2}\} > 0.$$

Thus, the Cauchy sequence property of $\{u_n\}_{n=1}^\infty$ implies

$$\lim_{m,n\to\infty} \|u_m - u_n\| = 0, \qquad \lim_{m,n\to\infty} \|u'_m - u'_n\| = 0.$$

By the completeness property of $L_2[a, b]$ with respect to the norm $\|\cdot\|$, there exist elements $u, \tilde{u} \in L_2[a, b]$ such that

$$\lim_{n\to\infty} \|u - u_n\| = 0, \qquad \lim_{n\to\infty} \|\tilde{u} - u'_n\| = 0.$$

We define $\overline{V}$ to be the set of all functions u that can be obtained by this process.

We call $\tilde{u}$ the *generalized derivative* of u. It can be shown that $\tilde{u}$ is uniquely determined by u, i.e., if two Cauchy sequences in V converge to the same u in $\overline{V}$, then they produce the same generalized derivative $\tilde{u}$. Further, if $u \in C^1[a, b]$, then $\tilde{u} = u'$. Hereafter we denote the generalized derivative by u'. With this convention the formulas

$$(u, v)_{\mathscr{L}} = \int_a^b [p(x)u'v' + q(x)uv] \, dx, \qquad u, v \in \overline{V},$$

$$\|u\|_{\mathscr{L}} = (u, u)_{\mathscr{L}}^{1/2}, \qquad u \in \overline{V},$$

define the energy inner product and norm for all of $\overline{V}$. In contrast to V, the space $\overline{V}$ is complete with respect to the energy norm (Exercise 3.3) and is therefore a Hilbert space.

The following example shows that $\overline{V}$ contains functions not contained in

V or even in $C^1[a, b]$. Let $[a, b] = [-1, 1]$, and for $n = 1, 2, \ldots$ let

$$u_n(x) = \begin{cases} 1 - (1/n) + [2/(n\pi)]\cos(n\pi x/2) & \text{for} \quad |x| < 1/n, \\ 1 - |x| & \text{for} \quad 1/n \le |x| \le 1. \end{cases} \tag{3.15a}$$

These functions belong to V, i.e., they are continuous and have continuous derivatives of first and second order, and they vanish at the endpoints of the interval. Their first derivatives are

$$u_n'(x) = \begin{cases} 1 & \text{for} \quad -1 \le x \le -1/n, \\ -\sin(n\pi x/2) & \text{for} \quad |x| < 1/n, \\ -1 & \text{for} \quad 1/n \le x \le 1. \end{cases} \tag{3.15b}$$

Functions of type (3.15a) and (3.15b) are sketched in Figs. 3.1a and 3.1b, respectively.

We have

$$\|u_m - u_n\|_{\mathscr{L}}^2 = \int_{-1}^{1} p(u_m' - u_n')^2 \, dx + \int_{-1}^{1} q(u_m - u_n)^2 \, dx$$

$$\le p_1 \int_{-1}^{1} (u_m' - u_n')^2 \, dx + q_1 \int_{-1}^{1} (u_m - u_n)^2 \, dx,$$

where, for $n \le m$,

$$|u_m'(x) - u_n'(x)| \le \begin{cases} 1 & \text{for} \quad |x| < 1/n, \\ 0 & \text{for} \quad 1/n \le |x| \le 1, \end{cases}$$

$$|u_m(x) - u_n(x)| \le \begin{cases} 1/n & \text{for} \quad |x| < 1/n, \\ 0 & \text{for} \quad 1/n \le |x| \le 1. \end{cases}$$

Thus,

$$\|u_m - u_n\|_{\mathscr{L}}^2 \le (2p_1/n) + (2q_1/n^3),$$

and this establishes that $\lim_{m,n \to \infty} \|u_m - u_n\|_{\mathscr{L}} = 0$. According to the preceding discussion, one of the elements of $\overline{V}$ is the function $u \in L_2[-1, 1]$ that satisfies $\lim_{n \to \infty} \|u - u_n\| = 0$. We leave it to the reader to verify that this function is in fact

$$u(x) = 1 - |x|, \qquad |x| \le 1. \tag{3.16a}$$

Since $u(x)$ is not differentiable at $x = 0$, it does not belong to $C^1[a, b]$.

The generalized derivative of u is the function $u' \in L_2[-1, 1]$ that satisfies $\lim_{n \to \infty} \|u' - u_n'\| = 0$, and it is easily seen that

$$u'(x) = \begin{cases} 1 & \text{for} \quad -1 \le x < 0, \\ 0 & \text{for} \quad x = 0, \\ -1 & \text{for} \quad 0 < x \le 1. \end{cases} \tag{3.16b}$$

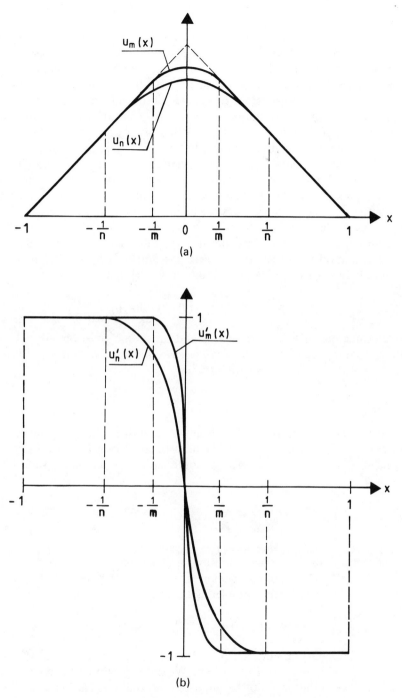

Fig. 3.1. Examples of the functions (a) (3.15a) and (b) (3.15b) for $n < m$.

This is an appropriate point to recall that an element of $L_2[a, b]$ is actually an equivalence class of functions, every pair of functions in the class being equal AE in the interval $[a, b]$. In choosing a representative function from an equivalence class, we always choose a function with continuity in as much of the interval as possible. In the case of the function $u(x)$ under consideration this convention uniquely selects (3.16a), since (3.16a) is continuous everywhere in $[a, b]$ and every other function in the same equivalence class has at least one point of discontinuity. In the case of $u'(x)$ the value $u'(0) = 0$ is arbitrary in the sense that no value can eliminate the discontinuity at $x = 0$. We shall often comment on the degree of smoothness of an element of some space $\overline{V}$ obtained by the process of completion. Since an element of $\overline{V}$ is actually an equivalence class, such statements must be understood to apply only to the smoothest function in the class.

Having seen that not all functions in $\overline{V}$ possess a continuous first derivative, it is natural to ask whether at least the functions themselves are continuous. It can be shown [see, e.g., Mikhlin (1970)] that

$$\overline{V} \subset \{v \in C[a, b]; v(a) = v(b) = 0\},$$

i.e., all functions in $\overline{V}$ are continuous and satisfy the given boundary conditions. We say that a function u is *piecewise differentiable* on $[a, b]$ if for some set of points $\{x_i\}_{i=1}^n$, where

$$a < x_1 < x_2 < \cdots < x_n < b,$$

it is true that $u'(x)$ exists and is continuous everywhere in $[a, b]$ except at $x_1, x_2, \ldots, x_n$. [Here $u'(x)$ denotes the derivative in the usual sense.] The set $\overline{V}$ includes all continuous piecewise differentiable functions u such that $u(a) = u(b) = 0$ and

$$\int_{x_{i-1}}^{x_i} [u'(x)]^2 \, dx < \infty \qquad \text{for} \quad i = 1, 2, \ldots, n + 1,$$

where $x_0 = a$ and $x_{n+1} = b$; (3.16a) is an example.

The fact that the boundary conditions imposed on V were carried over to all of $\overline{V}$ by the process of completion is typical of essential boundary conditions. On the other hand, completing the space

$$W = \{v \in C^2[a, b]; v(a) = v'(b) = 0\},$$

where the boundary condition $u'(b) = 0$ is natural, produces a space $\overline{W}$ such that $u \in \overline{W} \not\Rightarrow u'(b) = 0$. (See Exercise 3.4.) We saw in Section 2.2 that a natural boundary condition need not be imposed, and that one can replace W by the space $\{v \in C^2[a, b]; v(a) = 0\}$. Now we find that even if it is imposed, it becomes lost in the process of completion.

Let us now return to (3.9), replacing V by $\bar{V}$. In the analysis from (3.9) to (3.12) all statements remain valid, and in particular (3.11) becomes

$$f(u + \eta) = f(u) + [a(u, \eta) - G(\eta)] + \tfrac{1}{2}a(\eta, \eta), \qquad u, \eta \in \bar{V}. \quad (3.17)$$

A difficulty arises in attempting to integrate $a(u, \eta)$ by parts, however, since $\mathscr{L}u$ makes no immediate sense unless u has a continuous second-order derivative. Thus we can only write

$$a(u, \eta) - G(\eta) = (\mathscr{L}u - g, \eta), \qquad u \in V, \quad \eta \in \bar{V},$$

restricting u to V. But since we already know that the solution $\hat{u}$ of the boundary value problem $\mathscr{L}u = g, u(a) = u(b) = 0$ belongs to V, it follows that

$$a(\hat{u}, \eta) = G(\eta) \qquad \forall \eta \in \bar{V}.$$

Thus $\hat{u}$ is a solution of the problem of finding a function $u \in \bar{V}$ that satisfies

$$a(u, \eta) = G(\eta) \qquad \forall \eta \in \bar{V}. \quad (3.18)$$

Further, using (3.17) we find easily that

$$f(u) = f(\hat{u}) + \tfrac{1}{2}a(u - \hat{u}, u - \hat{u}), \qquad u \in \bar{V}, \quad (3.19)$$

and since $a(\eta, \eta) > 0 \ \forall \eta \in \bar{V}, \eta \neq 0$, it follows that

$$\min_{u \in \bar{V}} f(u) = \min_{u \in V} f(u) = f(\hat{u}).$$

Thus, if problem (3.18) had a second solution, then f would have two global minimizers; (3.19) shows this is impossible.

Conclusion: The solution of the boundary value problem $\mathscr{L}u = g, u(a) = u(b) = 0$ is the unique solution of the variational problem (3.18).

Sobolev Spaces (One Space Dimension)

Let

$$(u, v)_1 = \sum_{i=0}^{1} (u^{(i)}, v^{(i)}) = \int_a^b [uv + u'v'] \, dx, \qquad u, v \in V,$$

$$\|u\|_1 = (u, u)_1^{1/2} = \left\{ \int_a^b [u^2 + (u')^2] \, dx \right\}^{1/2}, \qquad u \in V,$$

where V is given by (3.9). It can be shown that $(\cdot, \cdot)_1$ and $\|\cdot\|_1$ are a well-defined inner product and norm, respectively, on V. They are called the *Sobolev inner product* and the *Sobolev norm of order one*. The Sobolev norm $\|\cdot\|_1$ and the energy norm

$$\|u\|_{\mathscr{E}} = \left\{\int_a^b [p(u')^2 + qu^2]\, dx\right\}^{1/2}, \qquad u \in V,$$

associated with (3.9) are *equivalent* in the sense that there exist constants $\rho, \beta > 0$ such that

$$\rho\|u\|_1^2 \le \|u\|_{\mathscr{E}}^2 \le \beta\|u\|_1^2 \qquad \forall u \in V. \tag{3.20}$$

It is clear from the assumptions on the functions p and q that we can take $\beta = \max\{p_1, q_1\}$ and that a suitable value of ρ is given by (3.14).

We have described how completing V with respect to the energy norm leads to a Hilbert space $\bar{V}$. Let $\tilde{V}$ denote the result of completing V with respect to the Sobolev norm. To obtain $\tilde{V}$ we must consider those sequences $\{u_n\}_{n=1}^{\infty}$ in V with the Cauchy sequence property $\lim_{m,n\to\infty} \|u_m - u_n\|_1 = 0$. It is obvious from the definition of the Sobolev norm that this implies $\lim_{m,n\to\infty} \|u_m - u_n\| = 0$, and the completeness of $L_2[a, b]$ with respect to the norm $\|\cdot\|$ determines some $u \in L_2[a, b]$ such that $\lim_{n\to\infty} \|u - u_n\| = 0$. The space $\tilde{V}$ is by definition the set of all functions that can be produced by this method. Comparing this process with the completion of V with respect to the energy norm, we see that $\tilde{V} = \bar{V}$ if and only if for every sequence $\{u_n\}_{n=1}^{\infty} \subset V$ it is true that

$$\lim_{m,n\to\infty} \|u_m - u_n\|_1 = 0 \quad \Leftrightarrow \quad \lim_{m,n\to\infty} \|u_m - u_n\|_{\mathscr{E}} = 0. \tag{3.21}$$

But the equivalence of the two norms obviously implies (3.21), and we conclude that $\tilde{V} = \bar{V}$. The Sobolev inner product and norm are defined on all of $\bar{V}$ when first-order derivatives are interpreted in the generalized sense, and $\bar{V}$ is a Hilbert space also with respect to this inner product and norm.

We shall now introduce a variety of so-called Sobolev spaces of which $\bar{V}$ is a special case. For any nonnegative integer k let $C^k(a, b)$ denote the set of functions defined on $a < x < b$ with continuous derivatives of order up to and including k. Let

$$\tilde{C}^k(a, b) = \left\{v \in C^k(a, b); \int_a^b (v^{(i)})^2\, dx < \infty, i = 0, 1, \ldots, k\right\}.$$

Since $C^k(a, b)$ includes functions that are unbounded near a or b and for which the integral $\int_a^b v^2\, dx$ diverges [e.g., $v(x) = (x - a)^{-1}$], we see that

$\tilde{C}^k(a, b)$ is a proper subset of $C^k(a, b)$. Let

$$(u, v)_k = \sum_{i=0}^{k} (u^{(i)}, v^{(i)})$$

$$= \int_a^b [uv + u'v' + \cdots + u^{(k)}v^{(k)}] \, dx, \qquad u, v \in \tilde{C}^k(a, b).$$

$$\|u\|_k = (u, u)_k^{1/2} = \left\{ \int_a^b [u^2 + (u')^2 + \cdots + (u^{(k)})^2] \, dx \right\}^{1/2}, \qquad u \in \tilde{C}^k(a, b).$$

$(\cdot, \cdot)_k$ and $\| \cdot \|_k$ are the Sobolev inner product and norm, respectively, of order k. The completion of $\tilde{C}^k(a, b)$ with respect to $\| \cdot \|_k$ produces a larger space that we denote $H^{(k)}(a, b)$ and call a *Sobolev space*. The process of completion allows us to extend the domain of definition of the Sobolev inner product and norm from $\tilde{C}^{(k)}(a, b)$ to all of $H^k(a, b)$.

A function u defined on the interval (a, b) is said to have *compact support* on (a, b) if there exist α, β such that $a < \alpha < \beta < b$ and $u(x) = 0$ for $a < x < \alpha$ and $\beta < x < b$. We define $\mathring{H}^k(a, b)$ to be the completion with respect to $\| \cdot \|_k$ of the subset of $C^k(a, b)$ with compact support on (a, b). We call also $\mathring{H}^k(a, b)$ a Sobolev space. $\mathring{H}^k(a, b)$ is a Hilbert space with respect to the Sobolev inner product and norm. Further,

$$\mathring{H}^k(a, b) = \{v \in H^k(a, b); v^{(i)}(a) = v^{(i)}(b) = 0, i = 0, 1, \ldots, k - 1\}.$$

Although the subspace of $C^1(a, b)$ with compact support on (a, b) is not identical to the space V in (3.9), it can be shown that their completions with respect to $\| \cdot \|_1$ are identical, i.e., $\overline{V} = \mathring{H}^1(a, b)$. Thus, the boundary value problem $\mathscr{L}u = g, u(a) = u(b) = 0$ associated with (3.9) has the variational formulation: find $u \in \mathring{H}^1(a, b)$ such that

$$a(u, \eta) = G(\eta) \qquad \forall \eta \in \mathring{H}^1(a, b).$$

Sobolev Spaces (Several Space Dimensions)

Let Ω be a bounded, open region of R^n. We denote by $L_2(\Omega)$ the set of functions u defined on Ω with the property that $\int_\Omega u^2 \, d\Omega < \infty$, the integral being in the sense of Lebesque. $L_2(\Omega)$ is a Hilbert space with respect to the inner product

$$(u, v) = \int_\Omega uv \, d\Omega$$

and the norm

$$\|u\| = \sqrt{(u, u)}.$$

[Since the boundary of Ω has measure zero (except in certain highly special cases of no physical interest), there is no essential distinction between $L_2(\Omega)$ and $L_2(\bar{\Omega})$ and, in particular, between $L_2(a, b)$ and $L_2[a, b]$. We work here with Ω rather than $\bar{\Omega}$ because Sobolev spaces are traditionally defined on open regions.]

It will occasionally be convenient to employ the following notation for the partial derivatives of a function $u(x_1, \ldots, x_n)$. Let $\alpha_1, \alpha_2, \ldots, \alpha_n$ be nonnegative integers. We define

$$\alpha = (\alpha_1, \ldots, \alpha_n), \qquad |\alpha| = \sum_{i=1}^{n} \alpha_i, \qquad D^\alpha = \frac{\partial^{|\alpha|}}{\partial x_1^{\alpha_1} \cdots \partial x_n^{\alpha_n}}, \qquad u^{(\alpha)} = D^\alpha u.$$

α is a *multi-index*, and $u^{(\alpha)}$, $D^\alpha u$ are multi-index notations for a partial derivative of order $|\alpha|$.

Let

$$\tilde{C}^k(\Omega) = \left\{ v \in C^k(\Omega); \int_\Omega (v^{(\alpha)})^2 \, d\Omega < \infty, 0 \le |\alpha| \le k \right\}.$$

The *Sobolev inner product* on $\tilde{C}^k(\Omega)$ is

$$(u, v)_k = \sum_{0 \le |\alpha| \le k} (u^{(\alpha)}, v^{(\alpha)}), \tag{3.22}$$

the summation being taken over all α such that $0 \le |\alpha| \le k$. The corresponding *Sobolev norm* is

$$\|u\|_k = \left\{ \sum_{0 \le |\alpha| \le k} \|u^{(\alpha)}\|^2 \right\}^{1/2}. \tag{3.23}$$

For example, in two space dimensions we have

$$\|u\|_2^2 = \int_\Omega (u^2 + u_x^2 + u_y^2 + u_{xx}^2 + u_{xy}^2 + u_{yy}^2) \, d\Omega.$$

The *Sobolev space* $H^k(\Omega)$ is the completion of $\tilde{C}^k(\Omega)$ with respect to the Sobolev norm. Thus if $\{u_n\}_{n=1}^\infty \subset \tilde{C}^{(k)}(\Omega)$ has the property that $\lim_{m,n \to \infty} \|u_m - u_n\|_k = 0$, then (3.23) implies $\lim_{m,n \to \infty} \|u_m^{(\alpha)} - u_n^{(\alpha)}\| = 0$ for all α such that $0 \le |\alpha| \le k$, and for all such α the completeness of $L_2(\Omega)$ determines a unique function $u_\alpha \in L_2(\Omega)$ satisfying $\lim_{n \to \infty} \|u_\alpha - u_n^{(\alpha)}\| = 0$. The function $u \equiv u_\alpha$, $|\alpha| = 0$ is then by definition an element of $H^k(\Omega)$, and each u_α, $0 < |\alpha| \le k$ is one of its generalized partial derivatives. It can be shown that if $u \in C^{|\alpha|}(\bar{\Omega})$, then $u_\alpha = u^{(\alpha)}$. Hereafter, generalized partial derivatives will be denoted by $u^{(\alpha)}$. With this convention, (3.22) and (3.23) are well defined for all $u, v \in H^k(\Omega)$. Further, $H^k(\Omega)$ is a Hilbert space with respect to this inner product and norm.

The existence of derivatives, in the ordinary sense, of $u \in H^k(\Omega)$ depends on k and the number of space dimensions. In the case of one space dimension, where $\Omega = (a, b)$, it can be shown that $H^k(\Omega) \subset C^{k-1}(\bar{\Omega})$. More generally, if $\Omega \subset R^n$, where n is arbitrary, and if the boundary is sufficiently smooth, then $H^k(\Omega) \subset C^s(\bar{\Omega})$, where s is the largest integer less than $(k - n/2)$. Further, there exists a constant C, dependent only on Ω and k, such that

$$\max_{x \in \Omega} |u^{(\alpha)}(x)| \leq C\|u\|_k \qquad \forall \alpha \ni |\alpha| \leq s. \tag{3.24}$$

This is one of the *Sobolev embedding theorems* (Adams, 1975). Note that $H^k(\Omega) \subset C^{k-2}(\bar{\Omega})$ in the case of two and three space dimensions. In contrast to the one-dimensional case, not all functions in $H^k(\Omega)$ have continuous derivatives of order $k - 1$.

The inclusions

$$L_2(\Omega) = H^0(\Omega) \supset H^1(\Omega) \supset H^2(\Omega) \cdots,$$

are valid and are analogous to

$$C^0(\bar{\Omega}) \supset C^1(\bar{\Omega}) \supset C^2(\bar{\Omega}) \supset \cdots.$$

We often tend to think of the "smoothness" (or "regularity") of a function u defined on $\bar{\Omega}$ as a property determined by the largest value of k for which it is true that $u \in C^k(\bar{\Omega})$. It is just as valid to associate this property with the largest value of k for which $u \in H^k(\Omega)$.

In the finite element method for solving differential equations, one approximates the solution of a boundary value problem with a continuous *piecewise polynomial*. We say that u is a piecewise polynomial on $\bar{\Omega}$ if

$$u(x) = P_l(x), \qquad x \in \Omega_l, \quad l = 1, 2, ..., L,$$

where $\{\Omega_l\}_{l=1}^{L}$ is a subdivision of $\bar{\Omega}$ and $P_l(x)$ a polynomial in the variables $x_1, ..., x_n \; \forall x \in \Omega_l$. A property of fundamental importance for the finite element method is that if $u \in C^{k-1}(\bar{\Omega})$, $u \notin C^k(\bar{\Omega})$, where u is a piecewise polynomial, then $u \in H^k(\Omega)$, $u \notin H^{k+1}(\Omega)$. The property $u \notin H^{k+1}(\Omega)$ is due to the fact that functions with step discontinuities do not have first-order generalized derivatives with respect to all of the variables $x_1, x_2, ..., x_n$.

A function u defined on a bounded open set $\Omega \subset R^n$ is said to have *compact support* on Ω if there exists a closed set $\Omega_0 \subset \Omega$ such that $u = 0$ everywhere in $\Omega - \Omega_0$. We define $\mathring{H}^k(\Omega)$ to be the completion with respect to norm $\|\cdot\|_k$ of the subset of $C^k(\Omega)$ with compact support on Ω. If the boundary Γ is sufficiently smooth, then we can characterize $\mathring{H}^k(\Omega)$ by

$$\mathring{H}^k(\Omega) = \{v \in H^k(\Omega); \partial^i v/\partial v^i = 0 \text{ on } \Gamma, i = 0, 1, ..., k - 1\},$$

provided the normal derivative $\partial^i v/\partial v^i$ is interpreted in the generalized sense.

In addition to the Sobolev norm $\|\cdot\|_k$, we shall occasionally have use for the *Sobolev seminorm*

$$|u|_k = \left\{ \sum_{|\alpha|=k} \|u^{(\alpha)}\|^2 \right\}^{1/2}. \tag{3.25}$$

This is well defined for $u \in H^m(\Omega)$, where $m \geq k$. A seminorm must satisfy all of the requirements of a norm except (3.5d). It can be shown that $|\cdot|_k$ is in fact a norm on $\mathring{H}^k(\Omega)$.

For treatments of Sobolev spaces see, e.g., Adams (1975), Barros-Neto (1973), and Friedman (1969).

3.2   The Lax–Milgram Lemma and Applications

The Lax–Milgram Lemma

We were able to express the quadratic functional (3.9) in the simple form $f(u) = \frac{1}{2}a(u, u) - G(u)$, $u \in V$, later replacing V by the Sobolev space $\mathring{H}^1(a, b)$, which is a Hilbert space with respect to the Sobolev inner product and its associated norm. The Lax–Milgram lemma deals with functionals of this form, but at an abstract level.

Thus let V now denote an arbitrary Hilbert space with inner product $(\cdot, \cdot)_V$ and norm

$$\|u\|_V \equiv (u, u)_V^{1/2}, \qquad u \in V.$$

Let $a: V \times V \to R$ be a mapping with the following properties:

(1) $a(\alpha u + \beta v, w) = \alpha a(u, w) + \beta a(v, w)$, $\quad u, v, w \in V$, $\quad \alpha, \beta \in R$;
(2) $a(w, \alpha u + \beta v) = \alpha a(w, u) + \beta a(w, v)$, $\quad u, v, w \in V$, $\quad \alpha, \beta \in R$;
(3) there exists a constant β such that

$$|a(u, v)| \leq \beta \|u\|_V \|v\|_V, \qquad u, v \in V;$$

(4) there exists a constant $\rho > 0$ such that

$$a(u, u) \geq \rho \|u\|_V^2, \qquad u \in V.$$

From (1) and (2) we recognize that $a(\cdot, \cdot)$ is a bilinear form. We say it is *bounded* by virtue of (3) and *coercive* by virtue of (4). It is also *symmetric* if it has the property

$$a(u, v) = a(v, u), \qquad u, v \in V.$$

Let $G: V \to R$ be a mapping with the following properties:

(5) $G(\alpha u + \beta v) = \alpha G(u) + \beta G(v),$ $u, v \in V,$ $\alpha, \beta \in R;$
(6)   there exists a constant δ such that

$$|G(u)| \le \delta \|u\|_V,   u \in V.$$

We note that G is a bounded linear functional on V. [Compare with (3.7).]

Theorem 3.3.   (Lax–Milgram Lemma)   Under assumptions (1)–(6) there exists a unique element $\hat{u} \in V$ such that

$$a(\hat{u}, u) = G(u)   \forall u \in V. \tag{3.26}$$

Further, if $a(\cdot, \cdot)$ is symmetric then $\hat{u}$ is the unique global minimizer of

$$f(u) = \tfrac{1}{2}a(u, u) - G(u),   u \in V. \tag{3.27}$$

PROOF: We confine ourselves here to the case when $a(\cdot, \cdot)$ is symmetric. For a proof of the general case, see Ciarlet (1978).

Assumptions (1), (4), and the assumption of symmetry imply that $a(u, v)$ and $\sqrt{a(u, u)}$ are a well-defined inner product and norm on V. Further, (3) and (4) imply that $\|u\|_V$ and $\sqrt{a(u, u)}$ are equivalent norms on V. Thus, for any sequence $\{u_n\}_{n=1}^{\infty} \subset V$,

$$\lim_{n \to \infty} \|u_n\|_V = 0   \Leftrightarrow   \lim_{n \to \infty} \sqrt{a(u_n, u_n)} = 0,$$

and it is easy to show (Exercise 3.8) that the completeness of V in the norm $\|\cdot\|_V$ then implies the completeness of V in the norm $\sqrt{a(u, u)}$. Thus V is a Hilbert space also with respect to inner product $a(u, v)$ and norm $\sqrt{a(u, u)}$.

The functional G is bounded with respect to this norm since

$$|G(u)| \le \delta \rho^{-1/2} \sqrt{a(u, u)},   u \in V.$$

We can then apply Theorem 3.1 (see the remark immediately after the theorem) to assert the existence of a unique $\hat{u} \in V$ such that $G(u) = a(\hat{u}, u)$ $\forall u \in V$, establishing (3.26).

To see that $\hat{u}$ minimizes f in the symmetric case we derive by simple operations the identity

$$f(u + v) = f(u) + [a(u, v) - G(v)] + \tfrac{1}{2}a(v, v),   u, v \in V.$$

Then by (3.26) and assumption (4),

$$f(\hat{u} + u) = f(\hat{u}) + \tfrac{1}{2}a(u, u) \ge f(\hat{u}) + (\rho/2)\|u\|_V^2 > f(\hat{u})$$

$$\forall u \in V,   u \ne 0. \qquad \blacksquare$$

It will be observed that when $a(\cdot, \cdot)$ is symmetric, assumption (2) is superfluous. Further, since symmetry together with (1) and (4) imply that $a(\cdot, \cdot)$ is an inner product on V, there is the Cauchy–Schwarz inequality

$$|a(u, v)| \le a(u, u)^{1/2}a(v, v)^{1/2}.$$

Suppose that for some constant $\beta > 0$ it is true that

$$(3)' \qquad\qquad a(u, u) \le \beta\|u\|_V^2, \qquad u \in V. \qquad\qquad (3.28)$$

Then property (3) follows. Conversely, putting $v = u$ in (3) we obtain (3)'. In the symmetric case, then, (3) and (3)' are equivalent.

Remarks. The following remarks concern the application of the Lax–Milgram lemma to a boundary value problem consisting of a differential equation $\mathscr{L}u = g$ of order $2m$ over some region Ω and specified boundary conditions.

1. Essential boundary conditions must be homogeneous. (See the end of this section for a discussion of the inhomogeneous case.)
2. The Hilbert space V is $H^m(\Omega)$ or some subspace of $H^m(\Omega)$, and $(\cdot, \cdot)_V = (\cdot, \cdot)_m$, $\|\cdot\|_V = \|\cdot\|_m$. When $V = H^m(\Omega)$, no boundary conditions are imposed. This choice of V corresponds to the case in which the specified boundary conditions are natural. If there are any essential boundary conditions, then these must be imposed. For example, the boundary conditions $u(a) = u(b) = 0$ for the second-order boundary value problem associated with (3.9) are essential. The appropriate choice of V in the Lax–Milgram lemma is thus $\mathring{H}^{(1)}(a, b)$, identical to the space $\overline{V}$ we obtained by completion. It is important to note that the space V defined in (3.9) is not suitable for the lemma, since it is not complete and therefore not a Hilbert space. If the boundary conditions had been $u(a) = u'(b) = 0$, the second one being natural, then we would have completed the space

$$V = \{v \in C^2[a, b]; v(a) = 0\}$$

to obtain a Hilbert space between $\mathring{H}^1(a, b)$ and $H^1(a, b)$.
3. The bilinear form is an integral over Ω, the integrand containing derivatives of u and v of order up to m. Further, $a(u, v)$ is well defined for all $u, v \in V \subseteq H^m(\Omega)$, because every function in $H^m(\Omega)$ has generalized derivatives of order at least m.
4. The differential equation $\mathscr{L}u = g$ appears through the relations

$$a(u, v) = (\mathscr{L}u, v) + \text{boundary integral}, \qquad u \in \hat{V} \subset V, \quad v \in V,$$

$$G(v) = (g, v), \qquad\qquad\qquad v \in V,$$

so we have

$$a(u, v) - G(v) = (\mathscr{L}u - g, v) + \text{boundary integral,}$$

$$u \in \hat{V} \subset V, \qquad v \in V, \qquad (3.29)$$

where $\hat{V}$ is any subset of V for which $\mathscr{L}u$ has meaning. (The boundary integral arises when there is a natural boundary condition.) Assuming the coefficients of $\mathscr{L}$ are smooth enough to allow any required differentiation (for example, p in $\mathscr{L}u = -(pu')'$ should be differentiable), we can take $\hat{V} = V \cap C^{2m}(\bar{\Omega})$.

5. We have seen that if the bilinear form is symmetric, then it is an inner product on V. As in the example of Section 3.1, we call it the *energy inner product* and the corresponding norm the *energy norm*, writing

$$(u, v)_{\mathscr{L}} \equiv a(u, v), \qquad u, v \in V,$$

$$\|u\|_{\mathscr{L}} \equiv a(u, u)^{1/2}, \qquad u \in V.$$

Since in our applications of the lemma the norm $\|\cdot\|_V$ is the Sobolev norm $\|\cdot\|_m$, assumptions (3)′ and (4) become the assumption that the energy and Sobolev norms are equivalent over V:

$$\rho \|u\|_m^2 \leq \|u\|_{\mathscr{L}}^2 \leq \beta \|u\|_m^2, \qquad u \in V. \qquad (3.30)$$

6. The lemma asserts the existence of a unique function $\hat{u} \in V$ satisfying (3.26). We call $\hat{u}$ the *generalized solution* of the boundary value problem. If $\hat{u} \in \hat{V} = V \cap C^{2m}(\bar{\Omega})$, then $\hat{u}$ is a solution of the boundary value problem in the classical sense. If the problem has a classical solution, then this solution is $\hat{u}$ [since the boundary integral in (3.29) typically vanishes for any $u \in V$ satisfying the natural boundary conditions].

7. It can happen that the linear functional $G(\cdot)$ is not of the form $G(u) = (g, u)$, in which case the differential equation lacks a right-hand side in the conventional sense. This situation leads to so-called "symbolic functions," the most common example being the Dirac delta function. See Section 3.3 for further discussion.

8. One often sees the terms *self-adjoint* or *symmetric* applied to boundary value problems. This usually means that the bilinear form in the variational formulation of the problem is symmetric, implying that

$$(\mathscr{L}u, v) = (u, \mathscr{L}v) + \text{boundary integral} \qquad \forall u, v \in \hat{V} = V \cap C^{2m}(\bar{\Omega}).$$

Typically the boundary integral vanishes when u and v are restricted to the subset $\hat{W}$ of functions in $\hat{V}$ that satisfy the natural boundary conditions, so

$$(\mathscr{L}u, v) = (u, \mathscr{L}v) \qquad \forall u, v \in \hat{W}.$$

By virtue of this relation $\mathscr{L}$ is said to be a *self-adjoint* or *symmetric operator* on $\hat{W}$.

Regardless of whether $\mathscr{L}$ has this property, by repeated application of integration by parts we can usually find an operator $\mathscr{L}^*$ that satisfies the identity

$$(\mathscr{L}u, v) = (u, \mathscr{L}^*v) + \text{boundary integral} \qquad \forall u, v \in C^{2m}(\bar{\Omega}).$$

This operator is called the *formal adjoint* of $\mathscr{L}$. If the boundary conditions of the problem make the boundary integral vanish (or, more generally, if we make this integral vanish by associating a possibly new set of boundary conditions with $\mathscr{L}^*$), then $\mathscr{L}^*$ is called the *adjoint* of $\mathscr{L}$. Thus, as the name implies, a self-adjoint operator is identical to its adjoint.

9. For a generalization of the Lax–Milgram lemma with applications to more general boundary value problems, see Babuška and Aziz (1972) and Exercise 3.14.

Examples

We shall now apply the Lax–Milgram lemma to four boundary value problems, our main source being Ciarlet (1978). In the following Ω denotes some open subset of R^n and Γ its boundary. Some of the inequalities to be presented require Γ to have a certain degree of smoothness, and we henceforth assume that Γ is Lipschitz continuous. [See Ciarlet (1978) for a precise definition of this property; almost all common boundary shapes not having cusps are Lipschitz continuous.] When we speak of a subset Γ_0 of Γ it will be understood to be a nontrivial subset. In the case $n = 2$, for example, when Γ is a curve, it will be assumed that the length (or more technically, "measure") of Γ_0 is not zero. According to a remark at the beginning of Section 3.1, Γ_0 cannot then consist of only a finite or denumerably infinite set of points.

It will be apparent in all of the examples that $a(\cdot, \cdot)$ is a symmetric bilinear form. What has to be established are the inequalities

$$\rho\|u\|_V^2 \leq a(u, u) \leq \beta\|u\|_V^2, \qquad u \in V.$$

The proof of coerciveness (existence of ρ) requires in each case some analog of Theorem 3.2. We do not prove these basic theorems but refer the reader to Nečas (1967). The proof of boundedness (existence of β) is usually straightforward. (Example 3.2 is an exception in this regard.)

In all of the examples G is a linear functional of the form

$$G(u) = \int_\Omega gu \, d\Omega, \qquad u \in V \qquad [V \subseteq H^1(\Omega) \text{ or } H^2(\Omega)],$$

where $g \in L_2(\Omega)$, and we give the proof of boundedness here. Using the

Cauchy–Schwarz inequality for $L_2(\Omega)$, we can write

$$|G(u)| \leq \|g\| \|u\| \leq \|g\| \|u\|_m, \qquad u \in H^m(\Omega),$$

and assumption (6) is satisfied for $\delta = \|g\|$.

To derive the boundary value problem associated with each example, one must integrate $[a(u, v) - (g, v)]$ by parts and consider boundary conditions. Since this is the kind of analysis done extensively in Chapter 2, we omit the details here.

Example 3.1.

$$V = \{v \in H^1(\Omega); v = 0 \text{ on } \Gamma_0\}, \qquad \|\cdot\|_V = \|\cdot\|_1,$$

$$a(u, v) = \int_\Omega (\nabla u)^T (\nabla v) \, d\Omega, \qquad u, v \in V,$$

$$G(u) = \int_\Omega gu \, d\Omega, \qquad u \in V,$$

where $\Gamma_0 \subseteq \Gamma$ and $g \in L_2(\Omega)$.

We wish to show first that $a(\cdot, \cdot)$ is coercive, i.e., that there exists a positive constant ρ such that

$$\int_\Omega |\nabla u|^2 \, d\Omega \geq \rho \|u\|_1^2 = \rho \left\{ \int_\Omega u^2 \, d\Omega + \int_\Omega |\nabla u|^2 \, d\Omega \right\}, \qquad u \in V.$$

This follows trivially from *Friedrichs' first inequality*,

$$\int_\Omega |\nabla u|^2 \, d\Omega \geq \alpha \int_\Omega u^2 \, d\Omega, \qquad u \in V, \tag{3.31}$$

where α is a positive constant. (Here we are using the above assumption that Γ_0 is a nontrivial subset of Γ.) Then,

$$\int_\Omega |\nabla u|^2 \, d\Omega = \frac{1}{2} \int_\Omega |\nabla u|^2 \, d\Omega + \frac{1}{2} \int_\Omega |\nabla u|^2 \, d\Omega$$

$$\geq \frac{1}{2} \int_\Omega |\nabla u|^2 \, d\Omega + \frac{\alpha}{2} \int_\Omega u^2 \, d\Omega \geq \rho \|u\|_1^2, \qquad u \in V,$$

where $\rho = \min\{1/2, \alpha/2\}$.

To prove the boundedness of $a(\cdot, \cdot)$, we note that

$$a(u, u) = \int_\Omega |\nabla u|^2 \, d\Omega \leq \int_\Omega (|\nabla u|^2 + u^2) \, d\Omega = \|u\|_1^2$$

and the boundedness inequality $|a(u, u)| \leq \beta \|u\|_1^2$ is valid for $\beta = 1$.

The boundary value problem of this example is readily found to be

$$-\Delta u = g \qquad \text{in } \Omega,$$

$$u = 0 \qquad \text{on } \Gamma_0,$$

$$u_\nu = 0 \qquad \text{on } \Gamma - \Gamma_0 \qquad \text{(natural boundary condition)},$$

where

$$\Delta u = \sum_{i=1}^{n} \partial^2 u / \partial x_i^2.$$

Example 3.2.

$$V = H^1(\Omega), \qquad\qquad\qquad \|\cdot\|_V = \|\cdot\|_1,$$

$$a(u, v) = \int_\Omega (\nabla u)^{\mathrm{T}} (\nabla v)\, d\Omega + \int_\Gamma \sigma uv\, d\Gamma, \qquad u, v \in V,$$

$$G(u) = \int_\Omega gu\, d\Omega, \qquad\qquad\qquad u \in V,$$

where $\sigma \in C(\Gamma)$ and $g \in L_2(\Omega)$. We assume that $0 < \sigma_0 \le \sigma(\mathbf{x}) \le \sigma_1\ \forall \mathbf{x} \in \Gamma$.

Friedrichs' second inequality states that if Γ_0 is a nontrivial subset of Γ, then there is a positive constant α such that

$$\int_\Omega |\nabla u|^2\, d\Omega + \int_{\Gamma_0} u^2\, d\Gamma \ge \alpha \|u\|_1^2 \qquad \forall u \in H^1(\Omega). \tag{3.32}$$

[Nečas (1967, p. 20); note that (3.32) implies (3.31).] Since

$$a(u, u) = \int_\Omega |\nabla u|^2\, d\Omega + \int_\Gamma \sigma u^2\, d\Gamma \ge \gamma \left(\int_\Omega |\nabla u|^2\, d\Omega + \int_\Gamma u^2\, d\Gamma \right),$$

where $\gamma = \min(\sigma_0, 1)$, we can apply (3.32) with $\Gamma_0 = \Gamma$ to obtain the coerciveness result $a(u, u) \ge \rho \|u\|_1^2$, $u \in H^1(\Omega)$, where $\rho = \gamma\alpha$.

To establish the boundedness of $a(\cdot, \cdot)$, we note that

$$a(u, u) \le \int_\Omega |\nabla u|^2 + \sigma_1 \int_\Gamma u^2\, d\Gamma \le \|u\|_1^2 + \sigma_1 \int_\Gamma u^2\, d\Gamma.$$

The *trace inequality* (Nečas, 1967, p. 84) asserts the existence of a constant $\hat{\alpha}$ such that

$$\int_\Gamma u^2\, d\Gamma \le \hat{\alpha} \|u\|_1^2, \qquad u \in H^1(\Omega). \tag{3.33}$$

Hence $a(u, u) \le \beta \|u\|_1^2$, $u \in H^1(\Omega)$, where $\beta = 1 + \sigma_1 \hat{\alpha}$.

The boundary value problem is

$$-\Delta u = g \qquad \text{in } \Omega,$$

$$u_v + \sigma u = 0 \qquad \text{on } \Gamma \qquad \text{(natural boundary condition)}.$$

If $\sigma(\mathbf{x}) = 0$ everywhere on Γ (the Neumann boundary condition), then $a(\cdot, \cdot)$ is not coercive over $H^1(\Omega)$. To see this we need only consider the function $u(\mathbf{x}) \equiv 1$, for which $a(u, u) = 0$ and $\|u\|_1 > 0$. The boundary value problem now has a solution only if g satisfies the "consistency condition" $\int_\Omega g \, d\Omega = 0$ (why?) and a solution is unique only up to a constant term. (See Exercise 3.10.) The coerciveness inequality can be established over the subset

$$V = \left\{ v \in H^1(\Omega); \int_\Omega v \, d\Omega = 0 \right\}.$$

[See Nečas (1967), pp. 19, 43.]

Example 3.3.

$$V = \{ v \in H^1(\Omega); v = 0 \text{ on } \Gamma_0 \}, \qquad\qquad \|\cdot\|_V = \|\cdot\|_1,$$

$$a(u, v) = \int_\Omega \sum_{i,j=1}^n a_{ij} \frac{\partial u}{\partial x_i} \frac{\partial v}{\partial x_j} \, d\Omega + \int_\Omega cuv \, d\Omega, \qquad u, v \in V,$$

$$G(u) = \int_\Omega gu \, d\Omega, \qquad\qquad u \in V,$$

where $\Gamma_0 \subset \Gamma$, $g \in L_2(\Omega)$, $c \in C(\bar{\Omega})$ and $a_{ij} = a_{ji} \in C(\bar{\Omega})$ for $i, j = 1, 2, \ldots, n$. (Note that the assumption $a_{ij} = a_{ji}$ makes the bilinear form symmetric.) We assume further that $c(\mathbf{x}) \geq 0 \; \forall \mathbf{x} \in \bar{\Omega}$ and that there exists a positive constant λ such that

$$\sum_{i,j=1}^n a_{ij}(\mathbf{x})\zeta_i\zeta_j \geq \lambda \sum_{i=1}^n \zeta_i^2 \qquad \forall \mathbf{x} \in \bar{\Omega}, \qquad \forall \zeta_i \in R, \quad i = 1, 2, \ldots, n.$$

This is equivalent to the assumption that all of the eigenvalues of the symmetric matrix $[a_{ij}(\mathbf{x})]_{i,j=1}^n$ are positive and that the smallest of them is bounded uniformly (with respect to $\mathbf{x}$) away from zero. The continuity assumptions on c and a_{ij}, $i, j = 1, 2, \ldots, n$, imply that there exist constants c_1 and $\hat{\lambda}$ such that $|c(\mathbf{x})| \leq c_1 \; \forall \mathbf{x} \in \bar{\Omega}$ and

$$\sum_{i,j=1}^n a_{ij}(\mathbf{x})\zeta_i\zeta_i \leq \hat{\lambda} \sum_{i=1}^n \zeta_i^2 \qquad \forall \mathbf{x} \in \bar{\Omega}, \quad \forall \zeta_i \in R, \quad i = 1, 2, \ldots, n.$$

The bilinear form is coercive since

$$a(u, u) = \int_\Omega \left[\sum_{i,j=1}^n a_{ij} \frac{\partial u}{\partial x_i} \frac{\partial u}{\partial x_j} \right] d\Omega + \int_\Omega c u^2 \, d\Omega$$

$$\geq \lambda \int_\Omega \sum_{i=1}^n \left(\frac{\partial u}{\partial x_i} \right)^2 d\Omega \geq \lambda \rho \|u\|_1^2, \qquad u \in V,$$

where ρ is the coerciveness constant in Example 3.1. It is also bounded, since

$$a(u, u) \leq \hat{\lambda} \int_\Omega \sum_{i=1}^n \left(\frac{\partial u}{\partial x_i} \right)^2 d\Omega + c_1 \int_\Omega u^2 \, d\Omega \leq \beta \|u\|_1^2, \qquad u \in V,$$

where $\beta = \max\{\hat{\lambda}, c_1\}$.

The boundary value problem here is

$$\mathscr{L}u = g \qquad \text{in } \Omega,$$

$$u = 0 \qquad \text{on } \Gamma_0,$$

$$\partial u / \partial v_{\mathscr{L}} = 0 \qquad \text{on } \Gamma - \Gamma_0 \qquad \text{(natural boundary condition)},$$

where

$$\mathscr{L}u = - \sum_{i,j=1}^n \frac{\partial}{\partial x_i} \left(a_{ij} \frac{\partial u}{\partial x_j} \right) + cu,$$

and where $\partial u / \partial v_{\mathscr{L}}$ is the *conormal* derivative defined by

$$\frac{\partial u}{\partial v_{\mathscr{L}}} = \sum_{i,j=1}^n v_i a_{ij} \frac{\partial u}{\partial x_j}.$$

v_i denotes, as usual, the direction cosine with respect to the x_i axis of the outer normal to Γ. (See Exercise 3.11.)

Example 3.4.

$$V = \overset{\circ}{H}{}^2(\Omega), \qquad\qquad \|\cdot\|_V = \|\cdot\|_2,$$

$$a(u, v) = \int_\Omega \Delta u \, \Delta v \, d\Omega, \qquad u, v \in V,$$

$$G(u) = \int_\Omega g u \, d\Omega, \qquad u \in V,$$

where $\Omega \subset R^2$ and $g \in L_2(\Omega)$.

Using the identity

$$\int_\Omega u_{xx} u_{yy} \, d\Omega = \int_\Omega u_{xy}^2 \, d\Omega, \qquad u \in \overset{\circ}{H}{}^2(\Omega)$$

(Exercise 2.16), we can write

$$a(u, u) = \int_\Omega (u_{xx} + u_{yy})^2 \, d\Omega = \int_\Omega (u_{xx}^2 + 2u_{xy}^2 + u_{yy}^2) \, d\Omega \geq |u|_2^2,$$

where

$$|u|_2 = \left[\int_\Omega (u_{xx}^2 + u_{xy}^2 + u_{yy}^2) \, d\Omega \right]^{1/2}.$$

But a Friedrichs-type inequality for $\mathring{H}^2(\Omega)$ states that

$$|u|_2^2 \geq \alpha \|u\|_2^2, \qquad u \in \mathring{H}^2(\Omega).$$

[See Nečas (1967, p. 14 .] Thus $a(\cdot, \cdot)$ is coercive. It is also bounded:

$$a(u, u) = \int_\Omega (u_{xx}^2 + 2u_{xy}^2 + u_{yy}^2) \, d\Omega$$

$$\leq 2 \int_\Omega (u_{xx}^2 + u_{xy}^2 + u_{yy}^2) \, d\Omega \leq 2\|u\|_2^2, \qquad u \in \mathring{H}^2(\Omega).$$

The boundary value problem for this example is

$$\Delta^2 u = g \qquad \text{in } \Omega,$$

$$u = u_\nu = 0 \qquad \text{on } \Gamma.$$

Inhomogeneous Boundary Conditions

We shall discuss the treatment of inhomogeneous boundary conditions by means of an example. Consider the differential equation $\mathscr{L}u = g$ given by

$$-[p(x, y)u_x]_x - [p(x, y)u_y]_y + q(x, y)u = g(x, y), \qquad (x, y) \in \Omega \subset R^2, \quad (3.34)$$

where $p, q \in C(\bar{\Omega})$, $g \in L_2(\Omega)$, $0 < p_0 \leq p(x, y) \leq p_1$, $0 \leq q(x, y) \leq q_1$, together with the boundary condition

$$u = \gamma(x, y), \qquad (x, y) \in \Gamma. \qquad (3.35)$$

In the homogeneous case ($\gamma = 0$), we can apply the Lax–Milgram lemma immediately, taking

$$V = \mathring{H}^1(\Omega),$$

$$a(u, v) = \int\!\!\int_\Omega [pu_x v_x + pu_y v_y + quv] \, dx \, dy,$$

$$G(u) = \int\!\!\int_\Omega gu \, dx \, dy.$$

Now $\mathring{H}^1(\Omega)$ is the subset of functions in $H^1(\Omega)$ satisfying the homogeneous boundary condition on Γ. What we need in the inhomogeneous case is the subset

$$H^1_\gamma(\Omega) \equiv \{u \in H^1(\Omega); u = \gamma \text{ on } \Gamma\}.$$

Two delicate questions arise here. Given some $u \in H^1(\Omega)$, how do we define its restriction to Γ? Given some γ defined on Γ, is there a $u \in H^1(\Omega)$ such that the restriction of u to Γ is γ? The answer to the first question is obvious for any $u \in H^1(\Omega) \cap C(\bar{\Omega})$ but not otherwise. This aspect of Sobolev spaces involves the concept of *traces* and leads to trace inequalities, an example of which appears in Example 3.2. The answer to the second question turns out to be positive if and only if $\gamma \in H^{1/2}(\Gamma)$, a so-called *fractional* Sobolev space. See Adams (1975) for a discussion of these matters. It suffices for our purpose to state that $H^{1/2}(\Gamma)$ contains almost all boundary functions of physical interest.

The functional to be minimized in our example is

$$f(u) = \tfrac{1}{2}a(u, u) - G(u), \qquad u \in H^1_\gamma(\Omega).$$

Now the Lax–Milgram lemma is not immediately applicable, since $H^1_\gamma(\Omega)$ is not a linear space. However, for any fixed $u^* \in H^1_\gamma(\Omega)$ we can write

$$H^1_\gamma(\Omega) = \{u \in H^1(\Omega); u = v + u^*, v \in \mathring{H}^1(\Omega)\} \tag{3.36}$$

and define

$$
\begin{aligned}
f^*(v) &= f(v + u^*) - f(u^*) \\
&= \tfrac{1}{2}a(v + u^*, v + u^*) - G(v + u^*) - \tfrac{1}{2}a(u^*, u^*) + G(u^*) \\
&= \tfrac{1}{2}a(v, v) - G^*(v), \qquad v \in \mathring{H}^1(\Omega),
\end{aligned}
$$

where

$$G^*(v) = G(v) - a(u^*, v).$$

We can now apply the Lax–Milgram lemma, taking the Hilbert space, bilinear form, and linear functional to be $\mathring{H}^1(\Omega)$, $a(\cdot, \cdot)$, and $G^*(\cdot)$, respectively. We leave it to the reader to verify that the assumptions of the lemma are satisfied. The lemma states that there exists a unique $\hat{v} \in \mathring{H}^1(\Omega)$ such that

$$a(\hat{v}, v) = G^*(v) \qquad \forall v \in \mathring{H}^1(\Omega),$$

and hence

$$a(\hat{v} + u^*, v) = G(v) \qquad \forall v \in \mathring{H}^1(\Omega). \tag{3.37}$$

It then follows from (3.36) that there exists a unique $\hat{u} \in H^1_\gamma(\Omega)$, namely, $\hat{u} \equiv \hat{v} + u^*$, such that

$$a(\hat{u}, v) = G(v) \qquad \forall v \in \mathring{H}^1(\Omega). \tag{3.38}$$

The function $\hat{v}$ minimizes f^* over $\mathring{H}^1(\Omega)$, and clearly

$$\min_{u \in H^1_\gamma(\Omega)} f(u) = f(\hat{u}).$$

The formal identity

$$a(u, v) - G(v) = (\mathscr{L}u - g, v), \qquad v \in \mathring{H}^1(\Omega)$$

together with (3.38) and the property $\hat{u} = \gamma$ on Γ imply that $\hat{u}$ is the generalized solution of the boundary value problem (3.34), (3.35).

There is an alternative inhomogeneous boundary condition that can be associated with (3.34), namely,

$$u_\nu + \sigma(x, y)u = \xi(x, y), \qquad (x, y) \in \Gamma, \tag{3.39}$$

where we shall assume that $\sigma \in C(\Gamma)$, $\xi \in L_2(\Gamma)$, and $0 < \sigma_0 \leq \sigma(x, y) \leq \sigma_1$. [Boundary conditions (3.35) and (3.39) can of course be mixed in the sense that each applies to a different part of Γ.] For the sake of comparison and future reference we shall briefly consider (3.39), illustrating at the same time how one proceeds from the boundary value problem to the variational formulation; we have hitherto always taken the opposite direction.

Formal integration by parts yields the identity

$$(\mathscr{L}u - g, v) = a(u, v) - G(v) - \int_\Gamma pu_\nu v \, ds, \tag{3.40}$$

where $a(\cdot, \cdot)$ and $G(\cdot)$ are the same as before. Incorporating the boundary condition (3.39) in the boundary integral, we obtain

$$(\mathscr{L}u - g, v) = \tilde{a}(u, v) - \tilde{G}(v),$$

where we have introduced

$$\tilde{a}(u, v) \equiv a(u, v) + \int_\Gamma p\sigma uv \, ds, \qquad u, v \in H^1(\Omega),$$
$$\tilde{G}(v) \equiv G(v) + \int_\Gamma p\xi v \, ds, \qquad v \in H^1(\Omega). \tag{3.41}$$

Note that we have defined $\tilde{a}(\cdot, \cdot)$ and $\tilde{G}(\cdot)$ for all functions in $H^1(\Omega)$, not just for those satisfying boundary condition (3.39).

We now apply the Lax–Milgram lemma to (3.41). The assumptions of the lemma are satisfied (Exercise 3.15), and hence there exists a unique $\hat{u} \in H^1(\Omega)$ such that

$$\tilde{a}(\hat{u}, v) = \tilde{G}(v) \qquad \forall v \in H^1(\Omega). \tag{3.42}$$

Since (3.40) and (3.41) give us the formal identity

$$\tilde{a}(u, v) - \tilde{G}(v) = (\mathscr{L}u - g, v) + \int_\Gamma p(u_\nu + \sigma u - \xi)v \, ds,$$

we deduce from (3.42) that $\hat{u}$ is the generalized solution of the boundary value problem (3.34), (3.39).

Note the difference in the effect of the functions γ and ξ in boundary conditions (3.35) and (3.39). When $\gamma \neq 0$ the set of admissible functions is no longer a linear space. When $\xi \neq 0$ a term is added to $G(\cdot)$.

3.3   Regularity, Symbolic Functions, and Green's Functions

Regularity

As will be seen in Chapter 5, the error estimates for a finite element approximation to the solution $\hat{u}$ of a boundary value problem assume some degree of regularity (or smoothness) of $\hat{u}$. The appropriate measure of regularity for the purpose of these estimates is the largest integer p such that $\hat{u} \in H^p(\Omega)$. When the conditions of the Lax–Milgram lemma are satisfied, then obviously $p \geq m$, where $2m$ is the order of the boundary value problem. Unfortunately, this is the only information on p the lemma can provide, and it is insufficient in as much as the error estimates usually require $p > m$.

The value of p depends on the various data of the problem: the coefficient functions appearing in $\mathcal{L}$, the function g on the right-hand side of the equation, the boundary Γ, and the functions defined on Γ in the boundary conditions. The determination of p is one of the fundamental topics of the theory of differential equations and lies for the most part beyond the scope of this book. (See, however, Section 5.6.) The interested reader is referred to the texts in the list of references.

Symbolic Functions

We have seen in the proof of the Lax–Milgram lemma that the lemma defines a one-to-one correspondence between the Hilbert space V and the set of bounded linear functionals defined on V. We denote this set by V^*. It becomes a normed linear space when for any $\alpha, \beta \in R$ and $G, H \in V^*$ we define $(\alpha G + \beta H) \in V^*$ by

$$(\alpha G + \beta H)(u) = \alpha G(u) + \beta H(u), \qquad u \in V$$

and introduce the norm

$$\|G\|_{V^*} = \sup_{u \in V} \frac{|G(u)|}{\|u\|_V}, \qquad G \in V^*;$$

V^* is commonly called the *dual space* of V.

Let now $V = \overset{\circ}{H}{}^1(-1, 1)$, the space of functions u that are continuous and possess a generalized derivative of order 1 and that satisfy the boundary conditions $u(-1) = u(1) = 0$. For any $g \in L_2[-1, 1]$ let

$$G(u) = \int_{-1}^{1} gu\, dx, \qquad u \in \overset{\circ}{H}{}^1(-1, 1). \qquad (3.43)$$

G is obviously a linear functional on $\overset{\circ}{H}{}^1(-1, 1)$. Moreover, it is bounded since by the Cauchy–Schwarz inequality,

$$|G(u)| \le \left[\int_{-1}^{1} g^2\, dx\right]^{1/2} \left[\int_{-1}^{1} u^2\, dx\right]^{1/2}$$

$$\le \left[\int_{-1}^{1} g^2\, dx\right]^{1/2} \|u\|_1, \qquad u \in \overset{\circ}{H}{}^1(-1, 1).$$

Thus $G \in V^*$, the dual space of $V = \overset{\circ}{H}{}^1(-1, 1)$.

An interesting and important fact is that not every $G \in V^*$ is of type (3.43). Consider, for example, the functional G_δ defined by

$$G_\delta(u) = u(0), \qquad u \in \overset{\circ}{H}{}^1(-1, 1).$$

G_δ is obviously linear. It is also bounded, since

$$|u(x)| = \left|\int_{-1}^{x} u'(t)\, dt\right| \le \left[\int_{-1}^{x} 1^2\, dt\right]^{1/2} \left[\int_{-1}^{x} [u'(t)]^2\, dt\right]^{1/2}$$

$$\le \sqrt{2}\left[\int_{-1}^{1} [u'(t)]^2\, dt\right]^{1/2} \le \sqrt{2}\|u\|_1$$

for any $x \in [-1, 1]$, and in particular for $x = 0$. Thus $G_\delta \in V^*$. (As we shall see shortly, this property fails to hold if the number of space dimensions exceeds one.)

Now suppose that for some $g \in L_2[-1, 1]$ it were true that

$$u(0) = \int_{-1}^{1} gu\, dx \qquad \forall u \in \overset{\circ}{H}{}^1(-1, 1). \qquad (3.44)$$

Then we would have

$$\int_{-1}^{1} gu\, dx = 0 \qquad \forall u \in \tilde{V} \equiv \{v \in \overset{\circ}{H}{}^1(-1, 1); v(0) = 0\}. \qquad (3.45)$$

But it can be shown that $\tilde{V}$ is so "rich" in functions that (3.45) implies $g = 0$, and hence (3.44) is false for every $u \in \mathring{H}^1(-1, 1) - \tilde{V}$. In other words, G_δ is not of type (3.43).

On the other hand, for any $u \in V$ we can easily approximate $G_\delta(u)$ by some $G(u)$ of type (3.43). To this end consider the functional G_{δ_ε} defined by

$$G_{\delta_\varepsilon}(u) = \int_{-1}^{1} \delta_\varepsilon(x)u(x)\, dx, \qquad u \in \mathring{H}^1(-1, 1),$$

where

$$\delta_\varepsilon(x) = \begin{cases} (1/\varepsilon)[1 - (|x|/\varepsilon)] & \text{for } |x| < \varepsilon, \\ 0 & \text{for } \varepsilon \le |x| \le 1, \end{cases} \qquad (3.46)$$

for any $0 < \varepsilon \le 1$. (See Fig. 3.2.) It is readily verified that $\delta_\varepsilon(x)$ has the following properties:

$$\int_{-1}^{x} \delta_\varepsilon(t)\, dt = \begin{cases} 0 & \text{for } x \le -\varepsilon, \\ 1 & \text{for } x \ge \varepsilon, \end{cases}$$

$$\lim_{\varepsilon \to 0} \int_{-1}^{1} \delta_\varepsilon(x)u(x)\, dx = u(0), \qquad u \in \mathring{H}^1(-1, 1).$$

The second property establishes that, given any $u \in \mathring{H}^1(-1, 1)$, we can approximate $G_\delta(u)$ as closely as we please by $G_{\delta_\varepsilon}(u)$ if we choose ε sufficiently small.

Now, since $\lim_{\varepsilon \to 0} \delta_\varepsilon(0) = \infty$, there is no classical function $\delta(x)$ with the property $\lim_{\varepsilon \to 0} \delta_\varepsilon(x) = \delta(x)$, $-1 \le x \le 1$. Further, the sequence $u_n(x) = \delta_\varepsilon(x)$, where $\varepsilon = 1/n$ for $n = 1, 2, 3, \ldots$, belongs to $L_2[-1, 1]$ but is not a Cauchy sequence in $L_2[-1, 1]$ since, as a simple calculation shows, $\lim_{n \to \infty} \|u_n - u_{2n}\| = \infty$. Hence there is no $\delta \in L_2[-1, 1]$ satisfying $\lim_{n \to \infty} \|\delta - u_n\| = 0$.

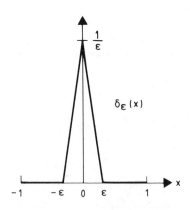

Fig. 3.2.   The function $\delta_\varepsilon(x)$.

Despite these failures to define a limit for $\delta_\varepsilon(x)$ as $\varepsilon \to 0$ [which reflect the fact that G_δ is not of type (3.43)], there is a tradition for introducing a "symbolic function" $\delta(x)$, the so-called *Dirac delta function*, with the "properties"

$$\delta(x) = 0, \qquad |x| > 0, \tag{3.47a}$$

$$\int_{-1}^{x} \delta(t)\,dt = \begin{cases} 0 & \text{for} \quad x < 0, \\ 1 & \text{for} \quad x > 0, \end{cases} \tag{3.47b}$$

$$\int_{-1}^{1} \delta(x)u(x)\,dx = u(0). \tag{3.47c}$$

Even though the delta function makes no immediate sense, it often provides a convenient shorthand for analysis. In the context of problems arising in science and engineering, $\delta(x)$ describes some kind of physical idealization. In structural mechanics, for example, it can denote a unit load concentrated at the single point $x = 0$. (More generally, $\delta(x - x_0)$ can describe a unit load at $x = x_0$.)

We now introduce the *Heaviside unit step function*

$$H(x) = \begin{cases} 0 & \text{for} \quad x < 0, \\ \alpha & \text{for} \quad x = 0, \\ 1 & \text{for} \quad x > 0, \end{cases} \tag{3.48}$$

where α is arbitrary. Considered as an element in $L_2(-1, 1)$, H is independent of α. Property (3.47b) motivates our writing $\int_{-1}^{x} \delta(t)\,dt = H(x)$ and hence

$$\delta(x) = H'(x). \tag{3.49}$$

Now, since H is not differentiable at $x = 0$ and δ lacks a rigorous definition, (3.49) is without meaning. We can replace it, however, by a valid mathematical statement based on the concept of a derivative of a functional. Thus let $G_1, G_2 \in \mathring{H}^1(-1, 1)^*$ be two functionals satisfying the relation

$$G_1(u') = -G_2(u) \qquad \forall u \in \mathring{H}^1(-1, 1). \tag{3.50}$$

Then we say that G_2 is the *derivative* of G_1 and write

$$G_2 = G_1'.$$

This definition is inspired by the fact that if G_1 and G_2 are of the form

$$G_1(u) = \int_{-1}^{1} g_1 u\,dx, \qquad u \in \mathring{H}^1(-1, 1),$$

$$G_2(u) = \int_{-1}^{1} g_2 u\,dx, \qquad u \in \mathring{H}^1(-1, 1),$$

where $g_2 = g_1'$, then (3.50) is valid and expresses integration by parts. [Note the importance of the boundary values $u(-1) = u(1) = 0$.]

Let

$$G_H(u) = \int_{-1}^{1} Hu \, dx, \qquad u \in \mathring{H}^1(-1, 1).$$

A simple calculation establishes that

$$G_H(u') = -G_\delta(u) \qquad \forall u \in \mathring{H}^1(a, b).$$

Hence by the definition of the derivative of a functional,

$$G_\delta = G_H', \tag{3.51}$$

which, in contrast to (3.49), is a mathematically rigorous statement.

If we replace $\mathring{H}^1(-1, 1)$ by the smoother space $\mathring{H}^k(-1, 1)$, $k > 1$, then we can differentiate G_δ. Thus consider the functionals $G_{\delta^{(i)}} \in \mathring{H}^k(-1, 1)^*$ defined by

$$G_{\delta^{(i)}}(u) = (-1)^i u^{(i)}(0), \qquad u \in \mathring{H}^k(-1, 1), \quad i = 0, 1, \ldots, k - 1.$$

Obviously $G_{\delta^{(0)}}(u) = G_\delta(u)$ and $G_{\delta^{(i)}}(u') = -G_{\delta^{(i+1)}}(u)$. Hence

$$G_{\delta^{(i+1)}} = G_{\delta^{(i)}}', \qquad i = 0, 1, \ldots, k - 2, \tag{3.52}$$

and the functional G_δ is $k - 1$ times differentiable.

One can verify that

$$\lim_{\varepsilon \to 0} \int_{-1}^{1} \delta_\varepsilon^{(i)}(x) u(x) \, dx = G_{\delta^{(i)}}(u), \qquad u \in \mathring{H}^k(-1, 1), \quad i = 0, 1, \ldots, k - 1,$$

where

$$\delta_\varepsilon(x) = \begin{cases} C_\varepsilon \exp[-\varepsilon^2/(\varepsilon^2 - x^2)] & \text{for } |x| < \varepsilon, \\ 0 & \text{for } |x| \geq \varepsilon, \end{cases} \tag{3.53}$$

the constant C_ε being chosen to make $\int_{-1}^{1} \delta_\varepsilon(x) \, dx = 1$. [The reason for replacing (3.46) by (3.53) is that the latter has continuous derivatives of all orders.] Letting $\varepsilon \to 0$, we associate with the functional $G_{\delta^{(i)}}$ a symbolic function $\delta^{(i)}(x)$ "satisfying"

$$\int_{-1}^{1} \delta^{(i)}(x) u(x) \, dx = G_{\delta^{(i)}}(u), \qquad u \in \mathring{H}^k(-1, 1);$$

(3.52) then suggests the relation

$$\delta^{(i+1)}(x) = \frac{d}{dx} \delta^{(i)}(x),$$

analogous to (3.49).

The foregoing discussion is intimately related to the theory of distributions. [See Schwartz (1966) and Stakgold (1979).]

An Application of Symbolic Functions

We shall illustrate the use of symbolic functions in connection with Example 2.5. A loaded, uniform, linearly elastic beam of unit length, clamped at both ends, satisfies the boundary value problem

$$\alpha u^{iv} = g(x), \qquad 0 < x < 1, \tag{3.54a}$$

$$u(0) = u'(0) = u(1) = u'(1) = 0, \tag{3.54b}$$

where α is a material constant and $g(x)$ the load density. We consider the case where $g(x)$ consists of a continuous load density $h(x)$ per unit length, a point load F_i at $x = x_i \in (0, 1)$, and a point moment m_j at $x = x_j \in (0, 1)$. This physically idealized load function is modeled by

$$g(x) = -h(x) - F_i\,\delta(x - x_i) + m_j\,\delta'(x - x_j). \tag{3.55}$$

By formal integration we obtain

$$\alpha u'''(x) = c_1(x) - F_i H(x - x_i) + m_j \delta(x - x_j), \qquad c_1 \in C[0, 1],$$

$$\alpha u''(x) = c_2(x) + m_j H(x - x_j), \qquad c_2 \in C[0, 1],$$

so u'' has a step discontinuity at x_j. Continuing, we see that $u \in C^1[0, 1]$.

Consider now the variational formulation of this problem in terms of the Lax–Milgram lemma. We have

$$V = \overset{\circ}{H}{}^2(0, 1),$$

$$a(u, v) = \alpha \int_0^1 u''v''\, dx,$$

$$G(u) = \int_0^1 g(x)u(x)\, dx$$

$$= -\int_0^1 h(x)u(x)\, dx - F_i \int_0^1 \delta(x - x_i)u(x)\, dx$$

$$+ m_j \int_0^1 \delta'(x - x_j)u(x)\, dx$$

$$= -\int_0^1 h(x)u(x)\, dx - F_i u(x_i) - m_j u'(x_j).$$

Note that the symbolic functions have disappeared and G is a perfectly well-defined linear functional on $\overset{\circ}{H}{}^2(0, 1)$. Further,

$$\left| \int_0^1 hu \, dx \right| \le \|h\| \|u\| \le \|h\| \|u\|_2,$$

$$|F_i u(x_i)| \le |F_i| \|u'\| \le |F_i| \|u\|_2$$

(see the proof of boundedness of G_δ), and similarly,

$$|m_j u'(x_j)| \le |m_j| \|u''\| \le |m_j| \|u\|_2.$$

Hence $|G(u)| \le \rho \|u\|_2 \ \forall u \in \overset{\circ}{H}{}^2(0, 1)$, where $\rho = \|h\| + |F_i| + |m_j|$ and G is bounded.

The bilinear form is bounded and coercive (the Friedrichs inequality in Example 3.4 establishes coerciveness), and according to the lemma there exists a unique $\hat{u} \in \overset{\circ}{H}{}^2(0, 1)$ such that

$$\int_0^1 \hat{u}'' u'' \, dx = - \int_0^1 hu \, dx - F_i u(x_i) - m_j u'(x_j) \qquad \forall u \in \overset{\circ}{H}{}^2(0, 1).$$

$\hat{u}$ is the generalized solution of boundary value problem (3.54). Further, the heuristic smoothness argument above indicates that $\hat{u} \in C^1[0, 1]$ with $\hat{u}''(x)$ having a step discontinuity at $x = x_j$. Such a function belongs to $H^2(0, 1)$ but not to $H^3(0, 1)$. The regularity parameter p defined at the beginning of this section is therefore $p = m = 2$, the minimum value.

If g in (3.55) is replaced by a smoother function, then the value of p increases. If the term $m_j \delta'(x - x_j)$ is removed, for example, then $p = 3$.

Green's Functions

Closely related to the concept of the delta function is that of the Green's function. Since the Green's function will be useful in Section 5.4 in connection with the error analysis of the finite element method, we shall now give a brief description of it. For literature on the subject see, e.g., Roach (1970) and Stakgold (1979).

In the Lax–Milgram lemma let

$$V = \overset{\circ}{H}{}^1(-1, 1),$$

$$a(u, v) = \int_{-1}^1 [p(x)u'v' + q(x)uv] \, dx, \qquad u, v \in \overset{\circ}{H}{}^1(-1, 1),$$

$$G(u) = u(\xi), \qquad\qquad u \in \overset{\circ}{H}{}^1(-1, 1),$$

where p and q satisfy the conditions stated under (3.9) and ξ is a fixed value in the interval $[-1, 1]$. We observe that G is the bounded linear functional on $\mathring{H}^1(-1, 1)$ that corresponds to the delta function

$$\delta(x - \xi), \qquad -1 \le x \le 1.$$

According to the lemma there exists a function in $\mathring{H}^1(-1, 1)$, which we denote by $K(x, \xi)$, such that

$$a[K(\cdot, \xi), u(\cdot)] = u(\xi) \qquad \forall u \in \mathring{H}^1(-1, 1). \tag{3.56}$$

[The notation $K(\cdot, \xi)$ indicates that the integration in the bilinear form is with respect to x.] We call $K(x, \xi)$ a *Green's function*. In the light of our earlier discussion of symbolic functions, we see that (3.56) is equivalent to the statement that $K(x, \xi)$ satisfies the boundary value problem

$$\begin{aligned}
\mathscr{L} K(x, \xi) &= \delta(x - \xi), \qquad -1 < x < 1, \\
K(-1, \xi) &= K(1, \xi) = 0,
\end{aligned} \tag{3.57}$$

where the operator $\mathscr{L}$ is formally defined by

$$\mathscr{L} u = -(pu')' + qu.$$

In addition to being the generalized solution of (3.57), the Green's function has the following properties:

$$K(x, \xi) \quad \text{is continuous for} \quad -1 \le x, \xi \le 1, \tag{3.58a}$$

$$K(x, \xi) = K(\xi, x), \qquad -1 \le x, \xi \le 1, \tag{3.58b}$$

$$\lim_{\xi \to x, \xi < x} \frac{\partial K}{\partial \xi}(x, \xi) - \lim_{\xi \to x, \xi > x} \frac{\partial K}{\partial \xi}(x, \xi) = 1. \tag{3.58c}$$

The importance of the Green's function is mainly due to the fact that it leads to an explicit formula for the (generalized) solution $\hat{u}$ of the boundary value problem

$$\begin{aligned}
\mathscr{L} u &= g, \qquad -1 < x < 1, \\
u(-1) &= u(1) = 0,
\end{aligned}$$

where g is an arbitrary function in $L_2[-1, 1]$. The formula is easily derived as follows:

$$\begin{aligned}
\hat{u}(\xi) &= a[K(\cdot, \xi), \hat{u}(\cdot)] = a[\hat{u}(\cdot), K(\cdot, \xi)] \\
&= ((\mathscr{L}\hat{u})(\cdot), K(\cdot, \xi)) = \int_{-1}^{1} K(x, \xi) g(x) \, dx,
\end{aligned}$$

and hence by (3.58b) and a switch of variables,

$$\hat{u}(x) = \int_{-1}^{1} K(x, \xi) g(\xi) \, d\xi. \tag{3.59}$$

Unfortunately, the Green's function can only rarely be obtained analytically. An exceptional case occurs when the coefficients in the operator are constant. If, for example, $p(x) = 1$ and $q(x) = 0$ for $-1 \leq x \leq 1$, then

$$K(x, \xi) = \begin{cases} \frac{1}{2}(1 - x)(1 + \xi) & \text{for} \quad -1 \leq \xi \leq x, \\ \frac{1}{2}(1 + x)(1 - \xi) & \text{for} \quad x \leq \xi \leq 1. \end{cases} \tag{3.60}$$

(See Exercise 3.18.)

Equation (3.59) leads to a bound on the *maximum norm* of $\hat{u}$ defined by

$$\|\hat{u}\|_{\infty} = \max_{-1 \leq x \leq 1} |\hat{u}(x)|.$$

To obtain this bound, we observe that the Cauchy–Schwarz inequality applied to (3.59) yields

$$|\hat{u}(x)| \leq \| K(x, \cdot) \| \, \| g \|,$$

so that

$$\|\hat{u}\|_{\infty} \leq M_1 \| g \| \qquad \forall g \in L_2[-1, 1],$$

where $M_1 = \max_{-1 \leq x \leq 1} \| K(x, \cdot) \|$. This should be compared with the bound that can be derived from condition (4) of the Lax–Milgram lemma (which is, of course, satisfied by the bilinear form of the present problem). Thus,

$$\rho \| \hat{u} \|_1^2 \leq a(\hat{u}, \hat{u}) = (\mathscr{L}\hat{u}, \hat{u}) = (g, \hat{u}) \leq \| g \| \, \| \hat{u} \| \leq \| g \| \, \| \hat{u} \|_1,$$

so that

$$\| \hat{u} \|_1 \leq M_2 \| g \| \qquad \forall g \in L_2[-1, 1],$$

where $M_2 = \rho^{-1}$.

The usefulness of the Green's function in Section 5.4 will be in connection with an investigation of the maximum norm of the error incurred in the finite element method.

We now consider second-order boundary value problems in n space variables, where $n > 1$. A major obstacle arises here since the functional

$$G(u) = u(\xi), \qquad u \in H^1(\Omega), \tag{3.61}$$

where ξ is a fixed point in Ω, is not bounded. To prove boundedness we would have to demonstrate the existence of a positive constant M such that

$$|u(\xi)| \leq M \| u \|_1 \qquad \forall u \in H^1(\Omega).$$

This is impossible since there are in fact functions in $H^1(\Omega)$ that are singular at ξ. For example, if

$$\Omega = \{\mathbf{x} \in R^2; \|\mathbf{x}\| < \tfrac{1}{2}\}, \qquad \xi = \mathbf{0},$$

then such a function is (Strang and Fix, 1973)

$$u(\mathbf{x}) = \ln[\ln(\|\mathbf{x}\|^{-1})]. \tag{3.62}$$

This state of affairs is consistent with the Sobolev embedding theorem in Section 3.1, according to which

$$H^1(\Omega) \not\subset C(\bar{\Omega}), \qquad n \geq 2.$$

It follows from the unboundedness of (3.61) that we cannot use our variational formulation of a boundary value problem to determine the corresponding Green's function as we could in the case of one space dimension. Nevertheless, it turns out that there still exists a Green's function, i.e., a function $K(\mathbf{x}, \xi)$, $\mathbf{x}, \xi \in \bar{\Omega}$, such that

$$\hat{u}(\mathbf{x}) = \int_\Omega K(\mathbf{x}, \xi) g(\xi) \, d\xi, \qquad g \in L_2(\Omega).$$

Further, it typically has the singular form

$$K(\mathbf{x}, \xi) = \begin{cases} \ln(\|\mathbf{x} - \xi\|) \cdot \tilde{K}(\mathbf{x}, \xi) & \text{for } n = 2 \\ \|\mathbf{x} - \xi\|^{2-n} \cdot \tilde{K}(\mathbf{x}, \xi) & \text{for } n \geq 3, \end{cases} \tag{3.63}$$

where $\tilde{K}(\mathbf{x}, \xi)$ is smooth and satisfies the boundary conditions (which we assume to be homogeneous).

An analysis of these functions is beyond the scope of this book. For further reading see the texts mentioned previously.

Exercises

3.1. Show that the norm property (3.5b) implies the inequality $\left| \|u\| - \|v\| \right| \leq \|u - v\|$.

3.2.

(i) Derive the Cauchy–Schwarz inequality (3.6).

HINT: Property (3.4c) implies $(\xi u + v, \xi u + v) \geq 0 \ \forall \xi \in R$.

(ii) Establish (3.5b) using the Cauchy–Schwarz inequality.

(iii)   Let

$$[u, v]_k = \int_a^b u^{(k)} v^{(k)} \, dx, \qquad u, v \in V,$$

$$|u|_k = \sqrt{[u, u]_k}, \qquad u \in V,$$

where V is either $C^k[a, b]$ or the Sobolev space $H^k(a, b)$.

Which of the four properties required of an inner product in (3.4) is not satisfied by $[\cdot, \cdot]_k$? Extend your analysis in (i) and (ii) to show that

$$\big|[u, v]_k\big| \le |u|_k |v|_k, \qquad u, v \in V,$$

$$|u + v|_k \le |u|_k + |v|_k, \qquad u, v \in V.$$

Which of the four properties required of a norm in (3.5) is not satisfied by $|\cdot|_k$? $[\cdot, \cdot]_k$ and $|\cdot|_k$ are the Sobolev semi-inner product and seminorm, respectively.

3.3   In Section 3.1 the linear space V defined in (3.9) was expanded to a larger space $\overline{V}$. Prove, by carrying out the following steps, that $\overline{V}$ is complete in the energy norm $\|\cdot\|_{\mathscr{L}}$.

(i)   Let $\{u_n\}_{n=1}^\infty$ be any sequence in $\overline{V}$, and let $\{\varepsilon_n\}_{n=1}^\infty$ be any sequence of positive real numbers. Justify the assertion that there exists a sequence $\{v_n\}_{n=1}^\infty$ in V such that $\|u_n - v_n\|_{\mathscr{L}} \le \varepsilon_n$ for $n = 1, 2, \dots$.

(ii)   Assume that the sequence $\{u_n\}_{n=1}^\infty$ in (i) has the property that $\lim_{m,n \to \infty} \|u_m - u_n\|_{\mathscr{L}} = 0$, and let $\{\varepsilon_n\}_{n=1}^\infty$ be chosen so that $\lim_{n \to \infty} \varepsilon_n = 0$. Use the results of (i) to show that $\lim_{m,n \to \infty} \|v_m - v_n\|_{\mathscr{L}} = 0$.

HINT: $v_m - v_n = (v_m - u_m) + (u_m - u_n) + (u_n - v_n)$.

(iii)   Justify the assertion that there exists $u \in \overline{V}$ such that $\lim_{n \to \infty} \|u - u_n\|_{\mathscr{L}} = 0$.

3.4.   Consider the operator $\mathscr{L}$ defined by

$$\mathscr{L}u = -u'', \qquad u \in V,$$

$$V = \{u \in C^2[a, b]; u(a) = u'(b) = 0\},$$

and let $\overline{V}$ denote the completion of V in the energy norm. It can be shown that every $u \in \overline{V}$ is continuous and satisfies the boundary condition $u(a) = 0$. By considering (3.15b) show that not every $u \in \overline{V}$ satisfies the second boundary condition $u'(b) = 0$.

3.5   Show that $\lim_{n \to \infty} \|u_n''\| = \infty$, where $\{u_n\}_{n=1}^\infty$ is given by (3.15a), and use Exercise 3.1 to deduce that there is no $v \in L_2[a, b]$ such that $\lim_{n \to \infty} \|v - u_n''\| = 0$. The function (3.16a) does not have a second-order generalized derivative.

3.6.   Let $\mathscr{L}$ be the linear differential operator defined by

$$\mathscr{L}u = \sum_{i=0}^m (-1)^i \big[p_i(x) u^{(i)}\big]^{(i)}, \qquad u \in V,$$

$$V = \{u \in C^{2m}[a, b]; u^{(i)}(a) = u^{(i)}(b) = 0, i = 0, 1, \dots, m - 1\},$$

where $p_i \in C^i[a, b]$.

(i)   What is the associated energy inner product $(\cdot, \cdot)_{\mathscr{L}}$?

(ii)   Assuming that $p_m(x) > 0$ and $p_i(x) \geq 0$ for $a \leq x \leq b$, where $i = 0, 1, ..., m - 1$, show that the energy norm $\|\cdot\|_{\mathscr{E}}$ and the Sobolev norm $\|\cdot\|_m$ are equivalent over V.

HINT: Note that u in Theorem 3.2 can be replaced by $u^{(i)}$, $i = 1, 2, ..., m - 1$.
The completion of V with respect to the Sobolev norm is the Sobolev space $\mathring{H}^{(m)}(a, b)$.

3.7. Verify that the Sobolev seminorm $|u|_1$ [see (3.25)] is a norm on $\mathring{H}^1(\Omega)$.

HINT: Friedrichs' first inequality (3.31) is useful.

3.8 Show in the proof of the Lax–Milgram lemma that V is complete in the norm $\sqrt{a(u, u)}$.

3.9. It is instructive to consider the Lax–Milgram lemma in the finite-dimensional case

$$V = R^N, \qquad a(\mathbf{u}, \mathbf{v}) = \mathbf{u}^T A \mathbf{v}, \qquad G(\mathbf{u}) = \mathbf{g}^T \mathbf{u},$$

where $\|\cdot\|_V$ is the usual Euclidean vector norm, A is an $(N \times N)$ real matrix, and $\mathbf{g}$ is an $(N \times 1)$ real vector.

(i)   Without assuming that the bilinear form is symmetric, prove (3.26) by a simple argument from linear algebra.
(ii)   Show that the assumption of coerciveness is by no means necessary for (3.26) to hold.

3.10. We consider the boundary value problem

$$-\Delta u = g, \quad (x, y) \in \Omega; \qquad u_\nu = \xi, \quad (x, y) \in \Gamma.$$

(i)   What are the appropriate choices of a Hilbert space V, a bilinear form $a(\cdot, \cdot)$, and a linear functional $G(\cdot)$ for the variational formulation of this problem?
(ii)   Show that a solution exists only if

$$\iint_\Omega g \, dx \, dy = - \int_\Gamma \xi \, ds,$$

and that if u is a solution then so is $u + c$, where c is an arbitrary constant.

3.11. Derive the boundary value problem associated with the functional f in Example 3.3.

3.12. The functional

$$f(u) = \int_\Omega \left[\tfrac{1}{2}(\Delta u)^2 - gu \right] d\Omega, \qquad u \in \mathring{H}^2(\Omega)$$

attains its minimum at $u = \hat{u}$, where

$$\Delta^2 \hat{u} = g \qquad \text{in } \Omega,$$
$$\hat{u} = \hat{u}_\nu = 0 \qquad \text{on } \Gamma.$$

(See Example 3.4.) The Ritz–Galerkin method (Chapter 4) produces an approximation $\hat{v} \simeq \hat{u}$ with the property that $f(\hat{v}) \geq f(\hat{u})$. The purpose of this exercise is to show how a *lower* bound of $f(\hat{u})$ may be obtained.

Thus, let $\hat{w} \in H^1(\Omega)$ be a solution of Poisson's equation $\Delta w = g$. Show that

(i) $$\int_\Omega gu \, d\Omega = \int_\Omega \hat{w}\Delta u \, d\Omega, \qquad\qquad u \in \mathring{H}^2(\Omega),$$

(ii) $$f(u) = \frac{1}{2}\int_\Omega (\Delta u - \hat{w})^2 \, d\Omega - \frac{1}{2}\int_\Omega \hat{w}^2 \, d\Omega, \qquad u \in \mathring{H}^2(\Omega),$$

and that therefore $f(\hat{u}) \geq -\frac{1}{2}\int_\Omega \hat{w}^2 \, d\Omega$ with equality if and only if $\Delta u = \hat{w}$.

3.13. In the Lax–Milgram lemma let

$$V = \mathring{H}^1(0, 1),$$

$$a(u, v) = \int_0^1 \left[u'v' + c(x)u'v \right] dx,$$

$$G(u) = \int_0^1 gu \, dx,$$

where $|c(x)| \leq c_1, 0 \leq x \leq 1$.

(i)   Show that $a(\cdot, \cdot)$ is a bounded, unsymmetric bilinear form.
(ii) Show that $a(\cdot, \cdot)$ is coercive if c_1 is sufficiently small or if $c(x)$ is a constant function.
(iii) Find some $c(x)$ and $u \in \mathring{H}^1(0, 1)$ such that $a(u, u) < 0$.
(iv) What is the boundary value problem associated with V, $a(\cdot, \cdot)$, and $G(\cdot)$?

3.14. Generalize the Lax–Milgram lemma so as to make it immediately applicable to the boundary value problem (3.34), (3.35).

3.15 Show that $\tilde{a}(\cdot, \cdot)$ and $\tilde{G}(\cdot)$ in (3.41) satisfy the conditions of the Lax–Milgram lemma.

3.16. Let $\hat{u}$ and $\hat{u}_r$ denote the solutions of the differential equation (3.34), which we denote $\mathscr{L}u = g$, with boundary conditions

$$u = \gamma(x, y) \qquad \text{on } \Gamma$$

and

$$u_v + ru = r\gamma(x, y) \qquad \text{on } \Gamma,$$

respectively, where r is a positive constant. Since the latter boundary condition can be written $r^{-1}u_v + u = \gamma$, we intuitively expect that $\hat{u}_r$ approximates $\hat{u}$ when r is large.

(i)   Show that the function $\hat{e}_r \equiv \hat{u} - \hat{u}_r$ is the solution of the boundary value problem $\mathscr{L}u = 0$ in Ω, $u_v + ru = \hat{u}_v$ on Γ.

(ii) Establish the relation

$$\iint_\Omega \left[p(\hat{e}_r)_x^2 + p(\hat{e}_r)_y^2 + q\hat{e}_r^2 \right] dx \, dy = \int_\Gamma p(\hat{u}_v - r\hat{e}_r)\hat{e}_r \, ds$$

and hence show that

(a) $\left(\int_\Gamma \hat{e}_r^2 \, ds\right)^{1/2} \le (p_1/p_0) r^{-1} \left(\int_\Gamma \hat{u}_v^2 \, ds\right)^{1/2},$

(b) $\iint_\Omega \left[p(\hat{e}_r)_x^2 + p(\hat{e}_r)_y^2 + q\hat{e}_r^2 \right] dx \, dy \le (p_1^2/p_0) r^{-1} \int_\Gamma \hat{u}_v^2 \, ds,$

where $0 < p_0 \le p(x, y) \le p_1 \ \forall (x, y) \in \bar{\Omega}$. [We are also assuming that $q(x, y)$ is nonnegative in $\bar{\Omega}$.]

(iii) Using Friedrichs' second inequality (3.32) and (ii) prove that there is a constant c such that

$$\| \hat{e}_r \|_1 \le c r^{-1/2} \left(\int_\Gamma \hat{u}_v^2 \, ds \right)^{1/2}, \qquad r \to \infty,$$

thus confirming the expectation that $\hat{u}_r$ approximates $\hat{u}$ when r is large.

(iv) Show that $\hat{u}_r$ is the minimizer of the functional

$$f_r(u) = \frac{1}{2} \iint_\Omega \left[pu_x^2 + pu_y^2 + qu^2 \right] dx \, dy - \int_\Omega gu \, dx \, dy + \frac{r}{2} \int_\Gamma p(u - \gamma)^2 \, ds, \quad u \in H^1(\Omega).$$

By minimizing this functional we are determining an approximation (if r is large) to the solution $\hat{u}$ of (3.34), (3.35) *without imposing the inhomogeneous Dirichlet boundary condition* (3.35) *on the admissible functions*. This is the "penalty method" for finding $\hat{u}$ (Babuška, 1973).

3.17. For $\Omega \subset R^2$ let

$$a(u, v) = \int_\Omega \left[u_x v_x + u_y v_y - u_x(rv)_y + u_y(rv)_x \right] dx \, dy, \qquad u, v \in H^1(\Omega),$$

$$G(u) = \int_\Omega gu \, dx \, dy + \int_\Gamma hu \, ds, \qquad u \in H^1(\Omega).$$

(i) Show that the differential equation and boundary condition (natural) associated with the variational problem of finding $u \in H^1(\Omega)$ such that $a(u, v) = G(v) \ \forall v \in H^1(\Omega)$ are

$$-\Delta u = g \quad \text{in } \Omega \quad \text{and} \quad u_v + ru_\tau = h \quad \text{on } \Gamma, \tag{3.64}$$

where u_v and u_τ are the normal and tangential derivatives of u, respectively. [See (2.24).]

(ii) Let $\boldsymbol{\beta} \equiv [\beta_1, \beta_2]^T$ denote a unit vector (not necessarily constant) defined on Γ and let $\tilde{h}$ be a function defined on Γ. Let u_β denote the derivative of u at Γ in the direction $\boldsymbol{\beta}$ (i.e., $u_\beta = \beta_1 u_x + \beta_2 u_y$). Show that (3.64) implies

$$u_\beta = \tilde{h} \quad \text{on } \Gamma$$

when

$$r = \boldsymbol{\beta}^T \boldsymbol{\tau} / \boldsymbol{\beta}^T \mathbf{v}, \qquad h = \tilde{h} / \boldsymbol{\beta}^T \mathbf{v},$$

where $\mathbf{v} \equiv [v_1, v_2]^T$ and $\boldsymbol{\tau} \equiv [-v_2, v_1]^T$ are the unit normal and tangential vectors, respectively. u_β is called an *oblique* derivative of u.

3.18. The Green's function associated with the boundary value problem

$$-u'' = g(x), \qquad -1 < x < 1,$$

$$u(-1) = u(1) = 0$$

is given by (3.60).

(i) Verify that it is the solution of variational problem (3.56).

(ii) Verify that the function $\hat{u}$ in (3.59) is the solution of the given boundary value problem.

3.19. Verify that the function u in (3.62) belongs to $H^1(\Omega)$.

References

Adams, R. A. (1975). "Sobolev Spaces." Academic Press, New York.

Babuška, I. (1973). The finite element method with penalty. *Math. Comp.* **27**, 221–228.

Babuška, I., and Aziz, A. K. (1972). Survey lectures on the mathematical foundations of the finite element method. *In* "The Mathematical Foundations of the Finite Element Method with Applications to Partial Differential Equations" (A. K. Aziz, ed.), pp. 5–359. Academic Press, New York.

Barros-Neto, J. (1973). "An Introduction to the Theory of Distributions." Marcel Dekker, New York.

Ciarlet, P. G. (1978). "The Finite Element Method for Elliptic Problems." North-Holland Publ., Amsterdam.

Friedman, A. (1969). "Partial Differential Equations." Holt, New York.

Gilbarg, D., and Trudinger, N. S. (1977). "Elliptic Partial Differential Equations of Second Order." Spring-Verlag, Berlin and New York.

Goffman, C., and Pedrick, G. (1965). "First Course in Functional Analysis." Prentice-Hall, Englewood Cliffs, New Jersey.

Gustafson, K. E. (1980). "Introduction to Partial Differential Equations and Hilbert Space Methods." Wiley, New York.

Lions, J. L., and Magenes, E. (1972). "Non-Homogeneous Boundary Value Problems and Applications, Vol. 1." Springer-Verlag, Berlin and New York.

Mikhlin, S. G. (1970). "Mathematical Physics, an Advanced Course." North-Holland Publ., Amsterdam.

Nečas, J. (1967). "Les Méthodes Directes en Théorie des Equations Elliptiques." Masson, Paris.

Rektorys, K. (1975). "Variational Methods in Mathematics, Science and Engineering." D. Reidel, Dordrecht.

Roach, G. F. (1970). "Green's Functions." Van Nostrand-Reinhold, Princeton, New Jersey.

Schwartz, L. (1966). "Theorie des Distributions." Hermann, Paris.

Showalter, R. E. (1977). "Hilbert Space Methods for Partial Differential Equations." Pitman, London.

Stakgold, I. (1979). "Green's Functions and Boundary Value Problems." Wiley, New York.

Strang, G., and Fix, G. J. (1973). "An Analysis of the Finite Element Method." Prentice-Hall, Englewood Cliffs, New Jersey.

Titchmarsh, E. C. (1939). "The Theory of Functions," 2nd ed. Oxford Univ. Press, London and New York.

CHAPTER 4

The Ritz–Galerkin Method

Introduction

In this chapter we shall describe the Ritz–Galerkin method for finding the approximate solution of a boundary value problem. We assume throughout the first three sections that the problem can be formulated so that the Lax–Milgram lemma is applicable, i.e., there is a coercive and bounded bilinear form $a(\cdot, \cdot)$ and a bounded linear functional $G(\cdot)$, both defined on a Hilbert space V, such that the solution of the boundary value problem is identical to the element $\hat{u} \in V$ whose existence is asserted by the Lax–Milgram lemma. We recall that this element satisfies the condition

$$a(\hat{u}, u) = G(u) \qquad \forall u \in V \tag{4.1}$$

and that if $a(\cdot, \cdot)$ is symmetric, then

$$\min_{u \in V} f(u) = f(\hat{u}), \tag{4.2}$$

where

$$f(u) = \tfrac{1}{2}a(u, u) - G(u), \qquad u \in V. \tag{4.3}$$

In Section 4.1 we assume that $a(\cdot, \cdot)$ is symmetric and derive the Ritz method by minimizing the energy functional f over an N-dimensional subspace of V. This leads directly to the problem of minimizing a quadratic functional with a positive definite Hessian over the vector space R^N, and the iterative methods of Chapter 1 are applicable. Alternatively, the corresponding system of N algebraic equations can be solved by the direct methods of Chapter 6.

In Section 4.2 we show how the minimal property of the Ritz method leads to important error estimates. The assumption that $a(\cdot, \cdot)$ is symmetric is dropped in Section 4.3, in which we derive the more general Galerkin method and examine the error associated with it. In Section 4.4 we replace the assumption that $a(\cdot, \cdot)$ is coercive by a weaker inequality and at the same time introduce a number of new assumptions. It is shown that the Galerkin method is sometimes applicable to problems of this type.

4.1   The Ritz Method

Every method of obtaining an approximate solution of a boundary value problem requires some kind of discretization. In the case of the Ritz method, considered in the setting of the Lax–Milgram lemma, this is done by selecting an N-dimensional subspace $V_N \subset V$. Since V_N is itself a Hilbert space (Exercise 4.1), conditions (1)–(6) of the Lax–Milgram lemma are obviously satisfied when V is replaced by V_N. This leads immediately to the following theorem.

Theorem 4.1. Let conditions (1)–(6) of the Lax–Milgram lemma be satisfied, and let V_N be an N-dimensional subspace of V. Then there exists a unique element $\hat{u}_N \in V_N$ such that

$$a(\hat{u}_N, u) = G(u) \qquad \forall u \in V_N. \tag{4.4}$$

Further, if $a(\cdot, \cdot)$ is symmetric, then

$$\min_{u \in V_N} f(u) = f(\hat{u}_N), \tag{4.5}$$

where f is given by (4.3).

Theorem 4.1 is nonconstructive in that it does not specify a procedure for finding $\hat{u}_N$. Nevertheless, we can easily exploit the finite dimensionality of V_N to obtain a procedure. Thus, assume that $a(\cdot, \cdot)$ is symmetric and let $\{\phi_i\}_{i=1}^N$ be a basis for V_N, i.e., any set of N linearly independent functions in V_N. Every $u \in V_N$ has a unique expansion of the form

$$u = \sum_{i=1}^N \alpha_i \phi_i, \tag{4.6}$$

where $\alpha_1, \ldots, \alpha_N \in R$. Substituting in (4.3) and using the bilinear property of $a(\cdot, \cdot)$ and the linear property of $G(\cdot)$, we find that

$$f(u) = \tfrac{1}{2} a \left(\sum_{i=1}^{N} \alpha_i \phi_i, \sum_{i=1}^{N} \alpha_i \phi_i \right) - G \left(\sum_{i=1}^{N} \alpha_i \phi_i \right)$$

$$= \tfrac{1}{2} \sum_{i,j=1}^{N} \alpha_i \alpha_j a(\phi_i, \phi_j) - \sum_{i=1}^{N} \alpha_i G(\phi_i)$$

$$= \tfrac{1}{2} \alpha^T K \alpha - \alpha^T G = F(\alpha), \qquad (4.7)$$

where

$$\alpha = \begin{bmatrix} \alpha_1 \\ \alpha_2 \\ \vdots \\ \alpha_N \end{bmatrix}, \qquad G = \begin{bmatrix} G(\phi_1) \\ G(\phi_2) \\ \vdots \\ G(\phi_N) \end{bmatrix},$$

$$K = \begin{bmatrix} a(\phi_1, \phi_1) & a(\phi_2, \phi_1) & \cdots & a(\phi_N, \phi_1) \\ a(\phi_1, \phi_2) & a(\phi_2, \phi_2) & \cdots & a(\phi_N, \phi_2) \\ \vdots & \vdots & \ddots & \vdots \\ a(\phi_1, \phi_N) & a(\phi_2, \phi_N) & \cdots & a(\phi_N, \phi_N) \end{bmatrix}.$$

$$(4.8)$$

The symmetry of $a(\cdot, \cdot)$ implies that K is symmetric. Moreover, from the coercive property of $a(\cdot, \cdot)$ we see that

$$\alpha^T K \alpha = a(u, u) \geq \rho \|u\|_V^2 \geq 0$$

for some positive ρ independent of u. Since $\alpha^T K \alpha = 0$ if and only if $\alpha = 0$, we have proved the next theorem.

Theorem 4.2. The assumption that the bilinear form $a(\cdot, \cdot)$ is symmetric and coercive implies that matrix K in (4.8) is positive definite.

It is clear from (4.7) that $\min_{u \in V_N} f(u) = \min_{\alpha \in R^N} F(\alpha)$. Now F is a quadratic functional over R^N with a positive definite Hessian, and we know from Section 1.1 that F is uniquely minimized by the α that satisfies

$$K \alpha = G. \qquad (4.9)$$

The minimizer $\hat{u}_N$ of f over V_N is related to this α by (4.6). Hence, we have derived the following procedure for finding $\hat{u}_N$.

(1) Choose a basis $\{\phi_i\}_{i=1}^{N}$ for V_N.
(2) Construct K and G defined in (4.8).

(3) Find $\alpha \in R^N$ that minimizes F in (4.7) or, equivalently, that satisfies (4.9).

(4) $\hat{u}_N = \sum_{i=1}^{N} \alpha_i \phi_i$.

This is the *Ritz method* for finding $\hat{u}_N$ (Ritz, 1908). Because of its physical significance in problems of elasticity, K is sometimes called the *stiffness matrix*.

Theorem 4.1 shows that $\hat{u}_N$ depends on the basis functions only to the extent that these determine the subspace V_N by the relation

$$V_N = \text{SPAN}\{\phi_1, ..., \phi_N\}.$$

Any other basis for the same subspace V_N must yield the same element $\hat{u}_N$. In spite of this observation, it turns out that the choice of basis functions has a great effect on the accuracy with which one can solve (4.9) in practice. We shall return to this point shortly.

From a computational point of view, the fact that K is positive definite is very advantageous, since some of the most effective numerical methods for solving systems of linear equations assume that the matrix has this property. In particular, the conjugate gradient method (Chapter 1) is applicable to (4.9), and so are the direct methods of Chapter 6.

The sets of basis functions used for the Ritz method may be divided into two general categories: dimension-independent and dimension-dependent. The characteristic property of dimension-independent basis functions is that in passing from dimension N to $(N + 1)$, we simply add a new function ϕ_{N+1} to the old set $\{\phi_i\}_{i=1}^{N}$. In the case of dimension-dependent basis functions, we replace the old set of N functions by an entirely new set of $(N + 1)$ functions. Thus, a more precise notation for dimension-dependent functions is $\{\phi_i^{(N)}\}_{i=1}^{N}$.

In implementing the Ritz method with dimension-independent basis functions, one selects a sequence $\{\phi_i\}_{i=1}^{\infty} \subset V$ and defines

$$V_N = \text{SPAN}\{\phi_1, ..., \phi_N\}, \qquad N = 1, 2, ...$$

The set $\{\phi_i\}_{i=1}^{\infty}$ should be large enough to permit any $u \in V$ to be well approximated by functions in V_N for N sufficiently large and small enough to avoid linear dependence, or "near" linear dependence. A precise formulation of the first requirement is the following: for any $u \in V$ and any $\varepsilon > 0$ there should be a positive integer N_0 such that u has a decomposition of the form

$$u = u_N + e_N, \qquad u_N \in V_N, \qquad \|e_N\|_V \leq \varepsilon$$

for $N \geq N_0$. If the set $\{\phi_i\}_{i=1}^{\infty}$ has this property then we say it is *complete in V*.

We now denote the matrix K of (4.8) by $K^{(N)}$ to emphasize its dependence on N. The most obvious formulation of the second requirement that the set

$\{\phi_i\}_{i=1}^{\infty}$ be "small enough" is that the functions $\{\phi_i\}_{i=1}^N$ be linearly independent for each of the values $N = 1, 2, \ldots$, since otherwise $K^{(N)}$ is singular for all N sufficiently large. However, this property by no means precludes $K^{(N)}$ from being nearly singular in the sense of having a very large spectral condition number $\kappa(K^{(N)})$. Unfortunately, if $K^{(N)}$ is nearly singular, then numerical solutions of (4.9) will often be contaminated by large rounding errors and iterative methods will typically have a low rate of convergence. Thus, with regard to practical computation, the requirement of simple linear independence is insufficient. We also want $\kappa(K^{(N)})$ to be reasonably small.

From a theoretical point of view, a natural choice of basis functions $\{\phi_i\}_{i=1}^{\infty}$ are the eigenfunctions of the operator $\mathscr{L}$ appearing in the boundary value problem. When the conditions of the Lax–Milgram lemma are satisfied and the bilinear form is symmetric, these and the corresponding eigenvalues $\{\lambda_i\}_{i=1}^{\infty}$ satisfy

$$\mathscr{L}\phi_i = \lambda_i\phi_i, \qquad i = 1, 2, 3, \ldots,$$

$$0 < \lambda_1 \le \lambda_2 \le \ldots, \qquad \lim_{i \to \infty} \lambda_i = \infty,$$

$$a(\phi_i, \phi_j) = \lambda_i\,\delta_{ij}, \qquad i, j = 1, 2, 3, \ldots.$$

The last relation shows that $K^{(N)} = \text{diag}(\lambda_1, \lambda_2, \ldots, \lambda_N)$, and the solution of (4.9) is

$$\alpha_i = G(\phi_i)/\lambda_i, \qquad i = 1, 2, \ldots, N.$$

The practical problem posed by eigensolutions in the Ritz method, of course, is that they must be found before they can be used. This, unfortunately, is a major task in itself.

With regard to the choice of basis functions, our main interest in this book is the dimension-dependent functions of the finite element method. We shall not discuss them here, however, since they are the subject of Chapter 5. Their main advantage is that they are reasonably easy to work with, and, in particular, they make $K^{(N)}$ a sparse matrix. (Dimension-independent basis functions that are easy to construct usually do not have this property.) Although $\kappa(K^{(N)})$ is not uniformly bounded with respect to N for the finite element basis functions, its rate of growth is quite modest. In Chapter 5 we shall show that for second-order boundary value problems in two space dimensions, $\kappa(K^{(N)})$ typically increases only linearly with N. The growth is even slower in the case of three dimensions.

For discussions on the use of dimension-independent basis functions in the Ritz method see, e.g., Delves and Freeman (1981) and Mikhlin (1971).

Inhomogeneous Boundary Conditions

Boundary value problems with inhomogeneous essential boundary conditions are special in the sense that they cannot be formulated directly in terms of the Lax–Milgram lemma. We shall illustrate here the Ritz method for such problems in the case of (3.34), (3.35). It was shown in Section 3.2 that the solution of this problem is

$$\hat{u} = \hat{v} + u^*,$$

where u^* is any chosen function in the set

$$H^1_\gamma(\Omega) = \{u \in H^1(\Omega); u = \gamma \text{ on } \Gamma\}$$

and $\hat{v}$ the minimizer of

$$f^*(v) = \tfrac{1}{2}a(v, v) - G^*(v), \qquad v \in \mathring{H}^1(\Omega).$$

We recall that

$$a(u, v) = \int\int_\Omega \left[p u_x v_x + p u_y v_y + q u v \right] dx \, dy,$$

$$G^*(v) = G(v) - a(u^*, v) = \int\int_\Omega g v \, dx \, dy - a(u^*, v).$$

Let V_N be an N-dimensional subspace of $\mathring{H}^1(\Omega)$, and let $\hat{v}_N \in V_N$ be defined by

$$\min_{v \in V_N} f^*(v) = f^*(\hat{v}_N).$$

The Ritz theory tells us that if $\phi_1, \phi_2, \ldots, \phi_N$ is a basis of V_N, then

$$\hat{v}_N = \sum_{i=1}^N \alpha_i \phi_i,$$

where

$$K\alpha = \mathbf{G}^*,$$

$$k_{ij} = a(\phi_j, \phi_i), \qquad\qquad i, j = 1, 2, \ldots, N, \qquad\qquad (4.10)$$

$$G_i^* = G(\phi_i) - a(u^*, \phi_i), \qquad i = 1, 2, \ldots, N.$$

$\hat{v}_N$ is the Ritz approximation to $\hat{v}$, and the corresponding Ritz approximation to $\hat{u}$ is

$$\hat{u}_N \equiv \hat{v}_N + u^* = \sum_{i=1}^N \alpha_i \phi_i + u^*. \qquad\qquad (4.11)$$

In practice one often tries to construct u^* in the form

$$u^* = \sum_{i=N+1}^{N+P} \alpha_i \phi_i,$$

where functions $\phi_{N+1}, \phi_{N+2}, \ldots, \phi_{N+P}$ and constants $\alpha_{N+1}, \alpha_{N+2}, \ldots, \alpha_{N+P}$ are chosen so that

$$\sum_{i=N+1}^{N+P} \alpha_i \phi_i(x, y) = \gamma(x, y), \qquad (x, y) \in \Gamma.$$

This makes

$$G_i^* = G(\phi_i) - \sum_{j=N+1}^{N+P} \alpha_j a(\phi_j, \phi_i), \qquad i = 1, 2, \ldots, N,$$

$$\hat{u}_N = \sum_{i=1}^{N+P} \alpha_i \phi_i.$$

4.2 Error Analysis of the Ritz Method

The functional f in (4.3) can be expressed as

$$f(u) = f(\hat{u}) + \tfrac{1}{2} a(\hat{u} - u, \hat{u} - u), \qquad u \in V.$$

It follows immediately from (4.5) that

$$\left[a(\hat{u} - \hat{u}_N, \hat{u} - \hat{u}_N) \right]^{1/2} = \min_{u \in V_N} \left[a(\hat{u} - u, \hat{u} - u) \right]^{1/2} \tag{4.12}$$

or, in the energy norm notation,

$$\| \hat{u} - \hat{u}_N \|_{\mathscr{L}} = \min_{u \in V_N} \| \hat{u} - u \|_{\mathscr{L}}.$$

(See Remark 5 after the Lax–Milgram lemma.) This fundamental result states that the Ritz method minimizes the error $(\hat{u} - \hat{u}_N)$ in the energy norm over the subspace V_N. An estimate of this type (in any norm) is called *optimal*.

Subtracting (4.4) from (4.1) we obtain the relation

$$a(\hat{u} - \hat{u}_N, u) = 0 \qquad \forall u \in V_N, \tag{4.13}$$

which in geometric terms states that $\hat{u}_N$ is the orthogonal projection with respect to the energy inner product of $\hat{u}$ onto V_N. Using elementary Fourier analysis, we can derive a simple expression for the error (4.12) in the case of dimension-independent basis functions $\{\phi_i\}_{i=1}^{\infty}$ that are complete in V and orthonormal with respect to the energy inner product [i.e., $a(\phi_i, \phi_j) = \delta_{ij}$].

The solution $\hat{u}$ has the Fourier expansion

$$\hat{u} = \sum_{i=1}^{\infty} b_i \phi_i, \qquad\qquad b_i = a(\hat{u}, \phi_i),$$

and if

$$V_N = \mathrm{SPAN}\{\phi_1, ..., \phi_N\}, \qquad N = 1, 2, ...,$$

then the partial sum $\sum_{i=1}^{N} b_i \phi_i$ is the orthogonal projection of $\hat{u}$ onto V_N with respect to the energy inner product. Thus,

$$\hat{u}_N = \sum_{i=1}^{N} b_i \phi_i, \qquad \hat{u} - \hat{u}_N = \sum_{i=N+1}^{\infty} b_i \phi_i,$$

and we have the desired result,

$$\|\hat{u} - \hat{u}_N\|_{\mathscr{L}} = \left(\sum_{i=N+1}^{\infty} b_i^2 \right)^{1/2}. \tag{4.14}$$

We shall now derive an error estimate in the norm $\|\cdot\|_V$. Since $a(\cdot, \cdot)$ is assumed to satisfy conditions (3) and (4) of the Lax–Milgram lemma, there exist positive constants ρ and β such that

$$\sqrt{\rho}\|u\|_V \le \sqrt{a(u, u)} \le \sqrt{\beta}\|u\|_V \qquad \forall u \in V,$$

and (4.12) implies

$$\|\hat{u} - \hat{u}_N\|_V \le C \min_{u \in V_N} \|\hat{u} - u\|_V, \tag{4.15}$$

where $C = \sqrt{\rho^{-1}\beta}$. An estimate of this type is called *quasi-optimal*.

This result brings us to a problem of approximation theory: How well can a function in V be approximated by a function in V_N in the norm $\|\cdot\|_V$? Since in boundary value problems of order $2m$ the norm $\|\cdot\|_V$ is the Sobolev norm $\|\cdot\|_m$, we are concerned with approximation errors measured in this norm. In Section 5.4 we shall return to this topic in the context of basis functions of finite element type.

Inhomogeneous Boundary Conditions

We shall again use (3.34) and (3.35) to illustrate the case of inhomogeneous boundary conditions, continuing the discussion at the end of the preceding section. Applying (4.15) to the functional f^*, we obtain

$$\|\hat{v} - \hat{v}_N\|_1 \le C \min_{v \in V_N} \|\hat{v} - v\|_1.$$

Since $\hat{v} = \hat{u} - u^*$ and $\hat{v}_N = \hat{u}_N - u^*$, this yields the error estimate

$$\|\hat{u} - \hat{u}_N\|_1 \leq C \min_{u \in \tilde{V}_N} \|\hat{u} - u\|_1, \tag{4.16}$$

where

$$\tilde{V}_N = \{u \in H^1_\gamma(\Omega); u = v + u^*, v \in V_N\}.$$

4.3 The Galerkin Method

Suppose now that the bilinear form $a(\cdot, \cdot)$ is not necessarily symmetric but that conditions (1)–(6) of the Lax–Milgram lemma are still satisfied. We can then use (4.4) to derive a procedure for finding $\hat{u}_N$. For if $\{\phi_i\}_{i=1}^N$ is a basis for V_N and if $\{\alpha_i\}_{i=1}^N$ is the unique set of coefficients for which

$$\hat{u}_N = \sum_{i=1}^N \alpha_i \phi_i, \tag{4.17}$$

then (4.4) implies that

$$\sum_{j=1}^N \alpha_j a(\phi_j, u) = G(u) \qquad \forall u \in V_N. \tag{4.18}$$

In particular, we have

$$\sum_{j=1}^N \alpha_j a(\phi_j, \phi_i) = G(\phi_i), \qquad i = 1, 2, \ldots, N,$$

or

$$K\alpha = G, \tag{4.19}$$

where

$$\alpha = \begin{bmatrix} \alpha_1 \\ \alpha_2 \\ \vdots \\ \alpha_N \end{bmatrix}, \qquad G = \begin{bmatrix} G(\phi_1) \\ G(\phi_2) \\ \vdots \\ G(\phi_N) \end{bmatrix},$$

$$K = \begin{bmatrix} a(\phi_1, \phi_1) & a(\phi_2, \phi_1) & \cdots & a(\phi_N, \phi_1) \\ a(\phi_1, \phi_2) & a(\phi_2, \phi_2) & \cdots & a(\phi_N, \phi_2) \\ \vdots & \vdots & \ddots & \vdots \\ a(\phi_1, \phi_N) & a(\phi_2, \phi_N) & \cdots & a(\phi_N, \phi_N) \end{bmatrix}.$$

It is easy to show that the linear independence of the basis functions $\{\phi_i\}_{i=1}^N$

and the coercive property of $a(\cdot, \cdot)$ imply that K is nonsingular (Exercise 4.2). Thus we can solve (4.19) to obtain $\boldsymbol{\alpha}$ and then determine $\hat{u}_N$ from (4.17).

This is the *Galerkin method* for finding $\hat{u}_N$ (Galerkin, 1915). It is obviously identical to the Ritz method when $a(\cdot, \cdot)$ is symmetric. Note that if $a(\cdot, \cdot)$ is not symmetric then neither is K. This fact makes the numerical solution of (4.19) more costly with respect to computer time and storage than in the symmetric case.

The error estimates we obtained for the Ritz method were derived from the minimum properties (4.2) and (4.5). In spite of the fact that these properties cannot be assumed in the case of the Galerkin method, it turns out that one can still obtain a quasi-optimal error estimate in the norm $\|\cdot\|_V$.

Theorem 4.3. Let assumptions (1)–(6) of the Lax–Milgram lemma be satisfied, and let V_N be an N-dimensional subspace of V. Let $\hat{u}$ and $\hat{u}_N$ be the elements identified in the Lax–Milgram lemma and Theorem 4.1, respectively. Then,

$$\|\hat{u} - \hat{u}_N\|_V \leq C \min_{u \in V_N} \|\hat{u} - u\|_V, \qquad (4.20)$$

where $C = \rho^{-1}\beta > 0$. [β and ρ are the constants in assumptions (3) and (4), respectively.]

PROOF:

$$a(\hat{u} - \hat{u}_N, \hat{u} - \hat{u}_N) = a(\hat{u} - \hat{u}_N, \hat{u} - u) + a(\hat{u} - \hat{u}_N, u - \hat{u}_N)$$

$$= a(\hat{u} - \hat{u}_N, \hat{u} - u) \qquad \forall u \in V_N.$$

We have used (4.13) here [which does not assume that $a(\cdot, \cdot)$ is symmetric] and the fact that $u - \hat{u}_N \in V_N \ \forall u \in V_N$. Then, from assumptions (3) and (4) we obtain

$$\rho\|\hat{u} - \hat{u}_N\|_V^2 \leq a(\hat{u} - \hat{u}_N, \hat{u} - \hat{u}_N) = a(\hat{u} - \hat{u}_N, \hat{u} - u)$$

$$\leq \beta\|\hat{u} - \hat{u}_N\|_V \|\hat{u} - u\|_V \qquad \forall u \in V_N,$$

and (4.20) follows.   ∎

A generalization of the Galerkin method is the *Petrov–Galerkin method* in which one chooses distinct N-dimensional subspaces $V_N \subset V$ and $W_N \subset V$ and determines $\hat{u}_N \in V_N$ such that

$$a(\hat{u}_N, u) = G(u) \qquad \forall u \in W_N.$$

If $\phi_1, \phi_2, ..., \phi_N$ and $\theta_1, \theta_2, ..., \theta_N$ are bases of V_N and W_N, respectively, then we can write

$$\hat{u}_N = \sum_{i=1}^{N} \alpha_i \phi_i$$

and determine $\alpha_1, \alpha_2, \ldots, \alpha_N$ from the requirement that

$$a\left(\sum_{j=1}^{N} \alpha_j \phi_j, \theta_i\right) = G(\theta_i), \qquad i = 1, 2, \ldots, N.$$

This yields the linear system $K\alpha = G$, where $k_{ij} = a(\phi_j, \theta_i)$ and $G_i = G(\theta_i)$.

The Petrov–Galerkin method is important, for example, when a second-order differential equation is dominated by its first-order terms. [For further information see Anderssen and Mitchell (1979).]

4.4 Application of the Galerkin Method to Noncoercive Problems

We shall now consider the application of the Galerkin method to a problem in which the bilinear form $a(\cdot, \cdot)$ is not coercive but satisfies a weaker inequality [(3) in the following list]. At the same time, we introduce two assumptions that have no analog in the Lax–Milgram lemma [(1) and (4) in the following list]. Assuming that the problem actually possesses a solution, we derive quasi-optimal error bounds for the Galerkin method. Our reference is Schatz (1974).

Let V and H be Hilbert spaces with norms $\|\cdot\|_V$ and $\|\cdot\|_H$, respectively. We assume that $V \subseteq H$ and that

(1) $$\|u\|_H \leq \|u\|_V \qquad \forall u \in V.$$

Let $a(\cdot, \cdot)$ be a bilinear form on $V \times V$ with the boundedness property

(2) $$|a(u, v)| \leq \beta \|u\|_V \|v\|_V \qquad \forall u, v \in V.$$

Let V_N, $N = 1, 2, \ldots$, be a sequence of finite-dimensional subspaces of V, and let there exist a positive constant ρ and a constant γ, both independent of u and N, such that

(3) $$\rho \|u\|_V - \gamma \|u\|_H \leq \sup_{\substack{v \in V_N \\ \|v\|_V = 1}} |a(u, v)| \qquad \forall u \in V_N.$$

Finally, let there exist a sequence of positive numbers $\{\delta_N\}_{N=1}^{\infty}$ such that $\lim_{N \to \infty} \delta_N = 0$, and such that for every $e \in V$ satisfying

$$a(e, u) = 0 \qquad \forall u \in V_N,$$

it is true that

(4) $$\|e\|_H \leq \delta_N \|e\|_V.$$

Theorem 4.4. Let $\hat{u} \in V$ be given and consider the problem of finding $\hat{u}_N \in V_N$ such that

$$a(\hat{u} - \hat{u}_N, u) = 0 \qquad \forall u \in V_N. \tag{4.21}$$

If conditions (1)–(4) are satisfied, then there exists an integer N_0, independent of $\hat{u}$, such that (4.21) has a unique solution $\hat{u}_N$ for $N \geq N_0$. Moreover, there exists a constant C, independent of $\hat{u}$ and N, such that

$$\|\hat{u} - \hat{u}_N\|_V \leq C \min_{u \in V_N} \|\hat{u} - u\|_V, \tag{4.22}$$

$$\|\hat{u} - \hat{u}_N\|_H \leq C \, \delta_N \min_{u \in V_N} \|\hat{u} - u\|_V \tag{4.23}$$

for $N \geq N_0$.

PROOF: Assume first that some $\hat{u}_N \in V_N$ is a solution of (4.21). Then,

$$a(\hat{u}_N - u, v) = a(\hat{u}_N - \hat{u}, v) + a(\hat{u} - u, v)$$
$$= a(\hat{u} - u, v) \qquad \forall u, v \in V_N.$$

Hence, from (3) and (2),

$$\rho\|\hat{u}_N - u\|_V - \gamma\|\hat{u}_N - u\|_H \leq \sup_{\substack{v \in V_N \\ \|v\|_V = 1}} |a(\hat{u}_N - u, v)| = \sup_{\substack{v \in V_N \\ \|v\|_V = 1}} |a(\hat{u} - u, v)|$$

$$\leq \beta\|\hat{u} - u\|_V \qquad \forall u \in V_N. \tag{4.24}$$

At this point we must take account of the sign of γ. If $\gamma > 0$ then we use (4), with $e = \hat{u} - \hat{u}_N$, to obtain

$$(\rho - \gamma \, \delta_N)\|\hat{u} - \hat{u}_N\|_V \leq \rho\|\hat{u} - \hat{u}_N\|_V - \gamma\|\hat{u} - \hat{u}_N\|_H.$$

From the standard norm inequalities

$$\|\hat{u} - \hat{u}_N\|_V \leq \|\hat{u} - u\|_V + \|u - \hat{u}_N\|_V,$$
$$\|\hat{u} - \hat{u}_N\|_H \geq -\|\hat{u} - u\|_H + \|u - \hat{u}_N\|_H,$$

we have

$$\rho\|\hat{u} - \hat{u}_N\|_V - \gamma\|\hat{u} - \hat{u}_N\|_H \leq \rho\|\hat{u} - u\|_V + \gamma\|\hat{u} - u\|_H$$
$$+ (\rho\|u - \hat{u}_N\|_V - \gamma\|u - \hat{u}_N\|_H).$$

Combining the foregoing results, we now obtain

$$(\rho - \gamma \, \delta_N)\|\hat{u} - \hat{u}_N\|_V \leq \rho\|\hat{u} - u\|_V + \gamma\|\hat{u} - u\|_H + \beta\|\hat{u} - u\|_V$$
$$\leq (\rho + \gamma + \beta)\|\hat{u} - u\|_V \qquad \forall u \in V_N,$$

the estimate $\|\hat{u} - u\|_H \leq \|\hat{u} - u\|_V$ coming from (1). Since $\lim_{N \to \infty} \delta_N = 0$, there exists an integer N_0 such that $\delta_N \le \rho/(2\gamma)$ for $N \ge N_0$. Then,

$$\|\hat{u} - \hat{u}_N\|_V \le C\|\hat{u} - u\|_V \qquad \forall u \in V_N, \quad \forall N \ge N_0,$$

where $C = 2\rho^{-1}(\rho + \gamma + \beta)$, which establishes (4.22). Inequality (4.23) follows immediately from (4).

We leave it to the reader to return to (4.24) and show that if $\gamma \le 0$, then (4.22) and (4.23) are valid for $C = \rho^{-1}(\rho + \beta)$ and $N_0 = 1$.

Thus far we have shown that if some $\hat{u}_N \in V_N$ is a solution of (4.21), then there is a value N_0, dependent on ρ, γ, and β, for which (4.22) and (4.23) are valid. We shall now show that given any $\hat{u} \in V$, the subspace V_N, $N \ge N_0$ in fact contains a unique element $\hat{u}_N$ that satisfies (4.21).

We consider uniqueness first. Suppose that

$$a(\hat{u} - \hat{u}_N, u) = 0 \qquad \forall u \in V_N,$$

$$a(\hat{u} - \hat{v}_N, u) = 0 \qquad \forall u \in V_N,$$

and let $\hat{w}_N = \hat{u}_N - \hat{v}_N$. We obtain by subtraction the relation

$$a(-\hat{w}_N, u) = 0 \qquad \forall u \in V_N,$$

which states that $\hat{w}_N$ is the solution of problem (4.21) for the case $\hat{u} = 0$. Then, from (4.22)

$$\|\hat{w}_N\|_V \le C \min_{u \in V_N} \|u\|_V = C\|0\|_V = 0,$$

and it follows that $\hat{u}_N = \hat{v}_N$ when $N \ge N_0$.

Finally, to prove the existence of $\hat{u}_N$ we rewrite problem (4.21) as

$$a(\hat{u}_N, u) = G(u) \qquad \forall u \in V_N, \tag{4.25}$$

where $G(u) = a(\hat{u}, u)$. This has the form of (4.4) and we consider the application of the Galerkin method to obtain $\hat{u}_N$, and in particular the system of equations (4.19). Since $\hat{u}_N$, if it exists, is unique, the solution α of (4.19), if it exists, must also be unique. But (4.19) is a finite system of linear equations, and a well-known theorem of algebra states that uniqueness implies existence. Hence (4.19) possesses a unique solution and $\hat{u}_N$ is given by (4.17). ∎

Remarks

1. In applications to second-order boundary value problems, V is usually $H^1(\Omega)$, or some subspace of $H^1(\Omega)$, and H is $L_2(\Omega)$. Assumption (4) then implies that the error in the L_2-norm goes to zero faster than the error in the H^1-norm as the number of basis functions increases.

2. Suppose that the solution $\hat{u}$ of some boundary value problem satisfies a relation of the type

$$a(\hat{u}, u) = G(u) \qquad \forall u \in V, \tag{4.26}$$

where $a(\cdot, \cdot)$ is a bilinear form on $V \times V$ and $G(\cdot)$ is a linear functional on V. Then problem (4.21) is identical to the problem of finding $\hat{u}_N \in V_N$ such that

$$a(\hat{u}_N, u) = G(u) \qquad \forall u \in V_N,$$

and if assumptions (1)–(4) are satisfied, then the theorem asserts the existence of a unique $\hat{u}_N \in V_N$, if $N \geq N_0$, that solves this problem. We can find $\hat{u}_N$ by applying the Galerkin method, and the quasi-optimal error estimates (4.22) and (4.23) are valid.

A very important point, however, is that we cannot deduce from Theorem 4.4 the existence of an element $\hat{u} \in V$ that satisfies (4.26). Thus, this theorem, in contrast to the Lax–Milgram lemma, cannot be used as an existence theorem for boundary value problems.

3. We leave it to the reader to show that assumption (3) of the theorem is implied by either of the following:

(3)' $a(\cdot, \cdot)$ is coercive on $V \times V$;
(3)'' there exist constants $\rho > 0$ and γ such that

$$\rho \|u\|_V^2 - \gamma \|u\|_H^2 \leq a(u, u) \qquad \forall u \in V. \tag{4.27}$$

(See Exercise 4.4.)

Example 4.1. For $\Omega \subset R^n$ let

$$V = \mathring{H}^1(\Omega), \qquad \|\cdot\|_V = \|\cdot\|_1,$$

$$a(u, v) = \int_\Omega \left[\sum_{i,j=1}^n a_{ij} \frac{\partial u}{\partial x_i} \frac{\partial v}{\partial x_j} + (\mathbf{b}^T \nabla u)v + cuv \right] d\Omega, \qquad u, v \in V,$$

$$G(u) = \int_\Omega gu \, d\Omega, \qquad u \in V.$$

Note that this problem differs from that of Example 3.3 in that $\Gamma_0 = \Gamma$ and, much more important, there is now the term $(\mathbf{b}^T \nabla u)v$ in the integrand of $a(u, v)$. We add to the assumptions of Example 3.3 that $b_i \in C^1(\bar{\Omega})$, $i = 1, 2, \ldots, n$. This implies that there are constants $\tilde{b}$ and $\hat{b}$ such that

$$|b_i(\mathbf{x})| \leq \tilde{b} \qquad \forall \mathbf{x} \in \bar{\Omega}, \quad i = 1, 2, \ldots, n,$$

and

$$|\mathrm{div}[\mathbf{b}(\mathbf{x})]| \leq \hat{b} \qquad \forall \mathbf{x} \in \bar{\Omega}.$$

From the inequality

$$\left| \int_\Omega (\mathbf{b}^T \nabla u)v \, d\Omega \right| \leq \sum_{i=1}^n \int_\Omega \left| b_i \frac{\partial u}{\partial x_i} v \right| d\Omega$$

$$\leq \tilde{b} \|v\| \sum_{i=1}^n \left\| \frac{\partial u}{\partial x_i} \right\| \leq \tilde{b}n \|u\|_1 \|v\|_1$$

and the boundedness of the bilinear form of Example 3.3 we see that $a(\cdot, \cdot)$ is bounded, i.e., assumption (2) of Theorem 4.4 is satisfied. Further, using the identities

$$-\int_{\Omega} (\mathbf{b}^T \nabla u)u \, d\Omega = \int_{\Omega} u \, \text{div}(u\mathbf{b}) \, d\Omega$$

$$= \int_{\Omega} u\mathbf{b}^T \nabla u \, d\Omega + \int_{\Omega} \text{div}(\mathbf{b})u^2 \, d\Omega, \qquad u \in \mathring{H}^1(\Omega),$$

we obtain

$$\int_{\Omega} (\mathbf{b}^T \nabla u)u \, d\Omega = -\frac{1}{2} \int_{\Omega} \text{div}(\mathbf{b})u^2 \, d\Omega,$$

and it follows that

$$a(u, u) = \int_{\Omega} \left[\sum_{i,j=1}^{n} a_{ij} \frac{\partial u}{\partial x_i} \frac{\partial u}{\partial x_j} \right] d\Omega + \int_{\Omega} \phi u^2 \, d\Omega,$$

where $\phi(\mathbf{x}) = c(\mathbf{x}) - \frac{1}{2} \text{div}[\mathbf{b}(\mathbf{x})]$. Example 3.3 shows that the first integral is bounded below by $\rho\|u\|_1^2$ for some positive ρ independent of $u \in \mathring{H}^1(\Omega)$. Hence, if we define

$$\phi_0 = \min_{\mathbf{x} \in \bar{\Omega}} \phi(\mathbf{x}) \geq -(c_1 + \tfrac{1}{2}\hat{b}), \qquad c_1 \equiv \max_{\mathbf{x} \in \bar{\Omega}} |c(\mathbf{x})|,$$

then

$$a(u, u) \geq \rho\|u\|_1^2 + \phi_0\|u\|^2 \qquad \forall u \in \mathring{H}^1(\Omega). \tag{4.28}$$

[This is a special case of *Gårding's inequality* (Friedman, 1969). Note that ϕ_0 may be negative.]

We now introduce $H = L_2(\Omega)$, $\|\cdot\|_H = \|\cdot\|$ and observe that assumption (1) of the theorem is satisfied and that (4.28) yields (4.27). Hence assumption (3) is also satisfied. We conclude from the theorem and Remark 2 that if there exists $\hat{u} \in \mathring{H}^1(\Omega)$ such that

$$a(\hat{u}, u) = G(u) \qquad \forall u \in \mathring{H}^1(\Omega),$$

then for any family of subspaces $\{V_N\}_{N=1}^{\infty} \subset \mathring{H}^1(\Omega)$ satisfying assumption (4), the Galerkin solution $\hat{u}_N$ exists and has the properties

$$\|\hat{u} - \hat{u}_N\|_1 \leq C \min_{u \in V_N} \|\hat{u} - u\|_1, \qquad \|\hat{u} - \hat{u}_N\| \leq C \, \delta_N \min_{u \in V_N} \|\hat{u} - u\|_1.$$

$\hat{u}$ is the generalized solution of the boundary value problem

$$-\sum_{i,j=1}^{n} \frac{\partial}{\partial x_i}\left(a_{ij} \frac{\partial u}{\partial x_j}\right) + \mathbf{b}^T \nabla u + cu = g \qquad \text{in } \Omega,$$

$$u = 0 \qquad \text{on } \Gamma.$$

Note that the assumption in Example 3.3 that $c(\mathbf{x}) \geq 0$ $\forall \mathbf{x} \in \bar{\Omega}$ is not needed here. Note, too, that if $\phi_0 > -\rho$, then $a(\cdot, \cdot)$ is coercive, the Lax–Milgram lemma is applicable, and the existence of $\hat{u}$ is guaranteed.

Exercises

4.1. The justification of Theorem 4.1 is the Lax–Milgram lemma together with the assertion that any finite-dimensional subspace V_N of a Hilbert space V is itself a Hilbert space. The only nontrivial aspect of this assertion is the completeness property. Show that V_N is complete, i.e., show that if $\{u_n\}_{n=1}^{\infty} \subset V_N$ has the Cauchy sequence property $\lim_{m,n \to \infty} \|u_n - u_m\|_V = 0$, then there exists $u \in V_N$ such that $\lim_{n \to \infty} \|u - u_n\|_V = 0$.

HINT: Write $u_n = \sum_{i=1}^{N} \alpha_i^{(n)} \phi_i$, where $\phi_1, \dots, \phi_N$ is an orthonormal basis of V_N [i.e., $(\phi_i, \phi_j)_V = \delta_{ij}$], and show that

$$\|u_n - u_m\|_V^2 = (u_n - u_m, u_n - u_m)_V = \sum_{i=1}^{N} (\alpha_i^{(n)} - \alpha_i^{(m)})^2.$$

If $\|u_n - u_m\|_V \to 0$ then $\{\alpha_i^{(n)}\}_{n=1}^{\infty}$, for each i, is a Cauchy sequence of real numbers.

4.2. Assuming that the bilinear form $a(\cdot, \cdot)$ is coercive, show that the matrix K in (4.19) is nonsingular if and only if $\phi_1, \dots, \phi_N$ are linearly independent.

4.3. Consider the boundary value problem

$$-u'' + u = g(x), \qquad 0 < x < 1,$$

$$u'(0) = u'(1) = 0.$$

(i)   Determine V, $a(\cdot, \cdot)$, and $G(\cdot)$ for this problem, and verify that the conditions of the Lax–Milgram lemma are satisfied.

(ii)   Calculate the stiffness matrix K corresponding to the choice of basis functions $\phi_i(x) = x^{i-1}$, $i = 1, 2, \dots, N$, where N is arbitrary.

(iii)   Using library routines, compute λ_1 and λ_N (the smallest and largest eigenvalues of K, respectively) and the spectral condition number $\kappa(K)$ for $N = 1, 2, \dots, 8$. What geometric property of the basis functions suggests that $\kappa(K)$ should be large?

4.4 Show that assumption (3) of Theorem 4.4 is implied by either of the following:

(i)   the coerciveness of $a(\cdot, \cdot)$;
(ii)   inequality (4.27) and assumption (1).

4.5. Discuss the assertion that in the Ritz–Galerkin method natural boundary conditions are in general only satisfied approximately.

4.6. The Ritz method, whose basic idea is to approximate the minimizer of a functional f over a space V by finding the minimizer over a subspace $V_N \subset V$, is by no means restricted to *quadratic* functionals defined on *infinite*-dimensional spaces. Thus, consider, for example, the Rayleigh quotient

$$f(\mathbf{x}) = \mathbf{x}^T A \mathbf{x} / \mathbf{x}^T B \mathbf{x}, \qquad \mathbf{x} \in R^N,$$

where A and B are $(N \times N)$ real symmetric matrices and B is positive definite. The eigenvalue problem $A\mathbf{x} = \lambda B\mathbf{x}$ has real eigensolutions $(\lambda, \mathbf{x}) = (\lambda_s, \mathbf{x}_s)$, $s = 1, 2, ..., N$, which can be ordered by $\lambda_1 \leq \lambda_2 \leq \cdots \leq \lambda_N$, and it can be shown that

$$\min_{\mathbf{x} \in R^N} f(\mathbf{x}) = f(\mathbf{x}_1) = \lambda_1.$$

(See Exercise 1.12.)

Let $\mathbf{y}_1, ..., \mathbf{y}_M$, where $M < N$, be linearly independent vectors in R^N and let $R_M^N = \text{SPAN}\{\mathbf{y}_1, ..., \mathbf{y}_M\}$. Show that

$$\min_{\mathbf{x} \in R_M^N} f(\mathbf{x}) = \eta_1 \geq \lambda_1,$$

where η_1 is the smallest eigenvalue of the Mth-order problem $C\mathbf{z} = \eta D\mathbf{z}$, $c_{ij} = \mathbf{y}_i^T A \mathbf{y}_j$, $d_{ij} = \mathbf{y}_i^T B \mathbf{y}_j$ for $i, j = 1, ..., M$.

4.7. Given a boundary value problem consisting of a differential equation $\mathscr{L}u = g$ and homogeneous boundary conditions, let V denote the space of all functions u such that $\mathscr{L}u$ is well defined and such that u satisfies the boundary conditions. If $\hat{u} \in V$ is a solution of the problem, then it minimizes the functional

$$f(u) = \int_\Omega (\mathscr{L}u - g)^2 \, d\Omega, \qquad u \in V.$$

Let $\phi_1, ..., \phi_N$ be a basis of a finite-dimensional subspace $V_N \subset V$. Show that

$$\min_{u \in V_N} f(u) = f(\hat{u}_N), \qquad \hat{u}_N = \sum_{i=1}^N \alpha_i \phi_i,$$

where $K\boldsymbol{\alpha} = \mathbf{G}$, $k_{ij} = \int_\Omega (\mathscr{L}\phi_i)(\mathscr{L}\phi_j) \, d\Omega$, $G_i = \int_\Omega g\mathscr{L}\phi_i \, d\Omega$ for $i, j = 1, 2, ..., N$.

This is a "least squares" approach to the given boundary value problem.

4.8. We continue here the discussion of the penalty method begun in Exercise 3.16 Let V_N be an N-dimensional subspace of $H^1(\Omega)$, and let $\hat{u}_r^{(N)}$ be defined by

$$\min_{u \in V_N} f_r(u) = f_r(\hat{u}_r^{(N)}).$$

(i)   Show that

$$a(\hat{u}_r - \hat{u}_r^{(N)}, \hat{u}_r - \hat{u}_r^{(N)}) = \min_{u \in V_N} a(\hat{u}_r - u, \hat{u}_r - u),$$

where

$$a(u, v) = \int \int_\Omega [pu_x v_x + pu_y v_y + quv] \, dx \, dy + r \int_\Gamma puv \, ds.$$

(ii)   Using Friedrichs' second inequality (3.32), the trace inequality (3.33), and (i), show that

$$\|\hat{u}_r - \hat{u}_r^{(N)}\|_1 \leq \tilde{c} r^{1/2} \min_{u \in V_N} \|\hat{u}_r - u\|_1, \qquad r \to \infty$$

for some constant $\tilde{c}$.

(iii)   Hence, deduce from Exercise 3.16 an inequality of the form

$$\|\hat{u} - \hat{u}_r^{(N)}\|_1 \le \hat{c}(r^{-1/2} + r^{1/2} \min_{u \in V_N} \|\hat{u}_r - u\|_1),$$

where $\hat{u}$ is the solution of the boundary value problem (3.34), (3.35).

For further information on the penalty method see Babuška (1973), King (1974), and Pasciak (1979).

References

Anderssen, R. S., and Mitchell, A. R. (1979). Analysis of generalized Galerkin methods in the numerical solution of elliptic equations. *Math. Meth. Appl. Sci.* **1**, 1–11.

Babuška, I. (1973). The finite element method with penalty. *Math. Comp.* **27**, 221–228.

Delves, L. M., and Freeman, T. L. (1981). "Analysis of Global Expansion Methods." Academic Press, New York.

Friedman, A. (1969). "Partial Differential Equations." Holt, New York.

Galerkin, B. G. (1915). Series occurring in various questions concerning the elastic equilibrium of rods and plates (Russian). *Eng. Bull. (Vestn. Inzh. Tech.)* **19**, 897–908.

King, J. T. (1974). New error bounds for the penalty method and extrapolation. *Numer. Math.* **23**, 153–165.

Mikhlin, S. G. (1971). "The Numerical Performance of Variational Methods." Wolters-Noordhoff, Groningen, Holland.

Pasciak, J. (1979). The penalty correction method for elliptic boundary value problems. *SIAM J. Numer. Anal.* **16**, 1046–1059.

Ritz, W. (1908). Über eine neue Methode zur Lösung gewisser Variationsprobleme der mathematischen Physik. *J. Reine Angew. Math.* **135**, 1–61.

Schatz, A. H. (1974). An observation concerning Ritz–Galerkin methods with indefinite bilinear forms. *Math. Comp.* **28**, 959–962.

CHAPTER 5

The Finite Element Method

Introduction

The term "finite element method," as used in this book, denotes the implementation of the Ritz–Galerkin method with finite element basis functions, i.e., basis functions that are continuous, piecewise polynomials and that have local support in the sense that each function vanishes outside of a small subregion of the domain Ω. Such functions are defined with respect to some chosen subdivision of $\bar{\Omega}$ into (normally) triangular or rectangular elements that, together with a choice of nodes, makes up a finite element mesh. The mesh is by no means required to be uniform, a fact that gives the finite element method great strength. Nonuniform meshes are desirable when the solution of the problem is known to vary more rapidly in certain parts of the domain than in others and essential when the domain has an irregular geometry.

Section 5.1 is devoted to the fundamental properties of finite element meshes and basis functions. By restricting a finite element basis function to a single element we arrive at the concept of a "local" basis function. Further, the fact that every element in the mesh is the image of a conveniently chosen "standard" element under an appropriate variable transformation makes it possible to restrict attention to the local basis functions defined on that one element. This turns out to be a property of very great importance for both computation and analysis. Three common types of basis functions are described in detail: the piecewise linear and piecewise quadratic functions, both defined on a mesh of triangular elements, and the piecewise bilinear functions defined on a mesh of rectangular elements.

Section 5.2 deals mainly with the computational details of constructing the Ritz–Galerkin system of equations for a boundary value problem, given a set of finite element basis functions. The computation proceeds element by element, i.e., the elements of the mesh are examined sequentially, each element yielding a contribution to the matrix and right-hand-side vector of the Ritz–Galerkin system. The contribution from an element is conveniently formulated in terms of an element matrix and element vector of low order. At the end of the section we derive some of the important properties of the element matrices and use these to obtain information on the matrix of the Ritz–Galerkin system.

In Section 5.3 we shall show how the class of basis functions described in Section 5.1 can be expanded to include the so-called isoparametric basis functions. The advantage of the latter is that they provide even more flexibility in the choice of a mesh than was available previously. For example, the elements can now have curved edges, a property that can be exploited when the domain $\bar{\Omega}$ has a curved boundary.

Section 5.4 is devoted to an error analysis of the finite element method. A thorough treatment of this important topic is beyond the scope of the book, but the material presented should convey some of the most essential ideas. At the heart of the analysis is the theory of interpolation in Sobolev spaces. This, combined with the quasi-optimal error results obtained for the Ritz–Galerkin method in Chapter 4, leads in the case of a second-order boundary value problem to a bound of the form $\|\hat{u} - \hat{u}_N\|_1 \leq Ch^k\|\hat{u}\|_{k+1}$, where $\hat{u}$ is the exact solution of the problem, $\hat{u}_N$ the finite element approximation, h the greatest element edgelength in the mesh, and the basis functions have the property of interpolating exactly any polynomial of degree $\leq k$. After deriving this fundamental result, we discuss briefly the task of finding corresponding bounds on $\|\hat{u} - \hat{u}_N\|$ and $\|\hat{u} - \hat{u}_N\|_\infty$.

Section 5.5 gives an analysis of the spectral condition number of the Ritz–Galerkin matrix in the context of the finite element method. The main result is that in the case of second-order boundary value problems the spectral condition number has order of magnitude $O(N^{2/n})$, where N is the order of the matrix and n the number of space variables. The size of the spectral condition number is important in connection with the numerical solution of the Ritz–Galerkin system, since it influences the size of rounding errors and, in the case of the iterative methods of Chapter 1, determines the rate of convergence.

In Section 5.6 we shall examine the effect of boundary corners and material interfaces on the smoothness of the exact solution of a boundary value problem. This is relevant to the effectiveness of the finite element method since the error estimates obtained in Section 5.4 assume a certain degree of smoothness. A few common numerical techniques for treating singularities are mentioned.

5.1 Finite Element Basis Functions

Notation

For the sake of easy reference we collect here the most important notation that will be introduced in this section.

L	number of elements in a finite element mesh
M	number of nodes in a finite element mesh
T	number of nodes in a single element
$e_l, l = 1, 2, ..., L$	the elements
$N_i = (x_i, y_i), i = 1, 2, ..., M$	the nodes
$i_r^{(l)}, r = 1, 2, ..., T$	node numbers of nodes in e_l
$\phi_i(x, y), i = 1, 2, ..., M$	global basis functions (defined on $\bar{\Omega}$)
$\phi_r^{(l)}(x, y), r = 1, 2, ..., T$	local basis functions (defined on e_l)
$\tilde{e}$	the standard element
$\tilde{\phi}_r(\tilde{x}, \tilde{y}), r = 1, 2, ..., T$	standard local basis functions (defined on $\tilde{e}$)

Finite Element Meshes

Let $\Omega \subset R^2$ be an open, bounded, simply connected domain of definition of a boundary value problem. We divide $\bar{\Omega}$ into a number of closed sub-regions, or *elements*, $\{e_l\}_{l=1}^L$. For the time being it will be assumed that the elements are polygons. This implies the assumption that $\bar{\Omega}$ itself is a polygon, since otherwise curved elements would be unavoidable at the boundary. The most common elements by far are triangles and quadrilaterals.

We select in $\bar{\Omega}$ a number of points or *nodes*, $\{N_i = (x_i, y_i)\}_{i=1}^M$. Each node, according to its location relative to the elements, is of *vertex*, *edge*, or *interior* type. A vertex node can belong to many elements, an edge node to at most two, and an interior node to only one. The choice of elements and nodes defines a *finite element mesh*. For simplicity we make the assumption that

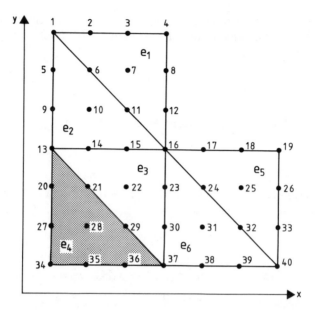

Fig. 5.1.   Example of a finite element mesh. $L = 6$, $M = 40$, $T = 10$.

all elements in a mesh are the same type of polygon and have the same number of vertex, edge, and interior nodes. We denote by T the total number of nodes in an element. Figure 5.1 shows a finite element mesh over an L-shaped domain.

The assignment of integers $i = 1, 2, ..., M$ to the nodes, which can be done

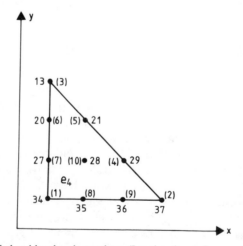

Fig. 5.2.   Global and local node numbers. (Local node numbers are in parentheses.)

in $M!$ different ways, defines a *global node ordering*. It is convenient to have also a *local node ordering* $r = 1, 2, ..., T$ of the nodes in each element, as illustrated in Fig. 5.2.

We shall need a notation for the global node numbers of nodes in an arbitrary element e_l. These will be designated $i_r^{(l)}$, $r = 1, 2, ..., T$, where r is the local node number. Thus, in the case of the element shown in Fig. 5.2,

$$i_1^{(4)} = 34, \quad i_2^{(4)} = 37, \quad i_3^{(4)} = 13, \quad i_4^{(4)} = 29, \quad i_5^{(4)} = 21, \quad \text{etc.}$$

The task of generating a suitable finite element mesh over a given domain is far from trivial. Three general rules, dictated by considerations of error analysis, are:

(1) very large and small element angles should be avoided;

(2) elements should be placed most densely in regions where the solution of the problem and its derivatives are expected to vary rapidly;

(3) high accuracy requires a fine mesh or many nodes per element (the latter condition yields high accuracy, however, only if the solution is sufficiently smooth).

One technique for generating a triangular mesh is to begin with a fairly coarse mesh and then refine it by placing new nodes at the midpoints of all element edges. (See Fig. 5.3.) The new triangles are geometrically similar to the old (i.e., they have the same angles), so if the coarse mesh satisfies requirement (1) then so does the finer mesh. Further, the relative element density in any subregion is roughly preserved. The refinement process can be repeated until the mesh is as fine as desired.

The important topic of computer-implemented mesh generation is too specialized to be treated here. Much has been written on the subject [see,

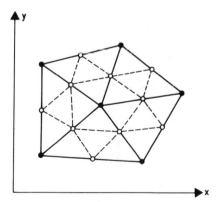

Fig. 5.3.   Refinement of a triangular mesh. Original nodes and new nodes are denoted by ● and ○, respectively.

e.g., Haber *et al.* (1981) and the references cited therein]. We shall assume that the mesh generation process, however performed, has had the result of establishing four arrays: ELNODE, NODECO, EDGE, and BONODE. Array ELNODE contains the global node numbers of every element, and NODECO the x, y coordinates of every node. EDGE and BONODE are used in connection with natural and essential boundary conditions, respectively. All of these arrays are described in detail in Section 5.2. (When the mesh is the result of one or more systematic refinements of an original coarse mesh, as described previously, then it is possible to store data for the coarse mesh only and compute the data for the refined mesh as needed. This can reduce the storage requirement substantially.)

Finite Element Basis Functions

Suppose that for a given finite element mesh there is associated with each node $N_i \equiv (x_i, y_i)$ a function ϕ_i, defined on $\bar{\Omega}$, with the following properties.

(1)   The restriction of ϕ_i to any element e_l has the polynomial form

$$\phi_i(x, y) = \sum_{s=1}^{T} c_{il}^{(s)} x^{p_s} y^{q_s}, \qquad (x, y) \in e_l, \tag{5.1}$$

where the powers p_s and q_s, $s = 1, 2, \ldots, T$, are independent of i and l.

(2) $\phi_i(N_j) = \delta_{ij}$ for $i, j = 1, 2, \ldots, M.$ (5.2)

(3) ϕ_i is uniquely determined on every element edge by its values at the nodes belonging to that edge.

Let

$$V_M = \text{SPAN}\{\phi_1, \phi_2, \ldots, \phi_M\}.$$

We call V_M a *finite element space* and $\phi_1, \phi_2, \ldots, \phi_M$ *finite element basis functions*. Property (2) implies that $\phi_1, \phi_2, \ldots, \phi_M$ are linearly independent (show this), and V_M has dimension M.

The coefficients in (5.1) are determined from (5.2) through the linear system of equations

$$\sum_{s=1}^{T} c_{il}^{(s)} x_{i_r^{(l)}}^{p_s} y_{i_r^{(l)}}^{q_s} = \begin{cases} 1, & \text{for } i_r^{(l)} = i, \\ 0, & \text{otherwise,} \end{cases} \qquad r = 1, 2, \ldots, T,$$

where $i_r^{(l)}$ is the global node number notation introduced previously. This system can be expressed in the matrix–vector form

$$S_l \mathbf{c}_{il} = \mathbf{d}_{il}, \tag{5.3}$$

where

$$
S_l = \begin{bmatrix}
x_{i_1^{(l)}}^{p_1} y_{i_1^{(l)}}^{q_1} & x_{i_1^{(l)}}^{p_2} y_{i_1^{(l)}}^{q_2} & \cdots & x_{i_1^{(l)}}^{p_T} y_{i_1^{(l)}}^{q_T} \\
x_{i_2^{(l)}}^{p_1} y_{i_2^{(l)}}^{q_1} & x_{i_2^{(l)}}^{p_2} y_{i_2^{(l)}}^{q_2} & \cdots & x_{i_2^{(l)}}^{p_T} y_{i_2^{(l)}}^{q_T} \\
\vdots & \vdots & \ddots & \vdots \\
x_{i_T^{(l)}}^{p_1} y_{i_T^{(l)}}^{q_1} & x_{i_T^{(l)}}^{p_2} y_{i_T^{(l)}}^{q_2} & \cdots & x_{i_T^{(l)}}^{p_T} y_{i_T^{(l)}}^{q_T}
\end{bmatrix}.
\tag{5.4}
$$

Except in very special "degenerate" cases, S_l is nonsingular and ϕ_i is well defined on e_l. Further, property (3) ensures that ϕ_i is continuous at element edges. This, together with the continuity of polynomials, implies that

(4)
$$
\phi_i \in C(\bar{\Omega}).
\tag{5.5}
$$

Suppose node N_i is not in element e_l. Then $\mathbf{d}_{il} = \mathbf{0}$, and it follows from (5.3) and (5.1) that ϕ_i vanishes everywhere in e_l. Hence,

(5) ϕ_i assumes nonzero values only in those elements to which N_i belongs.

We call the union of elements to which N_i belongs the *support* of ϕ_i. Thus (5) states that ϕ_i vanishes outside of its support. The continuity of ϕ_i together with (5) implies the following.

(6) If N_i is not on Γ (the boundary of Ω), then ϕ_i vanishes on the boundary of its support. If N_i is on Γ, then ϕ_i vanishes on that part of the boundary of its support that lies in Ω.

Since the support of ϕ_i is usually a small subset of $\bar{\Omega}$, we say that ϕ_i has *local support* (i.e., local to N_i). A rough geometrical description of ϕ_i is that of a "tent" centered about N_i. The "floor" of the tent is the support of ϕ_i.

By definition, a function u belongs to V_M if and only if it can be expressed as

$$
u(x, y) = \sum_{i=1}^{M} c_i \phi_i(x, y), \qquad (x, y) \in \bar{\Omega}.
$$

Every such u is a *continuous, piecewise polynomial* over $\bar{\Omega}$. Geometrically, it resembles a "quilt," i.e., a connected surface consisting of smooth pieces joined together along the edges.

For any $u \in C(\bar{\Omega})$ let $u_1 \in V_M$ be defined by

$$
u_1(x, y) = \sum_{i=1}^{M} u(N_i) \phi_i(x, y), \qquad (x, y) \in \bar{\Omega}.
\tag{5.6}
$$

Applying (5.2) we find that

$$
u_1(N_i) = u(N_i), \qquad i = 1, 2, \ldots, M.
$$

That is, u_1 *interpolates* u at the nodes. We call u_1 the V_M *interpolant* of u. Obviously,

$$u_1(x, y) = u(x, y) \quad \forall (x, y) \in \bar{\Omega} \quad \Leftrightarrow \quad u \in V_M. \tag{5.7}$$

In our error analysis of the finite element method in Section 5.4, we need the concept of a V_M interpolant of a function u in a Sobolev space $H^p(\Omega)$. It will be recalled that $H^p(\Omega)$ is a subset of the Hilbert space $L^2(\Omega)$, so u is actually an equivalence class of functions that are equal almost everywhere. Since changing the value of a function at some point does not change its equivalence class, $u(N_i)$ is not a well-defined value and hence (5.6) makes no sense.

An equivalence class can contain, however, at most one function in $C(\bar{\Omega})$. In the event that it does contain such a function, we shall define $u(N_i)$ to be the value of that function at N_i. It then follows from the Sobolev embedding theorem mentioned in Section 3.1 [see (3.24)] that the V_M interpolant of any $u \in H^p(\Omega)$ is well defined for $p \geq 1$ in the case of one space dimension and for $p \geq 2$ in the case of two or three space dimensions.

We define k and m to be the greatest integers for which it is true that

$$P_k(\bar{\Omega}) \subseteq V_M \subset C^{m-1}(\bar{\Omega}), \tag{5.8}$$

where $P_k(\bar{\Omega})$ denotes the space of all polynomials of degree at most k defined on $\bar{\Omega}$. (These are global, not piecewise, polynomials.) It is easy to see that k is the degree of the largest complete polynomial represented by (5.1); i.e., k is the largest integer such that every term of the form $x^{k_1} y^{k_2}$, where $k_1 + k_2 \leq k$, appears in (5.1). The terms necessary for a complete polynomial of degree k are shown in Fig. 5.4 for $0 \leq k \leq 3$. If (5.1), for example, is

$$\phi_i(x, y) = c_{il}^{(1)} + c_{il}^{(2)}x + c_{il}^{(3)}y + c_{il}^{(4)}x^2 + c_{il}^{(5)}y^2,$$

then $k = 1$ since the first three terms make up the complete first-degree polynomial, whereas the xy term required for the complete second-degree polynomial is missing.

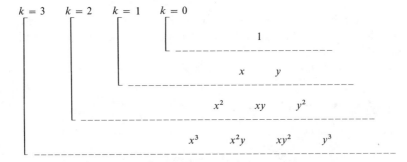

Fig. 5.4.   Terms in the complete polynomial of degree k for $k = 0, 1, 2, 3$.

It follows from (5.7) and (5.8) that

$$u \in P_k(\bar{\Omega}) \quad \Rightarrow \quad u_I(x, y) = u(x, y) \quad \forall (x, y) \in \bar{\Omega}; \qquad (5.9)$$

i.e., all polynomials of degree $\leq k$ are interpolated exactly in V_M. We shall see in Section 5.4 that this property makes k the fundamental parameter in the error analysis of finite element basis functions.

Regarding the value of m in (5.8), it is clear from (5.5) that $m \geq 1$. Now it is typical of the kind of finite element basis functions we are discussing that the normal derivative of a basis function at element edges in its support is discontinuous, implying that $V_M \not\subset C^1(\bar{\Omega})$ and $m = 1$. It turns out that to achieve C^1 continuity one has to enlarge the set of basis functions (assigning more than one basis function to at least some of the nodes) so that not only does u_I interpolate values of u but in addition certain derivatives of u_I interpolate the corresponding derivatives of u. This is known as *Hermite interpolation*, in contrast to *Lagrange interpolation*, in which only values of u are interpolated. Thus, the total number of basis functions, or "degrees of freedom," exceeds the number of nodes. C^1-continuous basis functions are easily constructed in the case of one space dimension (see Exercise 5.12), but tend to be complicated in several space dimensions.

The significance of m follows from a remark in Section 3.1 on continuous, piecewise polynomials and Sobolev spaces, namely, if u is any function of this type, then

$$u \in C^{m-1}(\bar{\Omega}), \quad u \notin C^m(\bar{\Omega}) \quad \Rightarrow \quad u \in H^m(\Omega), \quad u \notin H^{m+1}(\Omega).$$

The definition of m in (5.8) then implies that

$$V_M \subset H^m(\Omega), \qquad V_M \not\subset H^{m+1}(\Omega).$$

Finite element basis functions with $m = 1$ are appropriate, or *conforming*, for second-order boundary value problems in which the space V of the Lax–Milgram lemma is $H^1(\Omega)$ or a subspace of $H^1(\Omega)$. They are not sufficiently smooth for fourth-order problems, which require $m = 2$.

In view of the fact that basis functions for which $m = 2$ (i.e., C^1 continuity) are rather unwieldy, it is worth mentioning that the *mixed-variational* formulation of fourth-order problems makes it possible to work with basis functions having only C^0 continuity [see Ciarlet (1978) for details].

Local Basis Functions

We now introduce *local basis functions* over e_l, defined by

$$\phi_r^{(l)}(x, y) = \phi_{i_r^{(l)}}(x, y), \qquad (x, y) \in e_l, \quad r = 1, 2, \ldots, T.$$

A local basis function is simply the restriction of some global basis function to e_l. Note that it is locally determined by (5.1) and (5.3). Its name stems from the fact that if $V_T^{(l)}$ denotes the space of all polynomials of type (5.1) defined on e_l, then

$$V_T^{(l)} = \text{SPAN}\{\phi_1^{(l)}, \phi_2^{(l)}, ..., \phi_T^{(l)}\}.$$

Obviously,

$$\phi_r^{(l)}(N_{i_s^{(l)}}) = \delta_{rs}, \qquad r, s = 1, 2, ..., T.$$

Using the local basis functions we can rewrite (5.6) as

$$u_l(x, y) = \sum_{i=1}^{M} u(N_i)\phi_i(x, y)$$

$$= \sum_{r=1}^{T} u(N_{i_r^{(l)}})\phi_r^{(l)}(x, y), \qquad (x, y) \in e_l,$$

displaying the local nature of finite element interpolation.

We will henceforth assume that the finite element basis functions have the following property in addition to the six mentioned earlier.

(7)   It is possible to choose a *standard* (or *reference*) *element* $\tilde{e}$ in the $\tilde{x}$–$\tilde{y}$ plane, with local basis functions $\tilde{\phi}_1(\tilde{x}, \tilde{y}), \tilde{\phi}_2(\tilde{x}, \tilde{y}), ..., \tilde{\phi}_T(\tilde{x}, \tilde{y})$ of type (5.1), and find for every element e_l an invertible affine variable transformation

$$\left.\begin{array}{l} x = x(\tilde{x}, \tilde{y}) \equiv f_{11}\tilde{x} + f_{12}\tilde{y} + b_1 \\ y = y(\tilde{x}, \tilde{y}) \equiv f_{21}\tilde{x} + f_{22}\tilde{y} + b_2 \end{array}\right\} (\tilde{x}, \tilde{y}) \in \tilde{e} \qquad (5.10)$$

dependent on l, such that (5.10) maps $\tilde{e}$ onto e_l (mapping nodes onto nodes) and

$$\tilde{\phi}_r(\tilde{x}, \tilde{y}) = \phi_r^{(l)}(x(\tilde{x}, \tilde{y}), y(\tilde{x}, \tilde{y})). \qquad (5.11)$$

Denoting the inverse transformation of (5.10) by

$$\left.\begin{array}{l} \tilde{x} = \tilde{x}(x, y) \\ \tilde{y} = \tilde{y}(x, y) \end{array}\right\} (x, y) \in e_l, \qquad (5.12)$$

we can rewrite (5.11) as

$$\phi_r^{(l)}(x, y) = \tilde{\phi}_r(\tilde{x}(x, y), \tilde{y}(x, y)). \qquad (5.13)$$

Relation (5.11) implies that the local basis functions $\phi_r^{(l)}, l = 1, 2, ..., L$ can be reduced by variable transformations to the single function $\tilde{\phi}_r$. But since the global basis functions $\phi_1, \phi_2, ..., \phi_M$ are composites of the local basis functions, this means that *all operations on the global basis functions can be reduced to operations on* $\tilde{\phi}_1, \tilde{\phi}_2, ..., \tilde{\phi}_T$. We call these the *standard* (or *reference*) *local basis functions*. As will become clear, they lie at the heart of finite element analysis and computation.

Relation (5.13) shows that all of the local basis functions in the mesh can be generated from the standard local basis functions. This will be the point of departure for our derivation of isoparametric elements in Section 5.3.

We note for future reference that (5.10) and its inverse can be expressed in the matrix–vector form

$$\begin{bmatrix} x \\ y \end{bmatrix} = F \begin{bmatrix} \tilde{x} \\ \tilde{y} \end{bmatrix} + \mathbf{b}, \qquad \begin{bmatrix} \tilde{x} \\ \tilde{y} \end{bmatrix} = F^{-1} \begin{bmatrix} x \\ y \end{bmatrix} - F^{-1}\mathbf{b}. \tag{5.14}$$

Examples

Three examples of finite element basis functions follow, all of which are widely used in practice. The essential data in each case are

(1)   the standard element $\tilde{e}$,
(2)   the standard local basis functions,
(3)   the variable transformation (5.10),
(4)   the values of k and m in (5.8).

The choice of $\tilde{e}$, which is arbitrary, is made on the basis of simplicity.

Example 5.1. Piecewise Linear Basis Functions on Triangular Elements. Let the elements be triangles with nodes at the vertices and let (5.1) be

$$\phi_i(x, y) = c_{il}^{(1)} + c_{il}^{(2)}x + c_{il}^{(3)}y, \qquad (x, y) \in e_l. \tag{5.15}$$

A typical mesh is shown in Fig. 5.5.

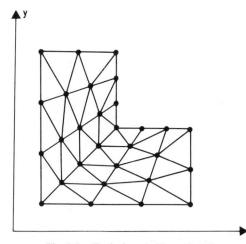

Fig. 5.5.   Typical mesh (Example 5.1).

The matrix S_l in (5.4) for this example is

$$S_l = \begin{bmatrix} 1 & x_{i_1^{(l)}} & y_{i_1^{(l)}} \\ 1 & x_{i_2^{(l)}} & y_{i_2^{(l)}} \\ 1 & x_{i_3^{(l)}} & y_{i_3^{(l)}} \end{bmatrix}.$$

It is easy to show that S_l is singular if and only if the three nodes lie on a straight line, i.e., if and only if e_l is a degenerate triangle. The basis functions are thus well defined for any normal mesh.

An element edge is described by an equation of the form $ax + by + c = 0$. By eliminating x or y in (5.15), we find that ϕ_i is a linear function of the remaining variable. Hence, ϕ_i is determined everywhere on the edge by its values at the two nodes, and property (3) is satisfied.

Figure 5.6 shows our choice of the standard element $\tilde{e}$.

The standard local basis function $\tilde{\phi}_r$ has the form

$$\tilde{\phi}_r(\tilde{x}, \tilde{y}) = \tilde{c}_r^{(1)} + \tilde{c}_r^{(2)}\tilde{x} + \tilde{c}_r^{(3)}\tilde{y},$$

the coefficients being determined so that $\tilde{\phi}_r$ has the value unity at node r and zero at the other two nodes. Simple calculations establish that

$$\tilde{\phi}_1(\tilde{x}, \tilde{y}) = 1 - \tilde{x} - \tilde{y}, \qquad \tilde{\phi}_2(\tilde{x}, \tilde{y}) = \tilde{x}, \qquad \tilde{\phi}_3(\tilde{x}, \tilde{y}) = \tilde{y}. \qquad (5.16)$$

The affine transformation

$$x = (x_{i_2^{(l)}} - x_{i_1^{(l)}})\tilde{x} + (x_{i_3^{(l)}} - x_{i_1^{(l)}})\tilde{y} + x_{i_1^{(l)}},$$
$$y = (y_{i_2^{(l)}} - y_{i_1^{(l)}})\tilde{x} + (y_{i_3^{(l)}} - y_{i_1^{(l)}})\tilde{y} + y_{i_1^{(l)}}, \qquad (5.17)$$

clearly maps the vertices of $\tilde{e}$ onto those of e_l as indicated in Fig. 5.7. Since every affine transformation maps straight lines onto straight lines (Exercise 5.1), it follows that (5.17) maps $\tilde{e}$ onto e_l.

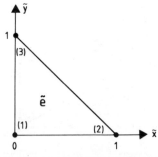

Fig. 5.6.   The standard element (Example 5.1).

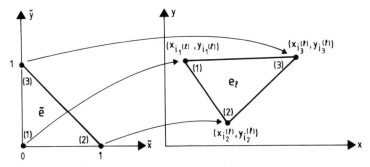

Fig. 5.7.   The mapping of $\tilde{e}$ onto e_l (Example 5.1).

For any element e_l there are six possible ways of assigning local node numbers to the nodes, three clockwise and three counterclockwise. The transformation (5.17) obviously depends on which choice is made. We shall henceforth adopt the convention (which will be useful later) that every element in the mesh has a counterclockwise local ordering of nodes.

We shall now verify that (5.11) is satisfied, taking as an example the case $r = 1$. Consider the function

$$\theta_1^{(l)}(\tilde{x}, \tilde{y}) \equiv \phi_1^{(l)}(x(\tilde{x}, \tilde{y}), y(\tilde{x}, \tilde{y})), \qquad (\tilde{x}, \tilde{y}) \in \tilde{e}.$$

Without determining $\phi_1^{(l)}(x, y)$ explicitly, we know that it is a linear function of x and y and that $\phi_1^{(l)}(N_{i_s^{(l)}}) = \delta_{1s}$, $s = 1, 2, 3$. By (5.17), $\theta_1^{(l)}(\tilde{x}, \tilde{y})$ must then be a linear function of $\tilde{x}$ and $\tilde{y}$. Further,

$$\theta_1^{(l)}(0, 0) = \phi_1^{(l)}(x(0, 0), y(0, 0)) = \phi_1^{(l)}(N_{i_1^{(l)}}) = 1,$$

and similar calculations establish that $\theta_1^{(l)}(1, 0) = \theta_1^{(l)}(0, 1) = 0$. But the only linear function on $\tilde{e}$ that has these values at the vertices is the function $\tilde{\phi}_1(\tilde{x}, \tilde{y})$ in (5.16). Hence, $\theta_1^{(l)}(\tilde{x}, \tilde{y}) \equiv \tilde{\phi}_1(\tilde{x}, \tilde{y})$, and (5.11) is established.

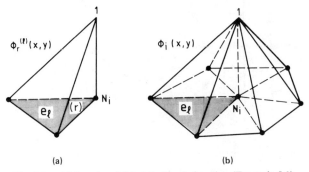

Fig. 5.8.   (a) Local and (b) global basis function (Example 5.1).

Figure 5.8 illustrates local and global basis functions and the relation between them; $\phi_r^{(l)}$ is just the restriction of ϕ_i to e_l.

Regarding the parameters k and m defined by (5.8), it is obvious from (5.15) that $k = 1$. Every function in V_M, the span of $\phi_1, \phi_2, ..., \phi_M$, is a surface made up of flat triangular pieces joined along the edges. Such functions have in general a discontinuous normal derivative at an element edge. Thus $m = 1$.

This choice of basis functions, proposed by Courant (1943) and Prager and Synge (1947), among others, is widely used because of its simplicity. Further, piecewise linear basis functions often give more accuracy, for the same computing time, than more refined basis functions when the solution of the boundary value problem has little regularity.

Example 5.2. Piecewise Quadratic Functions on Triangular Elements. Let the elements be triangular with nodes at the vertices and edge midpoints, and let (5.1) be

$$\phi_i(x, y) = c_{il}^{(1)} + c_{il}^{(2)}x + c_{il}^{(3)}y + c_{il}^{(4)}x^2 + c_{il}^{(5)}xy + c_{il}^{(6)}y^2, \qquad (x, y) \in e_l. \quad (5.18)$$

A typical mesh is shown in Fig. 5.9.

On an element edge, ϕ_i reduces to a quadratic function of x or y alone and is completely determined by its values at the three nodes on that edge. Hence, property (3) is established.

Our choice of the standard element $\tilde{e}$ is shown in Fig. 5.10. It is readily

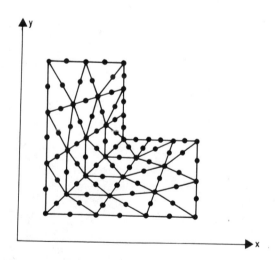

Fig. 5.9. Typical mesh (Example 5.2).

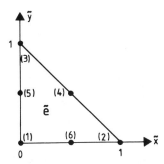

Fig. 5.10.   The standard element (Example 5.2).

verified that the corresponding standard local basis functions are

$$\tilde{\phi}_1(\tilde{x}, \tilde{y}) = \tilde{\lambda}_1(2\tilde{\lambda}_1 - 1), \qquad \tilde{\phi}_4(\tilde{x}, \tilde{y}) = 4\tilde{\lambda}_2\tilde{\lambda}_3,$$

$$\tilde{\phi}_2(\tilde{x}, \tilde{y}) = \tilde{\lambda}_2(2\tilde{\lambda}_2 - 1), \qquad \tilde{\phi}_5(\tilde{x}, \tilde{y}) = 4\tilde{\lambda}_1\tilde{\lambda}_3, \qquad (5.19)$$

$$\tilde{\phi}_3(\tilde{x}, \tilde{y}) = \tilde{\lambda}_3(2\tilde{\lambda}_3 - 1), \qquad \tilde{\phi}_6(\tilde{x}, \tilde{y}) = 4\tilde{\lambda}_1\tilde{\lambda}_2,$$

where $\tilde{\lambda}_1$, $\tilde{\lambda}_2$, and $\tilde{\lambda}_3$ are the standard local basis functions of the preceding example:

$$\tilde{\lambda}_1 = 1 - \tilde{x} - \tilde{y}, \qquad \tilde{\lambda}_2 = \tilde{x}, \qquad \tilde{\lambda}_3 = \tilde{y}.$$

(These relations are easily seen to hold for the local linear and quadratic basis functions on any element e_l.)

We adopt the convention that the local ordering of nodes in any element e_l is such that the vertex nodes are ordered first, counterclockwise, and that nodes 4, 5, and 6 are the mid-edge points opposite nodes 1, 2, and 3, respectively. The variable transformation (5.17) maps $\tilde{e}$ onto e_l and the mid-edge nodes 4, 5, and 6 of $\tilde{e}$ onto nodes 4, 5, and 6, respectively, of e_l. We leave it to the reader to verify that (5.11) is satisfied.

For these basis functions we have $k = 2$ and $m = 1$.

Example 5.3. Piecewise Bilinear Basis Functions on Rectangular Elements. Let the elements be axiparallel rectangles with nodes at the vertices, and let (5.1) be

$$\phi_i(x, y) = c_{il}^{(1)} + c_{il}^{(2)}x + c_{il}^{(3)}y + c_{il}^{(4)}xy, \qquad (x, y) \in e_l. \qquad (5.20)$$

The mesh must be formed by a set of axiparallel lines. This can be done whenever the boundary Γ is composed of axiparallel line segments, as illustrated in Fig. 5.11.

On any element edge ϕ_i reduces to a linear function of x or y and is uniquely determined by its values at the two vertex nodes. Hence, property (3) is established. (Note, however, that this property depends on the edges being axiparallel.)

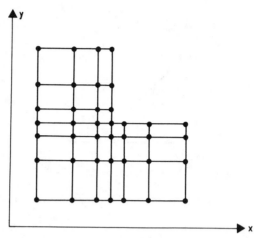

Fig. 5.11.   Typical mesh (Example 5.3).

We take as $\tilde{e}$ the element shown in Fig. 5.12. The standard local basis functions are

$$\tilde{\phi}_1(\tilde{x}, \tilde{y}) = \tfrac{1}{4}(1 - \tilde{x})(1 - \tilde{y}), \qquad \tilde{\phi}_2(\tilde{x}, \tilde{y}) = \tfrac{1}{4}(1 + \tilde{x})(1 - \tilde{y}),$$
$$\tilde{\phi}_3(\tilde{x}, \tilde{y}) = \tfrac{1}{4}(1 + \tilde{x})(1 + \tilde{y}), \qquad \tilde{\phi}_4(\tilde{x}, \tilde{y}) = \tfrac{1}{4}(1 - \tilde{x})(1 + \tilde{y}). \tag{5.21}$$

We adopt the convention that the local ordering of nodes in every element e_l is the same as shown for $\tilde{e}$ in Fig. 5.12, i.e., counterclockwise, starting at the lower left node. The affine mapping of $\tilde{e}$ onto e_l, illustrated in Fig. 5.13, can be described in terms of any three of the four nodes of e_l. In terms of the first three nodes, we have

$$x = \tfrac{1}{2}(x_{i_2^{(l)}} - x_{i_1^{(l)}})\tilde{x} + \tfrac{1}{2}(x_{i_2^{(l)}} + x_{i_1^{(l)}}),$$
$$y = \tfrac{1}{2}(y_{i_3^{(l)}} - y_{i_1^{(l)}})\tilde{y} + \tfrac{1}{2}(y_{i_3^{(l)}} + y_{i_1^{(l)}}). \tag{5.22}$$

It is easy to verify that (5.11) is satisfied.

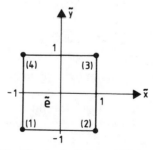

Fig. 5.12.   The standard element (Example 5.3).

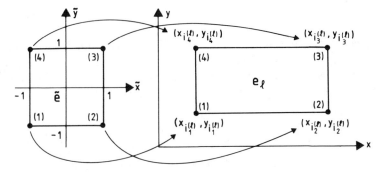

Fig. 5.13.   The mapping of $\tilde{e}$ onto e_l (Example 5.3).

Since (5.20) contains the complete first-degree polynomial but not the second, we have $k = 1$. First-order normal derivatives at element edges are generally discontinuous, and $m = 1$.

The typical global basis function ϕ_i is illustrated in Fig. 5.14. The support of ϕ_i is always four elements unless N_i belongs to Γ.

Obviously, the variety of finite element basis functions is endless. Many more examples can be found in Ciarlet (1978), Mitchell and Wait (1977), Schwarz (1980, 1981), Strang and Fix (1973), Zienkiewicz (1977), and the exercises. To keep our material within bounds we have considered only the

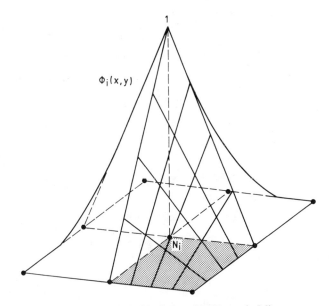

Fig. 5.14.   Global basis function (Example 5.3).

case of two space dimensions. For three-dimensional basis functions see the cited texts.

We have thus far restricted our attention to basis functions having the seven fundamental properties mentioned at the beginning of this section. Sometimes it is convenient to work with functions of a more general type, as we shall see in Sections 5.3 and 7.6.

5.2 Assembly of the Ritz–Galerkin System

Notation

We summarize here the most important notation to be introduced in this section.

Γ_0	part of Γ where an essential boundary condition is given
M_0	number of nodes on Γ_0
J_0	set of node numbers of nodes on Γ_0
Γ_1	part of Γ where a natural boundary condition is given
L_1	number of element edges on Γ_1
N	number of nodes in $\Omega \cup \Gamma_1$
J	set of node numbers of nodes in $\Omega \cup \Gamma_1$
Q	number of integration points in the standard element $\tilde{e}$
$(\tilde{x}^{(m)}, \tilde{y}^{(m)}), m = 1, 2, ..., Q$	integration points
$w_m, m = 1, 2, ..., Q$	integration weights

Program Arrays

$k(M \times M)$	stiffness matrix
$G(M)$	load vector
ELNODE $(L \times T)$	global node numbers for all elements
NODECO $(M \times 2)$	x, y coordinates of all nodes
BONODE (M_0)	set J_0
EDGE $(L_1 \times 2)$	data for all element edges on Γ_1
INTPT $(Q \times 2)$	integration points

$W(Q)$	integration weights
PHI $(T \times Q)$	values of $\tilde{\phi}_1, ..., \tilde{\phi}_T$ at the integration points
PHIX $(T \times Q)$	values of $(\tilde{\phi}_1)_x, ..., (\tilde{\phi}_T)_x$ at the integration points
PHIY $(T \times Q)$	values of $(\tilde{\phi}_1)_y, ..., (\tilde{\phi}_T)_y$ at the integration points

Preliminary Discussion

We shall show by an example how the Ritz–Galerkin method of Chapter 4 can be implemented with finite element basis functions. Thus, consider the boundary value problem

$$-(pu_x)_x - (pu_y)_y + qu = g \qquad \text{in } \Omega, \tag{5.23}$$

$$u = \gamma \qquad \text{on } \Gamma_0, \tag{5.24a}$$

$$u_\nu + \sigma u = \xi \qquad \text{on } \Gamma_1, \tag{5.24b}$$

on the domain shown in Fig. 5.15. ($\Gamma = \Gamma_0 \cup \Gamma_1$).

The differential equation is the same as (3.34), whereas the boundary conditions are a combination of (3.35) and (3.39). Regarding the various coefficients, all of the assumptions stated in the discussion of this problem in Section 3.2 are also made here.

It has to be stressed that the computational process to be described by no means requires Γ to have the simple geometry shown in Fig. 5.15. Indeed, one of the great advantages of the finite element method is its great flexibility in this respect. We note, however, that if Γ is curved, then it cannot be represented exactly by the boundary of a finite element mesh. (Isoparametric elements, however, allow a more accurate representation of Γ; see Section 5.3.)

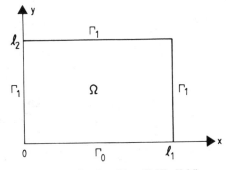

Fig. 5.15.   Domain of problem (5.23), (5.24).

The boundary segment Γ_0 should be viewed as variable in the sense that it can include as much or as little of Γ as we desire. The one extreme is

$$\Gamma_0 = \Gamma, \tag{5.25a}$$

in which case the problem reduces to (3.34), (3.35). At the other extreme we have

$$\Gamma_1 = \Gamma, \tag{5.25b}$$

yielding problem (3.34), (3.39).

Let

$$H_\gamma^1(\Omega) = \{v \in H^1(\Omega); v = \gamma \text{ on } \Gamma_0\},$$

$$H_0^1(\Omega) = \{v \in H^1(\Omega); v = 0 \text{ on } \Gamma_0\}.$$

It is easily seen from the analysis of (3.34), (3.35), and (3.39) in Chapter 3 that the variational formulation of (5.23), (5.24) is the problem of finding a function $\hat{u} \in H_\gamma^1(\Omega)$ that satisfies

$$a(\hat{u}, v) = G(v) \qquad \forall v \in H_0^1(\Omega), \tag{5.26}$$

where

$$a(u, v) = \int\!\!\int_\Omega \left[pu_x v_x + pu_y v_y + quv\right] dx\, dy + \int_{\Gamma_1} p\sigma uv\, ds$$

$$= a(u, v)_\Omega + a(u, v)_{\Gamma_1}, \quad \text{say};$$

$$G(v) = \int\!\!\int_\Omega gv\, dx\, dy + \int_{\Gamma_1} p\xi v\, ds$$

$$= G(v)_\Omega + G(v)_{\Gamma_1}, \quad \text{say}.$$

$\hat{u}$ minimizes the functional

$$f(u) = \tfrac{1}{2}a(u, u) - G(u), \qquad u \in H_\gamma^1(\Omega).$$

If u^* is any function in $H_\gamma^1(\Omega)$, then we can express $H_\gamma^1(\Omega)$ as

$$H_\gamma^1(\Omega) = \{u \in H^1(\Omega); u = v + u^*, v \in H_0^1(\Omega)\},$$

and (5.26) is equivalent to the problem of finding a function $\hat{v} \in H_0^1(\Omega)$ such that

$$a(\hat{v} + u^*, v) = G(v) \qquad \forall v \in H_0^1(\Omega).$$

Let V_N be an N-dimensional subspace of $H_0^1(\Omega)$ with basis functions ϕ_1, $\phi_2, ..., \phi_N$. According to the discussion at the end of Section 4.1, the Ritz–Galerkin equations for this problem are

$$K\alpha = G^*, \tag{5.27}$$

where

$$k_{ij} = a(\phi_j, \phi_i), \qquad\qquad i, j = 1, 2, ..., N,$$
$$G_i^* = G(\phi_i) - a(u^*, \phi_i), \qquad i = 1, 2, ..., N.$$

The corresponding Ritz–Galerkin approximations to $\hat{v}$ and $\hat{u}$ are

$$\hat{v}_N \equiv \sum_{i=1}^{N} \alpha_i \phi_i \qquad \text{and} \qquad \hat{u}_N \equiv \hat{v}_N + u^*,$$

respectively.

Application of Finite Element Basis Functions

Let there be given a mesh of L elements and M nodes on $\bar{\Omega}$ and finite element basis functions $\phi_1, \phi_2, ..., \phi_M$ with the seven properties described in Section 5.1. We define

M_0	number of nodes on Γ_0
J_0	set of node numbers of nodes on Γ_0
N	number of nodes in $\Omega \cup \Gamma_1$ ($N = M - M_0$)
J	set of node numbers of nodes in $\Omega \cup \Gamma_1$

J_0 and J refer to nodes where $\hat{u}$ is known and unknown, respectively. These sets are illustrated in Fig. 5.16 for a mesh suited to the piecewise linear basis functions of Example 5.1.

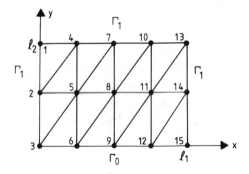

Fig. 5.16. An example of the sets J_0 and J: $M = 15$, $M_0 = 5$, $N = 10$; $J_0 = \{3, 6, 9, 12, 15\}$; $J = \{1, 2, 4, 5, 7, 8, 10, 11, 13, 14\}$.

The solution of boundary value problem (5.23), (5.24) is independent of whether Γ_0 is a closed interval. It is important for our application of the Ritz–Galerkin method, however, to

(1) place nodes at the endpoints of $\bar{\Gamma}_0$,
(2) assign these nodes to Γ_0 rather than to Γ_1.

Nodes 3 and 15 in Fig. 5.16, for example, have been assigned to Γ_0.

To be able to compute the right-hand side of (5.27), we need to find some $u^* \in H_\gamma^1(\Omega)$. Consider for this purpose the function

$$u_N^*(x, y) \equiv \sum_{i \in J_0} \gamma(N_i)\phi_i(x, y), \qquad (x, y) \in \bar{\Omega}.$$

It is readily verified that

(1) $u_N^* \in H^1(\Omega)$,
(2) $u_N^*(N_i) = \gamma(N_i) \quad \forall i \in J_0$.

That is, u_N^* is a function in $H^1(\Omega)$ that interpolates γ at all of the boundary nodes on Γ_0. However, in general u_N^* does not interpolate γ between the nodes. Thus,

$$u_N^* \notin H_\gamma^1(\Omega) \tag{5.28}$$

and u_N^* is not a mathematically valid choice of u^*. Nevertheless, if the mesh is sufficiently fine, then we expect u_N^* to be a good approximation to some function in $H_\gamma^1(\Omega)$, and we accordingly replace u^* in (5.27) by u_N^*. [A "variational crime" in the terminology of Strang and Fix (1973).]

The next step is to determine a suitable subspace $V_N \subset H_0^1(\Omega)$. Consider for this purpose

$$V_N = \mathrm{SPAN}\{\phi_i, i \in J\}.$$

Each of the N basis functions of V_N has the properties

(1) $\phi_i \in H^1(\Omega)$,
(2) $\phi_i = 0$ on Γ_0.

(Note, however, that the second property depends on the previously mentioned convention of placing nodes at the endpoints of $\bar{\Gamma}_0$ and of assigning these nodes to Γ_0.) It follows that V_N is a subspace of $H_0^1(\Omega)$, as required.

With the given choices of u^* and V_N, the data of the Ritz–Galerkin equations (5.27) become

$$k_{ij} = a(\phi_j, \phi_i), \qquad\qquad\qquad i, j \in J,$$

$$G_i^* = G(\phi_i) - \sum_{j \in J_0} \gamma(N_j)a(\phi_j, \phi_i), \qquad i \in J, \tag{5.29}$$

and the next task is that of computing these data.

Outline of the Computation

The computational procedure is most easily described in terms of two programming arrays, k and G, with dimensions $(M \times M)$ and $(M \times 1)$, respectively. In practice an $(M \times M)$ array would hardly ever be used, since the stiffness matrix it will contain turns out to be very sparse. However, it is a straightforward programming task to interpret an element $k[i,j]$ in terms of another data structure. The simplicity of an $(M \times M)$ array makes it preferable for clarifying the computation, and that is our purpose here.

Note that the size of the arrays is determined by M and not N. This reflects a basic principle in our approach, namely, to make the computation as independent of the boundary conditions as possible.

The calculation of the Ritz–Galerkin data (5.29) can be performed in the following major steps:

(1) $k[i,j] := a(\phi_j, \phi_i)_\Omega,$ $\qquad\qquad i,j = 1, 2, ..., M;$

(2) $G[i] := G(\phi_i)_\Omega,$ $\qquad\qquad\qquad i = 1, 2, ..., M;$

(3) $k[i,j] := k[i,j] + a(\phi_j, \phi_i)_{\Gamma_1},$ $\quad i,j = 1, 2, ..., M;$

(4) $G[i] := G[i] + G(\phi_i)_{\Gamma_1},$ $\qquad\quad i = 1, 2, ..., M;$

(5) $\forall j \in J_0:$

$$G[i] := G[i] - \gamma(N_j)k[i,j] \qquad \forall i \in J;$$

$$k[i,j] := 0, \quad k[j,i] := 0 \qquad \forall i \in J;$$

$$k[j,i] := 0 \qquad \forall i \in J_0, \quad i \neq j;$$

$$G[j] := \gamma(N_j); \quad k[j,j] := 1;$$

where $a(\cdot, \cdot)_\Omega$, $G(\cdot)_\Omega$, $a(\cdot, \cdot)_{\Gamma_1}$, and $G(\cdot)_{\Gamma_1}$ are defined under (5.26).

Remarks

1. The first two steps are independent of the boundary conditions, in accordance with the principle stated previously. Steps (3) and (4) bring in the natural boundary condition on Γ_1. Step (5) takes into account the essential boundary condition on Γ_0.

2. For every $i \in J_0$, the ith row and column of array k contain zeros at the end of the computation except in the diagonal position, where we have $k[i,i] = 1$. $G[i]$ contains the value $\gamma(N_i)$. If we were to "compress" k and G by removing all of these rows and columns, then the two arrays would assume dimensions $N \times N$ and $N \times 1$, respectively, and would contain precisely the

data of (5.29). In working with arrays of dimension $(M \times M)$ and $(M \times 1)$, we are appending the $(M - N)$ equations

$$u(N_i) = \gamma(N_i) \qquad \forall i \in J_0$$

to the original Nth-order Ritz–Galerkin system.

If the nodes of $\Omega \cup \Gamma_1$ are ordered before those of Γ_0, then the final contents of k assumes the form

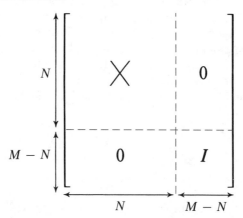

No such ordering is required, however, and no attempt need be made to delete the extra equations from the system prior to calling an equation solver. Since N/M is close to unity when the mesh is fine and the extra equations are extremely simple, the extra work involved in solving the Mth-order system instead of the Nth-order system is usually marginal.

3. The importance of the choice of a node ordering depends upon the nature of the equation solver. If the equation solver implements the simple conjugate gradient method of Chapter 1, then the node ordering is unimportant. If it implements the conjugate gradient method with either of the types of preconditioning discussed in Section 1.4, or if it implements a direct method (Chapter 6), then the ordering can have an important effect on computational labor and possibly data storage as well.

4. We can associate with the computation three normally distinct "stiffness" matrices, namely:

(1) K_1 of order M, the contents of array k at the end of step (1);   (5.30a)

(2) K_2 of order M, the contents of array k at the end of step (5);   (5.30b)

(3) K_3 of order N, the matrix obtained by removing the ith row
        and column of K_2 for all $i \in J_0$.   (5.30c)

K_2 and K_3 were discussed in Remark 2. We call K_1 the *primitive* stiffness matrix since it is formed without regard to the boundary conditions. In the remainder of this section we denote the primitive stiffness matrix, for convenience, by K.

5. A faster, if less neat, alternative to step (5) is

$$\forall j \in J_0:$$

$$k(j, j) := c; \qquad G(j) := c\gamma(N_j),$$

where c is a very large number (10^{20}, for example).

To make the computation as clear as possible, we did not exploit the symmetry of $a(\cdot, \cdot)$. We now give a more refined version that roughly halves the work and uses only the lower left triangle (main diagonal included) of array k.

(1) $k[i, j] := a(\phi_j, \phi_i)_\Omega,$ $\qquad\qquad i = 1, 2, ..., M; \quad j = 1, 2, ..., i,$ (5.31a)

(2) $G[i] := G(\phi_i)_\Omega,$ $\qquad\qquad\qquad\quad i = 1, 2, ..., M,$ (5.31b)

(3) $k[i, j] := k[i, j] + a(\phi_j, \phi_i)_{\Gamma_1},$ $\quad i = 1, 2, ..., M; \quad j = 1, 2, ..., i,$ (5.31c)

(4) $G[i] := G[i] + G(\phi_i)_{\Gamma_1},$ $\qquad\qquad i = 1, 2, ..., M,$ (5.31d)

(5) $\forall j \in J_0:$ (5.31e)

$$\left.\begin{array}{l} G[i] := G[i] - \gamma(N_j)k[j, i] \\ k[j, i] := 0 \end{array}\right\} \forall i \in J, i < j,$$

$$\left.\begin{array}{l} G[i] := G[i] - \gamma(N_j)k[i, j] \\ k[i, j] := 0 \end{array}\right\} \forall i \in J, i > j,$$

$$k[j, i] := 0 \qquad \forall i \in J_0, \quad i < j,$$

$$G[j] := \gamma(N_j); \qquad k[j, j] := 1.$$

In the case of the $(M \times M)$ array k we are using here, no computer storage is saved by exploiting symmetry. However, when (5.31) is rewritten for a storage scheme designed for a sparse symmetric matrix (such as those given in Sections 1.4 and 6.1), then there is an important reduction in storage. See Exercise 5.21 for further discussion.

The computation described by (5.31) is only an overview of the actual computational process. It is even misleading with regard to the sequence of operations within any of the five steps. We shall now describe in detail the implementation of each step.

Implementation of (5.31a): Element Matrices

The quantities to be computed in (5.31a) are

$$k_{ij} \equiv a(\phi_j, \phi_i)_\Omega = a(\phi_i, \phi_j)_\Omega = \int\int_\Omega F(\phi_i, \phi_j)\, dx\, dy, \qquad i, j = 1, 2, \ldots, M,$$

where

$$F(\phi_i, \phi_j) = p(\phi_i)_x(\phi_j)_x + p(\phi_i)_y(\phi_j)_y + q\phi_i\phi_j.$$

Property (5) of finite element basis functions (see Section 5.1) implies that $k_{ij} \neq 0$ only if nodes N_i and N_j belong to a common element. Thus, the primitive stiffness matrix $K = [k_{ij}]_{i,j=1}^M$ is sparse if the mesh is fine, and this is one of its important properties.

Let us decompose K according to the contributions from the individual elements. Thus,

$$K = \sum_{l=1}^L \hat{K}^{(l)},$$

where

$$\hat{k}_{ij}^{(l)} = \int\int_{e_l} F(\phi_i, \phi_j)\, dx\, dy, \qquad i, j = 1, 2, \ldots, M.$$

$\hat{K}^{(l)}$ is even sparser than K, having at most T^2 nonzero entries, where T is the number of nodes in an element. This follows from the fact that $\hat{k}_{ij}^{(l)}$ is nonzero only if N_i and N_j belong to e_l. If $\hat{k}_{ij}^{(l)}$ is nonzero, then clearly:

(1)   among the node numbers $i_1^{(l)}, i_2^{(l)}, \ldots, i_T^{(l)}$ are two, $i_r^{(l)}$ and $i_s^{(l)}$, such that

$$i = i_r^{(l)}, \qquad j = i_s^{(l)}; \tag{5.32}$$

(2) $$\hat{k}_{ij}^{(l)} = \int\int_{e_l} F(\phi_r^{(l)}, \phi_s^{(l)})\, dx\, dy.$$

Here we are using the notation for node numbers and local basis functions introduced in Section 5.1.

It is very convenient to associate with each element e_l a $T \times T$ matrix $K^{(l)}$ defined by

$$k_{rs}^{(l)} = \int\int_{e_l} F(\phi_r^{(l)}, \phi_s^{(l)})\, dx\, dy, \qquad r, s = 1, 2, \ldots, T. \tag{5.33}$$

We call $K^{(l)}$ the *element stiffness matrix*, or more simply, the *element matrix* of e_l. In view of the relations $K = \sum_{l=1}^L \hat{K}^{(l)}$ and $\hat{k}_{ij}^{(l)} = k_{rs}^{(l)}$ (for every $\hat{k}_{ij}^{(l)} \neq 0$) we can "assemble" K from the entries of the element matrices. Since both K

and the element matrices are symmetric, we need assemble only the lower left triangle of K, and this can be done using only the lower left triangle of the element matrices. The process is described by the following pseudo-ALGOL code:

```
for i := 1 step 1 until M do
for j := 1 step 1 until i do
k[i, j] := 0;
for l := 1 step 1 until L do
for r := 1 step 1 until T do
for s := 1 step 1 until r do
begin
    compute k_{rs}^{(l)};
    i := i_r^{(l)}; j := i_s^{(l)};
    if i ≥ j then
    k[i, j] := k[i, j] + k_{rs}^{(l)}
    else
    k[j, i] := k[j, i] + k_{rs}^{(l)}
end;
```

(5.34)

This computation, which implements (5.31a), proceeds by elements. The values of i and j, determined from l, r, and s by (5.32), are easily found if we have available a table of the global node numbers for all elements. Consider for this purpose an integer array ELNODE with dimensions $L \times T$. Suppose that in the process of generating the mesh we have put

$$\text{ELNODE}[l, r] := i_r^{(l)}, \qquad l = 1, 2, \ldots, L, \quad r = 1, 2, \ldots, T. \quad (5.35)$$

Then the statements $i := i_r^{(l)}$ and $j := i_s^{(l)}$ can be interpreted as $i := \text{ELNODE}[l, r]$ and $j := \text{ELNODE}[l, s]$, respectively.

We turn our attention now to the computation of the typical element matrix entry

$$k_{rs}^{(l)} = \int\int_{e_l} \left[p(\phi_r^{(l)})_x(\phi_s^{(l)})_x + p(\phi_r^{(l)})_y(\phi_s^{(l)})_y + q\phi_r^{(l)}\phi_s^{(l)} \right] dx \, dy. \quad (5.36)$$

We shall exploit here the variable transformation (5.10) and its inverse (5.12) to express $k_{rs}^{(l)}$ as an integral in the $\tilde{x}$, $\tilde{y}$ variables over the standard element $\tilde{e}$. Thus, let $x_{\tilde{x}}$, $x_{\tilde{y}}$, $y_{\tilde{x}}$, and $y_{\tilde{y}}$ denote the partial derivatives of (5.10). The change of variables requires $dx \, dy$ to be replaced by $|\tilde{D}| \, d\tilde{x} \, d\tilde{y}$, where $\tilde{D}$ is the Jacobian of (5.10), i.e.,

$$\tilde{D} = \det\begin{bmatrix} x_{\tilde{x}} & x_{\tilde{y}} \\ y_{\tilde{x}} & y_{\tilde{y}} \end{bmatrix} = x_{\tilde{x}}y_{\tilde{y}} - x_{\tilde{y}}y_{\tilde{x}}.$$

Let $\tilde{x}_x, \tilde{x}_y, \tilde{y}_x$, and $\tilde{y}_y$ denote the partial derivatives of (5.12). The derivatives $(\phi_r^{(l)})_x$ and $(\phi_r^{(l)})_y$ in (5.36) are transformed according to

$$(\phi_r^{(l)})_x = (\tilde{\phi}_r)_{\tilde{x}}\tilde{x}_x + (\tilde{\phi}_r)_{\tilde{y}}\tilde{y}_x,$$

$$(\phi_r^{(l)})_y = (\tilde{\phi}_r)_{\tilde{x}}\tilde{x}_y + (\tilde{\phi}_r)_{\tilde{y}}\tilde{y}_y,$$

and analogous identities hold for $(\phi_s^{(l)})_x$ and $(\phi_s^{(l)})_y$. It is expedient to express the partial derivatives of (5.12) in terms of those of (5.10). A theorem of calculus states that the relevant relations are

$$\tilde{x}_x = \tilde{D}^{-1}y_{\tilde{y}}, \qquad \tilde{x}_y = -\tilde{D}^{-1}x_{\tilde{y}}, \qquad \tilde{y}_x = -\tilde{D}^{-1}y_{\tilde{x}}, \qquad \tilde{y}_y = \tilde{D}^{-1}x_{\tilde{x}}. \quad (5.37)$$

Finally, let

$$\tilde{p}(\tilde{x}, \tilde{y}) = p(x(\tilde{x}, \tilde{y}), y(\tilde{x}, \tilde{y})), \qquad \tilde{q}(\tilde{x}, \tilde{y}) = q(x(\tilde{x}, \tilde{y}), y(\tilde{x}, \tilde{y})).$$

Combining all of these results we can rewrite (5.36) as

$$k_{rs}^{(l)} = \iint_{\tilde{e}} \{|\tilde{D}|^{-1}\tilde{p}[\tilde{E}_1(\tilde{\phi}_r)_{\tilde{x}}(\tilde{\phi}_s)_{\tilde{x}} - \tilde{E}_2((\tilde{\phi}_r)_{\tilde{y}}(\tilde{\phi}_s)_{\tilde{x}} + (\tilde{\phi}_r)_{\tilde{x}}(\tilde{\phi}_s)_{\tilde{y}})$$

$$+ \tilde{E}_3(\tilde{\phi}_r)_{\tilde{y}}(\tilde{\phi}_s)_{\tilde{y}}] + |\tilde{D}|\tilde{q}\tilde{\phi}_r\tilde{\phi}_s\} \, d\tilde{x} \, d\tilde{y}, \quad (5.38)$$

where

$$\tilde{D} = x_{\tilde{x}}y_{\tilde{y}} - x_{\tilde{y}}y_{\tilde{x}}, \qquad \tilde{E}_1 = x_{\tilde{y}}^2 + y_{\tilde{y}}^2,$$

$$\tilde{E}_2 = x_{\tilde{x}}x_{\tilde{y}} + y_{\tilde{x}}y_{\tilde{y}}, \qquad \tilde{E}_3 = x_{\tilde{x}}^2 + y_{\tilde{x}}^2.$$

Thus, if we have explicit knowledge of the standard local basis functions and the transformation (5.10), then the integrand of (5.38) is a known function of $\tilde{x}$ and $\tilde{y}$. Note that the dependency of (5.38) on l occurs through the variable transformation alone, since the standard local basis functions are independent of l.

A very essential point is that (5.38) is valid for a *general* variable transformation $x = x(\tilde{x}, \tilde{y})$, $y = y(\tilde{x}, \tilde{y})$, a fact that will be important in our discussion of isoparametric basis functions in Section 5.3. When the transformation has the affine form shown in (5.10), then obviously

$$\tilde{D} = f_{11}f_{22} - f_{12}f_{21}, \qquad \tilde{E}_1 = f_{12}^2 + f_{22}^2,$$

$$\tilde{E}_2 = f_{11}f_{12} + f_{21}f_{22}, \qquad \tilde{E}_3 = f_{11}^2 + f_{21}^2, \quad (5.39)$$

and f_{11}, f_{12}, f_{21}, and f_{22} are functions of the x, y coordinates of the vertex nodes in e_l. See (5.17) and (5.22) for the case of triangular and rectangular elements, respectively.

Let NODECO be an $(M \times 2)$ array and suppose that in the process of generating the mesh we have put

$$\text{NODECO}[i, 1] := x_i$$
$$\text{NODECO}[i, 2] := y_i$$

(5.40)

for $i = 1, 2, ..., M$, where (x_i, y_i) are the coordinates of node N_i. We can then compute $f_{11}, f_{12}, f_{21},$ and f_{22} easily by finding the global node numbers of e_l in ELNODE and then using NODECO to find the node coordinates.

Numerical Integration

The integral (5.38) can be determined numerically. A numerical method for computing

$$I = \int \int_{\tilde{e}} \tilde{\theta}(\tilde{x}, \tilde{y}) \, d\tilde{x} \, d\tilde{y}$$

typically has the form

$$I_A = \sum_{m=1}^{Q} w_m \tilde{\theta}(\tilde{x}^{(m)}, \tilde{y}^{(m)}),$$

(5.41)

where the *integration points* $\{(\tilde{x}^{(m)}, \tilde{y}^{(m)})\}_{m=1}^{Q}$ and the corresponding *weights* $\{w_m\}_{m=1}^{Q}$ are independent of $\tilde{\theta}$. For a given domain $\tilde{e}$ one can construct many formulas of this type. In the interest of low computational labor one obviously wants Q to be small. On the other hand, a requirement of high accuracy forces Q to be large. Table 5.1 gives integration formulas that are appropriate

Table 5.1

Integration Formulas for Examples 5.1–5.3

Example	Points	Weights
5.1	$(1/3, 1/3)$	$1/2$
5.2	$(1/2, 0)$	$1/6$
	$(1/2, 1/2)$	$1/6$
	$(0, 1/2)$	$1/6$
5.3	$(1/\sqrt{3}, 1/\sqrt{3})$	1
	$(-1/\sqrt{3}, 1/\sqrt{3})$	1
	$(-1/\sqrt{3}, -1/\sqrt{3})$	1
	$(1/\sqrt{3}, -1/\sqrt{3})$	1

for the basis functions of Examples 5.1–5.3. By "appropriate" we mean that they do not reduce the order of convergence associated with the basis functions. (See Section 5.4.) In each case, the domain $\tilde{e}$ is the standard element shown in the corresponding example.

The application of an integration formula of type (5.41) to the integral (5.38) is easily programmed in terms of arrays W, INTPT, PHI, PHIX, and PHIY with the following contents:

$$W(m) = w_m,$$

$$\text{INTPT}[m, 1] = \tilde{x}^{(m)}, \qquad\qquad (5.42a)$$

$$\text{INTPT}[m, 2] = \tilde{y}^{(m)},$$

for $m = 1, 2, ..., Q$;

$$\text{PHI}[r, m] = \tilde{\phi}_r(\tilde{x}^{(m)}, \tilde{y}^{(m)}),$$

$$\text{PHIX}[r, m] = (\tilde{\phi}_r)_{\tilde{x}}(\tilde{x}^{(m)}, \tilde{y}^{(m)}), \qquad\qquad (5.42b)$$

$$\text{PHIY}[r, m] = (\tilde{\phi}_r)_{\tilde{y}}(\tilde{x}^{(m)}, \tilde{y}^{(m)}),$$

for $r = 1, 2, ..., T$; $m = 1, 2, ..., Q$. These arrays can be established at the beginning of the computation since they are independent of the element e_l. The required values of $\tilde{p}$ and $\tilde{q}$, which have to be computed for each element, are given by

$$\tilde{p}(\tilde{x}^{(m)}, \tilde{y}^{(m)}) = p(x^{(m)}, y^{(m)}),$$

$$\tilde{q}(\tilde{x}^{(m)}, \tilde{y}^{(m)}) = q(x^{(m)}, y^{(m)}),$$

for $m = 1, 2, ..., Q$, where

$$x^{(m)} = f_{11}\tilde{x}^{(m)} + f_{12}\tilde{y}^{(m)} + b_1,$$

$$y^{(m)} = f_{21}\tilde{x}^{(m)} + f_{22}\tilde{y}^{(m)} + b_2.$$

We shall now describe briefly an alternative treatment of (5.38), based on the approximations

$$\tilde{p}(\tilde{x}, \tilde{y}) \simeq \tilde{p}_I(\tilde{x}, \tilde{y}) \equiv \sum_{r=1}^{T} \tilde{p}(\tilde{x}_r, \tilde{y}_r)\tilde{\phi}_r(\tilde{x}, \tilde{y}),$$

$$\tilde{q}(\tilde{x}, \tilde{y}) \simeq \tilde{q}_I(\tilde{x}, \tilde{y}) \equiv \sum_{r=1}^{T} \tilde{q}(\tilde{x}_r, \tilde{y}_r)\tilde{\phi}_r(\tilde{x}, \tilde{y}),$$

where $(\tilde{x}_r, \tilde{y}_r)$, $r = 1, 2, ..., T$, are the nodes of $\tilde{e}$. The functions $\tilde{p}_I$ and $\tilde{q}_I$ are the unique functions in $\text{SPAN}\{\tilde{\phi}_1, \tilde{\phi}_2, ..., \tilde{\phi}_T\}$ that interpolate $\tilde{p}$ and $\tilde{q}$, respectively, at the nodes. When $\tilde{p}_I$ and $\tilde{q}_I$ are substituted for $\tilde{p}$ and $\tilde{q}$ in (5.38), the integrand becomes a polynomial in $\tilde{x}$ and $\tilde{y}$. Now the integral

$$\iint_{\tilde{e}} \tilde{x}^\alpha \tilde{y}^\beta \, d\tilde{x} \, d\tilde{y},$$

where α and β are arbitrary nonnegative integers, can be determined analytically for each of our standard elements. (This is trivial for the square; see Exercise 5.20 for the case of the triangle.) Hence we can approximate (5.38).

In the special but by no means uncommon case when $p(x, y)$ and $q(x, y)$ are constant functions, the element matrices can in principle be found exactly. (See Exercises 5.14–5.17 and 7.18 for some examples.) Further, when the mesh is completely uniform, the element matrices are identical and the computational labor of the assembly process can be substantially reduced. An additional advantage of the analytically determined element matrices is the valuable insight they give into the influence of the geometry of the element.

Despite these observations, we prefer to emphasize the use of numerical integration in the assembly process because of its generality. Even though a program code based on numerical integration will often not have optimal efficiency, it is straightforward to write and easy to change from one type of basis function to another. Further, and very important, it is readily extended to the isoparametric basis functions of Section 5.3.

Implementation of (5.31b): Element Vectors

We now consider (5.31b), which requires the computation of the integrals

$$G_i \equiv \iint_\Omega g\phi_i \, dx \, dy, \qquad i = 1, 2, ..., M.$$

The procedure here is entirely analogous to that described for (5.31a). Thus, the primitive load vector

$$\mathbf{G} = [G_i]_{i=1}^M$$

is decomposed according to elements

$$\mathbf{G} = \sum_{l=1}^{L} \hat{\mathbf{G}}^{(l)},$$

where

$$\hat{g}_i^{(l)} = \iint_{e_l} g\phi_i \, dx \, dy, \qquad i = 1, 2, ..., M.$$

There are at most T nonzero components in any $\hat{\mathbf{G}}^{(l)}$, are these are conveniently collected in a $(T \times 1)$ *element vector* $\mathbf{G}^{(l)}$ defined by

$$g_r^{(l)} = \int\int_{e_l} g\phi_r^{(l)} \, dx \, dy, \qquad r = 1, 2, ..., T.$$

$\mathbf{G}$ can thus be assembled in array G as follows:

$$
\begin{aligned}
&\textbf{for } i := 1 \textbf{ step } 1 \textbf{ until } M \textbf{ do} \\
&G[i] := 0; \\
&\textbf{for } l := 1 \textbf{ step } 1 \textbf{ until } L \textbf{ do} \\
&\textbf{for } r := 1 \textbf{ step } 1 \textbf{ until } T \textbf{ do} \\
&\textbf{begin} \\
&\quad \text{compute } g_r^{(l)}; \\
&\quad i := i_r^{(l)}; \\
&\quad G[i] := G[i] + g_r^{(l)} \\
&\textbf{end};
\end{aligned}
\qquad (5.43)
$$

This implements (5.31b), but as in (5.34) the computation proceeds element by element. Using again the variable transformation that maps $\tilde{e}$ onto e_l, we find that

$$g_r^{(l)} = \int\int_{\tilde{e}} \tilde{g}\tilde{\phi}_r |\tilde{D}| \, d\tilde{x} \, d\tilde{y}, \qquad (5.44)$$

where

$$\tilde{g}(\tilde{x}, \tilde{y}) = g(x(\tilde{x}, \tilde{y}), y(\tilde{x}, \tilde{y}))$$

and

$$\tilde{D} = x_{\tilde{x}} y_{\tilde{y}} - x_{\tilde{y}} y_{\tilde{x}}.$$

Integral (5.44), like (5.38), does not require the variable transformation to be affine and hence is also applicable to isoparametric basis functions. In the affine case it reduces to

$$g_r^{(l)} = |f_{11}f_{22} - f_{12}f_{21}| \int\int_{\tilde{e}} \tilde{g}\tilde{\phi}_r \, d\tilde{x} \, d\tilde{y}. \qquad (5.45)$$

The numerical integration formulas of Table 5.1 can be used here.

Implementation of (5.31c,d): Edge Integrals

It follows from the properties of finite element basis functions that the integral

$$a(\phi_j, \phi_i)_{\Gamma_1} = \int_{\Gamma_1} p\sigma\phi_i\phi_j \, ds \qquad (5.46)$$

is nonzero only if nodes N_i and N_j belong to a common element edge lying on Γ_1. Let L_1 denote the number of element edges on Γ_1, and let EDGE be an integer array of dimensions $L_1 \times 2$. We suppose that during the construction of the finite element mesh we have stored information on each edge as follows:

$$\text{EDGE}[t, 1] := l,$$
$$\text{EDGE}[t, 2] := r_1, \tag{5.47}$$

for $t = 1, 2, \ldots, L_1$, where l is the element number and r_1 is the local node number of the first vertex node on the edge. By "first" we mean that motion along the edge from this node to the other vertex node on Γ_1 is in the counterclockwise sense of Γ. The order in which edges are recorded in EDGE is arbitrary. Note that a corner can lead to an element having more than one edge on Γ_1. Array EDGE then has an entry for each such edge.

To simplify the discussion somewhat, we shall henceforth restrict our attention to the three examples of finite element basis functions presented in Section 5.1. The treatment of other choices of basis functions is very similar.

Provided that the rules for local node orderings laid down in Examples 5.1–5.3 have been observed, we can determine from r_1 the local node number of the other vertex node on the edge. Let this number be denoted r_2. In the case of the six-node triangle, there is also a node on the midpoint of the edge. We denote its local node number r_3, and this number is also easily found from r_1. The vertex nodes of the edge can be written

$$N_{i_1} = (x_{i_1}, y_{i_1}), \qquad i_1 \equiv i_{r_1}^{(l)},$$
$$N_{i_2} = (x_{i_2}, y_{i_2}), \qquad i_2 \equiv i_{r_2}^{(l)}.$$

We shall need the sets $\hat{S}_t$ and S_t defined for each edge by

$$\hat{S}_t = \begin{cases} \{r_1, r_2\} & \text{(three-node triangle and four-node rectangle)}, \\ \{r_1, r_2, r_3\} & \text{(six-node triangle)}, \end{cases}$$

$$S_t = \{(r, s); r, s \in \hat{S}_t, r \geq s\}.$$

See Fig. 5.17.

The key to the implementation of (5.31c) is the fact that if the integral (5.46) is nonzero, then it can be assembled from *edge integrals* of the form

$$I_{r,s}^{(t)} = \int_{N_{i_1}}^{N_{i_2}} p\sigma\phi_r^{(l)}\phi_s^{(l)}\, ds, \qquad (r, s) \in S_t, \tag{5.48}$$

where $\phi_r^{(l)}$ and $\phi_s^{(l)}$ denote, as usual, local basis functions. [It is in fact the sum of at most two such integrals.] Hence, we have the following edgewise

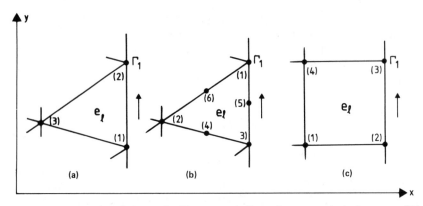

Fig. 5.17.   Examples of the set S_t. The arrows indicate the counterclockwise sense of Γ.
(a) $r_1 = 1$, $r_2 = 2$, $S_t = \{(1,1), (2,1), (2,2)\}$; (b) $r_1 = 3$, $r_2 = 1$, $r_3 = 5$, $S_t = \{(1,1), (3,1), (3,3),$
$(5,1), (5,3), (5,5)\}$; (c) $r_1 = 2, r_2 = 3, S_t = \{(2,2), (3,2), (3,3)\}$.

procedure for (5.31c):

$$
\begin{aligned}
&\textbf{for } t := 1 \textbf{ step } 1 \textbf{ until } L_1 \textbf{ do}\\
&\textbf{for all } (r, s) \in S_t \textbf{ do}\\
&\textbf{begin}\\
&\quad \text{compute } I_{rs}^{(t)};\\
&\quad i := i_r^{(l)};\, j := i_s^{(l)};\\
&\quad \textbf{if } i \geq j \textbf{ then}\\
&\quad k[i, j] := k[i, j] + I_{rs}^{(t)}\\
&\quad \textbf{else}\\
&\quad k[j, i] := k[j, i] + I_{rs}^{(t)}\\
&\textbf{end};
\end{aligned}
\qquad (5.49)
$$

For any choice of basis functions, the programming of "**for all** $(r, s) \in S_t$ **do**"
is easy given array EDGE.

To compute $I_{rs}^{(t)}$ we apply the variable transformation (5.10), expressing
$I_{rs}^{(t)}$ as an integral along the edge of the standard element $\tilde{e}$ with vertex nodes
$\tilde{N}_{r_1}$ and $\tilde{N}_{r_2}$. There are three cases to consider for triangular elements and
four for rectangular elements. The results of the variable transformation for
all seven cases is shown in Table 5.2. The parameter d is the length of the
edge in the original element e_l, i.e.,

$$
d = \{(x_{i_2} - x_{i_1})^2 + (y_{i_2} - y_{i_1})^2\}^{1/2}.
$$

The coordinates in this formula are found using ELNODE and NODECO.
$\tilde{f}$ is the result of applying the variable transformation to $p\sigma$; thus

$$
\tilde{f}(\tilde{x}, \tilde{y}) = p(x(\tilde{x}, \tilde{y}), y(\tilde{x}, \tilde{y})) \cdot \sigma(x(\tilde{x}, \tilde{y}), y(\tilde{x}, \tilde{y}));
$$

$\tilde{\phi}_r$ and $\tilde{\phi}_s$ denote, as usual, the standard local basis functions.

Table 5.2
Edge Integrals for the Triangular Elements of Examples 5.1 and 5.2
and the Rectangular Elements of Example 5.3

(r_1, r_2)	$I_{r,s}^{(t)}$
Triangular	
$(1, 2)$	$d \displaystyle\int_0^1 \tilde{f}(\tilde{x}, 0)\tilde{\phi}_r(\tilde{x}, 0)\tilde{\phi}_s(\tilde{x}, 0) \, d\tilde{x}$
$(2,3)$	$\dfrac{d}{\sqrt{2}} \displaystyle\int_0^{\sqrt{2}} \tilde{f}(\tilde{x}, \tilde{y})\tilde{\phi}_r(\tilde{x}, \tilde{y})\tilde{\phi}_s(\tilde{x}, \tilde{y}) \, d\tilde{s}, \qquad \tilde{x} = -\dfrac{\tilde{s}}{\sqrt{2}} + 1, \quad \tilde{y} = \dfrac{\tilde{s}}{\sqrt{2}}$
$(3, 1)$	$d \displaystyle\int_0^1 \tilde{f}(0, \tilde{y})\tilde{\phi}_r(0, \tilde{y})\tilde{\phi}_s(0, \tilde{y}) \, d\tilde{y}$
Rectangular	
$(1, 2)$	$\dfrac{d}{2} \displaystyle\int_{-1}^1 \tilde{f}(\tilde{x}, -1)\tilde{\phi}_r(\tilde{x}, -1)\tilde{\phi}_s(\tilde{x}, -1) \, d\tilde{x}$
$(2, 3)$	$\dfrac{d}{2} \displaystyle\int_{-1}^1 \tilde{f}(1, \tilde{y})\tilde{\phi}_r(1, \tilde{y})\tilde{\phi}_s(1, \tilde{y}) \, d\tilde{y}$
$(3, 4)$	$\dfrac{d}{2} \displaystyle\int_{-1}^1 \tilde{f}(\tilde{x}, 1)\tilde{\phi}_r(\tilde{x}, 1)\tilde{\phi}_s(\tilde{x}, 1) \, d\tilde{x}$
$(4, 1)$	$\dfrac{d}{2} \displaystyle\int_{-1}^1 \tilde{f}(-1, \tilde{y})\tilde{\phi}_r(-1, \tilde{y})\tilde{\phi}_s(-1, \tilde{y}) \, d\tilde{y}$

All of these integrals are of the form

$$I = \int_a^b g(\eta) \, d\eta.$$

A suitable numerical integration method for their computation is

$$I_A = \frac{b - a}{2} \left[g(\eta_1) + g(\eta_2) \right], \tag{5.50}$$

where

$$\eta_1 = -\frac{1}{2\sqrt{3}} (b - a) + \frac{1}{2} (b + a), \qquad \eta_2 = \frac{1}{2\sqrt{3}} (b - a) + \frac{1}{2} (b + a).$$

This is the *two-point Gauss–Legendre formula*, of which the third formula of Table 5.1 is a two-dimensional generalization. (See Exercise 5.19.)

We turn now to the implementation of (5.31d), where we must take account of the integrals

$$G(\phi_i)_{\Gamma_1} = \int_{\Gamma_1} p\xi\phi_i \, ds, \qquad i = 1, 2, \ldots, M.$$

Most of these integrals are zero, and the nonzero ones can be assembled from the edge integrals

$$\hat{I}_r^{(t)} \equiv \int_{N_{i_1}}^{N_{i_2}} p\xi\phi_r^{(l)} \, ds, \qquad r \in \hat{S}_t. \tag{5.51}$$

Step (5.31d) can thus be implemented as follows.

> **for** $t := 1$ **step** 1 **until** L_1 **do**
> **for all** $r \in \hat{S}_t$ **do**
> **begin**
>   compute $\hat{I}_r^{(t)}$; $\qquad\qquad\qquad\qquad\qquad$ (5.52)
> $i := i_r^{(l)}$;
> $G[i] := G[i] + \hat{I}_r^{(t)}$
> **end**;

The computation of $\hat{I}_r^{(t)}$ is entirely analogous to that of $I_{r,s}^{(t)}$. Application of the variable transformation (5.10) leads to edge integrals on the standard element, and these are obvious modifications of the integrals in Table 5.2. Corresponding to the first entry of this table, for example, we have

$$\hat{I}_r^{(t)} = d \int_0^1 \tilde{h}(\tilde{x}, 0)\tilde{\phi}_r(\tilde{x}, 0) \, d\tilde{x},$$

where

$$\tilde{h}(\tilde{x}, \tilde{y}) = p(x(\tilde{x}, \tilde{y}), y(\tilde{x}, \tilde{y})) \cdot \xi(x(\tilde{x}, \tilde{y}), y(\tilde{x}, \tilde{y})).$$

Formula (5.50) can again be used for numerical integration.

Implementation of (5.31e)

The implementation of (5.31e) requires an array for the node number set J_0. Thus let BONODE be an array of length M_0, and suppose that in the process of generating the mesh we have put

$$\text{BONODE}[i] := j$$

for every $j \in J_0$, i.e., for every j such that $N_j \in \Gamma_0$. The implementation of "$\forall j \in J_0$" is then just a pass through BONODE. Further, if the contents of BONODE have been sorted so that $\text{BONODE}[i + 1] > \text{BONODE}[i]$, $i = 1, 2, \ldots, M_0 - 1$, then "$\forall i \in J, i < j$" and "$\forall i \in J, i > j$" are also easily programmed.

Some Properties of the Element Matrices

The remainder of this section is devoted to the derivation of some of the properties of the matrices that have arisen in our treatment of the boundary value problem (5.23), (5.24), beginning with the element matrices. The assumptions on the coefficients p, q, and σ are $p, q \in C(\bar{\Omega})$, $\sigma \in C(\Gamma_1)$, and

$$0 < p_0 \le p(x, y) \le p_1 \qquad \forall (x, y) \in \bar{\Omega},$$
$$0 \le q(x, y) \le q_1 \qquad \forall (x, y) \in \bar{\Omega}, \qquad (5.53)$$
$$0 < \sigma_0 \le \sigma(x, y) \le \sigma_1 \qquad \forall (x, y) \in \Gamma_1.$$

For any functions $u, v \in H^1(\Omega)$ we define

$$F(u, v) = p u_x v_x + p u_y v_y + q u v.$$

(The results to follow are also easily established for the case of anisotropy, in which the coefficients of $u_x v_x$ and $u_y v_y$ are not identical.)

The entries of element matrix $K^{(l)}$ are

$$k_{rs}^{(l)} = \int\int_{e_l} F(\phi_r^{(l)}, \phi_s^{(l)}) \, dx \, dy, \qquad r, s = 1, 2, \ldots, T.$$

$K^{(l)}$ is obviously symmetric. Let

$$V_T^{(l)} = \text{SPAN}\{\phi_1^{(l)}, \phi_2^{(l)}, \ldots, \phi_T^{(l)}\}.$$

The relations

$$u^{(l)}(x, y) = \sum_{r=1}^{T} \alpha_r^{(l)} \phi_r^{(l)}(x, y), \qquad \boldsymbol{\alpha}^{(l)} = \begin{bmatrix} \alpha_1^{(l)} \\ \alpha_2^{(l)} \\ \vdots \\ \alpha_T^{(l)} \end{bmatrix}$$

establish a one-to-one correspondence between the function space $V_T^{(l)}$ and the T-dimensional vector space R^T. In particular,

$$\boldsymbol{\alpha}^{(l)} = \begin{bmatrix} 0 \\ 0 \\ \vdots \\ 0 \end{bmatrix} \quad \leftrightarrow \quad u^{(l)}(x, y) = 0 \quad \forall (x, y) \in e_l.$$

Further, if the parameter k defined by (5.8) satisfies $k \ge 0$ [which is the case whenever the polynomial (5.1) includes the constant term], then it is easily seen that

$$\alpha^{(l)} = \begin{bmatrix} 1 \\ 1 \\ \vdots \\ 1 \end{bmatrix} \quad \leftrightarrow \quad u^{(l)}(x, y) = 1 \quad \forall (x, y) \in e_l. \tag{5.54}$$

A straightforward computation establishes the key identity

$$\alpha^{(l)^T} K^{(l)} \beta^{(l)} = \iint_{e_l} F(u^{(l)}, v^{(l)}) \, dx \, dy,$$

where

$$u^{(l)} = \sum_{r=1}^{T} \alpha_r^{(l)} \phi_r^{(l)}, \qquad v^{(l)} = \sum_{r=1}^{T} \beta_r^{(l)} \phi_r^{(l)}.$$

From this follows

$$\alpha^{(l)^T} K^{(l)} \alpha^{(l)} = \iint_{e_l} \left[p(u_x^{(l)})^2 + p(u_y^{(l)})^2 + q(u^{(l)})^2 \right] dx \, dy, \tag{5.55a}$$

$$(K^{(l)} \alpha^{(l)})_r = \iint_{e_l} \left[p(\phi_r^{(l)})_x u_x^{(l)} + p(\phi_r^{(l)})_y u_y^{(l)} + q\phi_r^{(l)} u^{(l)} \right] dx \, dy, \tag{5.55b}$$

and hence, by (5.54),

$$\sum_{r,s=1}^{T} k_{rs}^{(l)} = \iint_{e_l} q \, dx \, dy, \tag{5.56a}$$

$$\sum_{s=1}^{T} k_{rs}^{(l)} = \iint_{e_l} q\phi_r^{(l)} \, dx \, dy. \tag{5.56b}$$

These relations lead to the following theorem.

Theorem 5.1.

(1) Suppose that $q(x, y) = 0 \; \forall (x, y) \in e_l$. Then,
    (a) $K^{(l)}$ is positive semidefinite;
    (b) $\sum_{s=1}^{T} k_{rs}^{(l)} = 0, r = 1, 2, ..., T$.
(2) Suppose that $q(x, y) > 0$ for some $(x, y) \in e_l$. Then,
    (a) $K^{(l)}$ is a positive definite.
Further, if the basis functions are piecewise linear (Example 5.1) or piecewise bilinear (Example 5.3), then
    (b) $\sum_{s=1}^{T} k_{rs}^{(l)} > 0, r = 1, 2, ..., T$.

PROOF: From (5.53) and (5.55a) we have the inequality

$$\alpha^{(l)^T} K^{(l)} \alpha^{(l)} \geq 0 \qquad \forall \alpha^{(l)},$$

so in each of the two cases above $K^{(l)}$ must be either positive definite or positive semidefinite. In case (1) $K^{(l)}$ is in fact positive semidefinite since, by (5.54) and (5.55a),

$$\alpha^{(l)^T} K^{(l)} \alpha^{(l)} = 0, \qquad \alpha^{(l)} = \begin{bmatrix} 1 \\ 1 \\ \vdots \\ 1 \end{bmatrix}.$$

Property (1b) follows immediately from (5.56b).

In case (2) let

$$\hat{e}_l = \{(x, y) \in e_l; q(x, y) > 0\},$$

and note that the continuity of q implies that the area of $\hat{e}_l$ is nonzero. We have

$$\alpha^{(l)^T} K^{(l)} \alpha^{(l)} \geq \int \int_{\hat{e}_l} q(u^{(l)})^2 \, dx \, dy \qquad \forall \alpha^{(l)}$$

so that

$$\alpha^{(l)^T} K^{(l)} \alpha^{(l)} = 0 \quad \Rightarrow \quad u^{(l)}(x, y) = 0 \qquad \forall (x, y) \in \hat{e}_l.$$

But since $u^{(l)}$ is a polynomial the last property implies $u^{(l)}(x, y) = 0 \; \forall (x, y) \in e_l$, and hence $\alpha^{(l)} = \mathbf{0}$. Thus $K^{(l)}$ is positive definite.

The basis functions of Examples 5.1 and 5.3 are positive everywhere in the interior of e_l, and (2b) follows from (5.56b). ∎

We now turn our attention to the signs of the entries of $K^{(l)}$. It is easily seen from (5.55) that

$$k_{rr}^{(l)} \geq p_0 \int \int_{e_l} [(\phi_r^{(l)})_x^2 + (\phi_r^{(l)})_y^2] \, dx \, dy,$$

and since this integral cannot vanish (why?), the diagonal entries are positive even in the semidefinite case.

The situation with respect to the signs of the off-diagonal entries is less simple. It is left as an exercise to establish that when $q(x, y) = 0 \; \forall (x, y) \in e_l$, then all off-diagonal entries of $K^{(l)}$ are nonpositive in the following cases.

(1) The basis functions are piecewise linear and $\theta \leq \pi/2$, where θ is any vertex angle in e_l.

(2) The basis functions are piecewise bilinear and

$$\sqrt{p_1/2p_0} \leq \beta \leq \sqrt{2p_0/p_1},$$

where β is the ratio of the two edge lengths of e_l (see Exercise 5.17).

If "$\leq$" is replaced by "$<$" in these inequalities, then all off-diagonal entries of $K^{(l)}$ are negative.

If $q(x, y) \geq 0$ in e_l, then it can be shown that all off-diagonal entries of $K^{(l)}$ are negative if e_l is sufficiently small and if either of the following holds.

(1) The basis functions are piecewise linear and

$$\theta \leq \theta_0 < \pi/2. \tag{5.57a}$$

(2) The basis functions are piecewise bilinear and

$$\sqrt{p_1/2p_0} < \beta_0 \leq \beta \leq \beta_1 < \sqrt{2p_0/p_1}. \tag{5.57b}$$

By "sufficiently small" we refer to a series of mesh refinements during which θ_0, or β_0 and β_1, are held constant. The key to this result is the fact that

$$\int\int_{e_l} p\left[(\phi_r^{(l)})_x(\phi_s^{(l)})_x + (\phi_r^{(l)})_y(\phi_s^{(l)})_y\right] dx \, dy = O(h^0),$$

$$\int\int_{e_l} q\phi_r^{(l)}\phi_s^{(l)} \, dx \, dy = O(h^2),$$

where h is the greatest element edge length in the mesh.

Some Properties of the Global Stiffness Matrices

We identified in (5.30) three normally distinct "global" stiffness matrices with the finite element treatment of problem (5.23), (5.24). We consider first the primitive stiffness matrix K whose entries are

$$k_{ij} = \int\int_{\Omega} F(\phi_i, \phi_j) \, dx \, dy, \qquad i, j = 1, 2, ..., M.$$

Proceeding as in the previous analysis of the element matrices, we find that

$$\boldsymbol{\alpha}^T K \boldsymbol{\beta} = \int\int_{\Omega} F(u, v) \, dx \, dy, \tag{5.58}$$

where

$$u = \sum_{i=1}^{M} \alpha_i \phi_i, \qquad v = \sum_{i=1}^{M} \beta_i \phi_i.$$

Relations (5.54)–(5.56) are valid for the primitive stiffness matrix if we replace T by M, e_l by Ω, and remove the superscript l. These relations give us the next theorem. We leave the details of the proof to the reader.

Theorem 5.2.

(1)   Suppose $q(x, y) = 0 \; \forall (x, y) \in \bar{\Omega}$. Then,
   (a) K is positive semidefinite;
   (b) $\sum_{j=1}^{M} k_{ij} = 0, \qquad i = 1, 2, ..., M$.
(2)   Suppose that $q(x, y) > 0$ for some $(x, y) \in \bar{\Omega}$. Then,
   (a) K is positive definite.
Further, if the basis functions are piecewise linear or bilinear, then
   (b) $\sum_{j=1}^{M} k_{ij} \geq 0, i = 1, 2, ..., M$,
strict inequality holding for certain rows.

We have seen that the element matrices always have positive diagonal entries and that under condition (5.57a) or (5.57b) all off-diagonal entries are negative, provided that the elements are sufficiently small. It is obvious from the assembly process that the same holds true for the primitive stiffness matrix K. Thus, when we use piecewise linear or bilinear basis functions and observe the restrictions on the element geometry given in (5.57), then K satisfies the first two requirements of an $\hat{M}$ matrix. (See Definition 1.11 in Section 1.4.) Further, the row sum results of Theorem 5.2 and consideration of signs establishes that K is diagonally dominant.

The third requirement of an $\hat{M}$ matrix is that in each of the first $(M - 1)$ rows there must be a nonzero entry to the right of the main diagonal. A necessary condition for this property is that for each node $N_i, i = 1, 2, ..., M - 1$, there is a node $N_j, j > i$, such that N_i and N_j belong to a common element. (This condition is also sufficient unless "uncoupling" occurs, as illustrated in Exercises 5.14 and 5.15.) Thus the choice of the global node ordering is the decisive factor here.

With the application of the boundary conditions in steps (5.31c) and (5.31e), the primitive stiffness matrix is transformed to K_2 [see (5.30b)], the matrix that is often given to the equation solver. As we have seen, K_2 is a trivial enlargement of the Nth-order Ritz–Galerkin matrix K_3 in (5.30c). Except for the case $-(pu_x)_x - (pu_y)_y = g$ in Ω, $u_\nu = \xi$ on Γ, boundary value problem (5.23), (5.24) has a symmetric, coercive bilinear form, and we know from Section 4.1 that K_3 is positive definite. But since the eigenvalues of K_2 are those of K_3 plus $(M - N)$ "ones," K_2 is also positive definite.

We want to know how the boundary conditions affect the signs of the off-diagonal entries of K_2 and the property of diagonal dominance. Regarding the natural boundary condition, it is easy to see that the ith row of K_2 is affected only if node N_i belongs to Γ_1. Let N_j, N_i, and N_m be three consecutive nodes on Γ_1 in the order of the counterclockwise sense of Γ. We restrict the discussion to the cases of piecewise linear or bilinear basis functions, so all three nodes are vertex nodes. The effect of the natural boundary condition on the ith row of K_2 is then

$$(K_2)_{ii} = k_{ii} + \int_{N_j}^{N_m} \sigma\phi_i^2 \, ds, \qquad (K_2)_{ij} = k_{ij} + \int_{N_j}^{N_i} \sigma\phi_i\phi_j \, ds,$$

$$(K_2)_{im} = k_{im} + \int_{N_i}^{N_m} \sigma\phi_i\phi_m \, ds,$$

where k_{ii}, k_{ij}, and k_{im} are nonzero entries of the primitive stiffness matrix. Each of the line integrals is positive.

Under a series of mesh refinements we typically find that the entries of K are $O(h^0)$, whereas the line integrals above are $O(h)$, h being the greatest element edge length. Thus, if the mesh is sufficiently fine, then the natural boundary condition does not alter the signs of matrix entries. Further, it never diminishes a row sum.

Inspection of (5.31e) shows that for any mesh the essential boundary condition does not alter the signs of matrix entries (except to replace certain nonzero entries by zero), nor does it change the sign of a row sum.

We conclude that under condition (5.57a) or (5.57b) and provided that the mesh is sufficiently fine, K_2 is a symmetric positive definite matrix with non-positive off-diagonal entries and nonnegative row sums. Thus, K_2 is diagonally dominant and satisfies the first two requirements of an $\hat{M}$ matrix. The same remarks are obviously also valid for K_3.

Note that regardless of the global node ordering, an essential boundary condition on any part of the boundary prevents K_2 from satisfying the third requirement of an $\hat{M}$ matrix. We shall see in Section 7.2 that this poses no practical problem.

Sparsity

As mentioned earlier, the primitive stiffness matrix K is usually very sparse since $k_{ij} \neq 0$ only if nodes N_i and N_j belong to a common element. Thus, the number of nonzero entries in the ith row cannot exceed the number of nodes in the support of ϕ_i. If N_i is the vertex node of s triangles and if the nodes are vertices only (Example 5.1), then the number of nodes in the support of ϕ_i is $s + 1$. If the nodes are vertices and midpoints (Example 5.2), then the number of nodes in the support of ϕ_i is $3s + 1$ if N_i is a vertex and 9 if N_i is a midpoint. In the case of rectangular elements with vertex nodes (Example 5.3), the support of ϕ_i contains 9 nodes. These remarks are illustrated in Fig. 5.18. In certain problems the number of nonzero entries in the ith row of K is appreciably less than the number of nodes in the support of ϕ_i. See Exercises 5.14 and 5.15 for examples.

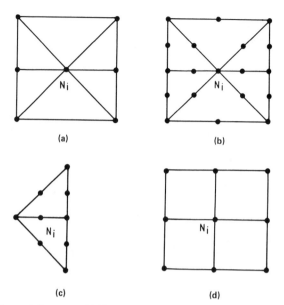

Fig. 5.18.   Support diagrams: (a) Example 5.1, $s = 6$, 7 nodes; (b) Example 5.2, $s = 6$, 19 nodes; (c) Example 5.2, 9 nodes; (d) Example 5.3, 9 nodes.

Historical Note. We conclude this section with the remark that engineers have long used a finite element method not based on the variational formulation of a boundary value problem. [See, e.g., Hrenikoff (1941), Kron (1944), and Langefors (1952).] We illustrate their method with the structured frame problem shown in Fig. 5.19. The unknowns to be determined are the deflections of the frame.

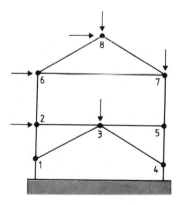

Fig. 5.19.   A structured frame.

Because of the indicated loadings, there occur deflections in the x and y directions. The 8 unconstrained points thus give rise to 16 variables, not all of which are coupled. Only nodal connections by a piece of the frame contribute to a nonzero element. The corresponding stiffness matrix has nonzero coefficients as indicated in the following matrix:

The element matrix associated with the element between nodes 6 and 8, for example, is

$$c_{68} \begin{bmatrix} 1 & -1 \\ -1 & 1 \end{bmatrix},$$

where c_{68} is a material constant for that element. Note that the matrix has a symmetric structure, a coupling from point i to j implying, of course, a coupling from j to i. In fact, the matrix for this problem is entirely symmetric.

A similar approach is sometimes used in the numerical solution of electromagnetic field problems, for which Maxwell's field equations are replaced by Kirchhoff's circuit laws for currents and voltages. The direct application of physical principles to make a discretization is appealing to many engineers; a disadvantage with such an approach is that an analysis of the errors that arise from the discretization is difficult. For further historical notes see Vichnevetsky (1981).

5.3   Isoparametric Basis Functions

Introduction

Given any set of finite element basis functions satisfying the assumptions of Section 5.1, we can derive new basis functions taking as the point of departure

(1)   the standard element $\tilde{e}$,
(2)   the standard local basis functions $\tilde{\phi}_1, \tilde{\phi}_2, ..., \tilde{\phi}_T$,
(3)   a new mesh.

As we shall see, the new mesh nodes can in general be chosen with greater freedom than was possible in Section 5.1. Another difference is that in the new mesh the typical element e_l has T prescribed nodes but not an explicitly prescribed boundary. The boundary, which in general is not a polygon, is defined implicitly through a variable transformation based on the standard local basis functions. It is assumed that the mesh nodes have been ordered globally and that the nodes of each element e_l have been ordered locally, so that the nodes of e_l can, as usual, be denoted

$$N_{i_r^{(l)}} \equiv (x_{i_r^{(l)}}, y_{i_r^{(l)}}), \qquad r = 1, 2, ..., T.$$

General Procedure

We introduce the variable transformation

$$\left.\begin{aligned} x &= \sum_{r=1}^{T} x_{i_r^{(l)}} \tilde{\phi}_r(\tilde{x}, \tilde{y}) \\ y &= \sum_{r=1}^{T} y_{i_r^{(l)}} \tilde{\phi}_r(\tilde{x}, \tilde{y}) \end{aligned}\right\} (\tilde{x}, \tilde{y}) \in \tilde{e} \tag{5.59}$$

and define e_l to be the image of $\tilde{e}$ under this transformation. Since the standard local basis functions have the property

$$\tilde{\phi}_r(\tilde{N}_s) = \delta_{rs}, \qquad r, s = 1, 2, ..., T,$$

where $\tilde{N}_1, \tilde{N}_2, ..., \tilde{N}_T$ denote the nodes of $\tilde{e}$, it is seen that (5.59) maps $\tilde{N}_r$ onto $N_{i_r^{(l)}}$, i.e., e_l contains the prescribed nodes. In addition, the boundary of e_l is now defined. When we speak of a vertex or edge of e_l we mean the image of a vertex or edge of $\tilde{e}$ under the transformation. It will be recalled that $\tilde{\phi}_r(\tilde{x}, \tilde{y})$ has the property of vanishing on any edge to which node $\tilde{N}_r$ does not belong. This implies that an edge of e_l, which in general is a curve, is independent of every node $N_{i_r^{(l)}}$ not belonging to that edge.

Assuming (5.59) to be invertible, we denote the inverse transformation by

$$\left.\begin{array}{l} \tilde{x} = \tilde{x}(x, y) \\ \tilde{y} = \tilde{y}(x, y) \end{array}\right\} (x, y) \in e_l \qquad\qquad (5.60)$$

and define local basis functions on e_l by

$$\phi_r^{(l)}(x, y) = \tilde{\phi}_r(\tilde{x}(x, y), \tilde{y}(x, y)), \qquad (x, y) \in e_l, \quad r = 1, 2, ..., T.$$

These clearly have the properties

$$\phi_r^{(l)}(N_{i_s^{(l)}}) = \delta_{rs}, \qquad r, s = 1, 2, ..., T;$$

$$\phi_r^{(l)}(x, y) = 0 \qquad \text{on every edge to which } N_{i_r^{(l)}} \text{ does not belong.}$$

Finally, we define for each node N_i a global basis function ϕ_i by piecing local basis functions together in the obvious way. Thus, the restriction of ϕ_i to any element e_l is given by

$$\phi_i(x, y) = \begin{cases} \phi_r^{(l)}(x, y), & \text{if } N_i \in e_l \quad (i_r^{(l)} = i), \\ 0, & \text{if } N_i \notin e_l. \end{cases}$$

We call e_l an *isoparametric element*, $\phi_r^{(l)}$, $r = 1, 2, ..., T$, *local isoparametric basis functions*, and ϕ_i, $i = 1, 2, ..., M$, *global isoparametric basis functions* (Ergatoudis, Irons, and Zienkiewicz, 1968; Zienkiewicz, 1977).

Remarks

1. All differences between isoparametric elements and basis functions and the nonisoparametric counterparts from which they are derived are due to the fact that the affine transformation (5.10) has been replaced by (5.59), which in general is nonaffine.

2. In choosing a mesh for nonisoparametric basis functions there are generally restrictions. For example, in the case of the six-node triangle the nonvertex nodes in any element e_l are determined by those in the standard triangle (which in practice should be the midedge points chosen in Example 5.2), and in the case of the four-node quadrilateral (Example 5.3) the nodes must define an axiparallel rectangle. These restrictions are relaxed for the isoparametric basis functions in so far as (5.59) is a well-defined transformation for any choice of nodes. It is typical that when these restrictions are observed, then (5.59) reduces to affine form.

3. The fact that (5.59) is a well-defined transformation for any choice of

nodes does not imply that it is always invertible. Generally speaking, the property of invertibility, which is of course essential, is present when the position of nodes in e_l is not greatly distorted from that in the corresponding nonisoparametric element.

4. The greater freedom permitted in the choice of a mesh for isoparametric basis functions can be exploited when the domain $\bar{\Omega}$ has a curved boundary.

5. $\phi_r^{(l)}$ is often a complicated nonlinear function of x and y. To determine it explicitly one would have to invert (5.59) explicitly, and this is rarely possible. Nevertheless, we shall see that isoparametric basis functions are easy to work with.

6. In Section 5.1 we mentioned seven properties of nonisoparametric basis functions. Of these, all but the first and seventh are valid for isoparametric basis functions.

7. Let

$$V_M = \text{SPAN}\{\phi_1, \phi_2, \ldots, \phi_M\},$$

where ϕ_1, ϕ_2, ..., ϕ_M are isoparametric, and let $\tilde{k}$ be defined as the largest integer for which it is true that

$$P_{\tilde{k}}(\tilde{\Omega}) \subseteq V_M, \qquad \tilde{\Omega} \equiv \bigcup_{l=1}^{L} e_l;$$

$\tilde{k}$ is usually less than the value k defined by (5.8) for the corresponding nonisoparametric basis functions. Fortunately, it turns out that the accuracy obtained from isoparametric basis functions is determined by k rather than $\tilde{k}$.

Examples

Example 5.4. Isoparametric Basis Functions Derived from Example 5.1. Substituting the standard local basis functions of Example 5.1 in (5.59), we obtain

$$x = x_{i_1^{(l)}}(1 - \tilde{x} - \tilde{y}) + x_{i_2^{(l)}}\tilde{x} + x_{i_3^{(l)}}\tilde{y}$$
$$= (x_{i_2^{(l)}} - x_{i_1^{(l)}})\tilde{x} + (x_{i_3^{(l)}} - x_{i_1^{(l)}})\tilde{y} + x_{i_1^{(l)}},$$

and similarly

$$y = (y_{i_2^{(l)}} - y_{i_1^{(l)}})\tilde{x} + (y_{i_3^{(l)}} - y_{i_1^{(l)}})\tilde{y} + y_{i_1^{(l)}}.$$

This is the affine transformation (5.17), and it follows that the isoparametric basis functions are identical to the nonisoparametric basis functions. The reason for this is that the standard local basis functions of Example 5.1 are affine.

Example 5.5. Isoparametric Basis Functions Derived from Example 5.2. When the functions of (5.19) are substituted in (5.59), the result can be expressed as

$$
\begin{bmatrix} x \\ y \end{bmatrix} = \begin{bmatrix} x_{i_1^{(l)}} \\ y_{i_1^{(l)}} \end{bmatrix} + \begin{bmatrix} x_{i_2^{(l)}} - x_{i_1^{(l)}} + Q_3 \\ y_{i_2^{(l)}} - y_{i_1^{(l)}} + R_3 \end{bmatrix} \tilde{x} + \begin{bmatrix} x_{i_3^{(l)}} - x_{i_1^{(l)}} + Q_2 \\ y_{i_3^{(l)}} - y_{i_1^{(l)}} + R_2 \end{bmatrix} \tilde{y}
$$

$$
- \begin{bmatrix} Q_3 \\ R_3 \end{bmatrix} \tilde{x}^2 + \begin{bmatrix} Q_1 - Q_2 - Q_3 \\ R_1 - R_2 - R_3 \end{bmatrix} \tilde{x}\tilde{y} - \begin{bmatrix} Q_2 \\ R_2 \end{bmatrix} \tilde{y}^2, \qquad (5.61)
$$

where

$$Q_1 = 2(2x_{i_4^{(l)}} - x_{i_2^{(l)}} - x_{i_3^{(l)}}), \qquad R_1 = 2(2y_{i_4^{(l)}} - y_{i_2^{(l)}} - y_{i_3^{(l)}}),$$

$$Q_2 = 2(2x_{i_5^{(l)}} - x_{i_3^{(l)}} - x_{i_1^{(l)}}), \qquad R_2 = 2(2y_{i_5^{(l)}} - y_{i_3^{(l)}} - y_{i_1^{(l)}}),$$

$$Q_3 = 2(2x_{i_6^{(l)}} - x_{i_1^{(l)}} - x_{i_2^{(l)}}), \qquad R_3 = 2(2y_{i_6^{(l)}} - y_{i_1^{(l)}} - y_{i_2^{(l)}}).$$

We have written (5.61) in this form to facilitate comparison with the affine transformation (5.17), which is used for the nonisoparametric case. Note that $Q_r = R_r = 0$ if and only if node $N_{i_{r+3}^{(l)}}$ is the midpoint of the straight line segment connecting the pair of vertex nodes that excludes $N_{i_r^{(l)}}$. It follows that (5.61) reduces to (5.17) if and only if $N_{i_4^{(l)}}$, $N_{i_5^{(l)}}$, and $N_{i_6^{(l)}}$ are all positioned in this fashion.

An edge of e_l is determined in parametric form by restricting $(\tilde{x}, \tilde{y})$ in (5.61) to the corresponding edge of the standard element $\tilde{e}$, the triangle with vertices $(0, 0)$, $(1, 0)$, and $(0, 1)$. Thus, for $\tilde{y} = 0$,

$$
\begin{bmatrix} x \\ y \end{bmatrix} = \begin{bmatrix} x_{i_1^{(l)}} \\ y_{i_1^{(l)}} \end{bmatrix} + \begin{bmatrix} x_{i_2^{(l)}} - x_{i_1^{(l)}} - Q_3 \\ y_{i_2^{(l)}} - y_{i_1^{(l)}} - R_3 \end{bmatrix} \tilde{x} - \begin{bmatrix} Q_3 \\ R_3 \end{bmatrix} \tilde{x}^2, \qquad 0 \le \tilde{x} \le 1;
$$

for $\tilde{y} = 1 - \tilde{x}$,

$$
\begin{bmatrix} x \\ y \end{bmatrix} = \begin{bmatrix} x_{i_3^{(l)}} \\ y_{i_3^{(l)}} \end{bmatrix} + \begin{bmatrix} x_{i_2^{(l)}} - x_{i_3^{(l)}} + Q_1 \\ y_{i_2^{(l)}} - y_{i_3^{(l)}} + R_1 \end{bmatrix} \tilde{x} - \begin{bmatrix} Q_1 \\ R_1 \end{bmatrix} \tilde{x}^2, \qquad 0 < \tilde{x} < 1;
$$

for $\tilde{x} = 0$,

$$
\begin{bmatrix} x \\ y \end{bmatrix} = \begin{bmatrix} x_{i_1^{(l)}} \\ y_{i_1^{(l)}} \end{bmatrix} + \begin{bmatrix} x_{i_3^{(l)}} - x_{i_1^{(l)}} + Q_2 \\ y_{i_3^{(l)}} - y_{i_1^{(l)}} + R_2 \end{bmatrix} \tilde{y} - \begin{bmatrix} Q_2 \\ R_2 \end{bmatrix} \tilde{y}^2, \qquad 0 \le \tilde{y} \le 1.
$$

These relations illustrate an earlier remark to the effect that an edge of e_l depends only on the nodes belonging to that edge. For example, the first edge depends only on $N_{i_1^{(l)}}$, $N_{i_2^{(l)}}$, and $N_{i_6^{(l)}}$. In particular, if these three nodes are chosen to make $Q_3 = R_3 = 0$, then this edge becomes a straight line, regardless of where the remaining nodes lie.

Figure 5.20 shows a typical application of isoparametric six-node elements. The "mid-edge node" $N_{i_4^{(l)}}$ has been placed on the boundary Γ. This edge of the element is a second-degree curve interpolating Γ at $N_{i_2^{(l)}}$, $N_{i_3^{(l)}}$, and $N_{i_4^{(l)}}$. The mapping of $\tilde{e}$ onto e_l is illustrated in Fig. 5.21.

Example 5.6. Isoparametric Basis Functions Derived from Example 5.3. Substituting the standard local basis functions (5.21) in (5.59), we obtain

$$\begin{bmatrix} x \\ y \end{bmatrix} = \frac{1}{2}\begin{bmatrix} x_{i_1^{(l)}} + x_{i_2^{(l)}} + Q \\ y_{i_1^{(l)}} + y_{i_3^{(l)}} + R \end{bmatrix} + \frac{1}{2}\begin{bmatrix} x_{i_2^{(l)}} - x_{i_1^{(l)}} + Q^* \\ R^* \end{bmatrix}\tilde{x}$$

$$+ \frac{1}{2}\begin{bmatrix} Q \\ y_{i_3^{(l)}} - y_{i_1^{(l)}} - R^* \end{bmatrix}\tilde{y} + \frac{1}{2}\begin{bmatrix} Q^* \\ -R \end{bmatrix}\tilde{x}\tilde{y}, \qquad (5.62)$$

where

$$Q = \tfrac{1}{2}(-x_{i_1^{(l)}} - x_{i_2^{(l)}} + x_{i_3^{(l)}} + x_{i_4^{(l)}}), \qquad R = \tfrac{1}{2}(-y_{i_1^{(l)}} + y_{i_2^{(l)}} - y_{i_3^{(l)}} + y_{i_4^{(l)}}),$$

$$Q^* = \tfrac{1}{2}(x_{i_1^{(l)}} - x_{i_2^{(l)}} + x_{i_3^{(l)}} - x_{i_4^{(l)}}), \qquad R^* = \tfrac{1}{2}(-y_{i_1^{(l)}} + y_{i_2^{(l)}} + y_{i_3^{(l)}} - y_{i_4^{(l)}}).$$

If the nodes $N_{i_r^{(l)}}$, $r = 1, 2, 3, 4$ are chosen to be the vertices of an axiparallel rectangle, then $Q = R = Q^* = R^* = 0$ and (5.62) reduces to (5.22). The element e_l is then this rectangle.

The transformation (5.62) maps any axiparallel line in the $\tilde{x}-\tilde{y}$ plane onto a straight line in the $x-y$ plane, so in all cases e_l is the quadrilateral with vertices $N_{i_r^{(l)}}$, $r = 1, 2, 3, 4$ (Fig. 5.22).

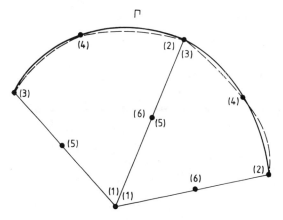

Fig. 5.20. The use of isoparametric elements to approximate a curved boundary: ———, boundary; — —, element edge (Example 5.5).

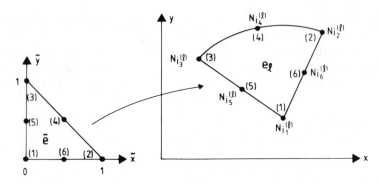

Fig. 5.21.   The mapping of $\tilde{e}$ onto e_l (Example 5.5).

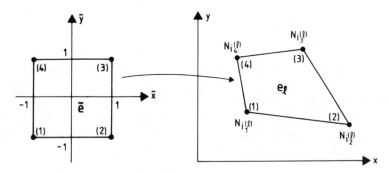

Fig. 5.22.   The mapping of $\tilde{e}$ onto e_l (Example 5.6).

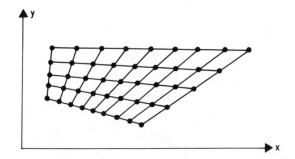

Fig. 5.23.   Isoparametric mesh for a quadrilateral domain (Example 5.6).

Figure 5.23 illustrates the application of these isoparametric elements in the case when the domain $\tilde{\Omega}$ is an arbitrary quadrilateral. The nonisoparametric elements would be clumsy here.

Computational Details

One might suppose that the use of isoparametric basis functions would be considerably more complicated than that of the nonisoparametric basis functions, but this is not the case. To begin with, all of the analysis of Section 5.2 up to and including (5.38) is still valid. Now, however, the partial derivatives $x_{\tilde{x}}$, $x_{\tilde{y}}$, $y_{\tilde{x}}$, and $y_{\tilde{y}}$ must be obtained from (5.59). Thus,

$$x_{\tilde{x}} = \sum_{r=1}^{T} x_{i_r^{(l)}} (\tilde{\phi}_r)_{\tilde{x}}, \qquad x_{\tilde{y}} = \sum_{r=1}^{T} x_{i_r^{(l)}} (\tilde{\phi}_r)_{\tilde{y}},$$

$$y_{\tilde{x}} = \sum_{r=1}^{T} y_{i_r^{(l)}} (\tilde{\phi}_r)_{\tilde{x}}, \qquad y_{\tilde{y}} = \sum_{r=1}^{T} y_{i_r^{(l)}} (\tilde{\phi}_r)_{\tilde{y}}.$$

These derivatives are in general functions of $\tilde{x}$ and $\tilde{y}$, but we need their values only at the integration points $(\tilde{x}^{(m)}, \tilde{y}^{(m)})$, $m = 1, 2, ..., Q$. (The integration formulas in Table 5.1 for Examples 5.2 and 5.3 are equally appropriate for Examples 5.5 and 5.6, respectively.) The computation of these values is straightforward in terms of the program arrays defined in (5.35), (5.40), and (5.42). The required values of the coefficients $\tilde{p}$ and $\tilde{q}$ in (5.38) are easily found using the relations

$$\tilde{p}(\tilde{x}^{(m)}, \tilde{y}^{(m)}) = p(x^{(m)}, y^{(m)}),$$

$$\tilde{q}(\tilde{x}^{(m)}, \tilde{y}^{(m)}) = q(x^{(m)}, y^{(m)}),$$

where

$$x^{(m)} = \sum_{r=1}^{T} x_{i_r^{(l)}} \tilde{\phi}_r(\tilde{x}^{(m)}, \tilde{y}^{(m)}),$$

$$y^{(m)} = \sum_{r=1}^{T} y_{i_r^{(l)}} \tilde{\phi}_r(\tilde{x}^{(m)}, \tilde{y}^{(m)}).$$

This accounts for the computation of the element matrix entry $k_{rs}^{(l)}$, and the treatment of the element vector component $g_r^{(l)}$ in (5.44) is similar. Regarding the edge integral $I_{r,s}^{(l)}$ defined in (5.48), Table 5.2 is equally applicable to the isoparametric basis functions of Examples 5.5 and 5.6.

For a generalization of the isoparametric concept see Frey, Hall, and Porsching (1978) and Gordon and Hall (1973). For finite element representation of surfaces in R^3, see also Nedelec (1976).

5.4 Error Analysis

Preliminary Remarks

To simplify the discussion we restrict our attention to second-order problems on polygonal domains, as exemplified by (5.23), (5.24). Thus, let

$$H_\gamma^1(\Omega) = \{u \in H^1(\Omega); u = \gamma \text{ on } \Gamma_0\},$$

$$H_0^1(\Omega) = \{v \in H^1(\Omega); v = 0 \text{ on } \Gamma_0\},$$

$$\tilde{V}_N = \{u \in H_\gamma^1(\Omega); u = v + u^*, v \in V_N\},$$

where u^* is an arbitrary but fixed function in $H_\gamma^1(\Omega)$ and V_N an N-dimensional subspace of $H_0^1(\Omega)$. Let $\hat{u}_N \in \tilde{V}_N$ denote the Ritz–Galerkin approximation to the exact solution $\hat{u} \in H_\gamma^1(\Omega)$. Inequality (4.16) shows that the *discretization error* $(\hat{u} - \hat{u}_N)$ satisfies

$$\|\hat{u} - \hat{u}_N\|_1 \le C\|\hat{u} - u\|_1 \qquad \forall u \in \tilde{V}_N, \tag{5.63}$$

where C is a constant.

Given finite element basis functions $\phi_1, \phi_2, \ldots, \phi_M$, we take

$$V_N = \text{SPAN}\{\phi_i; i \in J\}$$

and use for u^* the function

$$u_N^*(x, y) \equiv \sum_{i \in J_0} \gamma(N_i)\phi_i(x, y), \qquad (x, y) \in \bar{\Omega},$$

as discussed in Section 5.2. From a theoretical point of view this is acceptable only if $u_N^* \in H_\gamma^1(\Omega)$, since otherwise we are dealing with inadmissible functions. As mentioned earlier, this condition is satisfied only for very special boundary functions γ. Nevertheless, to keep our material within bounds we shall assume here that $u_N^* \in H_\gamma^1(\Omega)$. (See, however, Exercise 5.25.)

Further, we shall also assume that all integrals in the element matrices and vectors are determined exactly. (Information on the effect of integration errors can be obtained from the perturbation results of Sections 6.4 and 7.4.) For more thorough error analyses that take into account nonpolygonal domains, arbitrary boundary functions, and numerical integration see, e.g., Ciarlet (1978), Fairweather (1978), Mitchell and Wait (1977), Oden and Reddy (1976), and Strang and Fix (1973).

With the assumption $u_N^* \in H_\gamma^1(\Omega)$, we see that

$$u \in \tilde{V}_N \quad \Leftrightarrow \quad u = \sum_{i=1}^{M} \alpha_i \phi_i,$$

where the coefficients α_i, $i \in J$, are arbitrary and $\alpha_i = \gamma(N_i)$, $i \in J_0$. There are two functions in $\tilde{V}_N$ of importance for our error analysis. One is naturally the Ritz–Galerkin approximation $\hat{u}_N$, where the coefficients α_i, $i \in J$ are the solution of the Ritz–Galerkin equations. The other is $\hat{u}_I$, the V_M interpolant of $\hat{u}$. We recall that

$$V_M = \mathrm{SPAN}\{\phi_1, \phi_2, \ldots, \phi_M\}, \qquad \hat{u}_I = \sum_{i=1}^{M} \hat{u}(N_i)\phi_i \in V_M.$$

[We must make here the weak assumption that $\hat{u} \in C(\bar{\Omega})$, which holds in particular when $\hat{u} \in H_\gamma^1(\Omega) \cap H^2(\Omega)$.] Since $\hat{u}_I(N_i) = \hat{u}(N_i) = \gamma(N_i)$, $i \in J_0$, it follows that $\hat{u}_I \in \tilde{V}_N$.

Our aim is to use (5.63) to obtain a useful bound on the discretization error by taking u to be a function in $\tilde{V}_N$ such that $\|\hat{u} - u\|_1$ is reasonably easy to analyze and yet not much greater than $\min_{u \in \tilde{V}_N} \|\hat{u} - u\|_1$. It turns out that $\hat{u}_I$ satisfies both criteria. Thus, on the basis of the inequality

$$\|\hat{u} - \hat{u}_N\|_1 \le C\|\hat{u} - \hat{u}_I\|_1, \tag{5.64}$$

we turn our attention from the discretization error $(\hat{u} - \hat{u}_N)$ to the *interpolation error* $(\hat{u} - \hat{u}_I)$.

Interpolation Error: An Introductory Example

It is instructive to consider first a simple one-dimensional problem. On the interval $[a, b]$ we introduce a finite element mesh consisting of nodes

$$a = x_1 < x_2 < \cdots < x_M = b$$

and elements

$$[x_i, x_{i+1}], \qquad i = 1, 2, \ldots, M - 1,$$

and define the continuous, piecewise linear basis functions

$$\phi_i(x) = \begin{cases} (x - x_{i-1})/h_{i-1} & \text{for} \quad x_{i-1} \le x < x_i, \\ (x_{i+1} - x)/h_i & \text{for} \quad x_i \le x \le x_{i+1}, \\ 0 & \text{for} \quad a \le x < x_{i-1}, \quad x_{i+1} < x \le b, \end{cases}$$

$i = 1, 2, \ldots, M$, where $h_i = x_{i+1} - x_i$, $x_0 = x_1$ and $x_{M+1} = x_M$. These functions are illustrated in Fig. 5.24.

The V_M interpolant of a function u is the continuous, piecewise linear function u_I that interpolates u at the nodes, as illustrated in Fig. 5.25.

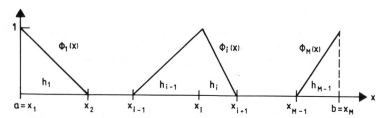

Fig. 5.24.   One-dimensional, continuous, piecewise linear basis functions.

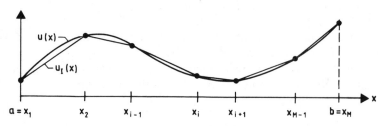

Fig. 5.25.   A function and its V_M interpolant.

Suppose that $u \in H^2(a, b)$, and let

$$|u|_2 = \left\{ \int_a^b (u''(x))^2 \, dx \right\}^{1/2}.$$

[This is the Sobolev seminorm introduced in (3.25).] Since u necessarily belongs to $C^1[a, b]$, the Mean Value Theorem states that there is some $\xi \in (x_i, x_{i+1})$ such that

$$u'(\xi) = h_i^{-1}[u(x_{i+1}) - u(x_i)].$$

Obviously $u_I'(x) = u'(\xi) \ \forall x \in (x_i, x_{i+1})$, and in this interval we have

$$u'(x) - u_I'(x) = u'(x) - u'(\xi) = \int_\xi^x u''(t) \, dt.$$

Applying the Cauchy–Schwarz inequality, we find that

$$|u'(x) - u_I'(x)| \leq \left\{ \int_\xi^x 1^2 \, dt \right\}^{1/2} \left\{ \int_\xi^x u''(t)^2 \, dt \right\}^{1/2}$$

$$\leq h_i^{1/2} \left\{ \int_{x_i}^{x_{i+1}} u''(t)^2 \, dt \right\}^{1/2}, \qquad x \in (x_i, x_{i+1}). \quad (5.65)$$

To derive a bound on $|u(x) - u_1(x)|$, we write

$$u(x) - u_1(x) = \int_{x_i}^{x} \left[u'(t) - u_1'(t) \right] dt$$

and use (5.65) to obtain

$$|u(x) - u_1(x)| \leq \int_{x_i}^{x_{i+1}} |u'(t) - u_1'(t)| \, dt$$

$$\leq h_i^{3/2} \left\{ \int_{x_i}^{x_{i+1}} u''(t)^2 \, dt \right\}^{1/2}, \qquad x \in [x_i, x_{i+1}]. \quad (5.66)$$

Squaring (5.65) and (5.66), integrating, summing over all elements, and taking square roots, we arrive at the bounds

$$|u - u_1|_1 \leq h|u|_2, \tag{5.67a}$$

$$|u - u_1|_0 \leq h^2|u|_2, \tag{5.67b}$$

where $h = \max_{1 \leq i \leq M-1} h_i$. Finally, since

$$\|u - u_1\|_1^2 = |u - u_1|_0^2 + |u - u_1|_1^2,$$

we find easily that

$$\|u - u_1\|_1 \leq Ch|u|_2, \tag{5.68}$$

where $C = [1 + (b - a)^2]^{1/2}$.

Remarks

1. Using more refined analysis one can show that for any $u \in H^2(a, b)$,

$$|u - u_1|_1 \leq \pi^{-1}h|u|_2, \qquad |u - u_1|_0 \leq \pi^{-2}h^2|u|_2,$$

and these are the strongest bounds possible (Schultz, 1973; Strang and Fix, 1973). Note that the bounds (5.67) are satisfactory in the sense that the powers of h are the best possible.

2. In Section 5.1 we defined k and m to be the largest integers such that

$$P_k(\bar{\Omega}) \subseteq V_M \subset C^{m-1}(\bar{\Omega})$$

and noted that this implies that $V_M \subset H^m(\Omega)$. Clearly, $k = m = 1$ for this example. It will be observed that the seminorm bounds we have obtained are of the form

$$|u - u_1|_s \leq C_s h^{k+1-s}|u|_{k+1}, \qquad s = 0, 1, \ldots, m, \tag{5.69}$$

where $C_0, C_1, \ldots, C_m$ are independent of u. This is typical of finite element interpolation, as we shall see.

Implicit in (5.69) is the important assumption that $u \in H^{k+1}(\Omega)$, since otherwise $|u|_{k+1}$ is undefined. If u does not have this degree of smoothness, then the bound on $|u - u_1|_s$ deteriorates. (See Exercise 5.26 for an example.)

Note that when $s > m$, then in general $u_1 \notin H^s(\Omega)$ and $|u - u_1|_s$ is not even defined.

3. One can also derive bounds on the interpolation error measured in other seminorms. Thus, for any $u \in C^s[a, b]$ consider the *maximum seminorm* defined by

$$|u|_{s,\infty} = \max_{a \le x \le b} |u^{(s)}(x)|.$$

From the previous analysis we can easily derive the bounds

$$|u - u_1|_{1,\infty} \le h|u|_{2,\infty}, \tag{5.70a}$$

$$|u - u_1|_{0,\infty} \le h^2|u|_{2,\infty} \tag{5.70b}$$

for any $u \in C^2[a, b]$.

Our interest in Sobolev seminorms and norms in preference to others is of course dictated by (5.64).

4. It was trivial to show that

$$[|u - u_1|_0 = O(h^2)] \wedge [|u - u_1|_1 = O(h)] \quad \Rightarrow \quad \|u - u_1\|_1 = O(h).$$

Note, however, that an attempt to establish the converse yields only

$$\|u - u_1\|_1 = O(h) \quad \Rightarrow \quad [|u - u_1|_0 = O(h)] \wedge [|u - u_1|_1 = O(h)],$$

hiding the second-order accuracy of $|u - u_1|_0$. The difficulty of deriving satisfactory bounds on seminorms of lower order from a given norm bound will be encountered later in our analysis of the discretization error $(\hat{u} - \hat{u}_N)$.

Interpolation Error: General Analysis

We begin now an analysis of two-dimensional finite element interpolation, our goal being to establish (5.69). The results are stated in Theorems 5.6 and 5.8 for the cases of triangular and rectangular elements, respectively.

For any $\theta \in H^s(e_l)$ let $|\theta|_{s,e_l}$ denote the Sobolev seminorm of order s over element e_l. Since

$$|u - u_1|_s^2 = \sum_{l=1}^{L} |u - u_1|_{s,e_l}^2, \tag{5.71}$$

we can restrict our attention to the interpolation error over individual elements. Further, by invoking property (7) of finite element basis functions

(Section 5.1), we can use an affine variable transformation to reduce the analysis of the interpolation error over any element e_l to that of an interpolation error over the standard element $\tilde{e}$. A significant part of the work in this approach consequently involves details of variable transformations (Theorems 5.3 and 5.7). The main results regarding interpolation error over the standard element (Theorem 5.5) will be obtained from the Bramble–Hilbert lemma (Theorem 5.4), which will be stated without proof.

We consider first the case of a mesh of triangular elements. The basis functions can be those of Examples 5.1 or 5.2, or they can be of higher degree. Our only assumption is that the vertices of the typical element e_l are nodes, and that the local node ordering begins with them (counterclockwise). We can then take as the standard element $\tilde{e}$ the triangle with vertices $(0, 0), (1, 0)$, and $(0, 1)$, and use the affine transformation (5.17),

$$x = (x_{i_2^{(l)}} - x_{i_1^{(l)}})\tilde{x} + (x_{i_3^{(l)}} - x_{i_1^{(l)}})\tilde{y} + x_{i_1^{(l)}},$$
$$y = (y_{i_2^{(l)}} - y_{i_1^{(l)}})\tilde{x} + (y_{i_3^{(l)}} - y_{i_1^{(l)}})\tilde{y} + y_{i_1^{(l)}},$$

(5.72)

to map $\tilde{e}$ onto e_l. The partial derivatives and Jacobian of this transformation are

$$x_{\tilde{x}} = x_{i_2^{(l)}} - x_{i_1^{(l)}}, \qquad x_{\tilde{y}} = x_{i_3^{(l)}} - x_{i_1^{(l)}},$$
$$y_{\tilde{x}} = y_{i_2^{(l)}} - y_{i_1^{(l)}}, \qquad y_{\tilde{y}} = y_{i_3^{(l)}} - y_{i_1^{(l)}},$$

and

$$\tilde{D} = (x_{i_2^{(l)}} - x_{i_1^{(l)}})(y_{i_3^{(l)}} - y_{i_1^{(l)}}) - (x_{i_3^{(l)}} - x_{i_1^{(l)}})(y_{i_2^{(l)}} - y_{i_1^{(l)}}),$$

respectively. The counterclockwise ordering of the vertex nodes of e_l implies that $\tilde{D} > 0$.

For a given element e_l let h be the largest edge length, and α the smallest angle. Obviously,

$$|x_{\tilde{x}}|, |x_{\tilde{y}}|, |y_{\tilde{x}}|, |y_{\tilde{y}}| \leq h.$$

(5.73a)

From elementary trigonometry we have

$$(h^2/2) \sin(\alpha) \leq \tilde{D} \leq h^2 \sin(\alpha).$$

(5.73b)

(See Exercise 5.28.)

Using (5.37) and (5.73) we find that the partial derivatives of the inverse transformation of (5.72) satisfy

$$|\tilde{x}_x|, |\tilde{x}_y|, |\tilde{y}_x|, |\tilde{y}_y| \leq 2/[h \sin(\alpha)].$$

(5.74a)

The determinant of the inverse transformation is

$$D \equiv \tilde{x}_x \tilde{y}_y - \tilde{x}_y \tilde{y}_x.$$

A well-known identity states that $D = \tilde{D}^{-1}$, and hence

$$1/[h^2 \sin(\alpha)] \le D \le 2/[h^2 \sin(\alpha)]. \qquad (5.74b)$$

These fundamental inequalities allow us to prove the following theorem.

Theorem 5.3. Let $\theta(x, y) \in H^s(e_l)$ and $\tilde{\theta}(\tilde{x}, \tilde{y}) \in H^s(\tilde{e})$ satisfy the relation $\theta(x, y) = \tilde{\theta}(\tilde{x}, \tilde{y})$ under the variable transformation (5.72). Then there exist constants D_s and E_s, independent of θ, $\tilde{\theta}$, h, and α, such that

$$D_s[\sin(\alpha)]^{s-1/2} h^{s-1} |\theta|_{s,e_l} \le |\tilde{\theta}|_{s,\tilde{e}} \le E_s[\sin(\alpha)]^{-1/2} h^{s-1} |\theta|_{s,e_l}. \qquad (5.75)$$

PROOF: We consider first the case $s = 0$. The identity

$$\iint_{e_l} \theta^2 \, dx \, dy = \tilde{D} \iint_{\tilde{e}} \tilde{\theta}^2 \, d\tilde{x} \, d\tilde{y}$$

immediately yields

$$|\theta|_{0,e_l} = \tilde{D}^{1/2} |\tilde{\theta}|_{0,\tilde{e}},$$

and it follows from (5.73b) that (5.75) is valid for $D_0 = 1$ and $E_0 = \sqrt{2}$.

To prove the theorem for $s = 1$ we need the identities

$$\theta_x = \tilde{\theta}_{\tilde{x}} \tilde{x}_x + \tilde{\theta}_{\tilde{y}} \tilde{y}_x, \qquad \theta_y = \tilde{\theta}_{\tilde{x}} \tilde{x}_y + \tilde{\theta}_{\tilde{y}} \tilde{y}_y. \qquad (5.76)$$

Then,

$$\iint_{e_l} (\theta_x^2 + \theta_y^2) \, dx \, dy = \tilde{D} \iint_{\tilde{e}} [c_1 \tilde{\theta}_{\tilde{x}}^2 + 2c_2 \tilde{\theta}_{\tilde{x}} \tilde{\theta}_{\tilde{y}} + c_3 \tilde{\theta}_{\tilde{y}}^2] \, d\tilde{x} \, d\tilde{y},$$

where

$$c_1 = \tilde{x}_x^2 + \tilde{x}_y^2, \qquad c_2 = \tilde{x}_x \tilde{y}_x + \tilde{x}_y \tilde{y}_y, \qquad c_3 = \tilde{y}_x^2 + \tilde{y}_y^2.$$

Applying the inequality

$$ab \le \tfrac{1}{2}(a^2 + b^2) \qquad (5.77)$$

in the preceding integral, we obtain

$$|\theta|_{1,e_l}^2 \le \tilde{D} c |\tilde{\theta}|_{1,\tilde{e}}^2, \qquad (5.78)$$

where $c = \max\{c_1 + c_2, c_3 + c_2\}$. Now, (5.74a) implies

$$c \le 16/[h \sin(\alpha)]^2.$$

Combining this result and (5.73b) with (5.78) we get

$$|\theta|_{1,e_l}^2 \le [16/\sin(\alpha)] |\tilde{\theta}|_{1,\tilde{e}}^2,$$

and hence the left-hand inequality of (5.75) is established with $D_1 = \tfrac{1}{4}$.

To find E_1 we reverse the roles of the "tilde" and "nontilde" variables in the preceding analysis. Inequality (5.78) then becomes

$$|\tilde{\theta}|^2_{1,\tilde{e}} \leq D\tilde{c}|\theta|^2_{1,e_l}, \tag{5.79}$$

where D is defined as before and

$$\tilde{c} = \max\{\tilde{c}_1 + \tilde{c}_2, \tilde{c}_3 + \tilde{c}_2\},$$

$$\tilde{c}_1 = x^2_{\tilde{x}} + x^2_{\tilde{y}}, \qquad \tilde{c}_2 = x_{\tilde{x}}y_{\tilde{x}} + x_{\tilde{y}}y_{\tilde{y}}, \qquad \tilde{c}_3 = y^2_{\tilde{x}} + y^2_{\tilde{y}}.$$

The inequalities in (5.73a) show that $\tilde{c} \leq 4h^2$, and using (5.74b) we derive

$$|\tilde{\theta}|^2_{1,\tilde{e}} \leq [8/\sin(\alpha)]|\theta|^2_{1,e_l}.$$

Thus, the right-hand inequality of (5.75) is valid with $E_1 = 2\sqrt{2}$.

To establish (5.75) for $s > 1$ we need the analog of (5.76) for derivatives of order s. For example, using (5.76) we find that

$$\begin{aligned}
\theta_{xx} &= (\theta_x)_x = (\tilde{\theta}_{\tilde{x}})_x\tilde{x}_x + (\tilde{\theta}_{\tilde{y}})_x\tilde{y}_x \\
&= [\tilde{\theta}_{\tilde{x}\tilde{x}}\tilde{x}_x + \tilde{\theta}_{\tilde{x}\tilde{y}}\tilde{y}_x]\tilde{x}_x + [\tilde{\theta}_{\tilde{y}\tilde{x}}\tilde{x}_x + \tilde{\theta}_{\tilde{y}\tilde{y}}\tilde{y}_x]\tilde{y}_x \\
&= \tilde{\theta}_{\tilde{x}\tilde{x}}\tilde{x}^2_x + 2\tilde{\theta}_{\tilde{x}\tilde{y}}\tilde{x}_x\tilde{y}_x + \tilde{\theta}_{\tilde{y}\tilde{y}}\tilde{y}^2_x.
\end{aligned}$$

The general situation is that every partial derivative of θ of order s is a polynomial of degree s with respect to $\tilde{x}_x$, $\tilde{x}_y$, $\tilde{y}_x$, and $\tilde{y}_y$, no term having degree less than s. Summing the squares of all sth-order derivatives and using (5.77) to eliminate cross products, we see that (5.78) becomes

$$|\theta|^2_{s,e_l} \leq \tilde{D}c|\tilde{\theta}|^2_{s,\tilde{e}},$$

where

$$c = O\{[h\sin(\alpha)]^{-2s}\}.$$

Similarly, (5.79) generalizes to

$$|\tilde{\theta}|^2_{s,\tilde{e}} < D\tilde{c}|\theta|^2_{s,e_l},$$

where $\tilde{c} = O(h^{2s})$. Using the upper bounds on $\tilde{D}$ and D we obtain (5.75). ■

Theorem 5.4. (Bramble–Hilbert Lemma) For some region $\Omega \subset R^2$ and some integer $k \geq -1$, let there be given a bounded linear functional

$$f: H^{k+1}(\Omega) \rightarrow R,$$

that is,

$$f(\alpha u + \beta v) = \alpha f(u) + \beta f(v), \qquad u, v \in H^{k+1}(\Omega), \quad \alpha, \beta \in R,$$

$$|f(u)| \leq \delta\|u\|_{k+1}, \qquad u \in H^{k+1}(\Omega),$$

for some δ independent of u. Suppose that

$$f(u) = 0 \qquad \forall u \in P_k(\bar{\Omega}),$$

where $P_k(\bar{\Omega})$ denotes (as usual) the space of polynomials of degree at most k defined on $\bar{\Omega}$.

Then there exists a constant C, dependent only on Ω, such that

$$|f(u)| \leq C\delta|u|_{k+1}, \qquad u \in H^{k+1}(\Omega).$$

We omit the proof. See, e.g., Bramble and Hilbert (1970) and Ciarlet (1978). [For related material see also Dupont and Scott (1978, 1980) and Meinguet (1977, 1978).] There is a technical condition on the geometry of Ω, the so-called "cone condition," which is satisfied by almost all domains of physical interest not having cusps.

The next theorem deals with finite element interpolation over the standard element $\tilde{e}$, and for the time being we can drop the assumption that $\tilde{e}$ is a triangle. The proof requires inequality (5.80), which we shall proceed to derive.

Thus, for some integer $k \geq 1$ and for some $\tilde{u} \in H^{k+1}(\tilde{e})$, consider the interpolant

$$\tilde{u}_1(\tilde{x}, \tilde{y}) = \sum_{r=1}^{T} \tilde{u}(\tilde{N}_r)\tilde{\phi}_r(\tilde{x}, \tilde{y}), \qquad (\tilde{x}, \tilde{y}) \in \tilde{e},$$

where $\tilde{N}_1, \tilde{N}_2, ..., \tilde{N}_T$ are the nodes of $\tilde{e}$ and $\tilde{\phi}_1, \tilde{\phi}_2, ..., \tilde{\phi}_T$ are the standard local basis functions. Differentiating, we obtain

$$\tilde{u}_1^{(\alpha)}(\tilde{x}, \tilde{y}) = \sum_{r=1}^{T} \tilde{u}(\tilde{N}_r)\tilde{\phi}_r^{(\alpha)}(\tilde{x}, \tilde{y}).$$

(We are employing the multi-index notation for arbitrary partial derivatives introduced in Section 3.1.) Since the standard local basis functions are polynomials, derivatives of sufficiently high order vanish. Clearly, there exists a value M such that

$$|\tilde{\phi}_r^{(\alpha)}(\tilde{x}, \tilde{y})| \leq M \qquad \forall(\tilde{x}, \tilde{y}) \in \tilde{e}, \quad \forall\alpha, \qquad r = 1, 2, ..., T.$$

Further, (3.24) leads to an inequality of the form

$$|\tilde{u}(\tilde{N}_r)| \leq \max_{(\tilde{x}, \tilde{y}) \in \tilde{e}} |\tilde{u}(\tilde{x}, \tilde{y})| \leq \eta\|\tilde{u}\|_{k+1,\tilde{e}} \qquad \forall\tilde{u} \in H^{k+1}(\tilde{e}),$$

where η depends only on k and $\tilde{e}$. Hence,

$$|\tilde{u}_1^{(\alpha)}(\tilde{x}, \tilde{y})| \leq \eta TM\|\tilde{u}\|_{k+1,\tilde{e}} \qquad \forall(\tilde{x}, \tilde{y}) \in \tilde{e}, \quad \forall\alpha, \quad \forall\tilde{u} \in H^{k+1}(\tilde{e}).$$

Finally, forming Sobolev seminorms of $\tilde{u}_1$ (of which only a finite number are nonzero), we see that there exists a value $\hat{M}$, independent of $\tilde{u}$ and s, such that

$$|\tilde{u}_1|_{s,\tilde{e}} \le \hat{M}\|\tilde{u}\|_{k+1,\tilde{e}} \qquad \forall \tilde{u} \in H^{k+1}(\tilde{e}), \qquad s = 0, 1, 2, \dots . \tag{5.80}$$

The proof of the theorem also requires the "semi-inner product" corresponding to the seminorm $|\cdot|_{s,\tilde{e}}$. This is defined by

$$[\tilde{u}, \tilde{v}]_{s,\tilde{e}} = \sum_{|\alpha|=s} \int\int_{\tilde{e}} \tilde{u}^{(\alpha)}\tilde{v}^{(\alpha)} \, d\tilde{x} \, d\tilde{y}, \qquad \tilde{u}, \tilde{v} \in H^s(\tilde{e}).$$

Obviously,

$$[\tilde{u}, \tilde{u}]_{s,\tilde{e}} = |\tilde{u}|^2_{s,\tilde{e}}, \qquad \tilde{u} \in H^s(\tilde{e}).$$

One can easily establish the Cauchy–Schwarz inequality

$$\left|[\tilde{u}, \tilde{v}]_{s,\tilde{e}}\right| \le |\tilde{u}|_{s,\tilde{e}}|\tilde{v}|_{s,\tilde{e}}, \qquad \tilde{u}, \tilde{v} \in H^s(\tilde{e}), \tag{5.81a}$$

and this leads to the basic seminorm inequality

$$|\tilde{u} + \tilde{v}|_{s,\tilde{e}} \le |\tilde{u}|_{s,\tilde{e}} + |\tilde{v}|_{s,\tilde{e}}, \qquad \tilde{u}, \tilde{v} \in H^s(\tilde{e}). \tag{5.81b}$$

(See Exercise 3.2.)

Theorem 5.5. Let there be given a standard element $\tilde{e}$ and standard local basis functions $\tilde{\phi}_1, \tilde{\phi}_2, \dots, \tilde{\phi}_T$. Let k be the largest integer satisfying

$$P_k(\tilde{e}) \subseteq \text{SPAN}\{\tilde{\phi}_1, \tilde{\phi}_2, \dots, \tilde{\phi}_T\}.$$

Then, there exists a constant $\hat{C}$, independent of $\tilde{u}$, such that

$$|\tilde{u} - \tilde{u}_1|_{s,\tilde{e}} \le \hat{C}|\tilde{u}|_{k+1,\tilde{e}} \qquad \forall \tilde{u} \in H^{k+1}(\tilde{e}), \quad s = 0, 1, \dots, k+1.$$

PROOF: For some integer s such that $0 \le s \le k+1$ and some $\tilde{v} \in H^s(\tilde{e})$, let a functional f be defined on $H^{k+1}(\tilde{e})$ by

$$f(\tilde{u}) = [\tilde{u} - \tilde{u}_1, \tilde{v}]_{s,\tilde{e}}, \qquad \tilde{u} \in H^{k+1}(\tilde{e}).$$

We leave it to the reader to verify that f is linear. Using (5.81), (5.80), and the trivial inequality $|\tilde{u}|_{s,\tilde{e}} \le \|\tilde{u}\|_{k+1,\tilde{e}}$, we find that

$$|f(\tilde{u})| \le |\tilde{u} - \tilde{u}_1|_{s,\tilde{e}}|\tilde{v}|_{s,\tilde{e}}$$
$$\le |\tilde{v}|_{s,\tilde{e}}(|\tilde{u}|_{s,\tilde{e}} + |\tilde{u}_1|_{s,\tilde{e}})$$
$$\le (1 + \hat{M})|\tilde{v}|_{s,\tilde{e}}\|\tilde{u}\|_{k+1,\tilde{e}}.$$

Thus, f is a bounded linear functional on $H^{k+1}(\tilde{e})$. Further, $\tilde{u} \in P_k(\tilde{e}) \Rightarrow \tilde{u}_1 = \tilde{u} \Rightarrow f(\tilde{u}) = 0$, so by the Bramble–Hilbert lemma there exists a constant C such that

$$|f(\tilde{u})| \le C(1 + \hat{M})|\tilde{v}|_{s,\tilde{e}}|\tilde{u}|_{k+1,\tilde{e}} \qquad \forall \tilde{u} \in H^{k+1}(\tilde{e}).$$

C depends only on $\tilde{e}$ and hence is independent of $\tilde{v}$. Putting $\tilde{v} = \tilde{u} - \tilde{u}_I$ we obtain

$$|\tilde{u} - \tilde{u}_I|^2_{s,\tilde{e}} \le C(1 + \hat{M})|\tilde{u} - \tilde{u}_I|_{s,\tilde{e}}|\tilde{u}|_{k+1,\tilde{e}},$$

and the theorem is established for $\hat{C} = C(1 + \hat{M})$. ∎

The preceding results lead to a fundamental theorem regarding finite element interpolation on a triangular mesh. The interpolation associated with the basis functions of Section 5.1 is the Lagrange type

$$u_I(x, y) = \sum_{i=1}^{M} u(N_i)\phi_i(x, y),$$

where, in contrast to Hermite interpolation, only values of u are interpolated. Accordingly, we assumed this type of interpolation in establishing the preceding theorem [more specifically, in deriving the bound in (5.80)]. As mentioned in Section 5.1, it is typical that the first-order derivatives of the global basis functions, and hence of u_I, have step discontinuities across element boundaries with the result that in general $u_I \notin H^2(\Omega)$. Hence, the Sobolev seminorm $|u - u_I|_s$ must be restricted to the values $s = 0, 1$. (This restriction is not necessary in Theorem 5.5 because the domain there is a single element.)

Theorem 5.6. Let there be given a polygonal domain $\bar{\Omega} \subset R^2$, a finite element mesh on $\bar{\Omega}$ with triangular elements, and associated basis functions $\phi_1, \phi_2, ..., \phi_M$. Let h and α denote the greatest edge length and smallest angle, respectively, in the mesh, and let k be the largest integer for which $P_k(\bar{\Omega}) \subseteq V_M$. Then, there exists a value C, independent of u and the mesh, such that

$$|u - u_I|_s \le C[\sin(\alpha)]^{-s}h^{k+1-s}|u|_{k+1} \qquad \forall u \in H^{k+1}(\Omega), \quad s = 0, 1,$$

where u_I is the V_M interpolant of u.

PROOF: The proof consists essentially of two applications of Theorem 5.3 and one of Theorem 5.5. Note that the above value of k is identical to the value defined in Theorem 5.5.

Let e_l be any element of the mesh, and let h and α denote for the moment the greatest edge length and smallest angle, respectively, of that element. Then,

$$|u - u_I|^2_{s,e_l} \le D_s^{-2}[\sin(\alpha)]^{-2s+1}h^{-2s+2}|\tilde{u} - \tilde{u}_I|^2_{s,\tilde{e}}$$

$$\le D_s^{-2}[\sin(\alpha)]^{-2s+1}h^{-2s+2}\hat{C}^2|\tilde{u}|^2_{k+1,\tilde{e}}$$

$$\le \{D_s^{-2}[\sin(\alpha)]^{-2s+1}h^{-2s+2}\}\hat{C}^2$$

$$\times \{E_{k+1}^2[\sin(\alpha)]^{-1}h^{2k}\}|u|^2_{k+1,e_l}.$$

This inequality obviously holds for all elements when h and α are the greatest edge length and smallest angle in the entire mesh. Summing over all elements and taking square roots, we establish the theorem with $C = \hat{C}E_{k+1}/\min\{D_0, D_1\} = 4\hat{C}E_{k+1}$. ∎

When $V_M \subset C^{m-1}(\bar{\Omega})$, where $m > 1$, u_I must be an Hermite interpolant of u and the preceding theorem can be extended to

$$|u - u_I|_s \leq C[\sin(\alpha)]^{-s}h^{k+1-s}|u|_{k+1} \qquad \forall u \in H^{k+1}(\Omega), \quad s = 0, 1, \ldots, m, \quad (5.82)$$

provided that $m \leq k + 1$.

Rectangular Elements

We consider now an axiparallel domain $\bar{\Omega}$ and a mesh of axiparallel rectangular elements. The basis functions can be the bilinear functions of Example 5.3 or of higher degree (such as those described in Exercises 5.7 and 5.9). We assume only that the four vertices in the typical element e_l are nodes, and that these are ordered first with the ordering shown in Example 5.3. If the standard element $\tilde{e}$ is taken to be the rectangle with vertices $(-1, -1), (1, -1), (1, 1),$ and $(-1, 1)$, then the mapping of $\tilde{e}$ onto e_l is given by (5.22):

$$x = \tfrac{1}{2}(x_{i_2^{(l)}} - x_{i_1^{(l)}})\tilde{x} + \tfrac{1}{2}(x_{i_2^{(l)}} + x_{i_1^{(l)}}),$$

$$y = \tfrac{1}{2}(y_{i_3^{(l)}} - y_{i_1^{(l)}})\tilde{y} + \tfrac{1}{2}(y_{i_3^{(l)}} + y_{i_1^{(l)}}).$$

For a given element e_l let h be the largest edge length, h^* the smallest edge length, and $\beta = h^*/h$ the element *edge ratio*. It is easily established that

$$|x_{\tilde{x}}|, |x_{\tilde{y}}|, |y_{\tilde{x}}|, |y_{\tilde{y}}| \leq h/2, \qquad \tilde{D} = \tfrac{1}{4}\beta h^2,$$

$$|\tilde{x}_x|, |\tilde{x}_y|, |\tilde{y}_x|, |\tilde{y}_y| \leq 2/(\beta h), \qquad D = 4/(\beta h^2),$$

where $\tilde{D}$ and D are the Jacobians of the transformation and its inverse, respectively. A comparison of these inequalities with (5.73) and (5.74) leads us to the following analogs of Theorems 5.3 and 5.6:

Theorem 5.7. Let $\theta(x, y) \in H^s(e_l)$ and $\tilde{\theta}(\tilde{x}, \tilde{y}) \in H^s(\tilde{e})$ satisfy the relation $\theta(x, y) = \tilde{\theta}(\tilde{x}, \tilde{y})$ under the given variable transformation. Then, there exist constants D_s and E_s such that

$$D_s\beta^{s-1/2}h^{s-1}|\theta|_{s,e_l} \leq |\tilde{\theta}|_{s,\tilde{e}} \leq E_s\beta^{-1/2}h^{s-1}|\theta|_{s,e_l}.$$

Theorem 5.8. Let there be given an axiparallel domain $\bar{\Omega} \subset R^2$, a finite element mesh on $\bar{\Omega}$ with axiparallel rectangular elements, and associated basis functions ϕ_1, ϕ_2, ..., ϕ_M. Let h and β denote the largest edge length and smallest edge ratio, respectively, in the mesh, and let k be the largest integer for which $P_k(\bar{\Omega}) \subseteq V_M$. Then, there exists a value C, independent of u and the mesh, such that

$$|u - u_1|_s \leq C\beta^{-s}h^{k+1-s}|u|_{k+1} \qquad \forall u \in H^{k+1}(\Omega), \quad s = 0, 1,$$

where u_1 is the V_M interpolant of u.

Theorems 5.6 and 5.8 suggest a cardinal rule regarding the generation of a finite element mesh: avoid small angles in a triangular mesh and small edge ratios in a rectangular mesh.

We shall now consider an ordered, infinite *family* of meshes $\{\mathcal{M}_p\}_{p=1}^{\infty}$ on $\bar{\Omega}$ with the property that the greatest edge length h in mesh $\mathcal{M}_p$ approaches zero as $p \to \infty$. If the elements are triangles, then we say the family is *regular* if all angles in all meshes are bounded below by some $\alpha > 0$. (The so-called *minimum angle condition*.) If the elements are rectangles, then we say the family is *regular* if all edge ratios in all meshes are bounded below by some $\beta > 0$. Let u be some fixed function in $H^{k+1}(\Omega)$ and let the corresponding interpolant u_1 be derived, successively, from all meshes in a regular family. Theorems 5.6 and 5.8 then imply an inequality of the form

$$|u - u_1|_s \leq \tilde{C}h^{k+1-s}|u|_{k+1}, \qquad h \to 0 \tag{5.83}$$

for $s = 0, 1$.

The derivation of (5.83) is based on the assumption that $u \in H^{k+1}(\Omega)$. If u does not have this degree of regularity but satisfies only $u \in H^{p+1}(\Omega)$ for some $p < k$, then it follows from the preceding analysis that there is some constant C^* such that

$$|u - u_1|_s \leq C^*h^{p+1-s}|u|_{p+1}, \qquad h \to 0 \tag{5.84}$$

for $s = 0, 1$.

It is an interesting fact that (5.83) and (5.84) are valid for at least $s = 1$ for certain nonregular families of meshes. More specifically, the minimum angle condition mentioned previously can be relaxed to the *maximum angle condition*, which requires all angles to be bounded above by $\pi - \alpha$ for some $\alpha > 0$. [See Babúska and Aziz (1976).]

Discretization Error

It was shown at the beginning of this section that the discretization error $(\hat{u} - \hat{u}_N)$ satisfies (5.64),

$$\|\hat{u} - \hat{u}_N\|_1 \leq C\|\hat{u} - \hat{u}_1\|_1.$$

Using the identity

$$\|\hat{u} - \hat{u}_1\|_1^2 = |\hat{u} - \hat{u}_1|_0^2 + |\hat{u} - \hat{u}_1|_1^2$$

and the bounds in (5.83), we see that if $\hat{u} \in H^{k+1}(\Omega)$, then

$$\|\hat{u} - \hat{u}_N\|_1 \leq \tilde{C}_1 h^k |\hat{u}|_{k+1} \tag{5.85}$$

for some constant $\tilde{C}_1$. If $\hat{u} \in H^{p+1}(\Omega)$, where $p < k$, then it follows from (5.84) that (5.85) must be replaced by a weaker bound,

$$\|\hat{u} - \hat{u}_N\|_1 \leq C_1^* h^p |\hat{u}|_{p+1}. \tag{5.86}$$

This brings out the important point that high-accuracy basis functions tend to be wasted when the solution of the boundary value problem has little regularity.

Inequality (5.85) leads trivially to the seminorm bounds

$$|\hat{u} - \hat{u}_N|_0 \leq \tilde{C}_1 h^k |\hat{u}|_{k+1}, \tag{5.87a}$$

$$|\hat{u} - \hat{u}_N|_1 \leq \tilde{C}_1 h^k |\hat{u}|_{k+1}. \tag{5.87b}$$

The *gradient error* $|\hat{u} - \hat{u}_N|_1$ (which is sometimes of most interest) has a bound that agrees with the bound on $|\hat{u} - \hat{u}_1|_1$ in (5.83) in the sense that the two bounds contain the same power of h. On the other hand, the above bound on $|\hat{u} - \hat{u}_N|_0$ is disappointing since it is $O(h^k)$, whereas the bound on $|\hat{u} - \hat{u}_1|_0$ in (5.83) is $O(h^{k+1})$, an order of magnitude better. We shall now present the *Aubin–Nitsche method* (Aubin, 1967; Nitsche, 1968), by which we can derive a bound on $|\hat{u} - \hat{u}_N|_0$ that is $O(h^{k+1})$, a process sometimes referred to as "L_2 lifting." Let us first recall that the seminorm $|\cdot|_0$ is identical to the $L_2(\Omega)$ norm $\|\cdot\|$. The latter notation will be used in the following analysis.

We shall illustrate the Aubin–Nitsche method in the case of the boundary value problem

$$\mathscr{L}u \equiv -\Delta u + \mathbf{b}(x, y)^T \nabla u + c(x, y)u = g(x, y) \qquad \text{in} \quad \Omega \subset R^2, \tag{5.88}$$

$$u = 0 \qquad \text{on} \quad \Gamma,$$

which was discussed in Example 4.1. Its variational formulation is the problem of finding $u \in \mathring{H}^1(\Omega)$ such that

$$a(u, v) = G(v) \qquad \forall v \in \mathring{H}^1(\Omega),$$

where

$$a(u, v) = \int\int_\Omega [(\nabla u)^T(\nabla v) + (\mathbf{b}^T \nabla u)v + cuv] \, dx \, dy, \qquad u, v \in \mathring{H}^1(\Omega),$$

$$G(v) = \int\int_\Omega gv \, dx \, dy.$$

We make the assumption that

$$\phi_0 \equiv \min_{(x,y)\in\Omega} \{c(x, y) - \tfrac{1}{2} \, \mathrm{div}[\mathbf{b}(x, y)]\} \geq -\rho,$$

ρ being the positive constant that satisfies

$$|u|_1^2 \geq \rho\|u\|_1^2 \qquad \forall u \in \mathring{H}^1(\Omega).$$

(See Example 3.1.) It then follows from (4.28) that

$$a(u, u) \geq \tilde{\rho}\|u\|_1^2 \qquad \forall u \in \mathring{H}^1(\Omega),$$

where $\tilde{\rho} = \min\{\rho, \phi_0 + \rho\}$, i.e., the bilinear form $a(\cdot, \cdot)$ is coercive. It was established in Example 4.1 that it is also bounded.

The Aubin–Nitsche method requires us to consider the so-called "adjoint" problem associated with (5.88). To derive this we observe from the identity

$$\int\int_\Omega (\mathbf{b}^\mathrm{T} \nabla u)v \; dx \; dy = -\int\int_\Omega \mathrm{div}(v\mathbf{b})u \; dx \; dy \qquad \forall u, v \in \mathring{H}^1(\Omega)$$

that

$$a(u, v) = a^*(v, u) \qquad \forall u, v \in \mathring{H}^1(\Omega), \tag{5.89}$$

where we have introduced the new bilinear form

$$a^*(v, u) = \int\int_\Omega [(\nabla v)^\mathrm{T}(\nabla u) - \mathrm{div}(v\mathbf{b})u + cvu] \; dx \; dy, \qquad u, v \in \mathring{H}^1(\Omega).$$

The variational problem of finding $v \in \mathring{H}^1(\Omega)$ such that

$$a^*(v, u) = G(u) \qquad \forall u \in \mathring{H}^1(\Omega) \tag{5.90}$$

leads to the boundary value problem

$$\mathscr{L}^*v \equiv -\Delta v - \mathrm{div}(v\mathbf{b}) + cv = g \qquad \text{in } \Omega,$$
$$v = 0 \qquad \text{on } \Gamma. \tag{5.91}$$

The identities $a(u, v) = (\mathscr{L}u, v)$, $a^*(v, u) = (u, \mathscr{L}^*v)$, and hence $(\mathscr{L}u, v) = (u, \mathscr{L}^*v)$ are valid for sufficiently smooth u and v in $\mathring{H}^1(\Omega)$, so $\mathscr{L}^*$ is the adjoint operator associated with $\mathscr{L}$. (See Remark 8 after the Lax–Milgram lemma in Section 3.2.) We call (5.91) the *adjoint problem* associated with (5.88).

We shall need the assumption that problem (5.90) has the property that for any $g \in L_2(\Omega)$, the solution $\hat{v}$ belongs to $H^2(\Omega) \cap \mathring{H}^1(\Omega)$ and

$$|\hat{v}|_2 \leq K\|g\|, \tag{5.92}$$

where K is independent of g. Whether this property (sometimes referred to as *elliptic regularity*) is present depends on the smoothness of $\mathbf{b}(x, y)$, $c(x, y)$, and Γ. [See Friedman (1969) and Nečas (1967) for further details.]

The Aubin–Nitsche method now proceeds as follows. Let $\hat{u}$ and $\hat{v}^{(N)}$ denote the solutions of boundary value problem (5.88) and the related problem

$$\mathscr{L}^*v = \hat{u} - \hat{u}_N \qquad \text{in } \Omega,$$

$$v = 0 \qquad \text{on } \Gamma,$$

respectively, where $\hat{u}_N$ is the Galerkin approximation to $\hat{u}$ based on some subspace $V_N \subset \overset{\circ}{H}{}^1(\Omega)$. Let $\hat{v}_N^{(N)}$ denote the Galerkin approximation to $\hat{v}^{(N)}$ from the same subspace. There are thus four variational problems:

$$a(\hat{u}, v) = (g, v) \qquad \forall v \in \overset{\circ}{H}{}^1(\Omega), \qquad (5.93\text{a})$$

$$a(\hat{u}_N, v) = (g, v) \qquad \forall v \in V_N, \qquad (5.93\text{b})$$

$$a(u, \hat{v}^{(N)}) = (\hat{u} - \hat{u}_N, u) \qquad \forall u \in \overset{\circ}{H}{}^1(\Omega), \qquad (5.93\text{c})$$

$$a(u, \hat{v}_N^{(N)}) = (\hat{u} - \hat{u}_N, u) \qquad \forall u \in V_N. \qquad (5.93\text{d})$$

Putting $u = \hat{u} - \hat{u}_N$ in (5.93c), we obtain

$$a(\hat{u} - \hat{u}_N, \hat{v}^{(N)}) = \|\hat{u} - \hat{u}_N\|^2.$$

From (5.93a) and (5.93b) we have

$$a(\hat{u} - \hat{u}_N, v) = 0 \qquad \forall v \in V_N$$

and hence in particular for $v = \hat{v}_N^{(N)}$. Thus,

$$a(\hat{u} - \hat{u}_N, \hat{v}^{(N)} - \hat{v}_N^{(N)}) = a(\hat{u} - \hat{u}_N, \hat{v}^{(N)}) = \|\hat{u} - \hat{u}_N\|^2,$$

and

$$\|\hat{u} - \hat{u}_N\|^2 \leq \beta \|\hat{u} - \hat{u}_N\|_1 \|\hat{v}^{(N)} - \hat{v}_N^{(N)}\|_1 \qquad [a(\cdot, \cdot) \text{ is bounded}],$$

$$\leq \beta C_1^* h |\hat{v}^{(N)}|_2 \|\hat{u} - \hat{u}_N\|_1 \qquad [(5.86), p = 1],$$

$$\leq \beta C_1^* h K \|\hat{u} - \hat{u}_N\| \, \|\hat{u} - \hat{u}_N\|_1 \qquad [(5.92)].$$

Hence,

$$\|\hat{u} - \hat{u}_N\| \leq \beta C_1^* K h \|\hat{u} - \hat{u}_N\|_1,$$

and from (5.85) we obtain the final bound

$$\|\hat{u} - \hat{u}_N\| \leq \beta C_1^* \tilde{C}_1 K h^{k+1} |\hat{u}|_{k+1},$$

which has the desired order of convergence.

Maximum-Norm and Pointwise Error Estimates

Using the Green's function (Section 3.3) one can analyze the behavior of the discretization error $\hat{u}(\mathbf{x}) - \hat{u}_N(\mathbf{x})$ at any point $\mathbf{x}$ in $\bar{\Omega}$ and hence derive bounds on the maximum norm of the error,

$$\|\hat{u} - \hat{u}_N\|_\infty \equiv \max_{\mathbf{x} \in \bar{\Omega}} |\hat{u}(\mathbf{x}) - \hat{u}_N(\mathbf{x})|.$$

To illustrate the procedure we consider the two-point boundary value problem

$$-(p(x)u')' + q(x)u = g(x), \qquad -1 < x < 1,$$
$$u(-1) = u(1) = 0,$$

where p and q satisfy the conditions given under (3.9). From (3.56) and (3.58b) we have the identity

$$u(x) = a(K(x, \cdot), u(\cdot)) \qquad \forall u \in \mathring{H}^1(-1, 1),$$

where $K(x, \xi)$ is the Green's function for the problem and the bilinear form is defined by

$$a(u, v) = \int_{-1}^{1} \left[pu'v' + quv\right] d\xi, \qquad u, v \in \mathring{H}^1(-1, 1).$$

The Ritz–Galerkin approximation $\hat{u}_N \in V_N$ satisfies

$$a(u, \hat{u} - \hat{u}_N) = 0 \qquad \forall u \in V_N.$$

Hence

$$\hat{u}(x) - \hat{u}_N(x) = a(K(x, \cdot), \hat{u}(\cdot) - \hat{u}_N(\cdot))$$
$$= a(K(x, \cdot) - u(\cdot), \hat{u}(\cdot) - \hat{u}_N(\cdot)) \qquad \forall u \in V_N.$$

The bilinear form is bounded, i.e., there exists a positive constant β such that

$$|a(u, v)| \le \beta \|u\|_1 \|v\|_1 \qquad \forall u, v \in \mathring{H}^1(-1, 1).$$

Further, (5.85) is also valid for this one-dimensional problem, so

$$\|\hat{u} - \hat{u}_N\|_1 = O(h^k)$$

under the assumption that $\hat{u} \in H^{k+1}(-1, 1)$. Denoting the V_M interpolant of $K(x, \xi)$, $-1 \le \xi \le 1$ by $K_I(x, \xi)$ and observing from the properties $K(x, 1) =$

$K(x, -1) = 0$ [see (3.57) and (3.58b)] that $K_1(x, \xi) \in V_N$, we obtain from the preceding results the *pointwise* error estimate

$$|\hat{u}(x) - \hat{u}_N(x)| = |a(K(x, \cdot) - K_1(x, \cdot), \hat{u}(\cdot) - \hat{u}_N(\cdot))|$$
$$= O(h^k)\|K(x, \cdot) - K_1(x, \cdot)\|_1.$$

Now the accuracy with which the Green's function is interpolated by the basis functions is determined by its smoothness. We know that it belongs to $\mathring{H}^1(-1, 1)$. Further, it is typically smooth in the subintervals $-1 \le \xi < x$ and $x < \xi \le 1$ (the degree of smoothness depending on that of the coefficients p and q), but its first-order derivative has a step discontinuity at $\xi = x$, implying $u \notin H^2(-1, 1)$. From (5.84) we then have

$$\|K(x, \cdot) - K_1(x, \cdot)\|_1 = O(h^0),$$

and combining this with the previous result we arrive at the maximum-norm estimate

$$\|\hat{u} - \hat{u}_N\|_\infty = O(h^k).$$

This is somewhat disappointing in so far as we know that $\|\hat{u} - \hat{u}_N\| = O(h^{k+1})$, an order of magnitude better. Fortunately, a more refined analysis does in fact establish that $\|\hat{u} - \hat{u}_N\|_\infty = O(h^{k+1})$. [See, e.g., Fairweather (1978).]

We shall now consider the pointwise error at a node $x = x_i$. A special situation arises here, namely, the step discontinuity in the first-order derivative of $K(x_i, \xi)$ has essentially no effect on the interpolation error because it occurs at a node. In fact, if the restrictions of $K(x_i, \xi)$ to $-1 < \xi < x_i$ and $x_i < \xi < 1$ belong to $H^{k+1}(-1, x_i)$ and $H^{k+1}(x_i, 1)$, respectively, then decomposing the interpolation error into contributions from each of these subintervals we can use (5.83) to obtain

$$\|K(x_i, \cdot) - K_1(x_i, \cdot)\|_1 = O(h^k)$$

and hence

$$|\hat{u}(x_i) - \hat{u}_N(x_i)| = O(h^{2k}).$$

If $k > 1$ then this is asymptotically faster than the $O(h^{k+1})$ convergence of $\|\hat{u} - \hat{u}_N\|_\infty$, and we speak of *superconvergence* at x_i.

An even more dramatic result is obtained if $p(x)$ is a positive constant and $q(x)$ is zero. Then, $K(x_i, \xi)$ is a linear function of ξ on each side of x_i [see (3.60)], and $K_1(x_i, \xi) = K(x_i, \xi)$, $-1 \le \xi \le 1$ provided only that $k \ge 1$. Hence,

$$|\hat{u}(x_i) - \hat{u}_N(x_i)| = 0.$$

Maximum-norm and pointwise error analysis in the case of a second-order boundary value problem in two or more dimensions is complicated by the fact that the Green's function does not belong to $H^1(\Omega)$. (See the end of Section 3.3.) Thus, more refined mathematical techniques are required. For a survey of papers on this advanced topic see Nitsche (1979); see also Goldstein (1980), Louis (1979), Natterer (1975), and Scott (1976). In the latter reference it is established that

$$\|\hat{u} - \hat{u}_N\|_\infty \leq \begin{cases} ch^2|\ln(h)| & \text{for} \quad k = 1, \\ ch^{k+1} & \text{for} \quad k \geq 2 \end{cases}$$

for the boundary value problem

$$-\Delta u + u = g \quad \text{in} \quad \Omega \subset R^2,$$

$$u_v = 0 \quad \text{on} \quad \Gamma$$

and the use of triangular elements. Regarding the case of piecewise linear basis functions $(k = 1)$, it is worth mentioning that the difference between $O(h^2|\ln(h)|)$ and $O(h^2)$ is insignificant in the sense that for any $\varepsilon > 0$ we have $h^2|\ln(h)| < h^{2-\varepsilon}$ for sufficiently small values of h.†

5.5   Condition Numbers

Introduction

We recall that the spectral condition number $\kappa(H)$ of an $N \times N$ positive definite matrix H with eigenvalues $0 < \lambda_1 \leq \cdots \leq \lambda_N$ is given by $\kappa(H) = \lambda_N/\lambda_1$. The main purpose of this section is to investigate the spectral condition number of the stiffness matrix K in the Ritz–Galerkin equations

$$K\alpha = G \tag{5.94}$$

when the basis functions are of finite element type. If $\kappa(K)$ is large, then a small change in G or K may cause a relatively large change in the solution α, and we say that (5.94) is *ill-conditioned*. Now the determination of K and G in practice often involves some form of approximation; e.g., numerical integration or experimentally determined data. Moreover, the inevitable occurrence of rounding errors in the process of solving (5.94) effectively

---

† For an analysis of the discretization error in norms other than those considered in this book see Rannacher and Scott (1982).

introduces perturbations in K and $\mathbf{G}$. Thus, the computed solution of (5.94) is unreliable if $\kappa(K)$ is very large. (Sometimes the effect of rounding errors on the computed solution can be reduced, however; see Section 7.4.) A further disadvantage of a large condition number is that it usually reduces the rate of convergence of iterative methods for solving (5.94), among them the conjugate gradient method of Chapter 1. All of these considerations make it important to assess the magnitude of $\kappa(K)$. We are particularly interested in how $\kappa(K)$ depends on N.

The Mass Matrix

We assume that the boundary value problem is of second order in n space dimensions and that the bilinear form $a(\cdot,\cdot)$ is symmetric, coercive, and bounded. Thus,

$$\rho\|u\|_1^2 \le a(u, u) \le \beta\|u\|_1^2 \qquad \forall u \in V \tag{5.95}$$

for some positive ρ and β independent of u, and $\mathring{H}^1(\Omega) \subseteq V \subseteq H^1(\Omega)$. The solution $\hat{u}$ belongs to V unless there is an inhomogeneous Dirichlet boundary condition on at least part of the boundary, in which case $\hat{u} = \hat{v} + u^*$ for some $\hat{v} \in V$ and some u^* satisfying the Dirichlet condition. [The right-hand side of (5.94) then has the form of $\mathbf{G}^*$ in (4.10).]

In our finite element treatment of problem (5.23), (5.24) in Section 5.2, we identified three distinct stiffness matrices, namely, K_1, K_2, and K_3 in (5.30), and we can obviously do the same for the more general problem. In the following analysis K denotes K_3, the "original" Ritz–Galerkin matrix. Since in practice it is often the larger matrix K_2 that is given to the equation solver, we shall return to this matrix later. The eigenvalues of both matrices are independent of the global node ordering because a reordering of nodes has the effect of multiplying the stiffness matrix from the left by a permutation matrix P and from the right by P^{T}, a similarity transformation since P is orthogonal. Hence, there is no loss of generality for our present purpose in assuming that the N nodes where $\hat{u}$ is unknown are ordered first. For material related to the following analysis see Descloux (1972) and Fried (1973, 1979).

Using the symmetry of the bilinear form, we can write the entries of K as

$$k_{ij} = a(\phi_i, \phi_j), \qquad i, j = 1, 2, \ldots, N.$$

To obtain bounds on the extreme eigenvalues of K [and thereby a bound on the condition number $\kappa(K)$], we must first examine the eigenvalues of the so-called *mass matrix* M defined by

$$m_{ij} = (\phi_i, \phi_j) = \int_\Omega \phi_i(\mathbf{x})\phi_j(\mathbf{x}) \, d\Omega, \qquad i, j = 1, 2, \ldots, N. \tag{5.96}$$

To this end it is convenient to introduce *element mass matrices* $\{M^{(l)}\}_{l=1}^L$ defined in terms of the local basis functions by

$$m_{rs}^{(l)} = \int_{e_l} \phi_r^{(l)}(\mathbf{x})\phi_s^{(l)}(\mathbf{x})\, d\Omega, \qquad r, s = 1, 2, \ldots, T. \qquad (5.97)$$

From the identity

$$\boldsymbol{\alpha}^{\mathrm{T}} M \boldsymbol{\alpha} = \int_\Omega u(\mathbf{x})^2 \, d\Omega, \qquad u(\mathbf{x}) \equiv \sum_{i=1}^N \alpha_i \phi_i(\mathbf{x})$$

we deduce that M is positive definite, and clearly the element mass matrices have the same property.

Let the eigenvalues of M and $M^{(l)}$ be denoted $\{\eta_i\}_{i=1}^N$ and $\{\eta_r^{(l)}\}_{r=1}^T$, respectively, with the orderings

$$0 < \eta_1 \le \eta_2 \le \cdots \le \eta_N; \qquad 0 < \eta_1^{(l)} \le \eta_2^{(l)} \le \cdots \le \eta_T^{(l)}.$$

By a well-known property of symmetric matrices, we have

$$\eta_1 = \min_{\boldsymbol{\alpha} \in R^N}(\boldsymbol{\alpha}^{\mathrm{T}} M \boldsymbol{\alpha}/\boldsymbol{\alpha}^{\mathrm{T}} \boldsymbol{\alpha}), \qquad \eta_N = \max_{\boldsymbol{\alpha} \in R^N}(\boldsymbol{\alpha}^{\mathrm{T}} M \boldsymbol{\alpha}/\boldsymbol{\alpha}^{\mathrm{T}} \boldsymbol{\alpha}), \qquad (5.98a)$$

$$\eta_1^{(l)} = \min_{\boldsymbol{\beta} \in R^T}(\boldsymbol{\beta}^{\mathrm{T}} M^{(l)} \boldsymbol{\beta}/\boldsymbol{\beta}^{\mathrm{T}} \boldsymbol{\beta}), \qquad \eta_T^{(l)} = \max_{\boldsymbol{\beta} \in R^T}(\boldsymbol{\beta}^{\mathrm{T}} M^{(l)} \boldsymbol{\beta}/\boldsymbol{\beta}^{\mathrm{T}} \boldsymbol{\beta}). \qquad (5.98b)$$

Our plan is to relate the eigenvalues of M to those of the element mass matrices by decomposing M in terms of the latter and applying (5.98). The key to this is the identity

$$\boldsymbol{\alpha}^{\mathrm{T}} M \boldsymbol{\alpha} = \sum_{l=1}^L \boldsymbol{\alpha}^{(l)\mathrm{T}} M^{(l)} \boldsymbol{\alpha}^{(l)}, \qquad (5.99)$$

where the components of $\boldsymbol{\alpha}^{(l)}$ are

$$\alpha_r^{(l)} = \begin{cases} \alpha_{i_r^{(l)}} & \text{if } 1 \le i_r^{(l)} \le N, \\ 0 & \text{if } i_r^{(l)} > N, \end{cases}$$

for $r = 1, 2, \ldots, T$. Here we are employing the global node number notation of Section 5.1. Note that since we have ordered the N nodes where $\hat{u}$ is unknown first, the condition $i_r^{(l)} > N$ occurs when the corresponding node belongs to a part of Γ where a Dirichlet boundary condition is prescribed.

From (5.99) and (5.98b) we have

$$\boldsymbol{\alpha}^{\mathrm{T}} M \boldsymbol{\alpha} \ge \sum_{l=1}^L \eta_1^{(l)} \boldsymbol{\alpha}^{(l)\mathrm{T}} \boldsymbol{\alpha}^{(l)} \ge (\min_{1 \le l \le L} \eta_1^{(l)}) \sum_{l=1}^L \boldsymbol{\alpha}^{(l)\mathrm{T}} \boldsymbol{\alpha}^{(l)}.$$

Now if node N_i belongs to p elements, then the term α_i^2 appears precisely p times in the last summation. Thus,

$$\boldsymbol{\alpha}^{\mathrm{T}} M \boldsymbol{\alpha} \ge p_1 (\min_{1 \le l \le L} \eta_1^{(l)}) \|\boldsymbol{\alpha}\|^2,$$

where p_1 is the smallest number of elements to which any of the first N nodes belongs. Similarly,

$$\boldsymbol{\alpha}^T M \boldsymbol{\alpha} \le p_2(\max_{1 \le l \le L} \eta_T^{(l)}) \|\boldsymbol{\alpha}\|^2,$$

where p_2 is the greatest number of elements to which any of the first N nodes belongs. Invoking (5.98a) we then obtain the inequalities

$$p_1 \min_{1 \le l \le L} \eta_1^{(l)} \le \eta_1 \le \eta_N \le p_2 \max_{1 \le l \le L} \eta_T^{(l)}. \tag{5.100}$$

Making the basic assumption that the mapping of the standard element $\tilde{e}$ onto e_l is affine, we can write

$$m_{rs}^{(l)} = |\tilde{D}| \int_{\tilde{e}} \tilde{\phi}_r(\tilde{\mathbf{x}}) \tilde{\phi}_s(\tilde{\mathbf{x}}) \, d\tilde{\Omega}, \qquad r, s = 1, 2, ..., T,$$

where $\tilde{D}$ denotes, as usual, the Jacobian of the mapping and $\tilde{\phi}_r, r = 1, 2, ..., T$ are the standard local basis functions. The dependency of $m_{rs}^{(l)}$ on l occurs through $\tilde{D}$ alone. A well-known identity states that

$$|\tilde{D}| = A_l/\tilde{A},$$

where A_l and $\tilde{A}$ are the area (or length or volume, depending on n) of e_l and $\tilde{e}$, respectively. Thus, introducing the *standard element mass matrix* $\tilde{M}$ of order T, defined by

$$\tilde{m}_{rs} = \int_{\tilde{e}} \tilde{\phi}_r(\tilde{\mathbf{x}}) \tilde{\phi}_s(\tilde{\mathbf{x}}) \, d\tilde{\Omega}, \qquad r, s = 1, 2, ..., T,$$

we have the relation

$$M^{(l)} = (A_l/\tilde{A})\tilde{M}.$$

Let $\tilde{\eta}_r, r = 1, 2, ..., T$ denote the eigenvalues of $\tilde{M}$ with the ordering $\tilde{\eta}_r \le \tilde{\eta}_{r+1}$. Obviously $\eta_r^{(l)} = A_l \tilde{\eta}_r / \tilde{A}$, so it follows from (5.100) that

$$p_1(\tilde{\eta}_1/\tilde{A}) \min_{1 \le l \le L} A_l \le \eta_1 \le \eta_N \le p_2(\tilde{\eta}_T/\tilde{A}) \max_{1 \le l \le L} A_l. \tag{5.101}$$

This is the key result regarding the extreme eigenvalues of the mass matrix. We shall now apply it to an infinite family of finite element meshes on $\bar{\Omega}$ having the property that there exist constants c_0, c_1, c_2, and c_3 (independent of the mesh) such that for every mesh,

$$p_2 \le c_0, \tag{5.102a}$$

$$c_1 N^{-1} \le A_l \le c_2 N^{-1}, \qquad l = 1, 2, ..., L, \tag{5.102b}$$

$$c_3 N^{-1/n} \le h_i \le c_4 N^{-1/n}, \tag{5.102c}$$

where h_i is the length of any element edge. From (5.101), (5.102a), and (5.102b) we deduce the existence of constants c_5 and c_6 such that

$$c_5 N^{-1} \leq \eta_1 \leq \eta_N \leq c_6 N^{-1}. \tag{5.103}$$

Note that the spectral condition number $\kappa(M)$ is uniformly bounded for all meshes in the family.

Estimation of $\kappa(K)$

We can now turn to the problem of obtaining bounds on the extreme eigenvalues of the stiffness matrix K. Combining the identities

$$a(u, u) = \boldsymbol{\alpha}^T K \boldsymbol{\alpha}, \qquad \|u\|^2 = \boldsymbol{\alpha}^T M \boldsymbol{\alpha}, \tag{5.104}$$

where

$$u(\mathbf{x}) = \sum_{i=1}^{N} \alpha_i \phi_i(\mathbf{x}),$$

with (5.95) and the inequality $\|u\|_1 \geq \|u\|$, we easily obtain

$$\boldsymbol{\alpha}^T K \boldsymbol{\alpha} / \boldsymbol{\alpha}^T \boldsymbol{\alpha} \geq \rho(\boldsymbol{\alpha}^T M \boldsymbol{\alpha} / \boldsymbol{\alpha}^T \boldsymbol{\alpha}) \qquad \forall \boldsymbol{\alpha} \in R^N, \quad \boldsymbol{\alpha} \neq \mathbf{0}.$$

From (5.98a), (5.101), and the relation

$$\lambda_1 = \min_{\boldsymbol{\alpha} \in R^N} (\boldsymbol{\alpha}^T K \boldsymbol{\alpha} / \boldsymbol{\alpha}^T \boldsymbol{\alpha}),$$

we then have

$$\lambda_1 \geq \rho \eta_1 \geq \rho p_1(\tilde{\eta}_1 / \tilde{A}) \min_{1 \leq l \leq L} A_l.$$

In the case of an infinite family of meshes satisfying (5.102), we can use (5.103) to obtain the bound

$$\lambda_1 \geq c_7 N^{-1}, \tag{5.105}$$

where $c_7 = \rho c_5$.

To derive an upper bound on λ_N, we introduce the $(N \times N)$ matrix Q with entries

$$q_{ij} = \int_\Omega \left[\sum_{k=1}^{n} \frac{\partial \phi_i}{\partial x_k} \frac{\partial \phi_j}{\partial x_k} \right] d\Omega, \qquad i, j = 1, 2, \ldots, N.$$

A simple computation establishes that

$$\boldsymbol{\alpha}^T Q \boldsymbol{\alpha} = |u|_1^2, \qquad u(\mathbf{x}) \equiv \sum_{i=1}^{N} \alpha_i \phi_i(\mathbf{x}), \tag{5.106}$$

and we see that Q is positive definite or semidefinite. Let the eigenvalues of Q be denoted $\{\xi_i\}_{i=1}^N$ with the ordering

$$0 \le \xi_1 \le \xi_2 \le \cdots \le \xi_N.$$

The right-hand inequality in (5.95) can be written

$$a(u, u) \le \beta(\|u\|^2 + |u|_1^2),$$

and using (5.104) and (5.106) we obtain

$$\alpha^T K\alpha/\alpha^T\alpha \le \beta[(\alpha^T M\alpha/\alpha^T\alpha) + (\alpha^T Q\alpha/\alpha^T\alpha)].$$

Since

$$\lambda_N = \max_{\alpha \in R^N} \frac{\alpha^T K\alpha}{\alpha^T\alpha}, \qquad \eta_N = \max_{\alpha \in R^N} \frac{\alpha^T M\alpha}{\alpha^T\alpha}, \qquad \xi_N = \max_{\alpha \in R^N} \frac{\alpha^T Q\alpha}{\alpha^T\alpha},$$

it follows that

$$\lambda_N \le \beta(\eta_N + \xi_N). \tag{5.107}$$

This leaves us with the problem of finding a bound on ξ_N. It is convenient to introduce element matrices $\{Q^{(l)}\}_{l=1}^L$ defined by

$$q_{rs}^{(l)} = \int_{e_l} \left[\sum_{k=1}^n \frac{\partial \phi_r^{(l)}}{\partial x_k} \frac{\partial \phi_s^{(l)}}{\partial x_k} \right] d\Omega, \qquad r, s = 1, 2, \ldots, T.$$

The analysis leading up to (5.100) makes it evident that

$$\xi_N \le p_2 \max_{1 \le l \le L} \xi_T^{(l)}, \tag{5.108}$$

where $\xi_T^{(l)}$ is the greatest eigenvalue of $Q^{(l)}$. Now $\xi_T^{(l)}$ is bounded by any norm of $Q^{(l)}$ and in particular by the maximum norm

$$\|Q^{(l)}\|_\infty \equiv \max_{1 \le r \le T} \sum_{s=1}^T |q_{rs}^{(l)}|.$$

Hence,

$$\xi_T^{(l)} \le T \max_{1 \le r, s \le T} |q_{rs}^{(l)}|. \tag{5.109}$$

To study the magnitude of the integral $q_{rs}^{(l)}$ it is helpful to use the affine transformation $\mathbf{x} = F\tilde{\mathbf{x}} + \mathbf{b}$, which maps the standard element $\tilde{e}$ onto e_l. We leave it to the reader to derive a bound of the form

$$|q_{rs}^{(l)}| \le c|\tilde{D}|\tau^2, \tag{5.110}$$

where c is independent of r, s and l, $\tilde{D}$ is the Jacobian $\det(F)$, and

$$\tau = \max_{1 \le i \le j \le n} |\partial \tilde{x}_i/\partial x_j|.$$

Section 5.4 shows that in the case of two space dimensions,

$$|\tilde{D}|\tau^2 \leq 4/\sin(\alpha) \qquad \text{when } e_l \text{ is a triangle,}$$

$$|\tilde{D}|\tau^2 \leq 1/\sigma \qquad \text{when } e_l \text{ is a rectangle,}$$

where α is the smallest angle and σ the smallest edge ratio. In the case of n space dimensions, the typical situation is $\tilde{D} = O(h^n)$, $\tau = O(h^{-1})$, and

$$|\tilde{D}|\tau^2 \leq c^*h^{n-2}, \tag{5.111}$$

where c^* depends on the shape but not the size of e_l and h is the largest edge length.

When an infinite family of meshes satisfies (5.102), then c^* is uniformly bounded for all elements in all meshes, and from (5.102c), (5.103), and (5.107)–(5.111) we obtain bounds of the form

$$\xi_N \leq c_8 N^{(2/n)-1}, \qquad \lambda_N \leq c_9 N^{(2/n)-1}.$$

Thus, we arrive at the main result of this section: when an infinite family of meshes has property (5.102), then the extreme eigenvalues of the stiffness matrix K satisfy

$$c_7 N^{-1} \leq \lambda_1 \leq \lambda_N \leq c_9 N^{(2/n)-1}, \tag{5.112}$$

and hence the spectral condition number of K has the bound

$$\kappa(K) \leq c_{10}N^{2/n}, \qquad c_{10} \equiv c_9/c_7. \tag{5.113}$$

Remarks

1. For a fixed value of N (sufficiently large), the stiffness matrix of a three-dimensional problem is better conditioned than that of a two-dimensional problem, which in turn is better conditioned than that of a one-dimensional problem. The same cannot be said when h is fixed, however, since (5.102c) and (5.113) imply

$$\kappa(K) \leq c_{11}h^{-2}, \qquad c_{11} \equiv c_4^2 c_{10},$$

and this bound is independent of n.

2. The bound on $\kappa(K)$ is independent of the accuracy of the finite element basis functions [i.e., independent of the value of k in (5.8)].

3. A similar analysis shows that for fourth-order problems $\kappa(K) = O(N^{4/n})$, roughly the square of $\kappa(K)$ for second-order problems. In view of the undesirable consequences of a large condition number mentioned at the beginning of this section, this fact provides yet another reason for attacking fourth-order problems with mixed element methods.

4. For certain problems, in particular those with discontinuous material coefficients a diagonal scaling of K (i.e., a transformation DKD, where D is a diagonal matrix) may reduce the condition number of K considerably.

5. Regarding the treatment of problem (5.23), (5.24) in Section 5.2, the stiffness matrix relevant to our discussion here is K_3, not K_2 [see (5.30)]. As remarked earlier, it is often the larger matrix K_2 that is given to the equation solver, so it is natural to inquire about the magnitude of $\kappa(K_2)$. Since the eigenvalues of K_2 are those of K_3 together with a number of "ones," we see immediately that $\kappa(K_2) \geq \kappa(K_3)$, suggesting that it might be disadvantageous to work with K_2 instead of K_3. A closer examination reveals, however, that the danger is illusory. Regardless of whether the iterative methods of Chapter 1 or the direct methods of Chapter 6 are used to solve the system of equations having matrix K_2, the numbers produced on the computer are essentially identical to those that would be obtained by applying the same method to the smaller system with matrix K_3. (This is a consequence of the fact that the extra rows and columns of K_2 contain zeros in all off-diagonal positions.) Thus, rounding errors are not worse for the larger system nor, in the case of an iterative method, is there a lower rate of convergence.

6. See Exercise 5.29 for more precise bounds on $\kappa(K)$.

7. Using various relations in this section, we find that

$$\alpha^T Q \alpha \leq \xi_N \alpha^T \alpha \leq \xi_N \eta_1^{-1} \alpha^T M \alpha$$

$$\leq c_8 N^{(2/n)-1} c_5^{-1} N \alpha^T M \alpha \qquad \forall \alpha \in R^N.$$

Hence, by (5.104) and (5.106),

$$|u|_1 \leq cN^{1/n}|u|_0 \qquad \forall u \in V_N,$$

where $c = \sqrt{c_8/c_5}$ and

$$V_N = \text{SPAN}\{\phi_1, \phi_2, ..., \phi_N\}.$$

This is an example of an *inverse estimate* in which a stronger norm (or seminorm; $|\cdot|_1$ here) is bounded by a constant times a weaker norm. As the property $\lim_{N \to \infty} N^{1/n} = \infty$ suggests, such a bound is possible only because we are restricting u to a finite-dimensional subspace of V.

8. The bound on λ_N can also be obtained in the following way:

$$\lambda_N \leq \|K\|_\infty \leq p_2 T \max_{1 \leq i,j \leq N} |a(\phi_i, \phi_j)|$$

$$\leq p_2 T \beta \max_{1 \leq i,j \leq N} (\|\phi_i\|_1 \|\phi_j\|_1)$$

$$\leq p_2 T \beta \max_{1 \leq i \leq N} (|\phi_i|_1^2 + |\phi_i|_0^2)$$

$$\leq p_2 T \beta (c^2 N^{2/n} + 1) \max_{1 \leq i \leq N} |\phi_i|_0^2$$

(from the previous remark), and since $\max_{1 \le i \le N} |\phi_i|_0^2 = O(N^{-1})$, we have $\lambda_N = O(N^{(2/n)-1})$.

Further Inequalities

We have established that for a second-order boundary value problem in n space dimensions and for an infinite family of meshes with the properties in (5.102), the extreme eigenvalues of K satisfy inequalities of the form

$$ch^n \le \lambda_1 \le \lambda_N \le dh^{n-2}.$$

Further analysis, which we omit, yields the more precise bounds

$$ch^n \le \lambda_1 \le dh^n, \qquad ch^{n-2} \le \lambda_N \le dh^{n-2},$$

and hence

$$ch^{-2} \le \kappa(K) \le dh^{-2}.$$

(c and d, of course, have various values in these inequalities.)

In Theorem 1.13 we introduced the parameter

$$\mu = \max_{\mathbf{x} \ne 0}(\mathbf{x}^T D \mathbf{x} / \mathbf{x}^T K \mathbf{x}),$$

where $D = \mathrm{diag}(k_{11}, k_{22}, ..., k_{NN})$, and later showed that $\mu \le \kappa(K)$. More generally, it can be established that for finite element matrices based on meshes satisfying (5.102),

$$ch^{-2} \le \mu \le dh^{-2}.$$

These bounds on μ will be important in Chapter 7.

5.6   Singularities

Introduction

Depending on the degree of smoothness of the data for a given boundary value problem, the solution $\hat{u}$, or some of its derivatives, may have singularities somewhere in the domain $\bar{\Omega}$. There will then be some p such that $\hat{u} \in H^p(\Omega)$, $\hat{u} \notin H^{p+1}(\Omega)$. The value of p is important since the quasi-optimal error estimates corresponding to a choice of finite element basis functions are based on the assumption that $\hat{u} \in H^{k+1}(\Omega)$, where the basis functions have the property of interpolating exactly all polynominals of degree at most k.

In this section we shall indicate how the presence of a corner, which may be formed by the boundary Γ or by internal material interfaces, can give rise to singularities in certain derivatives of the solution $\hat{u}$. Such singularities tend to make the discretization error of the finite element method large, and a few common techniques for improving accuracy are mentioned. We then examine the behavior of the solution along an internal interface and show that its first-order normal derivative typically has a step discontinuity. In contrast to the singularity caused by a corner, the step discontinuity does not necessarily degrade the accuracy of the finite element solution. Our main reference is Strang and Fix (1973).

Singularity at a Corner

Much insight into the effect of a corner on the smoothness of the solution of a boundary value problem is afforded by the simple problem shown in Fig. 5.26. The domain $\bar{\Omega}$ is a section of a circle of radius R with center at the origin.

In polar coordinates we have

$$\Delta u \equiv u_{rr} + (1/r)u_r + (1/r^2)u_{\theta\theta}.$$

When f and g are sufficiently smooth functions and $g(0) = g(\omega) = 0$, the solution can be expressed in the form of the Fourier expansion

$$\hat{u}(r, \theta) = S_1(r, \theta) + S_2(r, \theta)$$

$$= \sum_{j=1}^{\infty} g_j r^{\nu_j} \psi_j(\theta) + \sum_{j=1}^{\infty} \sum_{l=0}^{\infty} f_{jl} b_{jl} \chi_l(r) \psi_j(\theta), \qquad (5.114)$$

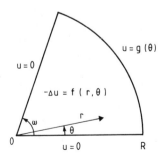

Fig. 5.26. A boundary value problem on a nonsmooth domain.

where

$$v_j = j\pi/\omega, \qquad \psi_j(\theta) = \sqrt{2/\omega}\,\sin(v_j\theta),$$

$$b_{jl}\chi_l(r) = \begin{cases} [(l+2)^2 - v_j^2]^{-1}r^{l+2} & \text{if } v_j \neq l+2, \\ [2(v_j+1)]^{-1}r^{l+2}\ln(r) & \text{if } v_j = l+2. \end{cases}$$

The constants $\{g_j\}_{j=1}^{\infty}$ and $\{f_{jl}\}_{j,l=1}^{\infty}$ depend on the functions g and f, respectively (Lehman, 1959). The first terms of (5.114) are

$$\hat{u} = g_1 r^{\pi/\omega}\sqrt{\frac{2}{\omega}}\,\sin\left(\frac{\pi}{\omega}\theta\right) + f_{1,0}b_{1,0}\chi_0(r)\sqrt{\frac{2}{\omega}}\,\sin\left(\frac{\pi}{\omega}\theta\right) + \cdots,$$

where

$$g_1 = c_1 \int_0^{\omega} \sqrt{\frac{2}{\omega}}\,\sin\left(\frac{\pi}{\omega}\theta\right)[g(\theta) - S_2(R,\omega)]R^{-\pi/\omega}\,d\theta,$$

$$f_{1,0} = d_{1,0} \int_0^{\omega} \int_0^R b_{1,0}\chi_0(r)\sqrt{\frac{2}{\omega}}\,\sin\left(\frac{\pi}{\omega}\theta\right)f(r,\theta)\,dr\,d\theta,$$

c_1 and $d_{1,0}$ being (normalization) constants independent of g and f.

Now every term in S_1 and S_2 is a continuous function of r and θ everywhere in $\bar{\Omega}$, but if we form partial derivatives with respect to r, then singularities may eventually begin to appear at the origin. (For terms with an integer power of r and no $\ln(r)$ factor, however, these derivatives eventually vanish and hence cause no singularity.) Of greatest importance are those terms in S_1 and S_2 where the first singularity occurs. These "critical terms" are shown (with coefficients omitted) in Table 5.3. We define $\alpha = \pi/\omega$; the parameters m and n denote positive integers; n/m is reduced to lowest terms.

In Case 2 the term $r^{\alpha}\sin(\alpha\theta)$ dominates since

$$\alpha < n \quad \Rightarrow \quad \lim_{r \to 0}[r^n \ln(r)/r^{\alpha}] = 0.$$

Note that in all three cases the first singular derivative of the critical term of $\hat{u}$ is of order s, where s is the smallest integer satisfying $s \geq \alpha$.

We now want to determine the largest integer p such that $\hat{u} \in H^p(\Omega)$, or equivalently, such that $|\hat{u}|_p < \infty$, and to this end it suffices to examine the critical term of $\hat{u}$. Using the identity

$$\iint_{\Omega} F(x,y)\,dx\,dy = \iint_{\Omega} \tilde{F}(r,\theta)r\,dr\,d\theta,$$

Table 5.3
Critical Terms in S_1, S_2, and $\hat{u}$

Case	$\alpha = \pi/\omega$	in S_1	in S_2	in $\hat{u}$
			Critical terms	
1	Irrational	$r^\alpha \sin(\alpha\theta)$	None	$r^\alpha \sin(\alpha\theta)$
2	n/m $(m > 1)$	$r^\alpha \sin(\alpha\theta)$	$r^n \ln(r) \sin(n\theta)$	$r^\alpha \sin(\alpha\theta)$
3	n $(n > 1)$	None	$r^\alpha \ln(r) \sin(\alpha\theta)$	$r^\alpha \ln(r) \sin(\alpha\theta)$

where $F(x, y) = \tilde{F}(r, \theta)$ under the variable transformation $x = r\cos(\theta)$, $y = r\sin(\theta)$, and letting

$$F(x, y) = \sum_{|v| = p} (\hat{u}_c^{(v)})^2,$$

where $\hat{u}_c$ denotes the critical term of $\hat{u}$ and v is the multi-index notation for partial differentiation, it is straightforward to show that

$$|\hat{u}_c|_p < \infty \quad \Leftrightarrow \quad \begin{cases} \displaystyle\int_0^R r^{2\alpha - 2p + 1} \, dr < \infty & \text{(Cases 1, 2)} \\ \\ \displaystyle\int_0^R r^{2\alpha - 2p + 1} \left[\ln(r)\right]^2 \, dr < \infty & \text{(Case 3)} \end{cases}$$

$$\Leftrightarrow \quad p < \alpha + 1. \tag{5.115}$$

The largest such integer p is identical to s; hence, the following regularity results:

$$\pi \leq \omega \leq 2\pi \quad \Rightarrow \quad \hat{u} \in H^1(\Omega),$$

$$\pi/2 \leq \omega < \pi \quad \Rightarrow \quad \hat{u} \in H^2(\Omega),$$

$$\pi/3 \leq \omega < \pi/2 \quad \Rightarrow \quad \hat{u} \in H^3(\Omega),$$

and so on. (This state of affairs may appear to be unsatisfactory in as much as one intuitively expects "smoothness" to be a continuous property of ω, whereas the order of the Sobolev space is seen to be a step function with respect to this variable. The problem is removed by the concept of a *fractional* Sobolev space $H^t(\Omega)$, defined for any real number t. [See, e.g., Nečas (1967).] One can show that for any $\alpha > 0$,

$$\omega = \pi/\alpha \quad \Rightarrow \quad \hat{u} \in H^{\alpha + 1 - \varepsilon}(\Omega),$$

where $\varepsilon > 0$ is arbitrarily small.)

The main conclusion to be drawn from our analysis is that the solution of the boundary value problem becomes less smooth as the angle of the corner increases. From the above regularity results and (5.85) and (5.86) we obtain the following estimate for the discretization error of the finite element method: if $\pi/(p + 1) \leq \omega < \pi/p$, where p is an integer, then

$$\|\hat{u} - \hat{u}_N\|_1 \leq Ch^q |\hat{u}|_{q+1},$$

where $q = \min\{p, k\}$, k being the usual accuracy parameter of the basis functions.

The use of special techniques in the finite element solution of a problem with one or more corners can lead to a significant gain of accuracy. These include the following.

(1)   The set of ordinary basis functions is extended to include a few of the leading critical terms of the solution near a corner. Since these new basis functions have global support, it is a common practice to multiply them by a smooth function with support only in a neighborhood of the corner.

(2)   Singular isoparametric basis functions are used [see Mitchell and Wait (1977)].

(3)   The mesh is refined in the neighborhood of the corner. This may be done with basis functions of the type described in Section 5.1 or with polar-coordinate elements. Two possibilities are illustrated in Fig. 5.27.

Of course, one can simply ignore the singularity at a corner in implementing the finite element method. The low accuracy obtained using a coarse uniform mesh may be sufficient for the purpose of the analysis. Uniform refinement of the mesh (in contrast to the third technique given above) will improve accuracy, but at a considerable cost in computing time.

For further reading see Babuška and Rheinboldt (1978, 1980), Barnhill and Whiteman (1975), Blum and Dobrowolski (1982), Dobrowolski (1981), Grisvard (1976, 1980), Schatz and Wahlbin (1978, 1979), Strang and Fix (1973), Whiteman (1982), and Whiteman and Akin (1979).

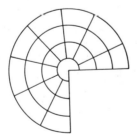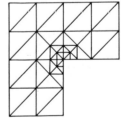

Fig. 5.27.   Meshes for treating a singularity.

Material Interfaces

Very often the physical object to be analyzed is a composite of various materials. Where different materials meet, internal boundaries, or interfaces, are formed. In the mathematical model of such an object, coefficients that describe parameters of the material usually have step discontinuities across the interfaces. We shall show by a simple example how the variational formulation of the problem determines the behavior of the solution at the interfaces, and at the same time derive "natural" interface conditions.

Thus, consider the boundary value problem

$$-(pu_x)_x - (pu_y)_y = g \quad \text{in } \Omega,$$
$$u = 0 \quad \text{on } \Gamma, \tag{5.116}$$

for the domain shown in Fig. 5.28. Let $p = p_i$ in Ω_i for $i = 1, 2$. The functions p_1 and p_2 are assumed to be positive and individually smooth, but p may be discontinuous at the interface $\tilde{\Gamma}$ of Ω_1 and Ω_2. In the variational formulation we have

$$V = \mathring{H}^1(\Omega), \qquad G(u) = \int\!\!\int_\Omega gu \, dx \, dy, \qquad u \in V,$$

$$a(u, v) = \int\!\!\int_\Omega p(u_x v_x + u_y v_y) \, dx \, dy, \qquad u, v \in V.$$

By the Lax–Milgram lemma, the problem has a generalized solution $\hat{u} \in V$ and

$$a(\hat{u}, u) = G(u) \qquad \forall u \in V. \tag{5.117}$$

Now, provided the data of the problem are sufficiently smooth, $\hat{u}$ is continuous everywhere in $\bar{\Omega}$ and has continuous partial derivatives of second order in Ω_1 and Ω_2. Thus, we may integrate by parts in Ω_1 and Ω_2 to obtain

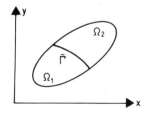

Fig. 5.28.   Domain of an interface problem: $\bar{\Omega} = \bar{\Omega}_1 \cup \bar{\Omega}_2$; $\tilde{\Gamma} = \bar{\Omega}_1 \cap \bar{\Omega}_2$.

the identity

$$a(\hat{u}, u) - G(u) = \sum_{i=1}^{2} \int\int_{\Omega_i} \left[p_i(\hat{u}_x u_x + \hat{u}_y u_y) - gu \right] dx\, dy$$

$$= \sum_{i=1}^{2} \left\{ \int\int_{\Omega_i} \left[-(p_i\hat{u}_x)_x - (p_i\hat{u}_y)_y - g \right] u\, dx\, dy + \int_{\Gamma_i} p_i\hat{u}_{n_i} u\, ds \right\},$$

where Γ_i is the boundary of Ω_i and $\hat{u}_{n_i}$ is the outer normal derivative of $\hat{u}$ on Γ_i. Using (5.117) and the fact that every $u \in \mathring{H}^1(\Omega)$ vanishes on Γ, we see that the differential equation of (5.116) is satisfied in Ω_1 and Ω_2, and that

$$p_1\hat{u}_{n_1} = -p_2\hat{u}_{n_2} \qquad \text{on } \tilde{\Gamma}. \tag{5.118}$$

Thus the variational formulation of the problem automatically imposes the interface condition (5.118). Note that if $p_1 = p_2$ on $\tilde{\Gamma}$, then (5.118) asserts the continuity of the normal derivative of $\hat{u}$ on $\tilde{\Gamma}$.

More generally, if Ω is a composite of subregions $\{\Omega_i\}_{i=1}^{m}$, then the condition at the interface of Ω_i and Ω_j is

$$p_i\hat{u}_{n_i} = -p_j\hat{u}_{n_j}, \tag{5.119}$$

and this result is independent of the boundary condition on Γ.

When the boundaries of $\Omega_1, \Omega_2, \ldots, \Omega_m$ are polygons, it is usually possible to choose the finite element mesh so that all material interfaces coincide with element edges. (If the interfaces are not axiparallel, then quadrilateral elements must be of the isoparametric type.) There are two important (and related) reasons for doing this. First, if this is not done then continuity is imposed on the normal derivative of the finite element solution $\hat{u}_N$ at those parts of the interfaces that are interior to elements, an undesirable property since it is not shared by the exact solution $\hat{u}$.

Second, the following considerations indicate that the discretization error will be smaller. Let $\hat{u}_I$ denote the interpolant of $\hat{u}$ in the span of the basis functions. Let $\hat{u}_l$ and $(\hat{u}_I)_l$ denote the restrictions of $\hat{u}$ and $\hat{u}_I$, respectively, to element e_l. If there are L elements then, by (5.64),

$$\|\hat{u} - \hat{u}_N\|_1^2 \leq C^2 \|\hat{u} - \hat{u}_I\|_1^2 = C^2 \sum_{l=1}^{L} \|\hat{u}_l - (\hat{u}_I)_l\|_1^2.$$

Now, it is clear from the analysis of Section 5.4 that the interpolation error $\|\hat{u}_l - (\hat{u}_I)_l\|_1$ is related to the smoothness of $\hat{u}_l$, i.e., to the largest r_l such that $\hat{u}_l \in H^{r_l+1}(e_l)$. If an interface passes through the interior of e_l, then the step discontinuity of the normal derivative implies that $\hat{u}_l \notin H^2(e_l)$, and the smallest integer value of r_l is zero. (In the context of fractional Sobolev spaces, it can be shown (Kellogg, 1982) that $r_l = \frac{1}{2} - \varepsilon$, where $\varepsilon > 0$ is arbitrarily small.) Hence, the interpolation error for this element tends to be

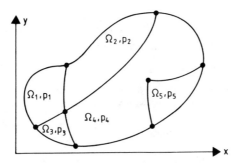

Fig. 5.29.   Interface corners (● indicates a corner point).

large regardless of the degree of the basis functions. On the other hand, an interface that does not pass through the interior of e_l, but which may possibly coincide with an edge of this element, has no influence on r_l.

An exception to this is the case in which e_l touches an interface corner. Interface corners, whether in Ω or Γ (see Fig. 5.29), commonly give rise to singularities of the type discussed at the beginning of this section. See Strang and Fix (1973) for further details.

Returning to the domain of Fig. 5.28, suppose that $p_1 \gg p_2$ on the interface $\tilde{\Gamma}$, making

$$\hat{u}_{n_1} = -(p_2/p_1)\hat{u}_{n_2} \simeq 0 \qquad \text{on } \tilde{\Gamma}.$$

An approximate solution may be obtained as follows.

(1)   Solve the boundary value problem on Ω_1 alone, using the condition $u_{n_1} = 0$ on $\tilde{\Gamma}$.

(2)   Solve the problem on Ω_2 alone, taking $u = u_1$ on $\tilde{\Gamma}$, where u_1 is the solution obtained in the previous step.

For further reading on interface problems see Kellogg (1971, 1975).

Exercises

5.1. Show that the affine transformation

$$\begin{bmatrix} x \\ y \end{bmatrix} = \begin{bmatrix} f_{11} & f_{12} \\ f_{21} & f_{22} \end{bmatrix} \begin{bmatrix} \tilde{x} \\ \tilde{y} \end{bmatrix} + \begin{bmatrix} b_1 \\ b_2 \end{bmatrix} \qquad \forall \begin{bmatrix} \tilde{x} \\ \tilde{y} \end{bmatrix} \in R^2$$

has the following properties.

(i)   If F is nonsingular then every straight line $\tilde{L}$ in the $\tilde{x}$–$\tilde{y}$ plane is mapped onto a straight line L in the x–y plane, and the midpoint of a straight line segment in the $\tilde{x}$–$\tilde{y}$ plane is mapped onto the midpoint of the corresponding segment in the x–y plane.

(ii)   Let L_1 and L_2 be the images of straight lines $\tilde{L}_1$ and $\tilde{L}_2$, respectively. Let θ be the angle measured from L_1 to L_2 in the counterclockwise sense, and let $\tilde{\theta}$ be the angle measured from $\tilde{L}_1$ to $\tilde{L}_2$ in the counterclockwise sense. Then,

$$F = \sigma Q, \quad \sigma \in R, \quad Q^{-1} = Q^T \quad \Rightarrow \quad \theta = \tilde{\theta} \text{ or } \pi - \tilde{\theta}.$$

What further property of F implies $\theta = \tilde{\theta}$?

5.2. Let A be the area of a triangle with vertices (x_i, y_i), $i = 1, 2, 3$, and let

$$F = \begin{bmatrix} x_2 - x_1 & x_3 - x_1 \\ y_2 - y_1 & y_3 - y_1 \end{bmatrix}.$$

Show that $A = \frac{1}{2} \det(F)$ if the vertices are ordered counterclockwise and $A = -\frac{1}{2} \det(F)$ otherwise.

5.3.

(i)   We define a mapping $\hat{x} = \hat{x}(x, y)$, $\hat{y} = \hat{y}(x, y)$ $\forall (x, y) \in e_l$ by

$$\hat{x} = \text{area}(N_1 N N_3)/\text{area}(N_1 N_2 N_3) \quad \text{and} \quad \hat{y} = \text{area}(N_1 N_2 N)/\text{area}(N_1 N_2 N_3).$$

(See the accompanying illustration.) The inverse transformation of (5.17) defines a mapping $\tilde{x} = \tilde{x}(x, y)$, $\tilde{y} = \tilde{y}(x, y)$ $\forall (x, y) \in e_l$. Show that $\hat{x} = \tilde{x}$ and $\hat{y} = \tilde{y}$.

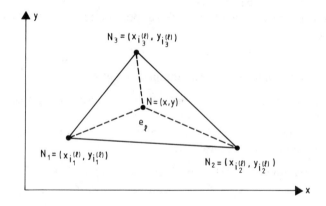

HINT: Solve (5.17) for $\tilde{x}$ and $\tilde{y}$ by Cramer's rule and use Exercise 5.2.

(ii)   The preceding question gives a geometrical interpretation of the $\tilde{x}$, $\tilde{y}$ variables of Section 5.1 in the case of a triangular element. Find an analogous interpretation of these variables when the element is rectangular.

5.4. Show that matrix S_l in Example 5.1 is singular if and only if the three nodes lie on a straight line.

HINT: Use Exercise 5.2.

5.5. Show that the piecewise quadratic basis functions of Example 5.2 do not belong to $C^1(\Omega)$.

5.6. This exercise generalizes the basis functions of Examples 5.1 and 5.2. Consider a mesh of triangular elements on a region $\bar{\Omega} \subset R^2$ and a positive integer k such that each element e_l has the following nodes:

   (i) the vertices of e_l;
   (ii) if $k \geq 2$, the $(k - 1)$ points on each edge that divide the edge into equal segments;
   (iii) if $k \geq 3$, the $\frac{1}{2}(k - 1)(k - 2)$ points in the interior of e_l determined as shown in the accompanying illustration for the case $k = 4$.

Show that there are basis functions of the type described in Section 5.1 with the property that $P_k(\bar{\Omega}) \subseteq V_M$.

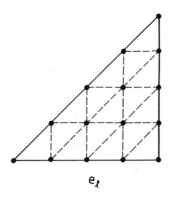

e_l

HINT: Compare e_l with the triangular arrangement of terms shown in Fig. 5.4.

5.7. The biquadratic polynomial

$$\tilde{\phi}(\tilde{x}, \tilde{y}) = a + b\tilde{x} + c\tilde{y} + d\tilde{x}^2 + e\tilde{x}\tilde{y} + f\tilde{y}^2 + g\tilde{x}^2\tilde{y} + h\tilde{x}\tilde{y}^2 + i\tilde{x}^2\tilde{y}^2$$

is in general uniquely determined by its values at 9 points.

   (i) Find standard local basis functions $\tilde{\phi}_r(\tilde{x}, \tilde{y})$, $r = 1, 2, \ldots, 9$ of this type for the standard element shown in the accompanying illustration.

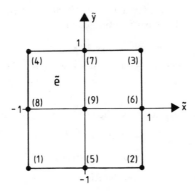

HINT: A special case of the above polynomial is

$$\tilde{\phi}(\tilde{x}, \tilde{y}) = (A + B\tilde{x} + C\tilde{x}^2)(D + E\tilde{y} + F\tilde{y}^2).$$

(ii)   The corresponding global basis functions $\phi_i(x, y)$, $i = 1, 2, \ldots, M$ can be defined piecewise on a mesh of axiparallel rectangular elements, each element e_l having the same distribution and ordering of nodes as $\tilde{e}$. What is the affine transformation that maps $\tilde{e}$ onto e_l? What are the values of k and m in (5.8)?

5.8. Repeat Exercise 5.7, eliminating the term $i\tilde{x}^2\tilde{y}^2$ from $\tilde{\phi}(\tilde{x}, \tilde{y})$ and node $(0, 0)$ from $\tilde{e}$.

HINT: Special cases of $\tilde{\phi}(\tilde{x}, \tilde{y})$ are $(A + B\tilde{x})(C + D\tilde{y})(E + F\tilde{x} + G\tilde{y})$, $(A + B\tilde{x} + C\tilde{x}^2)$ $\cdot(D + E\tilde{y})$, and $(A + B\tilde{x})(C + D\tilde{y} + E\tilde{y}^2)$. This is one of the so-called *Serendipity* elements (Zienkiewicz, 1977).

5.9. This exercise generalizes the basis functions of Example 5.3 and Exercise 5.7. Consider a mesh of axiparallel rectangular elements on a region $\bar{\Omega} \subset R^2$ and a positive integer k such that each element has $(k + 1)^2$ nodes located as shown in the accompanying illustration for the case $k = 4$. Show that there are basis functions of the type described in Section 5.1 with the property that $P_k(\bar{\Omega}) \subseteq V_M$.

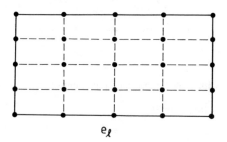

e_l

5.10. We consider here piecewise linear basis functions in one space dimension.

(i)   Taking as the standard element $\tilde{e}$ the interval $-1 \leq \tilde{x} \leq 1$ with nodes at ± 1, derive and sketch standard local basis functions $\tilde{\phi}_1(\tilde{x})$ and $\tilde{\phi}_2(\tilde{x})$ of the form $\tilde{\phi}(\tilde{x}) = a + b\tilde{x}$.
(ii)   Given the mesh on the interval $0 \leq x \leq 1$ shown in the accompanying illustration, sketch the typical global basis function $\phi_i(x)$.

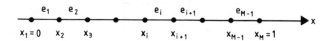

(iii)   These basis functions can be applied to the boundary value problem

$$-u'' = g(x), \qquad 0 < x < 1,$$

$$u(0) = \alpha, \qquad u'(1) = \beta.$$

Derive the typical element matrix and the Ritz–Galerkin system.

5.11. Repeat exercise 5.10 for the case of piecewise quadratic basis functions, adding a midpoint node to every element.

5.12. Given the mesh on the interval $0 \le x \le 1$ shown in Exerice 5.10, we associate with each node x_i *two* basis functions, $\phi_{2i-1}(x)$ and $\phi_{2i}(x)$, $0 \le x \le 1$, with the following properties: each is a cubic polynomial in every element,

$$\phi_{2i-1}(x_j) = \delta_{ij}, \qquad \phi'_{2i-1}(x_j) = 0,$$

$$\phi_{2i}(x_j) = 0, \qquad \phi'_{2i}(x_j) = \delta_{ij},$$

for $j = 1, 2, ..., M$.

(i)   Taking as the standard element $\tilde{e}$ the interval $-1 \le \tilde{x} \le 1$ with nodes at ± 1, derive the four standard local basis functions. Sketch these and the typical global basis functions $\phi_{2i-1}(x)$ and $\phi_{2i}(x)$.

(ii)   Let $V_M = \text{SPAN}\{\phi_1, \phi_2, ..., \phi_{2M}\}$. What are the values of k and m in (5.8)? For any $u \in C^1[0, 1]$ we define $u_I \in V_M$ by

$$u_I(x) = \sum_{i=1}^{M} u(x_i)\phi_{2i-1}(x) + \sum_{i=1}^{M} u'(x_i)\phi_{2i}(x).$$

Verify that

$$u_I(x_i) = u(x_i), \qquad u_I'(x_i) = u'(x_i), \qquad i = 1, 2, ..., M.$$

This is an example of Hermite interpolation.

(iii)   The application of these basis functions to the fourth-order boundary value problem

$$u^{iv} = g(x), \qquad 0 < x < 1,$$

$$u(0) = u'(0) = u(1) = u'(1) = 0,$$

leads to element matrices $K^{(i)}$, $i = 1, 2, ..., M - 1$, where

$$k_{rs}^{(i)} = \int_{e_i} \phi''_{2i-2+r}\phi''_{2i-2+s} \, dx, \qquad r, s = 1, 2, 3, 4.$$

Compute $k_{rs}^{(i)}$ and determine the Ritz–Galerkin system.

5.13. Given the mesh of Fig. 5.16, determine the positions of the nonzero entries of the matrices K_1 and K_3 in (5.30).

5.14. This exercise deals with the application of piecewise linear basis functions to problem (5.23), (5.24) on the domain shown in Fig. 5.15. For any given positive integers m_1 and m_2, we construct a uniform mesh of $2m_1 m_2$ right triangles as illustrated in Fig. 5.16 for the case $m_1 = 4$ and $m_2 = 2$. We take the global node ordering to be that illustrated in the figure, and the local node ordering of every element to be counterclockwise, starting at the vertex of the right angle.

(i)   Write a piece of program code that establishes the contents of arrays ELNODE, NODECO, BONODE, and EDGE from the input data l_1, l_2, m_1, and m_2.

(ii)   Assume that $p(x, y) = 1$ and $q(x, y) = 0$ in (5.23), and let $l_1/m_1 = l_2/m_2$, making the elements isosceles right triangles. Use (5.38) together with the affine transformation and standard local basis functions of Example 5.1 to show that the element matrix for any element e_l is

$$K^{(l)} = \frac{1}{2}\begin{bmatrix} 2 & -1 & -1 \\ -1 & 1 & 0 \\ -1 & 0 & 1 \end{bmatrix}.$$

(For a more general result see Exercise 5.17.)

(iii) Use $K^{(l)}$ to assemble part of the primitive stiffness matrix and verify that there are at most five nonzero entries in the ith row, despite the fact that there are seven nodes in the support of ϕ_i. The two "uncoupled" nodes are shown in the accompanying *support diagram*.

Does uncoupling occur when $p(x, y)$ and $q(x, y)$ are arbitrary?

(iv) We now drop the assumptions of question (ii). Write a piece of program code to compute (5.38) by numerical integration, using arrays ELNODE, NODECO, and the arrays of (5.42). Assume that the coefficients $p(x, y)$ and $q(x, y)$ are available in the form of subroutines of "function" type.

5.15. Repeat Exercise 5.14 for the case of the piecewise quadratic basis functions, ordering the nodes of each element as shown for the standard element in Example 5.2 (starting always with the vertex at the right angle). In evaluating (5.38) in question (ii) one can use the identity

$$\int\int_{\tilde{e}} \tilde{\phi}(\tilde{x}, \tilde{y})\, d\tilde{x}\, d\tilde{y} = \tfrac{1}{6}[\phi(\tilde{N}_4) + \phi(\tilde{N}_5) + \phi(\tilde{N}_6)],$$

which is valid for any polynomial $\tilde{\phi}(\tilde{x}, \tilde{y})$ of degree ≤ 2 (Exercise 5.20). $\tilde{N}_4$, $\tilde{N}_5$, and $\tilde{N}_6$ denote the midedge nodes of $\tilde{e}$.

REMARK:

The answer to question (ii) is

$$K^{(l)} = \frac{1}{6}\begin{bmatrix} 6 & 1 & 1 & 0 & -4 & -4 \\ 1 & 3 & 0 & 0 & 0 & -4 \\ 1 & 0 & 3 & 0 & -4 & 0 \\ 0 & 0 & 0 & 16 & -8 & -8 \\ -4 & 0 & -4 & -8 & 16 & 0 \\ -4 & -4 & 0 & -8 & 0 & 16 \end{bmatrix}.$$

In question (iii) one should obtain three distinct patterns of uncoupling, according to whether node N_i is (a) a vertex node, (b) a midedge node on the long edge, or (c) a midedge node on one of the short edges (see the accompanying diagrams).

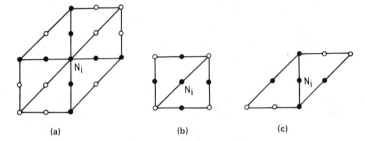

(a) (b) (c)

Regarding question (iv), note that the program code is virtually unchanged.

5.16. By removing all diagonals from the mesh of Exercise 5.14, we obtain a new mesh of $m_1 m_2$ axiparallel rectangles. Repeat Exercise 5.14 for the case of piecewise bilinear basis functions defined on this mesh. The answer to question (ii) is

$$K^{(l)} = \frac{1}{6} \begin{bmatrix} 4 & -1 & -2 & -1 \\ -1 & 4 & -1 & -2 \\ -2 & -1 & 4 & -1 \\ -1 & -2 & -1 & 4 \end{bmatrix}.$$

(For a more general result see the following exercise.)

5.17.

(i) Show that the element matrix $K^{(l)}$ that arises from the bilinear form

$$a(u, v) = \int\!\!\int_\Omega p(u_x v_x + u_y v_y)\, dx\, dy, \qquad p(x, y) \geq p_0 > 0$$

and the basis functions of Example 5.1 can be expressed as

$$k_{rs}^{(l)} = \frac{1}{2A} \int\!\!\int_{\tilde{e}} \tilde{p}\, d\tilde{x}\, d\tilde{y}\, \mathbf{v}_r^T \mathbf{v}_s, \qquad r, s = 1, 2, 3,$$

where A is the area of element e_l and $\mathbf{v}_1$, $\mathbf{v}_2$, and $\mathbf{v}_3$ are as shown in the accompanying diagram. Hence, deduce that if e_l has no angle greater than $\pi/2$, then all off-diagonal entries of $K^{(l)}$ are nonpositive.

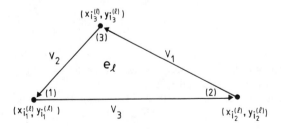

(For an equivalent formulation of this element matrix and a specific technique for deriving it, see Exercise 7.18.)

(ii)   In the bilinear form in (i) let $p(x, y) = p_1 > 0$, where p_1 is a constant. Show that the element matrix obtained from the basis functions of Example 5.3 is

$$K^{(l)} = \frac{p_1}{6} \begin{bmatrix} 2(\beta + \beta^{-1}) & & & \\ -(2\beta - \beta^{-1}) & 2(\beta + \beta^{-1}) & \text{SYM} & \\ -(\beta + \beta^{-1}) & -(2\beta^{-1} - \beta) & 2(\beta + \beta^{-1}) & \\ -(2\beta^{-1} - \beta) & -(\beta + \beta^{-1}) & -(2\beta - \beta^{-1}) & 2(\beta + \beta^{-1}) \end{bmatrix},$$

where β is the height of the element divided by its length. Hence, deduce that all off-diagonal entries of $K^{(l)}$ are nonpositive if and only if $1/\sqrt{2} \le \beta \le \sqrt{2}$.

(iii)   In question (ii) let $p(x, y)$ now satisfy $0 < p_0 \le p(x, y) \le p_1$, where p_0 and p_1 are constants. Show that all off-diagonal entries of $K^{(l)}$ are nonpositive if $\sqrt{p_1/2p_0} \le \beta \le \sqrt{2p_0/p_1}$.

5.18.   From a computational point of view, the only data we need in order to use finite element basis functions of a given type are the values of the standard local basis functions and their first partial derivatives at the integration points [see (5.42)]. Compute these data for the basis functions of Examples 5.1–5.3, using the integration points in Table 5.1.

5.19.   This exercise is concerned with numerical integration over rectangular elements.

(i)   Show that the numerical integration formula

$$\int_{-1}^{1} \tilde{\theta}(\tilde{x}) \, d\tilde{x} \simeq \sum_{i=1}^{Q} w_i \tilde{\theta}(\tilde{x}_i) \tag{5.120}$$

is exact for any polynomial $\tilde{\theta}(\tilde{x})$ of degree $\le d$ if

$$\sum_{i=1}^{Q} w_i \tilde{x}_i^r = \frac{1}{r+1}\left[1 - (-1)^{r+1}\right], \qquad r = 0, 1, ..., d. \tag{5.121}$$

This system of equations, with $d = 2Q - 1$, can be used to determine the parameters $\{w_i, \tilde{x}_i\}_{i=1}^{Q}$. Solve the system for the case $Q = 2$.

This strategy for choosing the parameters in (5.120) defines a *Gauss–Legendre formula* for every value of Q. See Stroud and Secrest (1966) for a table of parameter values.

(ii)   For any given integration formula of type (5.120), we can define a corresponding two-dimensional formula by

$$\iint_{\tilde{e}} \tilde{\theta}(\tilde{x}, \tilde{y}) \, d\tilde{x} \, d\tilde{y} \simeq \sum_{i,j=1}^{Q} w_i w_j \tilde{\theta}(\tilde{x}_i, \tilde{y}_j), \tag{5.122}$$

where $\tilde{e}$ is the square $-1 \le \tilde{x}, \tilde{y} \le 1$ and $\tilde{y}_i = \tilde{x}_i, i = 1, 2, ..., Q$. Show that if (5.120) is a Gauss–Legendre formula, then (5.122) is exact when $\tilde{\theta}(\tilde{x}) = \tilde{\alpha}(\tilde{x})\tilde{\beta}(\tilde{y})$, where $\tilde{\alpha}(\tilde{x})$ and $\tilde{\beta}(\tilde{y})$ are arbitrary polynomials of degree $\le (2Q - 1)$.

It can be shown (Ciarlet, 1978) that (5.122), with Gauss–Legendre parameters, is appropriate for the rectangular elements of Exercise 5.9 provided that $Q \ge k + 1$.

Note from your answer to question (i) that the third integration formula of Table 5.1 is appropriate for the case $k = 1$.

5.20. This exercise is concerned with numerical integration over triangular elements.

(i)   Let $\tilde{e}$ denote the triangle with vertices $(0, 0)$, $(1, 0)$, and $(0, 1)$, and let

$$I(r, s) = \int\int_{\tilde{e}} \tilde{x}^r \tilde{y}^s \, d\tilde{x} \, d\tilde{y},$$

where r and s are arbitrary nonnegative integers. Show that

$$I(r - 1, s + 1) = [(s + 1)/r]I(r, s), \qquad I(r, 0) = 1/[(r + 1)(r + 2)],$$

and hence establish by recursion that

$$I(r, s) = r!s!/(r + s + 2)!.$$

(ii)   It follows that an integration formula of the form

$$\int\int_{\tilde{e}} \tilde{\theta}(\tilde{x}, \tilde{y}) \, d\tilde{x} \, d\tilde{y} \simeq \sum_{i=1}^{Q} w_i \tilde{\theta}(\tilde{x}_i, \tilde{y}_i) \tag{5.123}$$

is exact for any polynomial of degree $\leq d$ if

$$\sum_{i=1}^{Q} w_i \tilde{x}_i^r \tilde{y}_i^s = r!s!/(r + s + 2)! \qquad \forall r, s \ni r + s \leq d.$$

Show that the first and second integration formulas of Table 5.1 are exact for polynomials of degree 1 and 2, respectively.

It can be shown (Ciarlet, 1978) that (5.123) is appropriate for the triangular elements of Exercise 5.6 if it is exact for at least all polynomials of degree $\leq 2(k - 1)$.

5.21. The pseudocode given in Section 5.2 for the assembly of the Ritz–Galerkin equations arising from problem (5.23), (5.24) assumes the use of an $(M \times M)$ array for the stiffness matrix. The purpose of the present exercise is to show how this data structure can be replaced by a much more economical one, namely, a row-ordered list for the nonzero entries in the lower left triangle of the matrix. Such a list was described in (and preceding) Fig. 1.8, in terms of variables N, Z, H, (we shall now use K instead of H), CN, and RS.

(i)   Assume first that the basis functions are piecewise linear and that the mesh is the one described at the beginning of Exercise 5.14. Verify that the appropriate value of Z is in general

$$Z = 4m_1 m_2 + 2(m_1 + m_2) + 1$$

and write a piece of program code that generates the contents of CN and RS.

To rewrite (5.34), (5.49), and (5.31e) in terms of array K, we need the function $m = m(i, j)$ that makes $K[m] = k[i, j]$. Find this function.

(ii)   We now drop all assumptions regarding the choice of basis functions and the geometry of the mesh and assume only that array ELNODE [see (5.35)] is available. Analyze the problem of computing Z and the contents of CN and RS and also that of computing from i and j the value of m that makes $K[m] = k[i, j]$.

5.22. We consider the quadratic isoparametric transformation

$$\begin{bmatrix} x \\ y \end{bmatrix} = \mathbf{F}(\tilde{x}, \tilde{y}) \equiv \sum_{r=1}^{6} \begin{bmatrix} x_r \\ y_r \end{bmatrix} \tilde{\phi}_r(\tilde{x}, \tilde{y}), \qquad (\tilde{x}, \tilde{y}) \in \tilde{e}$$

(see Example 5.5) that maps the standard triangle $\tilde{e}$ onto the triangle e shown in the accompanying diagrams. Nodes 5 and 6 of e are mid-edge points.

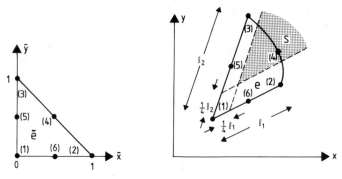

Show in the following steps that the transformation $\mathbf{F}(\tilde{x}, \tilde{y})$ is invertible if node 4 of e is placed in the shadowed region S.

(i) Let

$$\begin{bmatrix} \xi \\ \eta \end{bmatrix} = \mathbf{F}_1(\tilde{x}, \tilde{y}) \equiv \sum_{r=1}^{6} \begin{bmatrix} \xi_r \\ \eta_r \end{bmatrix} \tilde{\phi}_r(\tilde{x}, \tilde{y}), \qquad (\tilde{x}, \tilde{y}) \in \tilde{e}$$

map the standard triangle $\tilde{e}$ onto the element $\hat{e}$ shown in the accompanying illustration.

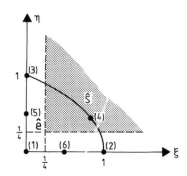

Let

$$\begin{bmatrix} x \\ y \end{bmatrix} = \mathbf{F}_2(\xi, \eta) \equiv B \begin{bmatrix} \xi \\ \eta \end{bmatrix} + \begin{bmatrix} x_1 \\ y_1 \end{bmatrix}, \qquad (\xi, \eta) \in \hat{e},$$

where

$$B = \begin{bmatrix} x_2 - x_1 & x_3 - x_1 \\ y_2 - y_1 & y_3 - y_1 \end{bmatrix}.$$

Show that if (ξ_4, η_4) is chosen to make $\begin{bmatrix} x_4 \\ y_4 \end{bmatrix} = \mathbf{F}_2(\xi_4, \eta_4)$, then

$$\mathbf{F}(\tilde{x}, \tilde{y}) = \mathbf{F}_2(\mathbf{F}_1(\tilde{x}, \tilde{y})) \qquad \forall (\tilde{x}, \tilde{y}) \in \tilde{e}.$$

Note that $\mathbf{F}_2(\xi, \eta)$ maps the shadowed region $\hat{S}$ onto S.

(ii) Since $\mathbf{F}_2(\xi, \eta)$ is an invertible affine transformation of $\hat{e}$ onto e whenever e is nondegenerate, we can now restrict our attention to $\mathbf{F}_1(\tilde{x}, \tilde{y})$. By a well-known theorem of analysis, $\mathbf{F}_1(\tilde{x}, \tilde{y})$ is invertible if $\det(J(\tilde{x}, \tilde{y})) \neq 0$, where

$$J(\tilde{x}, \tilde{y}) = \begin{bmatrix} \dfrac{\partial (\mathbf{F}_1)_1}{\partial \tilde{x}} & \dfrac{\partial (\mathbf{F}_1)_1}{\partial \tilde{y}} \\[2mm] \dfrac{\partial (\mathbf{F}_1)_2}{\partial \tilde{x}} & \dfrac{\partial (\mathbf{F}_1)_2}{\partial \tilde{y}} \end{bmatrix}, \qquad \mathbf{F}_1(\tilde{x}, \tilde{y}) = \begin{bmatrix} (\mathbf{F}_1)_1(\tilde{x}, \tilde{y}) \\ (\mathbf{F}_1)_2(\tilde{x}, \tilde{y}) \end{bmatrix}.$$

Show that

$$\det(J(\tilde{x}, \tilde{y})) = 1 + d_1 \tilde{y} + d_2 \tilde{x},$$

where $d_1 = 4\xi_4 - 2$ and $d_2 = 4\eta_4 - 2$, and hence deduce that

$$\det(J(\tilde{x}, \tilde{y})) > 0 \qquad \forall (\tilde{x}, \tilde{y}) \in \tilde{e}$$

$$\Leftrightarrow \quad \det(J(\tilde{x}_r, \tilde{y}_r)) > 0, \qquad r = 1, 2, 3$$

$$\Leftrightarrow \quad \xi_4 > \tfrac{1}{4}, \quad \eta_4 > \tfrac{1}{4} \qquad [\text{i.e., } (\xi_4, \eta_4) \in \hat{S}].$$

5.23. Find the local basis functions $\phi_r^{(l)}(x, y)$, $r = 1, 2, 3, 4$ for the isoparametric element shown in the accompanying illustration (see Example 5.6).

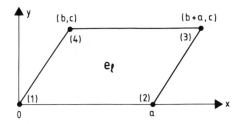

5.24. Rewrite the code of Exercise 5.15, question (iv), for the case of the isoparametric basis functions of Example 5.5.

5.25. Let $\mathscr{L}$ be defined by

$$\mathscr{L}u = -a(x, y)u_{xx} - b(x, y)u_{yy} + c(x, y)u_x + d(x, y)u_y, \qquad u \in C^2(\bar{\Omega}),$$

where Ω is a bounded region in R^2, all coefficients belong to $C(\bar{\Omega})$, and

$$0 < a_0 \leq a(x, y) \leq a_1, \qquad 0 < b_0 \leq b(x, y) \leq b_1 \qquad \forall (x, y) \in \bar{\Omega}.$$

It can be shown that if a function u satisfies $\mathscr{L}u = 0$ in Ω, then

$$\max_{(x,y)\in\Omega} |u(x, y)| = \max_{(x,y)\in\Gamma} |u(x, y)|,$$

where Γ is the boundary of Ω. This is a *maximum principle* [see, e.g., Gilbarg and Trudinger (1977).]

We consider the boundary value problems

$$\mathscr{L}u = f \quad \text{in } \Omega, \qquad u = \gamma \quad \text{on } \Gamma,$$

$$\mathscr{L}u_h = f \quad \text{in } \Omega_h, \qquad u = \gamma_h \quad \text{on } \Gamma_h,$$

where Γ_h, the boundary of Ω_h, is a polygon interpolating Γ, as illustrated in the accompanying diagram, and where $\gamma_h(x, y) = \gamma(x^*, y^*)$, (x^*, y^*) being the point on Γ closest

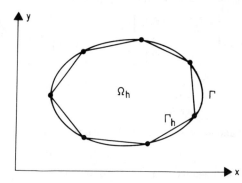

to (x, y). The parameter h denotes the maximum edge length in the polygon. Assuming Γ is a smooth boundary, use the maximum principle to establish that

$$\max_{(x,y)\in\Omega_h} |u - u_h| = O(h^2), \qquad h \to 0.$$

5.26. In Fig. 5.25 let $a = -1, b = 1$,

$$u(x) = \begin{cases} x + 1, & -1 \le x \le 0, \\ -x + 1, & 0 < x \le 1, \end{cases}$$

and let the mesh be uniform, i.e.,

$$h_i = h = 2/(M - 1), \qquad i = 1, 2, ..., M - 1.$$

Show that

$$|u - u_1|_0 = |u - u_1|_1 = 0 \qquad\qquad\qquad \text{if} \quad M \text{ is odd,}$$

$$|u - u_1|_0 = (\sqrt{3}/6)h^{3/2}, \qquad |u - u_1|_1 = h^{1/2} \qquad \text{if} \quad M \text{ is even,}$$

and compare with (5.67).

5.27. Derive the interpolation error bounds in (5.70).

5.28. Consider the triangular element shown in the accompanying diagram, where $\alpha_1 \le \alpha_2 \le \alpha_3$.

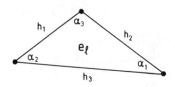

(i)   Deduce from the law of sines,

$$\sin(\alpha_1)/h_1 = \sin(\alpha_2)/h_2 = \sin(\alpha_3)/h_3,$$

and the inequality $h_1 + h_2 > h_3$ that $h_1 \leq h_2 \leq h_3$ and $h_2 \geq h_3/2$.

(ii)   Hence, use Exercise 5.2 and the relation

$$A = \tfrac{1}{2}h_2 h_3 \sin(\alpha_1),$$

where A is the area of e_l, to derive (5.73b).

5.29.

(i)   Using the analysis of Section 5.5, derive the inequality

$$\kappa(K) \leq \rho^{-1}(p_2/p_1)(\max_{1 \leq l \leq L} \lambda_T^{(l)}/ \min_{1 \leq l \leq L} \eta_1^{(l)}). \tag{5.124}$$

(ii)   The parameter ρ in (5.124) comes from the coerciveness of the bilinear form:

$$\rho\|u\|_1^2 \leq a(u, u) \qquad \forall u \in V.$$

There obviously exists a constant σ, where $\sigma \geq \rho$, such that

$$\sigma\|u\|^2 \leq a(u, u) \qquad \forall u \in V.$$

Derive the sharper inequality

$$\kappa(K) \leq \sigma^{-1}(p_2/p_1)(\max_{1 \leq l \leq L} \lambda_T^{(l)}/ \min_{1 \leq l \leq L} \eta_1^{(l)}). \tag{5.125}$$

(The largest possible value of σ is the smallest eigenvalue of the operator $\mathcal{L}$ in the boundary value problem.)

5.30.   We consider the boundary value problem

$$-u_{xx} - u_{yy} = g(x, y), \qquad (x, y) \in \Omega \equiv \{(x, y); 0 < x, y < 1\},$$

$$u = \gamma(x, y), \qquad (x, y) \in \Gamma,$$

and the use of piecewise linear basis functions on a mesh of $2m^2$ identical isosceles right triangles. (This is the mesh of Exercise 5.14, question (ii), with $l_1 = l_2 = 1$ and $m_1 = m_2 = m$.)

(i)   Show that the element mass matrix for every element is

$$M^{(l)} = \frac{1}{24m^2}\begin{bmatrix} 2 & 1 & 1 \\ 1 & 2 & 1 \\ 1 & 1 & 2 \end{bmatrix}$$

and compute its eigenvalues.

(ii)   The element stiffness matrix $K^{(l)}$ is given in Exercise 5.14, question (ii). Compute its eigenvalues.

(iii)   Given that

$$2\pi^2|u|_0^2 \leq |u|_1^2 \qquad \forall u \in \mathring{H}^1(\Omega),$$

use (5.125) to derive the bound

$$\kappa(K) \leq 18(m/\pi)^2.$$

5.31. Repeat Exercise 5.30 for the case of piecewise bilinear basis functions on a mesh of m^2 identical squares. The mass matrix obtained should be

$$
M^{(l)} = \frac{1}{36m^2} \begin{bmatrix} 4 & 2 & 1 & 2 \\ 2 & 4 & 2 & 1 \\ 1 & 2 & 4 & 2 \\ 2 & 1 & 2 & 4 \end{bmatrix}.
$$

To compute the eigenvalues of $M^{(l)}$ and $K^{(l)}$ (Exercise 5.16) show first that each of these matrices can be expressed as a second-degree polynomial in terms of

$$
T = \begin{bmatrix} 0 & 1 & 0 & 1 \\ 1 & 0 & 1 & 0 \\ 0 & 1 & 0 & 1 \\ 1 & 0 & 1 & 0 \end{bmatrix}.
$$

Find the eigenvalues of T and hence those of $M^{(l)}$ and $K^{(l)}$ and use (5.125) to derive the bound $\kappa(K) \le 18(m/\pi)^2$.

5.32. We consider the application of the finite element method with piecewise quadratic (Example 5.2) or biquadratic (Exercise 5.7) basis functions $\phi_1, \phi_2, ..., \phi_N$ to the problem

$$
-\Delta u = g(x, y) \qquad \text{in } \Omega,
$$

$$
u = 0 \qquad \text{on } \Gamma,
$$

where $\bar{\Omega}$ is an axiparallel rectangle with corners P_i, $i = 1, 2, 3, 4$. Let $\hat{u}$ denote the exact solution.

(i)   The Fourier expansion (5.114) expresses $\hat{u}$ in the neighborhood of P_i in terms of the local polar coordinates. Verify that $\hat{u} \notin H^3(\Omega)$ because of the single term

$$
c_i^* r^2 \ln(r) \sin(2\theta),
$$

where c_i^* is a certain constant.

(ii)   If g is sufficiently smooth, then $\hat{u} \in H^2(\Omega)$. Deduce from (5.86) that

$$
\|\hat{u} - \hat{u}_N\|_1 = O(h), \qquad h \to 0,
$$

where $\hat{u}_N$ is the Ritz–Galerkin approximation to $\hat{u}$ based on

$$
V_N = \text{SPAN}\{\phi_1, \phi_2, ..., \phi_N\}.
$$

Why is this result disappointing?

(iii)   For each corner P_i construct a function v_i on $\bar{\Omega}$ such that

$$
v_i = \begin{cases} r^2 \ln(r) \sin(2\theta), & 0 \le r \le r_0, \quad 0 \le \theta \le \pi/2, \\ 0, & (r, \theta) \in \bar{\Omega}, \qquad r \ge r_1, \\ 0, & r_0 < r < r_1, \quad \theta = 0, \pi/2 \end{cases}
$$

(see the accompanying figure) and such that $v_i \in C^2(\tilde{\Omega})$, where $\tilde{\Omega}$ is any closed subset of $\bar{\Omega}$ that excludes P_i.

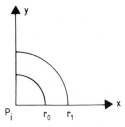

It follows that v_i, $i = 1, 2, 3, 4$, vanish on Γ and that

$$\hat{u} - \sum_{i=1}^{4} c_i^* v_i \in H^3(\Omega)$$

if g is sufficiently smooth.

(iv)   Let $\hat{u}_N$ denote the Ritz–Galerkin approximation to $\hat{u}$ based on

$$V_N = \text{SPAN}\{v_1, v_2, v_3, v_4, \phi_1, \phi_2, \dots, \phi_N\}.$$

(Note that v_i, $i = 1, 2, 3, 4$, are independent of the mesh.) Show that we now have

$$\|\hat{u} - \hat{u}_N\|_1 = O(h^2), \qquad h \to 0.$$

For further analysis of this and related problems see Strang and Fix (1973).

5.33. Let $\hat{u}$ denote the solution of the boundary value problem

$$-\Delta u = 0 \qquad \text{in } \Omega,$$

$$u = \gamma(x, y) \qquad \text{on } \Gamma,$$

on the domain with a crack, $\overline{PQ}$, shown in the accompanying figure. The crack is part of Γ and gives rise to an internal corner at Q with angle $\omega = 2\pi$.

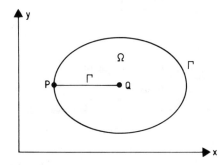

(i)   Assuming that $\gamma(x, y) = 0$ on the crack and that $\hat{u}$ is sufficiently smooth outside any neighborhood of Q, construct functions v_i, $i = 1, 2, 3$ that vanish on Γ such that

$$\hat{u} - \sum_{i=1}^{3} c_i^* v_i \in H^4(\Omega)$$

for certain constants c_i^*, $i = 1, 2, 3$.

NOTE: The sum $S_2(r, \theta)$ in (5.114) vanishes for this problem.

(ii) Why is it appropriate to supplement piecewise cubic or bicubic basis functions (the case $k = 3$ in Exercises 5.6 and 5.9, respectively) with v_i, $i = 1, 2, 3$? (Ignore the error due to the curvature of the boundary.)

(iii) Let ϕ_i, $i = 1, 2, \ldots, N$ denote piecewise cubic or bicubic basis functions and let $\phi_{N+i} = v_i$, $i = 1, 2, 3$. Let K denote the corresponding stiffness matrix of order $(N + 3)$. Verify that when the Ritz–Galerkin system $K\alpha = G$ is solved by Gaussian elimination, the amount of extra storage due to v_1, v_2, and v_3 does not exceed $3(N + 3)$.

Can this be said for the case when the ordering of the basis functions begins with v_1, v_2, and v_3?

5.34. How should (5.114) be modified if the boundary conditions shown in Fig. 5.26 are generalized to $u(r, 0) = u_0$ and $u(r, \omega) = u_1$ for $0 \leq r \leq R$, where u_0 and u_1 are constants and $g(0) = u_0$, $g(\omega) = u_1$?

5.35. Consider a bounded bilinear form

$$a(u, v), \qquad u \in U, \quad v \in V,$$

where U, V are Hilbert spaces; U does not have to be equal to V. Assume that $\hat{u}$ is a solution of

$$a(\hat{u}, v) = g(v) \qquad \forall v \in V,$$

where $g(\cdot)$ is a bounded linear functional on V. Let $U_N \subset U$, $V_M \subset V$ be finite-dimensional subspaces. Then, the *Petrov–Galerkin method* is defined as follows: find $\hat{u}_N \in U_N$ such that

$$a(\hat{u}_N, v) = g(v) \qquad \forall v \in V_M.$$

ERROR ESTIMATE: [see Babuška (1971), Babuška and Aziz (1973), and Brezzi (1974)] Assume that

$$\inf_{u \in U_N} \sup_{v \in V_N} \frac{a(u, v)}{\|u\|_U \|v\|_V} = \gamma_N > 0, \qquad u \neq 0, \quad v \neq 0. \tag{5.126}$$

(i) Prove that

$$\|\hat{u} - \hat{u}_N\|_U \leq (1 + C/\gamma_N)\|\hat{u} - u\|_U, \qquad \forall u \in U_N,$$

where C is the boundedness constant in the inequality

$$|a(u, v)| \leq C\|u\|_U \|v\|_V \qquad \forall u \in U, \quad v \in V,$$

where $\|\cdot\|_U$ is not weaker than $\|\cdot\|_V$, i.e., $\|u\|_V \leq \|u\|_U \; \forall u \in U_N$.

HINT: Write $\hat{u} - \hat{u}_N = \hat{u} - u + u - \hat{u}_N$, $u \in U_N$ and use (5.126) to prove that

$$\gamma_N \|u - \hat{u}_N\|_U \leq C\|u - \hat{u}\|_U.$$

(ii) Prove that (5.126) is satisfied if $U_N \subset V_M$, $\|u\|_V \leq \|u\|_U \; \forall u \in U_N$ and $a(\cdot, \cdot)$ is coercive, i.e., $a(u, u) \geq \rho\|u\|_U^2 \; \forall u \in U_N$.

HINT: Choose $v = u$ in (5.126).

(iii)   Apply (i) and (ii) to the bilinear form (see Example 4.1)

$$a_\varepsilon(u, v) = \int_\Omega \left[\varepsilon (\nabla u)^{\mathrm{T}} \nabla v + \mathbf{b} \, \nabla u v + u v \right] d\Omega,$$

where $u = 0$ on Γ, $\varepsilon > 0$, and, for simplicity, $\mathbf{b}$ is a constant vector.

(iv)   Let

$$V = U = \left\{ u \in \mathring{H}^1(\Omega); \, \|u\|_U = \int_\Omega \left(\varepsilon |\nabla u|^2 + u^2 \right) d\Omega \right\},$$

$$U' = \left\{ u \in \mathring{H}^1(\Omega); \, \|u\|_{U'} = \int_\Omega \left(\varepsilon |\nabla u|^2 + \varepsilon^{-1} u^2 \right) d\Omega \right\}.$$

Prove that if $U_N \subset V_M$, then the Petrov–Galerkin error satisfies

$$\|u - \hat{u}_N\|_U \leq C' \|\hat{u} - u\|_{U'} \qquad \forall u \in U_N$$

for some constant C' that is independent of ε and h.

(v)   Prove also that if $h \leq \varepsilon$, then

$$\|\hat{u} - \hat{u}_N\|_1 \leq O(h^k) \|\hat{u}\|_{k+1}$$

if U_N is a finite element space of piecewise polynomials of degree k. Note that this means that the error in $\|\cdot\|_U$ is of optimal order for all ε, $\varepsilon \geq h$.

5.36.   We shall consider two approaches to handle *numerical integration errors* in the finite element method. Let V_N be a finite element space of piecewise polynomial continuous functions of degree k. To be specific, consider the following variational problem: find $\hat{u}_N \in V_N$ such that

$$a(\hat{u}_N, v) = g(v) \qquad \forall v \in V_N, \tag{5.127}$$

where

$$a(u, v) = \int_\Omega p (\nabla u)^{\mathrm{T}} \nabla v \, d\Omega, \qquad g(v) = \int_\Omega g v \, d\Omega,$$

and $p \geq p_0 > 0$, and p, g are given functions that are sufficiently smooth on each element e_l, $l = 1, 2, \ldots, T$. In general, it is not possible to calculate the integrals exactly. Therefore, let

$$a_h(\tilde{u}_N, v) = g_h(v) \qquad \forall v \in V_N$$

be the problem that is actually solved and is derived from (5.127) by one of the following approximations [see Strang and Fix (1973)]:

$$a_h^{(1)}(\phi_j, \phi_i) = \sum_{l=1}^{T} \int_{e_l} \tilde{p} \, \nabla \phi_j \, \nabla \phi_i \, d\Omega,$$

$$g_h^{(1)}(\phi_i) = \sum_{l=1}^{T} \int_{e_l} \tilde{g} \phi_i \, d\Omega. \tag{5.128a}$$

Here $\tilde{p}, \tilde{g}$ are the interpolants in V_N of p and g, respectively, and the integrals are evaluated exactly (possible by some quadrature rule of sufficiently high order).

$$a_h^{(2)}(\phi_j, \phi_i) = \sum_{l=1}^{T} \sum_{q=1}^{r} w_q (p \, \nabla\phi_j \, \nabla\phi_i)\Big|_{x_q^{(l)}},$$

$$g_h^{(2)}(\phi_i) = \sum_{l=1}^{T} \sum_{q=1}^{r} w_q (g\phi_i)\Big|_{x_q^{(l)}},$$

(5.128b)

where w_q are the quadrature weights and $x_q^{(l)} \in e_l$ the corresponding points in e_l.

(i) Assume that $a_h(\cdot, \cdot)$ is coercive on V_N (i.e., positive definite),

$$a_h(v_N, v_N) \geq \zeta\|v_N\|_1^2 \qquad \forall v_N \in V_N$$

for some $\zeta > 0$. Show that

$$\|\hat{u}_N - \tilde{u}_N\|_1^2 \leq \zeta^{-1} a_h(\hat{u}_N - \tilde{u}_N, \hat{u}_N - \tilde{u}_N)$$
$$= \zeta^{-1}[(a_h - a)(\hat{u}_N, \hat{u}_N - \tilde{u}_N) + (g - g_h)(\hat{u}_N - \tilde{u}_N)].$$

(ii) Show that, if the mesh is fine enough ($h \leq h_0$), then $a_h^{(1)}(\cdot, \cdot)$ is coercive.

HINT: Prove that $\tilde{p} \geq \frac{1}{2}p_0$.

(iii) Prove that for (5.128), if $h \leq h_0$,

$$\|\hat{u}_N - \tilde{u}_N\|_1 \leq C\zeta^{-1} \max\{|p - \tilde{p}|_\infty\|g\|, |g - \tilde{g}|_\infty\} = O(h^{k+1}), \qquad h \to 0,$$

where $|v|_\infty = \max_{x \in \Omega} |v(\mathbf{x})|$.

(iv) Consider the example

$$-u_{xx} = g, \qquad 0 < x < 1, \qquad u(0) = u(1) = 0.$$

Show that the corresponding bilinear form

$$a_h^{(2)}(u, v) = \sum_{l} \sum_{q=1}^{r} w_q [(u_N)_x (v_N)_x]\Big|_{x_q^{(l)}}$$

with positive weights w_q is coercive only if there are at least k quadrature points on each interval, i.e., if $r \geq k$.

HINT: If $r \leq k - 1$, then choose u_N of degree k such that $(u_N)_x$ vanishes at $x_q^{(l)}$, $q = 1, 2, ..., r, l = 1, 2, ..., T$. Prove that $|u_N|_1^2 = a(u_N, u_N) > 0$ but $a_h^{(2)}(u_N, u_N) = 0$.

(v) Show that if a quadrature rule of order $O(h^{2k})$ is used, then the errors $|\hat{u}_N - \tilde{u}_N|_1$ due to quadrature are $O(h^{k+1})$.

HINT: First write

$$(a_h^{(2)} - a)(\hat{u}_N, \hat{u}_N - \tilde{u}_N) = (a_h^{(2)} - a)(\hat{u}, \hat{u}_N - \tilde{u}_N) + (a - a_h^{(2)})(\hat{u} - \hat{u}_N, \hat{u}_N - \tilde{u}_N),$$

where the Galerkin error $\|\hat{u} - \hat{u}_N\|_1 = O(h^k)$, then show that the second term is bounded by $O(h^{k+1})|\hat{u}_N - \tilde{u}_N|_1$. To prove the same estimate for the first term, note that for every derivative $|\hat{u}_N - \tilde{u}_N|_s \leq Ch^{-1}|\hat{u}_N - \tilde{u}_N|_{s-1} \leq (Ch^{-1})^{s-1}|\hat{u}_N - \tilde{u}_N|_1, s = 1, 2, \ldots, k,$

$$|\hat{u}_N - \tilde{u}_N|_s = 0, \qquad s \geq k + 1. \tag{5.129}$$

Then note that the remainder term in the numerical integration formula contains derivatives of order $2k$ and of the $2k$ powers of h, only $k - 1$ are lost due to differentiation of the factor $\nabla(\hat{u}_N - \tilde{u}_N)$ in the integrand. Similarly, one can treat the second term $(g - g_h^{(2)})(\hat{u}_N - \tilde{u}_N)$. Note that in this case the first derivative gives us $|\hat{u}_N - \tilde{u}_N|_1$, so only the last $k - 1$ gives us losses of powers of h.

REMARK: For the same reason, the same quadrature rule may be applied on the lower order terms in a more general bilinear form,

$$a(u, v) = \int_\Omega \left[p(\nabla u)^{\mathrm{T}} \nabla v + \mathbf{b}^{\mathrm{T}} \nabla uv + cuv \right] d\Omega.$$

(vi)   Indicate why it is sufficient in (v) that $\hat{u} \in H^{k+1}(\Omega)$ (i.e., the same regularity needed for the estimate of the optimal order of the Galerkin error $\|\hat{u} - \tilde{u}_N\|_1$.

References

Aubin, J. P. (1967). Behavior of the error of the approximate solutions of boundary value problems for linear elliptic operators by Galerkin's and finite difference methods. *Ann. Scuola Norm. Sup. Pisa Cl. Sci., Series 3* **21**, 599–637.

Babuška, I. (1971). Error bounds for finite element method. *Numer. Math.* **16**, 322–333.

Babuška, I., and Aziz, A. K. (1973). Survey lectures on the mathematical foundations of the finite element method. *In* "The Mathematical Foundations of the Finite Element Method with Applications to Partial Differential Equations" (A. K. Aziz, ed.), pp. 5–359. Academic Press, New York.

Babuška, I., and Aziz, A. K. (1976). On the angle condition in the finite element method. *SIAM J. Numer. Anal.* **13**, 214–226.

Babuška, I., and Rheinboldt, W. (1978). Error estimates for adaptive finite element computations. *SIAM J. Numer. Anal.* **15**, 736–754.

Babuška, I., and Rheinboldt, W. (1980). Reliable error estimation and mesh adaption for the finite element method. *In* "Computational Methods in Nonlinear Mechanics" (J. T. Oden, ed.), pp. 67–108. North-Holland Publ., Amsterdam.

Barnhill, R. E., and Whiteman, J. R. (1975). Error analysis of Galerkin methods for Dirichlet problems containing boundary singularities. *J. Inst. Math. Appl.* **15**, 121–125.

Blum, H., and Dobrowolski, M. (1982). On finite element methods for elliptic equations on domains with corners. *Computing* **28**, 53–63.

Bramble, J. H., and Hilbert, S. R. (1970). Estimation of linear functionals on Sobolev spaces with application to Fourier transforms and spline interpolation. *SIAM J. Numer. Anal.* **7**, 112–124.

Brezzi, F. (1974). On the existence, uniqueness, and approximation of saddle-point problems arising from Lagrangian multipliers. *RAIRO Sér. Rouge Anal. Numér.* **8**, 129–151.

Ciarlet, P. G. (1978). "The Finite Element Method for Elliptic Problems." North-Holland Publ., Amsterdam.

Courant, R. (1943). Variational methods for the solution of problems of equilibrium and vibrations. *Bull. Amer. Math. Soc.* **49**, 1–23.

Descloux, J. (1972). On finite element matrices. *SIAM J. Numer. Anal.* **9**, 260–265.

Dobrowolski, M. (1981). "Numerical approximation of elliptic interface and corner problems." Habilitationsschrift, Bonn, Federal Republic of Germany.

Dupont, T., and Scott, R. (1978). Constructive polynomial approximation in Sobolev spaces. *In* "Recent Advances in Numerical Analysis" (C. de Boor and G. Golub, eds.), pp. 31–44. Academic Press, New York.

Dupont, T., and Scott, R. (1980). Polynomial approximation of functions in Sobolev spaces. *Math. Comp.* **34**, 441–463.

Ergatoudis, I., Irons, B. M., and Zienkiewicz, O. C. (1968). Curved isoparametric "quadrilateral" elements for finite element analysis. *Internat. J. Solids and Structures* **4**, 31–42.

Fairweather, G. (1978). "Finite Element Galerkin Methods for Differential Equations." Marcel Dekker, New York.

Frey, A. E., Hall, C. A., and Porsching, T. A. (1978). Some results on the global inversion of bilinear and quadratic isoparametric finite element transformations. *Math. Comp.* **32**, 725–749.

Fried, I. (1973). The l_2 and l_∞ condition numbers of the finite element stiffness and mass matrices, and pointwise convergence of the method. *In* "The Mathematics of Finite Elements and Applications" (J. R. Whiteman, ed.), pp. 163–174. Academic Press, New York.

Fried, I. (1979). "Numerical Solution of Differential Equations." Academic Press, New York.

Friedman, A. (1969). "Partial Differential Equations." Holt, New York.

Gilbarg, D., and Trudinger, N. S. (1977). "Elliptic Partial Differential Equations of Second Order." Springer-Verlag, Berlin and New York.

Goldstein, C. I. (1980). Variational crimes and L^∞ error estimates in the finite element method. *Math. Comp.* **35**, 1131–1157.

Gordon, W. J., and Hall, C. A. (1973). Transfinite element methods: blending function interpolation over arbitrary curved element domains. *Numer. Math.* **21**, 109–129.

Grisvard, P. (1976). Behavior of solutions of an elliptic boundary value problem in polygonal or polyhedral domains. *In* "Numerical Solution of Partial Differential Equations III" (B. Hubbard, ed.), pp. 207–274. Academic Press, New York.

Grisvard, P. (1980). "Boundary Value Problems in Nonsmooth Domains." Lecture Notes No. 19, Institute of Fluid Dynamics and Applied Mathematics, University of Maryland, College Park, Maryland.

Haber, R., Shepard, M. S., Abel, J. F., Gallagher, R. H., and Greenberg, D. P. (1981). A general two-dimensional graphical finite element preprocessor utilizing discrete transfinite mappings. *Internat. J. Numer. Methods Engr.* **17**, 1015–1044.

Hrenikoff, A. (1941). Solution of problems in elasticity by the framework method. *J. Appl. Mech.* **8**, 169–175.

Kellogg, R. B. (1971). Singularities in interface problems. *In* "Numerical Solution of Partial Differential Equations II" (B. Hubbard, ed.), pp. 351–400. Academic Press, New York.

Kellogg, R. B. (1975). On the Poisson equation with intersecting interfaces. *Applicable Anal.* **4**, 101–129.

Kellogg, R. B. (1982). Unpublished lecture notes, Institute of Fluid Dynamics and Applied Mathematics, University of Maryland, College Park, Maryland.

Kron, G. (1944). Tensorial analysis and equivalent circuits of elastic structures. *J. Franklin Inst.* **238**, 400–452.

Langefors, B. (1952). Analysis of elastic structures by matrix transformation with special regard to semimonocoque structures. *J. Aeronautical Sci.* **19**, 451–458.

Lehman, R. S. (1959). Developments near an analytic corner of solutions of elliptic partial differential equations. *J. Math. Mech.* **8,** 727–760.

Louis, A. (1979). Acceleration of convergence for finite element solutions of the Poisson equation. *Numer. Math.* **33,** 43–53.

Meinguet, J. (1977). Structure et estimations de coefficients d'erreurs. *RAIRO Anal. Numér.* **11,** 355–368.

Meinguet, J. (1978). A practical method for estimating approximation errors. *In* "Multivariate Approximation" (D. C. Handscomb, ed.), pp. 169–187. Academic Press, New York.

Mitchell, A. R., and Wait, R. (1977). "The Finite Element Method in Partial Differential Equations." Wiley, New York.

Natterer, F. (1975). Über die punktweise Konvergenz Finiter Elemente. *Numer. Math.* **25,** 67–77.

Nečas, J. (1967). "Les Méthodes Directes en Théorie des Equations Elliptiques." Masson, Paris.

Nedelec, J. C. (1976). Curved finite element methods for the solution of singular integral equations on surfaces in R^3. *Comput. Methods Appl. Mech. Engrg.* **8,** 61–80.

Nitsche, J. (1968). Ein Kriterium fur die Quasi-Optimalitet des Ritzchen Verfahrens. *Numer. Math.* **11,** 346–348.

Nitsche, J. (1979). L_∞-error analysis for finite elements. *In* "The Mathematics of Finite Elements and Applications III" (J. R. Whiteman, ed.), pp. 173–186. Academic Press, New York.

Oden, J. T., and Reddy, J. N. (1976). "An Introduction to the Mathematical Theory of Finite Elements." Wiley, New York.

Prager, W., and Synge, J. L. (1947). Approximations in elasticity based on the concept of function space. *Quart. Appl. Math.* **5,** 241–269.

Rannacher, R., and Scott, R. (1982). Some optimal error estimates for piecewise linear finite element approximations. *Math. Comp.* **38,** 437–445.

Schatz, A. H., and Wahlbin, L. B. (1978). Maximum norm estimates in the finite element method on plane polygonal domains, I. *Math. Comp.* **32,** 73–109.

Schatz, A. H., and Wahlbin, L. B. (1979). Maximum norm estimates in the finite element method on plane polygonal domains, II. *Math. Comp.* **33,** 485–492.

Schultz, M. H. (1973). "Spline Analysis." Prentice-Hall, Englewood Cliffs, New Jersey.

Schwarz, H. R. (1980). "Methode der Finiten Elemente." Teubner, Stuttgart, Federal Republic of Germany.

Schwarz, H. R. (1981). "FORTRAN—Programme zur Methode der Finiten Elemente." Teubner, Stuttgart, Federal Republic of Germany.

Scott, R. (1976). Optimal L^∞ estimates for the finite element method on irregular meshes. *Math. Comp.* **30,** 681–698.

Strang, G., and Fix, G. J. (1973). "An Analysis of the Finite Element Method." Prentice-Hall, Englewood Cliffs, New Jersey.

Stroud, A. H., and Secrest, D. (1966). "Gaussian Quadrature Formulas." Prentice-Hall, Englewood Cliffs, New Jersey.

Vichnevetsky, R. (1981). "Computer Methods for Partial Differential Equations, Vol. 1: Elliptic Equations and the Finite Element Method." Prentice-Hall, Englewood Cliffs, New Jersey.

Whiteman, J. R. (1982). Finite elements for singularities in two- and three-dimensions. *In* "The Mathematics of Finite Elements and Applications IV" (J. R. Whiteman, ed.), pp. 37–55. Academic Press, New York.

Whiteman, J. R., and Akin, J. E. (1979). Finite elements, singularities and fracture. *In* "The Mathematics of Finite Elements and Applications III" (J. R. Whiteman, ed.), pp. 35–54. Academic Press, New York.

Zienkiewicz, O. C. (1977). "The Finite Element Method," 3rd ed. McGraw-Hill, New York.

CHAPTER 6

Direct Methods for Solving Finite Element Equations

Introduction

We have seen that the application of the finite element method to a boundary value problem leads to a system of equations $K\alpha = \mathbf{G}$, where the stiffness matrix K is often large, sparse, and positive definite. In this chapter we shall consider the solution of such systems by Gaussian elimination and the closely related Cholesky method. These so-called "direct" (i.e., noniterative) methods are probably the most widely used for finite element computation today. (The extent to which they deserve this honor is examined in Section 7.5, where we compare their performance with that of the iterative methods.) In addition to being important in their own right, the direct methods provide the basis for the incomplete factorization technique used to precondition the conjugate gradient method.

In the process of solving a sparse system of equations by Gaussian elimination "fill-in" occurs, i.e., nonzero entries are created in certain positions where the coefficient matrix K has zeros. Fill-in is undesirable because it increases both the computing time and the storage requirement. A fact of great importance for the finite element method is that fill-in is very much influenced by the choice of the global ordering of the mesh nodes. This leads to the fundamental question, How can the nodes be ordered to minimize computing time and storage?

This problem has been the topic of intense research in recent years, and much of the current state-of-the-art is well described in George and Liu (1981). It turns out that there are a number of competing node-ordering strategies, and the answer to the question of which is best depends very much on the specific problem to be solved. Further, the choice of an efficient storage scheme (or data structure) for implementing Gaussian elimination, as well as the organization of the computation, depends on the ordering strategy that has been adopted. Space limitations prevent us from dealing with all aspects of this important subject, and the reader interested in a more thorough treatment should consult George and Liu (1981) and the references given therein.

Section 6.1 is concerned with node-ordering strategies aimed at making K a matrix with a small band or envelope and presents storage schemes appropriate for such matrices. The simplicity of working with these storage schemes makes ordering strategies of this type the most popular of all. Roughly speaking, these orderings are most efficient when the mesh is "long and narrow."

Section 6.2 is devoted to a description of the mathematics of Gaussian elimination and the Cholesky method and is basic regardless of how the nodes are ordered. The essential fact of these methods is that they effectively decompose K into triangular factors and thereby reduce the problem of solving the original system to the much simpler problem of solving two triangular systems. An ALGOL code for factorizing a positive definite matrix by Gaussian elimination is given in Fig. 6.9.

In Section 6.3 we examine some "special techniques" for solving the stiffness equations. Each essentially corresponds to a node-ordering strategy that differs from the band-minimizing type described in Section 6.1, and the implementation of Gaussian elimination differs accordingly.

Section 6.4 deals with the main types of errors that arise in constructing and solving finite element equations.

6.1 Band Matrices

We are concerned with the solution of the Ritz–Galerkin equations

$$K\alpha = \mathbf{G},$$

where K is an $(N \times N)$ positive definite symmetric matrix. It will be recalled from Section 5.2 that $k_{ij} \neq 0$ only if nodes i and j in the finite element mesh belong to a common element. If the mesh is fine then most of the matrix entries are zeros, the distribution of the nonzero entries depending on which

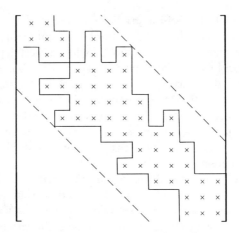

Fig. 6.1.   The band and envelope of a symmetric matrix.

of the $N!$ possible node orderings has been chosen. (The diagonal entries $k_{11}, ..., k_{NN}$ are nonzero for all orderings, however.)

We define the *bandwidth* of K to be $2w(K) + 1$, where the *half band-width* $w(K)$ is the smallest integer such that $k_{ij} = 0$ for all (i, j) satisfying $|i - j| > w(K)$. The *band* of K consists of the positions of all entries k_{ij} for which $|i - j| \leq w(K)$. Thus the band is a strip, centered on the main di-agonal, containing all the nonzero entries and possibly some zero entries as well. We show in Fig. 6.1 a symmetric band matrix of bandwidth 9. The dashed lines are the boundary of the band. By the foregoing definition every matrix has a band. When we speak of a *band matrix*, however, we usually mean a matrix whose bandwidth is fairly small relative to the order N. Thus, band matrices are examples of sparse matrices.

Let $m(i)$ denote the column number of the first nonzero entry in the ith row of a symmetric band matrix K. The entries k_{ij} and k_{ji}, where $j = m(i)$, $m(i) + 1, ..., i$, form the following pattern:

$$
\begin{matrix}
 & & & \times \\
 & & & \times \\
 & & & \times \\
\times & \times & \times & \times
\end{matrix}
$$

The positions of these entries for $i = 1, 2, ..., N$ define the *envelope* of K. The envelope of the matrix in Fig. 6.1 is bounded by the solid lines. The *size* of the envelope is $2e(K) + N$, where

$$ e(K) = \sum_{i=2}^{N} [i - m(i)]. $$

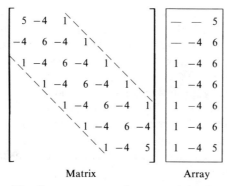

Matrix   Array

Fig. 6.2. Computer storage of a symmetric band matrix.

A standard storage scheme for a symmetric band matrix is a two-dimensional array, the diagonals in the lower half-band (including the main diagonal) being stored as columns in the array as illustrated in Fig. 6.2.

If the envelope of the matrix is appreciably smaller than the band, then it is usually preferable to store just the lower half-envelope. This can be accomplished with the help of two one-dimensional arrays, one for the row-wise storage of the matrix entries and the other for the storage of "pointers" to the diagonal elements $k_{11}, ..., k_{NN}$. The pointers provide easy access to any row of the matrix. This scheme, often called *variable bandwidth storage* (Jennings, 1977), is illustrated in Fig. 6.3.

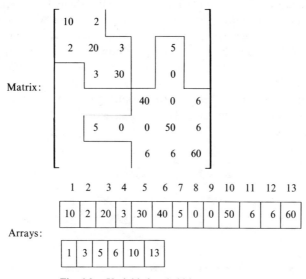

Fig. 6.3. Variable bandwidth storage.

As the matrix of Fig. 6.3 shows, there may be zeros within the envelope of a band matrix. Now a very important fact is that when Gaussian elimination (without pivoting) is applied to a system of equations, then *fill-in* (the creation of nonzero entries in positions originally occupied by zeros) is confined to the envelope of the matrix. Each of the storage schemes we have described provides space for any fill-in that might arise and hence can be used for the computer implementation of Gaussian elimination.

The computational labor required by Gaussian elimination depends on the size of the band or envelope, and it is natural to ask the following questions concerning the stiffness matrix K arising from an application of the finite element method.

(1)   How can one find a node ordering that is optimal in the sense of yielding the smallest band or smallest envelope?

(2)   How small is the smallest band and the smallest envelope?

The smaller the band or envelope, the more efficient Gaussian elimination is as a solution method.

Matrix Graphs

An indispensable tool in any discussion of these questions is the *graph* of a symmetric matrix (Parter, 1961). To construct the graph of an $N \times N$ symmetric matrix K, we draw N nodes, labeling them 1, ..., N, and draw a line from node i to node j for all (i, j) such that $i > j$ and $k_{ij} \neq 0$. When K arises from an application of the finite element method, it is natural to use the mesh nodes as graph nodes. As a rule, however, the mesh edges are only a subset of the graph edges. The relation between the mesh and the graph is illustrated in Fig. 6.4. Note that a reordering of mesh nodes leads only to a reordering of graph nodes, i.e., the "topological" properties of the graph are independent of the mesh node ordering.

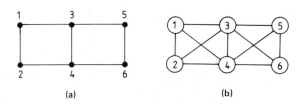

(a)   (b)

Fig. 6.4.   (a) A finite element mesh for piecewise bilinear basis functions and (b) the corresponding matrix graph.

We say that two nodes of a graph are *neighbors* if they are connected by an edge. Under the assumption that the matrix has nonzero entries in all positions on the main diagonal (this is always true of positive definite matrices), the column number $m(i)$ of the first nonzero entry in the ith row of the matrix is given by

$$m(i) = \min\{\tilde{m}(i), i\},$$

where $\tilde{m}(i)$ is the smallest label of all neighbors of node i. Thus, by inspecting the graph we can determine $m(i)$ for every node and hence the band and envelope parameters

$$w(K) = \max_{2 \leq i \leq N} [i - m(i)], \qquad e(K) = \sum_{i=2}^{N} [i - m(i)].$$

Clearly, the problem of numbering the mesh nodes for the purpose of obtaining a small band or envelope is essentially that of numbering the graph nodes so that the label of any node is close to the labels of all its neighbors.

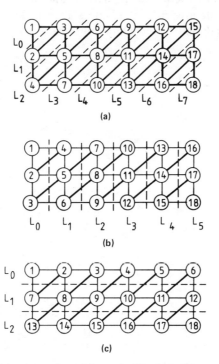

(a)

(b)

(c)

Fig. 6.5. Some level structures of a matrix graph. (The dashed lines separate levels.) In each case the node ordering has been based on the level structure. (a) $p = 7$, $d = 3$, $w(K) = 3$, $e(K) = 46$; (b) $p = 5$, $d = 3$, $w(K) = 3$, $e(K) = 47$; (c) $p = 2$, $d = 6$, $w(K) = 6$, $e(K) = 77$.

It will be observed, however, that the problems of *minimizing* the band and envelope are distinct, the first requiring the minimization of $w(K)$ and the second of $e(K)$.

We define a *level structure* of a matrix graph to be a partitioning of the nodes into sets L_0, L_1, ..., L_p such that all neighbors of any node in L_i belong to L_{i-1}, L_i, or L_{i+1}. (L_{-1} and L_{p+1} are understood to be the null set.) We call p the *length* of the level structure, and the *width d* is defined as the largest number of nodes in any of the sets L_0, ..., L_p. There are many ways to assign a level structure to a given matrix graph. In particular, by taking as L_0 a single node we generate a level structure called a *rooted level structure*.

Figure 6.5 shows some level structures for a graph that arises from a mesh of the type shown in Fig. 5.16. The first level structure is rooted in the upper left node.

When the nodes of set L_i in a level structure are ordered immediately after those of L_{i-1}, as illustrated in Fig. 6.5, then the node ordering induces a block tridiagonal structure in the matrix. The matrices corresponding to the three level structures in Fig. 6.5 are shown in Fig. 6.6. In the interest of obtaining a small band or envelope, an obvious strategy is to seek a level

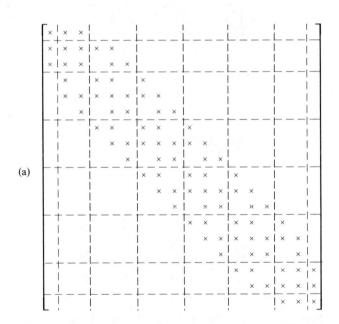

Fig. 6.6.   Matrices corresponding to the node orderings of Fig. 6.5.

(b)

(c)

structure with a small width and consequently large length. This property is often attained by a level structure rooted in a "remote" node; a corner, for example, in the case of a rectangular domain. When a level structure has been found, the node ordering is only partially determined by the requirement that the nodes of each L_i be labeled after those of L_{i-1}. In choosing the ordering of nodes within L_i, one should bear in mind the general principle that the label of a node should be close to those of all its neighbors. Note, for example, that if node labels 13 and 18 are exchanged in set L_2 of the third level structure in Fig. 6.5, then the half bandwidth increases from 6 to 11.

We shall now present the algorithm of Cuthill and McKee (1969) which, given a graph node, produces a node ordering based on the level structure rooted at that node. We define the *degree* of a node to be the number of its neighbors.

(1) Label the given node "1".

(2) For $i = 1, 2, ..., N$, find all the unlabeled neighbors of node i and label them in order of increasing degree.

The order in which neighbors of the same degree are labeled in step (2) is arbitrary. It will be observed that the first node ordering in Fig. 6.5 is a Cuthill–McKee ordering with the upper left node as starting node.

An important fact is that the reverse ordering of that produced by the Cuthill–McKee algorithm sometimes yields a smaller envelope and never a larger one. The bandwidth is unchanged. Thus, the *reverse Cuthill–McKee algorithm* obtained by adding the following step is to be preferred.

(3) For $i = 1, 2, ..., N$, change the label of node i in the Cuthill–McKee ordering to $(N - i + 1)$.

As mentioned above, it is desirable to choose a starting node that is at an extremity of the graph. For many problems, a visual inspection of the finite element mesh yields one or more obvious choices. However, there is sometimes a need for an automatic procedure for determining a remote node. An algorithm for this purpose, proposed in Gibbs, Poole, and Stockmeyer (1976) and modified as explained in George and Liu (1979), has proved to be effective. Both this and the reverse Cuthill–McKee algorithm can be fully implemented on a computer. See George and Liu (1981) for details. The two algorithms together constitute a node-ordering procedure that often yields a matrix with a nearly minimum band and envelope. It should be mentioned that there are no known true minimization procedures that do not require excessive computing time.

The Size of the Band

We now turn to the question posed earlier concerning the size of the smallest band that can be achieved by a suitable ordering of nodes. Let

$$q = \text{the average number of nonzeros in a row of } K$$

and

$$r = q/[2w(K) + 1].$$

r is approximately the density of nonzero entries in the band. Since q is independent of the ordering of the nodes, the ordering that minimizes the band is the one that maximizes r. The ideal situation would be a "compact" band, i.e., a band with few zero entries, corresponding to $r \simeq 1$. Unfortunately, this turns out to be unachievable for finite element problems in two or more space dimensions unless the mesh is very coarse. Indeed, the value of r typically tends to zero as the number of elements tends to infinity.

We illustrate this state of affairs for the case of a second-order boundary value problem on a square domain and the use of three kinds of basis functions; namely, the piecewise linear, quadratic, and bilinear functions of Examples 5.1, 5.2, and 5.3, respectively. We suppose that in each case the nodes of the mesh form a uniform $m \times m$ pattern, where m is odd, and that the elements are formed as illustrated in Fig. 6.7 for $m = 3$.

The maximum value of r over all node orderings is approximately (not exactly because we have ignored boundary effects) that given in Table 6.1. The data in brackets reflect the "uncoupling" of nodes that occurs in the case of Poisson's equation (see Exercises 5.14 and 5.15). The essential information of Table 6.1 is that the density of nonzero entries in the band of K is $O(m^{-1})$ for $m \to \infty$, or equivalently $O(N^{-1/2})$ for $N \to \infty$, where N is the number of nodes. This result, entirely typical for finite element applications to two-dimensional problems, implies that the storage scheme described

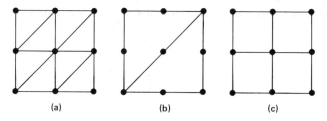

(a)   (b)   (c)

Fig. 6.7.   A mesh for piecewise (a) linear, (b) quadratic, and (c) bilinear basis functions.

Table 6.1
Density r of Nonzero Entries in the Band of K

Basis functions	q	$w(K)$	r
Linear	7	m	$7/(2m + 1)$
	[5]	$[m]$	$[5/(2m + 1)]$
Quadratic	11.5	$2m$	$23/(8m + 2)$
	[6]	$[2m]$	$[6/(4m + 1)]$
Bilinear	9	$m + 1$	$9/(2m + 3)$

earlier for band matrices (Fig. 6.2) becomes increasingly inefficient as the mesh is refined.

In the case of some mesh geometries, the size of the smallest envelope is significantly less than the size of the smallest band and justifies the use of the variable bandwidth storage scheme of Fig. 6.3. Nevertheless, it is typical also of the smallest envelope that the density of nonzero entries is $O(N^{-1/2})$ as the mesh is refined.

Problems in three space dimensions lead to even smaller densities of non-zero entries in the band and envelope. Consider, for example, the case of piecewise trilinear basis functions on a regular m^3 mesh (m nodes along each edge), where the typical element is the 8-noded right rectangular prism shown in Fig. 6.8. The typical row in K has 27 nonzero entries and the smallest half-bandwidth is about m^2. Thus, the density of nonzero entries in the band is $O(m^{-2})$ for $m \to \infty$, or $O(N^{-2/3})$ for $N \to \infty$.

In Section 1.4 we described a data structure for the storage of only the nonzero entries in the lower triangle of K. Because of the occurrence of fill-in within the envelope, such a scheme is obviously unsuited to Gaussian elimination. (This is a fundamental difference between the iterative and direct methods.) Further, a node ordering that minimizes the envelope typically produces very dense fill-in, making it impossible to store less than the entire half envelope. All of these considerations explain why orderings that minimize the band or envelope are of limited usefulness for finite element problems, and in Section 6.3 we shall look at some alternatives.

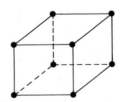

Fig. 6.8.   Typical element for piecewise trilinear basis functions.

6.2 Direct Methods

Gaussian Elimination

A *direct method* for solving the system of equations

$$K\alpha = G,$$

where K is an $(N \times N)$ nonsingular matrix, is commonly defined to be any method that (in the absence of rounding errors) produces the solution α after a finite number of elementary operations. What is to be regarded as an "elementary operation" is somewhat a matter of taste. We shall mean by this expression any of the four basic arithmetical operations or the extraction of a square root. (It is a source of some confusion that the conjugate gradient method, in either its simple or preconditioned form, is thus technically a direct method. However, the fact that in our applications we rarely carry out the full number of iterations justifies our viewing the method as iterative.) The best known direct methods, and the subject of this section, are Gaussian elimination and the closely related Cholesky method. Our treatment of this material will be concise since we assume it is part of the reader's background.

It will be recalled that Gaussian elimination entails a sequence of matrix and vector transformations

$$K^{(r)} \to K^{(r+1)},$$

$$G^{(r)} \to G^{(r+1)},$$

for $r = 1, 2, ..., N - 1$, where $K^{(1)} = K$, $G^{(1)} = G$, $K^{(N)}$ is upper triangular and

$$K^{(r)}\alpha = G^{(r)}, \qquad r = 1, 2, ..., N.$$

The purpose of the rth transformation is to eliminate the variable α_r from the last $(N - r)$ equations in the system $K^{(r)}\alpha = G^{(r)}$. The algorithm for the transformation is

$$l_{ir} = k_{ir}^{(r)}/k_{rr}^{(r)},$$

$$k_{ij}^{(r+1)} = k_{ij}^{(r)} - l_{ir}k_{rj}^{(r)}, \qquad j = r + 1, r + 2, ..., N, \tag{6.1}$$

$$G_i^{(r+1)} = G_i^{(r)} - l_{ir}G_r^{(r)},$$

for $i = r + 1, r + 2, ..., N$. $K^{(r+1)}$ is a completely defined $(N \times N)$ matrix when we supplement (6.1) with

$$k_{ij}^{(r+1)} = \begin{cases} 0, & \text{for } j = 1, ..., r, \quad i = j + 1, ..., N, \\ k_{ij}^{(i)}, & \text{for } i = 1, ..., r, \quad j = i, ..., N. \end{cases}$$

This matrix and the vector $\mathbf{G}^{(r+1)}$ are as follows for $r = 2$ and $N = 6$:

$$K^{(3)} = \begin{bmatrix} k_{11}^{(1)} & k_{12}^{(1)} & k_{13}^{(1)} & k_{14}^{(1)} & k_{15}^{(1)} & k_{16}^{(1)} \\ 0 & k_{22}^{(2)} & k_{23}^{(2)} & k_{24}^{(2)} & k_{25}^{(2)} & k_{26}^{(2)} \\ 0 & 0 & k_{33}^{(3)} & k_{34}^{(3)} & k_{35}^{(3)} & k_{36}^{(3)} \\ 0 & 0 & k_{43}^{(3)} & k_{44}^{(3)} & k_{45}^{(3)} & k_{46}^{(3)} \\ 0 & 0 & k_{53}^{(3)} & k_{54}^{(3)} & k_{55}^{(3)} & k_{56}^{(3)} \\ 0 & 0 & k_{63}^{(3)} & k_{64}^{(3)} & k_{65}^{(3)} & k_{66}^{(3)} \end{bmatrix}, \qquad \mathbf{G}^{(3)} = \begin{bmatrix} G_1^{(1)} \\ G_2^{(2)} \\ G_3^{(3)} \\ G_4^{(3)} \\ G_5^{(3)} \\ G_6^{(3)} \end{bmatrix}$$

When the upper triangular matrix $U \equiv K^{(N)}$ and the vector $\mathbf{G}^{(N)}$ have been found from (6.1), the vector $\boldsymbol{\alpha}$ is obtained by solving the system

$$U\boldsymbol{\alpha} = \mathbf{G}^{(N)} \tag{6.2}$$

by the familiar "back substitution" algorithm:

$$\alpha_N = G_N^{(N)}/u_{NN},$$

$$\alpha_i = \left(G_i^{(i)} - \sum_{j=i+1}^{N} u_{ij}\alpha_j \right) \bigg/ u_{ii}, \qquad i = N-1, N-2, \ldots, 1. \tag{6.3}$$

An important fact of Gaussian elimination is that it effectively produces a factorization of K of the form

$$K = LU, \tag{6.4}$$

where L is a lower triangular matrix with unit diagonal entries and U is the upper triangular matrix defined previously. To see this, we note from (6.1) that

$$K^{(r+1)} = \hat{L}^{(r)}K^{(r)},$$

where $\hat{L}^{(r)}$ is the identity matrix modified by the insertion of the entries $-l_{r+1,r}, \ldots, -l_{N,r}$ at the end of the rth column. The matrix $\hat{L}^{(r)}$ and its inverse are as follows for $r = 3$ and $N = 6$:

$$\hat{L}^{(3)} = \begin{bmatrix} 1 & 0 & 0 & 0 & 0 & 0 \\ 0 & 1 & 0 & 0 & 0 & 0 \\ 0 & 0 & 1 & 0 & 0 & 0 \\ 0 & 0 & -l_{43} & 1 & 0 & 0 \\ 0 & 0 & -l_{53} & 0 & 1 & 0 \\ 0 & 0 & -l_{63} & 0 & 0 & 1 \end{bmatrix}, \qquad \hat{L}^{(3)-1} = \begin{bmatrix} 1 & 0 & 0 & 0 & 0 & 0 \\ 0 & 1 & 0 & 0 & 0 & 0 \\ 0 & 0 & 1 & 0 & 0 & 0 \\ 0 & 0 & l_{43} & 1 & 0 & 0 \\ 0 & 0 & l_{53} & 0 & 1 & 0 \\ 0 & 0 & l_{63} & 0 & 0 & 1 \end{bmatrix}.$$

Thus, we obtain by recursion the relation

$$U = (\hat{L}^{(N-1)}\hat{L}^{(N-2)}\cdots\hat{L}^{(1)})K,$$

and we see that $K = LU$, where

$$L = (\hat{L}^{(N-1)}\hat{L}^{(N-2)} \cdots \hat{L}^{(1)})^{-1} = \prod_{r=1}^{N-1} \hat{L}^{(r)-1}.$$

Now the special form of $\hat{L}^{(r)-1}$ makes this product easy to compute. The case when $N = 6$ is typical:

$$L = \begin{bmatrix} 1 & 0 & 0 & 0 & 0 & 0 \\ l_{21} & 1 & 0 & 0 & 0 & 0 \\ l_{31} & l_{32} & 1 & 0 & 0 & 0 \\ l_{41} & l_{42} & l_{43} & 1 & 0 & 0 \\ l_{51} & l_{52} & l_{53} & l_{54} & 1 & 0 \\ l_{61} & l_{62} & l_{63} & l_{64} & l_{65} & 1 \end{bmatrix}.$$

Thus (6.4) is established.

From a theoretical point of view, the process defined by (6.1) and (6.3) breaks down only if at some stage it happens that $k_{rr}^{(r)} = 0$, and this happens if and only if some principal minor of K is zero. (The rth principal minor of K is the determinant of the upper left $(r \times r)$ submatrix of K.) Since this condition is satisfied by some nonsingular matrices, the algorithm as it stands is obviously insufficient as a general computational procedure. Just as important, it is numerically unstable for many matrices for which all principal minors are nonzero, because of rounding errors caused by the finite precision of the computer. (Numerical instability is defined in Section 6.4.)

It is well known that for many systems of equations the problem of instability is much improved by the use of pivoting, i.e., row and/or column interchanges. The process of solving the system $K\alpha = G$ by Gaussian elimination with pivoting is essentially identical (even in the presence of rounding errors) to that of solving the system $(PKQ^T)(Q\alpha) = (PG)$ by Gaussian elimination without pivoting, where P and Q are $(N \times N)$ permutation matrices determined by the row and column interchanges, respectively. A special case of pivoting is "symmetric" pivoting, where $Q = P$ and $PKQ^T = PKP^T$. In the case of finite element problems, the matrix PKP^T has a simple interpretation: it is the stiffness matrix corresponding to a reordering of the mesh nodes.

Now a fact of fundamental importance is that when K is positive definite, then pivoting is unnecessary in Gaussian elimination (Section 6.4 and Exercise 6.8). The consequence of this for finite element problems with a positive definite stiffness matrix is that any node ordering is acceptable from the point of view of stability. Thus, the choice of a node ordering can be based exclusively on considerations of computing time and storage and ease of programming.

However, the statement that pivoting is unnecessary when K is positive definite must not be interpreted as meaning that the computed solution of the system is accurate when no pivoting takes place. It means only that pivoting has no essential effect on accuracy. If the system is ill-conditioned (i.e., if the spectral condition number $\kappa(K)$ is large), then the computed solution may indeed have large relative errors due to rounding. See Section 6.4 for further discussion. Ill-conditioning is generally revealed during the computation by cancellation (Exercise 6.22).

Row-wise Gaussian Elimination

It is instructive to seek L and U explicitly by assuming that (6.4) holds for some lower triangular matrix L with unit diagonal entries and some upper triangular matrix U, and by equating k_{ij} with the (i, j) entry of the product LU. This yields the equations

$$k_{ij} = \sum_{r=1}^{\min\{i,j\}} l_{ir}u_{rj}, \qquad i, j = 1, 2, \ldots, N, \qquad (6.5)$$

where $l_{ii} = 1$ for $i = 1, 2, \ldots, N$. Depending on the relation between i and j, we may rewrite (6.5) as

$$u_{ij} = k_{ij} - \sum_{r=1}^{i-1} l_{ir}u_{rj} \qquad \text{for} \quad i \le j, \qquad (6.6a)$$

$$l_{ij} = \left(k_{ij} - \sum_{r=1}^{j-1} l_{ir}u_{rj}\right)\bigg/ u_{jj} \qquad \text{for} \quad i > j. \qquad (6.6b)$$

By choosing a suitable sequence of values of (i, j), we can compute all of the unknown entries of L and U recursively from these two formulas. There are many possible sequences, for example, the row-wise sequence

$$(i, j) = (1, 1), (1, 2), \ldots, (1, N), (2, 1), (2, 2), \ldots, (2, N), \ldots, (N, N). \quad (6.7)$$

Having obtained the L and U factors of K, we can solve the system of equations $K\alpha = G$ by solving the lower triangular system $L\tilde{G} = G$ for $\tilde{G}$ and then the upper triangular system $U\alpha = \tilde{G}$ for α. This is accomplished by

$$\tilde{G}_1 = G_1,$$

$$\tilde{G}_i = G_i - \sum_{j=1}^{i-1} l_{ij}\tilde{G}_j, \qquad i = 2, 3, \ldots, N, \qquad (6.8a)$$

and

$$\alpha_N = \tilde{G}_N / u_{NN},$$

$$\alpha_i = \left(\tilde{G}_i - \sum_{j=i+1}^{N} u_{ij} \alpha_j \right) \Big/ u_{ii}, \qquad i = N - 1, N - 2, ..., 1, \qquad (6.8b)$$

respectively.

Now if K is any matrix with the property that all of its principal minors are nonzero (a positive definite matrix has this property), then the LU factorization of K is unique. Thus, the Gaussian elimination process (6.1) and the "direct" method, with ordering (6.7), produce the same factorization of any such K. Further, an inspection of the algorithms shows that they do it using identical arithmetical steps. Only the sequence of the steps differs. Similarly, $\tilde{G}$ and $G^{(N)}$ are identical and are produced by the same arithmetic.

From a mathematical point of view, the difference in the two algorithms is obviously trivial, and we shall refer to (6.6), (6.7) as *row-wise Gaussian elimination*. From the point of view of practical computation, however, the difference may not be trivial. For example, (6.6) is formulated in terms of inner products, whereas (6.1) is not. Thus, computers that provide for the accumulation of inner products in double precision make (6.6) attractive with regard to accuracy. Even more important, the relative efficiency of the computer implementation of these algorithms depends on the choice of a storage scheme for K. We shall return to this point later.

The Symmetric Case

Suppose now that K is symmetric. Putting $r = 1$ in (6.1), we find that for any (i, j) such that $2 \leq i, j \leq N$,

$$k_{ij}^{(2)} = k_{ij}^{(1)} - (k_{i1}^{(1)} / k_{11}^{(1)}) k_{1j}^{(1)}$$

and

$$k_{ji}^{(2)} = k_{ji}^{(1)} - (k_{j1}^{(1)} / k_{11}^{(1)}) k_{1i}^{(1)}.$$

Since $K^{(1)} \equiv K$ is symmetric, we see that

$$k_{ij}^{(2)} = k_{ji}^{(2)}, \qquad i, j = 2, 3, ..., N,$$

and we can clearly continue the analysis to obtain

$$k_{ij}^{(r)} = k_{ji}^{(r)}, \qquad i, j = r, r + 1, ..., N$$

for $r = 3, 4, ..., N$. Using these symmetry results and the first relation in (6.1), we find that

$$u_{rj} = k_{rj}^{(r)} = k_{jr}^{(r)} = k_{rr}^{(r)} l_{jr}, \qquad j = r, r + 1, ..., N \qquad (6.9)$$

for $r = 1, 2, ..., N$. This establishes that $U = DL^T$, where

$$D = \mathrm{diag}(k_{11}^{(1)}, k_{22}^{(2)}, ..., k_{NN}^{(N)}) = \mathrm{diag}(u_{11}, u_{22}, ..., u_{NN}), \qquad (6.10)$$

and hence that the LU factorization of a symmetric matrix K may be re-written in the symmetric form

$$K = LDL^T. \qquad (6.11)$$

Now the number of negative diagonal entries in D is equal to the number of negative eigenvalues of K. This is so because $L^{-1}KL^{-T}$ is a so-called *congruence* transformation of K, and all nonsingular congruence transformations preserve the number of positive and negative eigenvalues. [See, e.g., Strang (1976).] Thus, if K is positive definite, then D has a real square root, namely, the matrix

$$D^{1/2} = \mathrm{diag}(\sqrt{u_{11}}, \sqrt{u_{22}}, ..., \sqrt{u_{NN}}),$$

and defining the lower triangular matrix $\tilde{L} = LD^{1/2}$, we obtain from (6.11) the *Cholesky factorization*

$$K = \tilde{L}\tilde{L}^T. \qquad (6.12)$$

To find $\tilde{L}$ it is not necessary to find L and D first. Equating k_{ij} with the entry in position (i, j) of the product $\tilde{L}\tilde{L}^T$ and using the fact that $\tilde{L}$ has lower triangular form, we obtain the relation

$$k_{ij} = \sum_{r=1}^{\min\{i, j\}} \tilde{l}_{ir}\tilde{l}_{jr}$$

and hence the following formulas for the direct computation of $\tilde{L}$:

$$\tilde{l}_{ii} = \left(k_{ii} - \sum_{r=1}^{i-1} \tilde{l}_{ir}^2 \right)^{1/2}, \qquad (6.13a)$$

$$\tilde{l}_{ij} = \left(k_{ij} - \sum_{r=1}^{j-1} \tilde{l}_{ir}\tilde{l}_{jr} \right) \bigg/ \tilde{l}_{jj}, \qquad j < i. \qquad (6.13b)$$

As with the direct LU factorization, there is considerable freedom in choosing the sequence of values (i, j). In particular, we may take the row-wise sequence obtained from (6.7) by deleting all (i, j) for which $j > i$.

A Code for Symmetric Row-wise Gaussian Elimination

All of the factorization procedures described previously are applicable to a positive definite system of equations. Regarding the choice between the Cholesky method and Gaussian elimination, there is very little difference for our purpose, and in the remainder of this section we shall confine our attention to Gaussian elimination. Regarding the "ordinary" and "row-wise" versions of Gaussian elimination, in each case it is important to take advantage of symmetry to halve both storage and computational labor. For the storage schemes we consider for K, the row-wise version is always at least as efficient as the ordinary one and sometimes more so. Further, we have seen that it is also occasionally more accurate.

We shall now give a code for factorizing a symmetric matrix by row-wise Gaussian elimination. Following Martin et al. (1965) we define

$$\tilde{k}_{ij} = u_{ji}, \qquad j \le i,$$

rewrite (6.6a) as

$$\tilde{k}_{ij} = k_{ij} - \sum_{r=1}^{j-1} l_{jr}\tilde{k}_{ir}, \qquad j < i, \tag{6.14a}$$

$$\tilde{k}_{ii} = k_{ii} - \sum_{r=1}^{i-1} l_{ir}\tilde{k}_{ir}, \tag{6.14b}$$

and rewrite (6.6b) as

$$l_{ij} = \tilde{k}_{ij}/\tilde{k}_{jj}, \qquad j < i. \tag{6.14c}$$

The program code naturally depends on the choice of a storage scheme, and for clarity of presentation we shall work with the lower triangle (main diagonal included) of an $N \times N$ array whose typical entry is denoted $k[i,j]$. Initially the lower triangle of K is stored in the array. At the end of the computation K has been overwritten by L (under the main diagonal) and D (on the main diagonal). The unit entries on the main diagonal of L are not stored. The task of rewriting the code for the storage schemes of Figs 6.2 and 6.3 is left to the exercises.

The code (in ALGOL) is shown in Fig. 6.9. At the beginning of the computation for row i, the entries k_{rs} and k_{rr} have been previously overwritten

```
for i := 2 step 1 until N do
for j := 2 step 1 until i do
begin x := k[i,j];
    if j < i then
    for r := 1 step 1 until j − 1 do
    x := x − k[j,r] × k[i,r]
    else
    for r := 1 step 1 until j − 1 do
    begin y := k[i,r];
        z := y/k[r, r]; k[i, r] := z;
        x := x − z × y
    end;
    k[i,j] := x
end;
```

Fig. 6.9. ALGOL code for factorizing a symmetric ($N \times N$) matrix by row-wise Gaussian elimination.

by l_{rs} and u_{rr}, respectively, for $r = 1, 2, ..., i - 1$ and $s = 1, 2, ..., r - 1$. The entries $\tilde{k}_{ij}, j = 1, 2, ..., i - 1$, are found recursively from (6.14a) and written over k_{ij}. Then $u_{ii} \equiv \tilde{k}_{ii}$ is found from (6.14b), and during this computation the entries $l_{ij}, j = 1, 2, ..., i - 1$ are found from (6.14c) and written over $\tilde{k}_{ij}$. Finally, u_{ii} is written over k_{ii}.

An inspection of the code reveals that the computational labor required to find L and D is about $\frac{1}{6}N^3$ flops. (We recall that a flop is a floating-point addition or subtraction together with a floating-point multiplication.) This is not a particularly relevant fact for us, however, since the code does nothing to exploit the sparsity of K. As mentioned earlier, the entire computation can be restricted to the envelope of K and therefore also to the band. When the computation is restricted to the band (more specifically, to the lower "half band" since we are exploiting symmetry), the computational labor is reduced to about $\frac{1}{2}Nw(K)^2$ flops provided that the half bandwidth $w(K)$ is significantly less than N. For variable bandwidth matrices there is the possibility of even further reduction, since the envelope is smaller than the band.

A variable bandwidth matrix (stored as shown in Fig. 6.3) provides a case in which row-wise Gaussian elimination is more efficient than the ordinary version. The disadvantage of ordinary Gaussian elimination is that in the rth stage of the computation in (6.1) it must be determined which of the entries $k_{ir}^{(r)}, i = r + 1, r + 2, ..., N$ are nonzero, and this entails a time-consuming search. The problem is especially acute if the matrix is too large for the main storage of the computer (not unusual for large-scale finite element problems), for then the search will require a large number of data transfers from peripheral storage (usually tape or disc). With row-wise Gaussian elimination, on the other hand, the part of the matrix that is necessary for the computation of the ith row is limited to the illustrated triangle.

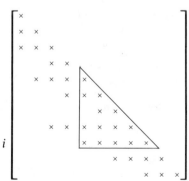

Row i of a variable bandwidth matrix is said to be *re-entrant* if the column number of the first nonzero entry in that row is less than that of the first nonzero entry in row $(i - 1)$. In the foregoing matrix, for example, rows 5 and 8 are re-entrant. Note that ordinary Gaussian elimination can be programmed efficiently for variable bandwidth matrices if it can be assumed that the matrix has no re-entrant rows.

Large-scale finite element problems often require double-precision accuracy. Although execution time for a double-precision flop need not be twice that for a single-precision flop (dependent on the computer), double-precision storage can significantly increase the number of data transfers between peripheral and main storage and thereby increase computing time.

Use of L and D

Having obtained L and D we can exploit the factorization $K = LDL^T$ to solve the system of equations $K\alpha = G$. The procedure is to solve first the lower triangular system $L\tilde{G} = G$ by forward substitution and then the upper triangular system $L^T\alpha = D^{-1}\tilde{G}$ for α by back substitution. The formulas are given by (6.8a) and a trivial modification of (6.8b). The computational labor is about N^2 flops if K is a full matrix (we assume N is large) and $2Nw(K)$ flops if K is a constant bandwidth matrix with half-bandwidth $w(K)$.

Note that these operation counts are significantly less than those for the factorization of K. It follows that the computational labor (including the factorization) required to solve m systems of equations with the same matrix K is usually much less than m times the labor required for one system. This is an advantage of factorization methods over iterative methods.

The QR Factorization

For the sake of completeness we shall describe yet another factorization of K, namely, $K = QR$, where Q is orthogonal and R is upper triangular. If K is nonsingular and if we impose the condition that the diagonal entries of R must be positive, then Q and R are uniquely determined. [See, e.g., Wilkinson (1965).] The factorization is conveniently performed with the help of so-called Householder matrices of the form

$$H = H(v) = I - (2/\|v\|^2)vv^T.$$

The matrix vv^T, whose typical entry is $v_i v_j$, is symmetric and hence H is symmetric. Further, since

$$(vv^T)^T(vv^T) = v(v^Tv)v^T = \|v\|^2vv^T,$$

it follows by a simple computation that $H^T H = I$, establishing that H is also orthogonal. The relations $H = H^T = H^{-1}$ make Householder matrices convenient to work with. (Thus for any matrix A, $HAH^{-1} = HAH^T = HAH$ is both a similarity and a congruence transformation of A.)

The usefulness of Householder matrices in numerical analysis stems partly from the following property: if $\mathbf{x}$ and $\mathbf{y}$ are any pair of distinct vectors such that $\|\mathbf{x}\| = \|\mathbf{y}\|$, then

$$\mathbf{y} = H(\mathbf{v})\mathbf{x}, \qquad \mathbf{v} \equiv \pm(\mathbf{x} - \mathbf{y}).$$

The proof is simple:

$$H(\mathbf{v})\mathbf{x} = \left[I - (2/\|\mathbf{v}\|^2)\mathbf{v}\mathbf{v}^T\right]\mathbf{x} = \mathbf{x} - (\mathbf{x} - \mathbf{y})[2(\mathbf{x} - \mathbf{y})^T\mathbf{x}/(\mathbf{x} - \mathbf{y})^T(\mathbf{x} - \mathbf{y})]$$

$$= \mathbf{x} - (\mathbf{x} - \mathbf{y})[(2\mathbf{x}^T\mathbf{x} - 2\mathbf{y}^T\mathbf{x})/(\mathbf{x}^T\mathbf{x} + \mathbf{y}^T\mathbf{y} - 2\mathbf{y}^T\mathbf{x})] = \mathbf{x} - (\mathbf{x} - \mathbf{y}) = \mathbf{y}.$$

We shall now describe briefly how Householder matrices can be used to perform the QR factorization of a given matrix K. Consider the recursions

$$K^{(r+1)} = H^{(r)}K^{(r)}, \qquad Q^{(r)} = Q^{(r-1)}H^{(r)}$$

for $r = 1, 2, \ldots, N - 1$, where $K^{(1)} = K$, $Q^{(0)} = I$ and each $H^{(r)}$ is a Householder matrix. Defining $R = K^{(N)}$ and $Q = Q^{(N-1)}$, we see that

$$R = H^{(N-1)}H^{(N-2)}\cdots H^{(1)}K, \qquad Q = H^{(1)}H^{(2)}\cdots H^{(N-1)},$$

and since $(H^{(r)})^2 = I$ for $r = 1, \ldots, N - 1$, we have $QR = K$.

Q is obviously orthogonal for any choice of $H^{(1)}, \ldots, H^{(N-1)}$, and we want to choose these matrices to make R upper triangular. In the first step, we use the previously mentioned property of Householder matrices to find a vector $\mathbf{v}_1$ such that the product of $H^{(1)} \equiv H(\mathbf{v}_1)$ with the first column of $K^{(1)}$ is of the form $c[1, 0, \ldots, 0]^T$. Since $K^{(2)} = H^{(1)}K^{(1)}$, this puts zeros in the last $N - 1$ positions of the first column of $K^{(2)}$. In the rth step of the recursion, where we compute $K^{(r+1)} = H^{(r)}K^{(r)}$ and $Q^{(r)} = Q^{(r-1)}H^{(r)}$, $H^{(r)}$ is chosen so that zeros are put in the last $(N - r)$ positions of the rth column of $K^{(r+1)}$ without destroying zeros in the previous columns. $H^{(r)}$ has the form

$$H^{(r)} = \left[\begin{array}{c|c} I & 0 \\ \hline 0 & \tilde{H}^{(r)} \end{array}\right],$$

and in practice we work only with the smaller Householder matrix $\tilde{H}^{(r)}$.

The fact that each $H^{(r)}$ is an orthogonal matrix and hence has condition number 1 makes the QR factorization described above a stable numerical process (Wilkinson, 1965). However, because of fill-in and the loss of symmetry and bandwidth properties, the QR factorization is rarely used in the context of the finite element method. [It plays an important role, however, in the Natural Factor Formulation method of Argyris and Brønlund (1975).]

6.3 Special Techniques

Introduction

On the basis of the material presented in Sections 6.1 and 6.2, a natural approach to the problem of solving the Ritz–Galerkin equations is to order the mesh nodes using the reverse Cuthill–McKee (RCM) algorithm, assemble and store K in variable bandwidth form, and apply the Cholesky or symmetric Gauss factorization method. This procedure is ideally suited to the case when the envelope of K is dense. As shown in Section 6.1, however, the envelope tends to be sparse for finite element problems in two or three space dimensions when the mesh is fine. The following remarks are therefore relevant.

1. For certain problems a non-RCM ordering can be found that effectively makes it possible to carry out part of the Gaussian elimination process in advance, so that the system to be solved on the computer is of reduced size.

2. If there are "identical substructures," an RCM ordering would fail to take account of them. The exploitation of identical substructures reduces both storage and computational labor. (For large-scale problems requiring the use of peripheral storage, there are also fewer time-consuming data transfers.)

3. An RCM ordering of the mesh nodes is usually far from optimal in the sense that there exist other orderings whose associated stiffness matrices can be factorized with many fewer arithmetical operations (we assume that operations on zeros are avoided) and with less storage.

4. The possibility of performing the assembly of K simultaneously with Gaussian elimination provides a flexibility hitherto unconsidered.

These remarks motivate the methods described in this section. For example, "static condensation" at either element level or "superelement" level is a technique for eliminating unknowns at an early stage. The notion of a superelement, i.e., a group of contiguous mesh elements, also provides the basis for exploiting physically identical components, or substructures, in the system being analyzed. Superelements arise in a purely mathematical way from node orderings of "one-way dissection" type.

The search for node orderings that minimize computational labor and fill-in for the Gauss and Cholesky factorizations of K have led to so-called "nested dissection orderings." By treating them from the point of view of recursive static condensation, we are able to derive bounds on the computational labor and storage for a model problem and show that these orderings are superior to band-minimizing orderings.

Our final topic is the "frontal method," which by an interlacing of the processes of assembly and elimination achieves an efficient use of core and peripheral storage and which replaces the problem of finding a good ordering of nodes with the easier problem of finding a good ordering of elements.

Static Condensation at Element Level: An Example

The simplest form of static condensation, *static condensation at element level*, is applicable to finite element problems in which the elements contain interior nodes. It is the technique whereby one eliminates at an early stage the unknowns associated with the interior nodes, so that only a reduced system of Ritz–Galerkin equations is assembled and solved.

A simple example is afforded by the one-dimensional problem

$$-u'' = g(x), \qquad 0 < x < 1,$$
$$u(0) = u(1) = 0. \tag{6.15}$$

Let the elements be the nonuniform subintervals $e_i = [x_{2i}, x_{2i+2}]$, $i = 0$, $1, \ldots, N$ of length h_i, with nodes at the endpoints and midpoint of each subinterval (see Fig. 6.10).

For the basis functions $\phi_0(x)$, $\phi_1(x)$, ..., $\phi_{2N+2}(x)$ we choose continuous, piecewise quadratic polynomials, the analog in one space dimension of the basis functions of Example 5.2. Taking as the standard element $\tilde{e}$ the interval $0 \leq \tilde{x} \leq 1$ with nodes $\tilde{x}_1 = 0$, $\tilde{x}_2 = \frac{1}{2}$, and $\tilde{x}_3 = 1$, we easily find that the standard local basis functions are

$$\tilde{\phi}_1(\tilde{x}) = 1 - 3\tilde{x} + 2\tilde{x}^2,$$
$$\tilde{\phi}_2(\tilde{x}) = 4(\tilde{x} - \tilde{x}^2), \tag{6.16}$$
$$\tilde{\phi}_3(\tilde{x}) = -\tilde{x} + 2\tilde{x}^2.$$

These are shown in Fig. 6.11.

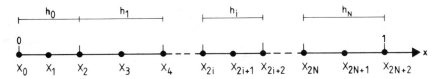

Fig. 6.10. A finite element mesh for problem (6.15).

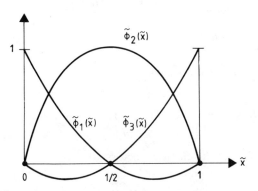

Fig. 6.11. The standard local basis functions.

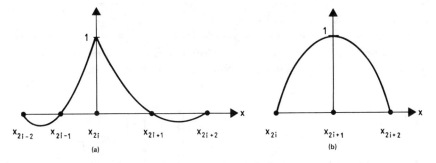

Fig. 6.12. The typical global basis functions: (a) $\phi_{2i}(x)$, (b) $\phi_{2i+1}(x)$.

The affine transformation

$$\tilde{x} = (x - x_{2i})/h_i, \qquad x_{2i} \leq x \leq x_{2i+2} \tag{6.17}$$

allows us to construct the global basis functions from the standard local basis functions (see Fig. 6.12).

The bilinear form associated with (6.15) is

$$a(u, v) = \int_0^1 u'v' \, dx, \qquad u, v \in \mathring{H}^1(0, 1),$$

and proceeding as in the derivation of (5.38) we find that the entries of element matrix $K^{(i)}$ are

$$
\begin{aligned}
k_{rs}^{(i)} &= \int_{e_i} \left[(\phi_r^{(i)})'(x) \right]\left[(\phi_s^{(i)})'(x) \right] dx \\
&= \int_0^1 \left[\tilde{\phi}_r'(\tilde{x}) \frac{d\tilde{x}}{dx} \right]\left[\tilde{\phi}_s'(\tilde{x}) \frac{d\tilde{x}}{dx} \right] \frac{dx}{d\tilde{x}} \, d\tilde{x} \\
&= h_i^{-1} \int_0^1 \tilde{\phi}_r'(\tilde{x}) \tilde{\phi}_s'(\tilde{x}) \, d\tilde{x}, \qquad r, s = 1, 2, 3.
\end{aligned}
$$

Straightforward integration yields

$$
K^{(i)} = \frac{1}{3h_i} \begin{bmatrix} 7 & -8 & 1 \\ -8 & 16 & -8 \\ 1 & -8 & 7 \end{bmatrix}, \qquad i = 0, 1, \ldots, N. \tag{6.18}
$$

Similarly, we find that the element vectors are

$$
\mathbf{G}^{(i)} = \begin{bmatrix} G_1^{(i)} \\ G_2^{(i)} \\ G_3^{(i)} \end{bmatrix}, \qquad G_r^{(i)} = h_i \int_0^1 \tilde{g}(\tilde{x}) \tilde{\phi}_r(\tilde{x}) \, d\tilde{x}
$$

for $i = 0, 1, \ldots, N$, where $\tilde{g}(\tilde{x}) = g(x(\tilde{x}))$.

We shall now suppose that the mesh is uniform, i.e., $h_i = h \equiv 1/(N + 1)$. The assembly of the Ritz–Galerkin system and removal of the first and last unknowns through the Dirichlet boundary conditions yields the system (6.19).

$$
\frac{1}{3h}
\begin{bmatrix}
16 & -8 & & & & & & & & \\
-8 & 14 & -8 & 1 & & & & & & \\
& -8 & 16 & -8 & & & & & & \\
& 1 & -8 & 14 & -8 & 1 & & & & \\
& & & \cdot & \cdot & \cdot & & & & \\
& & & 1 & -8 & 14 & -8 & 1 & & \\
& & & & & -8 & 16 & -8 & & \\
& & & & & 1 & -8 & 14 & -8 & 1 \\
& & & & & & & \cdot & \cdot & \cdot \\
& & & & & & & 1 & -8 & 14 & -8 \\
& & & & & & & & & -8 & 16
\end{bmatrix}
\begin{bmatrix}
\alpha_1 \\
\alpha_2 \\
\alpha_3 \\
\alpha_4 \\
\cdot \\
\alpha_{2i} \\
\alpha_{2i+1} \\
\alpha_{2i+2} \\
\cdot \\
\alpha_{2N} \\
\alpha_{2N+1}
\end{bmatrix}
=
\begin{bmatrix}
G_2^{(0)} \\
G_3^{(0)} + G_1^{(1)} \\
G_2^{(1)} \\
G_3^{(1)} + G_1^{(2)} \\
\cdot \\
G_3^{(i-1)} + G_1^{(i)} \\
G_2^{(i)} \\
G_3^{(i)} + G_1^{(i+1)} \\
\cdot \\
G_3^{(N-1)} + G_1^{(N)} \\
G_2^{(N)}
\end{bmatrix}. \tag{6.19}
$$

The special form of K makes it possible to eliminate easily the unknowns $\alpha_1, \alpha_3, \ldots, \alpha_{2N+1}$ corresponding to the interior nodes of the mesh. Thus, from rows $(2i - 1)$ and $(2i + 1)$ in (6.19) we obtain

$$\begin{aligned}
\alpha_{2i-1} &= \tfrac{1}{2}(\alpha_{2i-2} + \alpha_{2i} + \tfrac{3}{8}hG_{2i-1}), \\
\alpha_{2i+1} &= \tfrac{1}{2}(\alpha_{2i} + \alpha_{2i+2} + \tfrac{3}{8}hG_{2i+1}),
\end{aligned} \tag{6.20}$$

and substituting these expressions in row $(2i)$ we find, after simplification, that

$$\begin{aligned}
-\alpha_{2i-2} + 2\alpha_{2i} - \alpha_{2i+2} &= h\big[G_{2i} + \tfrac{1}{2}(G_{2i-1} + G_{2i+1})\big] \\
&= h\big[G_3^{(i-1)} + G_1^{(i)} + \tfrac{1}{2}(G_2^{(i-1)} + G_2^{(i)})\big] \\
&= h\hat{G}_{2i}, \quad \text{say,}
\end{aligned} \tag{6.21}$$

where $\alpha_0 = \alpha_{2N+2} = 0$. Thus, we have reduced the Ritz–Galerkin equations to

$$\frac{1}{h}\begin{bmatrix} 2 & -1 & & & & \\ -1 & 2 & -1 & & & \\ & \cdot & \cdot & \cdot & & \\ & & \cdot & \cdot & \cdot & \\ & & & -1 & 2 & -1 \\ & & & & -1 & 2 \end{bmatrix}\begin{bmatrix} \alpha_2 \\ \alpha_4 \\ \vdots \\ \vdots \\ \alpha_{2N-2} \\ \alpha_{2N} \end{bmatrix} = \begin{bmatrix} \hat{G}_2 \\ \hat{G}_4 \\ \vdots \\ \vdots \\ \hat{G}_{2N-2} \\ \hat{G}_{2N} \end{bmatrix}.$$

We observe that the bandwidth, as well as the order, has been reduced. When this system has been solved, the remaining unknowns can be found, if desired, from (6.20).

Remarks

1. The described procedure is equivalent to ordering the $N + 1$ interior nodes before the remaining nodes and then carrying out the first $N + 1$ steps of ordinary Gaussian elimination on the corresponding Ritz–Galerkin system. Since the matrix of this system has a band that is very much larger than the one in (6.19), we conclude that static condensation involves node orderings that are far from band-minimizing.

2. The new system can be obtained directly by the assembly of suitably defined "modified" element matrices $\hat{K}^{(0)}, \ldots, \hat{K}^{(N)}$ and element vectors $\hat{\mathbf{G}}^{(0)}, \ldots, \hat{\mathbf{G}}^{(N)}$. This is seen by rewriting (6.21) as

$$\hat{k}_{21}^{(i-1)}\alpha_{2i-2} + \big[\hat{k}_{22}^{(i-1)} + \hat{k}_{11}^{(i)}\big]\alpha_{2i} + \hat{k}_{12}^{(i)}\alpha_{2i+2} = \hat{G}_2^{(i-1)} + \hat{G}_1^{(i)}, \tag{6.22}$$

where we have defined

$$\hat{K}^{(i)} = \frac{1}{h}\begin{bmatrix} 1 & -1 \\ -1 & 1 \end{bmatrix}, \qquad \hat{\mathbf{G}}^{(i)} = \begin{bmatrix} G_1^{(i)} + \tfrac{1}{2}G_2^{(i)} \\ G_3^{(i)} + \tfrac{1}{2}G_2^{(i)} \end{bmatrix}.$$

The form of (6.22) establishes that the reduced set of Ritz–Galerkin equations is obtained directly by assembling the modified element matrices and vectors.

Static Condensation at Element Level: Generalities

We shall now describe static condensation at element level in general terms. Suppose that an element e_l has T nodes of which q are interior, and suppose that the nodes are ordered locally 1, 2, ..., T with the interior nodes ordered first. Let $\alpha_1^{(l)}, \alpha_2^{(l)}, ..., \alpha_T^{(l)}$ denote those unknowns of the Ritz–Galerkin equations that are associated with the nodes of e_l, and let the element matrix $K^{(l)}$ and element vector $\mathbf{G}^{(l)}$ be partitioned as follows:

$$
K^{(l)} = \begin{bmatrix} K_{11}^{(l)} & K_{21}^{(l)\mathrm{T}} \\ K_{21}^{(l)} & K_{22}^{(l)} \end{bmatrix} \begin{matrix} \updownarrow q \\ \updownarrow_{T-q} \end{matrix}, \qquad \mathbf{G}^{(l)} = \begin{bmatrix} \mathbf{G}_1^{(l)} \\ \mathbf{G}_2^{(l)} \end{bmatrix} \begin{matrix} \updownarrow q \\ \updownarrow_{T-q} \end{matrix}
$$

$K_{11}^{(l)}$ is positive definite or semidefinite because its determinant is a principal minor of $K^{(l)}$ and $K^{(l)}$ has one of these properties. We shall assume that $K_{11}^{(l)}$ is in fact positive definite.

The set of Ritz–Galerkin equations associated with the q interior nodes is

$$
K_{11}^{(l)}\boldsymbol{\alpha}_1^{(l)} + K_{21}^{(l)\mathrm{T}}\boldsymbol{\alpha}_2^{(l)} = \mathbf{G}_1^{(l)}, \tag{6.23}
$$

where $\boldsymbol{\alpha}_1^{(l)} = [\alpha_1^{(l)}, ..., \alpha_q^{(l)}]^{\mathrm{T}}$ and $\boldsymbol{\alpha}_2^{(l)} = [\alpha_{q+1}^{(l)}, ..., \alpha_T^{(l)}]^{\mathrm{T}}$. The contributions from e_l to the left- and right-hand (LHS and RHS) sides of the Ritz–Galerkin equations associated with the $(T - q)$ nodes on the boundary of e_l are

$$
K_{21}^{(l)}\boldsymbol{\alpha}_1^{(l)} + K_{22}^{(l)}\boldsymbol{\alpha}_2^{(l)}, \qquad \text{contribution to LHS;}
$$

$$
\mathbf{G}_2^{(l)}, \qquad \text{contribution to RHS.}
$$

Using (6.23) to eliminate $\boldsymbol{\alpha}_1^{(l)}$ and defining the *modified element matrix* and *modified element vector*

$$
\hat{K}^{(l)} = K_{22}^{(l)} - K_{21}^{(l)}K_{11}^{(l)-1}K_{21}^{(l)\mathrm{T}}, \tag{6.24}
$$

$$
\hat{\mathbf{G}}^{(l)} = \mathbf{G}_2^{(l)} - K_{21}^{(l)}K_{11}^{(l)-1}\mathbf{G}_1^{(l)}, \tag{6.25}
$$

we find that an equivalent formulation of the above contributions is

$$
\hat{K}^{(l)}\boldsymbol{\alpha}_2^{(l)}, \qquad \text{contribution to LHS;}
$$

$$
\hat{\mathbf{G}}^{(l)}, \qquad \text{contribution to RHS.}
$$

We deduce from this that the reduced set of Ritz–Galerkin equations, in which equations and unknowns associated with interior nodes have been eliminated, is obtained by the assembly of the modified element matrices and vectors over all elements in the mesh. (Note that since $K^{(l)}$ is positive definite or semidefinite, $\hat{K}^{(l)}$ must have the same property being a submatrix derived by Gaussian elimination on a part of $K^{(l)}$.) Thus, proceeding through the mesh an element at a time, we can

(1) compute the element matrix and vector $K^{(l)}$ and $\mathbf{G}^{(l)}$,
(2) compute $\hat{K}^{(l)}$ and $\hat{\mathbf{G}}^{(l)}$, defined by (6.24) and (6.25), respectively,
(3) "add" $\hat{K}^{(l)}$ and $\hat{\mathbf{G}}^{(l)}$ to the partially assembled global stiffness matrix and global load vector, respectively, of the reduced set of Ritz–Galerkin equations.

The essential feature of this process is that the reduction in the size of the Ritz–Galerkin equations is being performed at element level; at no point is the full set of equations assembled.

There are various ways to compute $\hat{K}^{(l)}$ in step (2), two of which are shown below. For convenience we formulate them in terms of the Cholesky factorization of $K_{11}^{(l)}$; the Gaussian factorization is of course equally applicable.

Method 1

(1) Perform the Cholesky factorization $K_{11}^{(l)} = \tilde{L}_{11}^{(l)} \tilde{L}_{11}^{(l)\mathrm{T}}$.
(2) Solve $\tilde{L}_{11}^{(l)} X = K_{21}^{(l)\mathrm{T}}$ for X. (Every column of $K_{21}^{(l)\mathrm{T}}$ determines a column of X.)
(3) Compute $\hat{K}^{(l)} = K_{22}^{(l)} - X^{\mathrm{T}} X$, taking advantage of symmetry to halve the work.

Method 2

(1) As in Method 1.
(2) As in Method 1.
(3) Solve $\tilde{L}_{11}^{(l)\mathrm{T}} Y = X$ for Y.
(4) Compute $\hat{K}^{(l)} = K_{22}^{(l)} - K_{21}^{(l)} Y$, taking advantage of symmetry to halve the work.

If $K^{(l)}$ is a dense matrix, which is usually the case for element matrices, then Method 1 involves less computational labor than Method 2, the difference being the work required for step (3) in the latter method. Our reason for presenting Method 2 is that in the context of static condensation at *super-element* level (discussed below), $K^{(l)}$ is usually sparse. In this situation, Method 2 is often faster if care is taken to avoid operating on zeros (George, 1977a).

The vector $\hat{\mathbf{G}}^{(l)}$ can be computed by an obvious modification of Method 2.

If it is desired to find the unknowns $\boldsymbol{\alpha}_1^{(l)}$ associated with the interior nodes of e_l, then $\tilde{L}_{11}^{(l)}$, $K_{21}^{(l)}$, and $\mathbf{G}_1^{(l)}$ must be saved. When the reduced set of Ritz–Galerkin equations has been solved, $\boldsymbol{\alpha}_2^{(l)}$ is known and $\boldsymbol{\alpha}_1^{(l)}$ can be found by solving

$$\tilde{L}_{11}^{(l)}(\tilde{L}_{11}^{(l)\mathrm{T}}\boldsymbol{\alpha}_1^{(l)}) = \mathbf{G}_1^{(l)} - K_{21}^{(l)\mathrm{T}}\boldsymbol{\alpha}_2^{(l)}$$

[see (6.23)] using a forward and backward substitution.

Superelements and Substructures

The technique of static condensation at element level can be extended to *superelement* level, a superelement being defined as any cluster of contiguous elements (see Fig. 6.13). Very often, the physical system being analyzed in a finite element problem is built up of components, or *substructures*. Given a finite element mesh over the entire structure with the property that substructure boundaries coincide with element edges, the restriction of the mesh to a particular substructure provides an example of a superelement.

The extension of static condensation to superelement level is straightforward. Thus, suppose that a finite element mesh is divided into superelements E_l, $l = 1, 2, \ldots, R$, and suppose that a superelement E_l has p nodes, q of which are interior to E_l. When the element matrices and vectors of all elements in E_l have been computed, the q Ritz–Galerkin equations associated with the interior nodes can be completely assembled and a relation analogous to (6.23) can be derived. Then, by analyzing the contributions to those Ritz–Galerkin equations associated with the remaining nodes of E_l, one can derive a *superelement matrix* $\hat{K}^{(l)}$ of order $p - q$ (sometimes called the

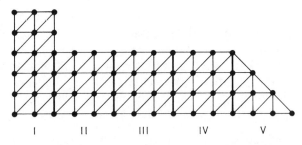

Fig. 6.13. A finite element mesh divided into five superelements.

condensed matrix) and a *superelement vector* $\hat{\mathbf{G}}^{(l)}$ of dimension $p - q$, analogous to $\hat{K}^{(l)}$ and $\hat{\mathbf{G}}^{(l)}$ in (6.24) and (6.25), respectively. As soon as $\hat{K}^{(l)}$ and $\hat{\mathbf{G}}^{(l)}$ have been computed, they can be used to update the assembly of the reduced set of Ritz–Galerkin equations whose unknowns are associated with only those nodes on superelement boundaries.

For problems with a sufficient degree of physical uniformity, the mesh and its division into superelements can be chosen so that a number of superelements and their matrices are the same. Naturally, in such cases $\hat{K}^{(l)}$ will be computed only once. The savings in computational labor thus achieved may be very substantial, and this is an important advantage of static condensation. Further, a superelement may represent a substructure that appears in many problems. The corresponding superelement matrix can be factored and stored in a "library" for future use. (Being dependent on the mesh as well as the physical properties of the substructure, however, the matrix will have to be recomputed if the mesh or these properties are altered.) If

(1) identical superelements are not exploited,

(2) the interior nodes of superelements are removed by Gaussian elimination (this is equivalent to Method 1 with the Cholesky factorization of $K_{11}^{(l)}$ replaced by the symmetric Gaussian factorization),

(3) Gaussian elimination is applied to the reduced stiffness matrix,

then, for an appropriate ordering of nodes, the computation is essentially identical to Gaussian elimination applied to the unreduced system of equations.

The literature on the use of superelement techniques is considerable, and much of it has appeared in engineering publications. [See, e.g., Bathe and Wilson (1976), Dodds and Lopez (1980) and Noor, Kamel, and Fulton (1977).] In principle, the process of static condensation can be repeated on a recursive basis by grouping "old" superelements (with interior nodes removed) into "new" superelements. We shall return to this idea shortly in connection with nested dissection orderings.

A Matrix Partitioning Method

In the foregoing discussion we primarily viewed the division of a finite element mesh into superelements as a process suggested by the division of the system being analyzed into physical components, and we described how, by an early elimination of unknowns, the order of the set of stiffness equations could be reduced. We shall now consider the choice of superelements to be a purely mathematical procedure connected with a certain node-ordering strategy and involving the assembly of the full set of equations. For the time being we shall concentrate on how the computation proceeds after the superelements have been determined, returning later to the problem of how to determine them in a systematic way.

Let the superelements be designated $E_1, E_2, ..., E_{R-1}$, and let the global ordering of nodes be such that

(1) nodes interior to superelements are ordered first,
(2) nodes interior to E_l are ordered before those interior to E_{l+1}.

This ordering induces a partitioned form in the Ritz–Galerkin equations $K\alpha = G$, which we illustrate for the case $R = 4$:

$$\begin{bmatrix} K_{11} & & & K_{41}^T \\ & K_{22} & & K_{42}^T \\ & & K_{33} & K_{43}^T \\ K_{41} & K_{42} & K_{43} & K_{44} \end{bmatrix} \begin{bmatrix} \alpha_1 \\ \alpha_2 \\ \alpha_3 \\ \alpha_4 \end{bmatrix} = \begin{bmatrix} G_1 \\ G_2 \\ G_3 \\ G_4 \end{bmatrix}. \tag{6.26}$$

The Cholesky factor $\tilde{L}$ of K is found to have the partitioned form

$$\tilde{L} = \begin{bmatrix} \tilde{L}_{11} & & & \\ & \tilde{L}_{22} & & \\ & & \tilde{L}_{33} & \\ \tilde{L}_{41} & \tilde{L}_{42} & \tilde{L}_{43} & \tilde{L}_{44} \end{bmatrix}, \tag{6.27}$$

where each submatrix $\tilde{L}_{rs}$ has the same dimensions as K_{rs} and each $\tilde{L}_{rr}$ is of course lower triangular. Equating corresponding submatrices in K and the product $\tilde{L}\tilde{L}^T$, we obtain the relations

$$K_{rr} = \tilde{L}_{rr}\tilde{L}_{rr}^T, \qquad r = 1, 2, ..., R - 1, \tag{6.28a}$$

$$K_{Rr} = \tilde{L}_{Rr}\tilde{L}_{rr}^T, \qquad r = 1, 2, ..., R - 1, \tag{6.28b}$$

$$K_{RR} - \sum_{r=1}^{R-1} \tilde{L}_{Rr}\tilde{L}_{Rr}^T = \tilde{L}_{RR}\tilde{L}_{RR}^T. \tag{6.28c}$$

Our objective is to solve the system $K\alpha = G$, and there are methods for this purpose analogous to Methods 1 and 2 described in the discussion of static condensation. They differ in that the first requires the computation and storage of each submatrix $\tilde{L}_{Rr}$ $(r < R)$, which can be written over K_{Rr} in memory, whereas the second retains K_{Rr} and uses the relation $\tilde{L}_{Rr} = K_{Rr}\tilde{L}_{rr}^{-T}$ whenever $\tilde{L}_{Rr}$ is needed. We shall describe only the second method as it is usually superior in terms of both storage and computational labor when K_{Rr}

is sparse, the typical situation with finite element problems. It is convenient to introduce first the matrices

$$M_r = \tilde{L}_{Rr}\tilde{L}_{Rr}^T = K_{Rr}\tilde{L}_{rr}^{-T}\tilde{L}_{rr}^{-1}K_{Rr}^T, \qquad r = 1, 2, ..., R - 1,$$

$$\hat{K}_{RR} = K_{RR} - \sum_{r=1}^{R-1} M_r.$$

The computation begins as follows.

(1) For $r = 1, 2, ..., R - 1$ do the following.
    (a) Compute $\tilde{L}_{rr}$ by the Cholesky factorization of K_{rr}, overwriting K_{rr} with $\tilde{L}_{rr}$.
    (b) For each column vector of the matrix K_{Rr}^T find the corresponding column vector of M_r and update $\hat{K}_{RR}$, as follows.
       (i) Solve $\tilde{L}_{rr}\mathbf{y} = \mathbf{x}$, where $\mathbf{x}$ is the column of K_{Rr}^T.
       (ii) Solve $\tilde{L}_{rr}^T\mathbf{z} = \mathbf{y}$.
       (iii) Compute $\mathbf{w} = K_{Rr}\mathbf{z}$.
       (iv) Subtract $\mathbf{w}$, which is the column of M_r, from the corresponding column of the partially assembled matrix $\hat{K}_{RR}$. This takes place in the space originally occupied by K_{RR}.
(2) Compute $\tilde{L}_{RR}$ by the Cholesky factorization of $\hat{K}_{RR}$, overwriting $\hat{K}_{RR}$ with $\tilde{L}_{RR}$.

This completes the factorization of K. Note that the systems in (i) and (ii) are triangular and hence easy to solve.

It remains to solve the system $(\tilde{L}\tilde{L}^T)\boldsymbol{\alpha} = \mathbf{G}$. This is done by first solving $\tilde{L}\boldsymbol{\beta} = \mathbf{G}$ and then $\tilde{L}^T\boldsymbol{\alpha} = \boldsymbol{\beta}$. Since the two computations are very similar, it is sufficient to describe the first. Writing the system $\tilde{L}\boldsymbol{\beta} = \mathbf{G}$ in the partitioned form (illustrated for $R = 4$),

$$\begin{bmatrix} \tilde{L}_{11} & & & \\ & \tilde{L}_{22} & & \\ & & \tilde{L}_{33} & \\ \tilde{L}_{41} & \tilde{L}_{42} & \tilde{L}_{43} & \tilde{L}_{44} \end{bmatrix} \begin{bmatrix} \boldsymbol{\beta}_1 \\ \boldsymbol{\beta}_2 \\ \boldsymbol{\beta}_3 \\ \boldsymbol{\beta}_4 \end{bmatrix} = \begin{bmatrix} \mathbf{G}_1 \\ \mathbf{G}_2 \\ \mathbf{G}_3 \\ \mathbf{G}_4 \end{bmatrix},$$

we can derive the relations

$$\tilde{L}_{rr}\boldsymbol{\beta}_r = \mathbf{G}_r, \qquad r = 1, 2, ..., R - 1, \tag{6.29a}$$

$$\tilde{L}_{RR}\boldsymbol{\beta}_R = \mathbf{G}_R - \sum_{r=1}^{R-1} \tilde{L}_{Rr}\boldsymbol{\beta}_r. \tag{6.29b}$$

Let

$$\mathbf{m}_r = \tilde{L}_{Rr}\boldsymbol{\beta}_r = K_{Rr}\tilde{L}_{rr}^{-T}\boldsymbol{\beta}_r, \qquad \hat{\mathbf{G}}_R = \mathbf{G}_R - \sum_{r=1}^{R-1} \mathbf{m}_r.$$

The computation of $\boldsymbol{\beta}$ proceeds as follows.

(1) For $r = 1, 2, ..., R - 1$ do the following.
    (a) Solve $\tilde{L}_{rr}\boldsymbol{\beta}_r = \mathbf{G}_r$.
    (b) Find $\mathbf{m}_r$ and update $\hat{\mathbf{G}}_R$ as follows.
        (i) Solve $\tilde{L}_{rr}^T\mathbf{x} = \boldsymbol{\beta}_r$.
        (ii) Compute $\mathbf{y} = K_{Rr}\mathbf{x}$ $(\mathbf{y} = \mathbf{m}_r)$.
        (iii) Subtract $\mathbf{y}$ from the partially assembled vector $\hat{\mathbf{G}}_R$.
(2) Solve $\tilde{L}_{RR}\boldsymbol{\beta}_R = \hat{\mathbf{G}}_R$.

An analogous computation is employed to solve the system $\tilde{L}^T\boldsymbol{\alpha} = \boldsymbol{\beta}$, yielding the desired vector $\boldsymbol{\alpha}$.

Regarding a storage scheme for the computation, since each of the submatrices K_{rr} is to be overwritten by $\tilde{L}_{rr}$, the storage scheme for K_{rr} must include space for fill-in and must of course exploit symmetry. This can be achieved, for example, by ordering the nodes of the corresponding superelement so as to obtain as small a bandwidth or envelope as possible and by storing K_{rr} in one of the ways described in Section 6.1. With the nodes so ordered, all of the submatrices $K_{rr}, r = 1, 2, ..., R$, could in fact be stored in an array for a single symmetric variable-bandwidth matrix of order N.

The case of an off-diagonal submatrix K_{Rr} is different, since this submatrix is retained throughout the computation. Here, a compact storage scheme for nonzero entries only is called for. In addition to storage for submatrices, a few one-dimensional arrays are needed for $\mathbf{G}, \boldsymbol{\alpha}, \boldsymbol{\beta}, \mathbf{x}, \mathbf{y}, \mathbf{z}$, and $\mathbf{w}$. With appropriate programming some of these vectors can share the same array. For a detailed discussion of the computer implementation of the computation described see George and Liu (1981).

One-Way Dissection Orderings

We now turn to the problem of dividing the mesh into superelements. A general technique for this purpose is *one-way dissection* (George, 1977b). We define the *separator* of a matrix graph to be any set of nodes with the property that when these nodes and the edges connected to them are removed, then the graph is separated into two (or more) disconnected pieces. In the case of a finite element problem, we can construct a separator by choosing an unbroken path of element edges that divides the mesh into two parts. The set of nodes belonging to the path is readily seen to constitute a separator of the associated matrix graph. We shall also call such a set a separator of the mesh itself.

The essential idea of one-way dissection is to choose S nonintersecting and more or less equally spaced separators of the mesh, thereby forming $S + 1$ superelements. This is illustrated in Fig. 6.13, where four separators (each a vertical mesh line) divide the mesh into five superelements. When the nodes are ordered as described preceding (6.26) (with $R = S + 2$), we speak of a *one-way dissection ordering.*† In George and Liu (1981) an analysis is made of the optimal choice of separators in a uniform mesh for piecewise quadratic basis functions, the nodes forming a pattern of m rows and l columns with $m \leq l$. It is found that the optimal number of vertical separators is of the form $S \simeq cl/\sqrt{m}$ when l and m are large, the value of c depending on what is to be minimized. Thus $c \simeq 0.82$ for the minimization of storage, $c \simeq 1.31$ for the minimization of the computational labor to factorize K, and $c \simeq 1.15$ for the minimization of the computational labor to solve $K\alpha = G$ after K has been factorized. It must be stressed that these values depend on details of storage and computation. [See George and Liu (1981) for further discussion.]

Nested Dissection

Consider a square domain and a finite element mesh made up of n^2 square elements with nodes at all vertices, the basis functions being the bilinear ones of Example 5.3. A row of the stiffness matrix K has at most nine nonzero entries, and the order of K is $N = (n + 1)^2$. Assuming that $n = 2^t$, for some integer t, we can solve the Ritz–Galerkin equations by the recursive use of static condensation, choosing superelements at the beginning of the rth stage $(r = 1, 2, ..., t)$ as illustrated in Fig. 6.14 for the case $n = 8$. At the end of the tth stage, the only unknowns not yet eliminated are those corresponding to the boundary nodes.

Let b_r denote the number of superelements at the rth stage, q_r the number of interior nodes in a superelement, and p_r the total number of nodes in a superelement. Then,

$$b_r = 4^{t-r},$$

$$p_r = 6 \cdot 2^r - 3, \tag{6.30}$$

$$q_r = 2^{r+1} - 3,$$

where $r = 1, 2, ..., t$. The number of boundary nodes is $(p_t - q_t) = 4(2^t)$.

Without going into details of computer implementation, we would like to assess the computational labor required to solve the Ritz–Galerkin system

---

† Boundary nodes not belonging to a separator may be viewed here as interior nodes of a superelement and ordered accordingly.

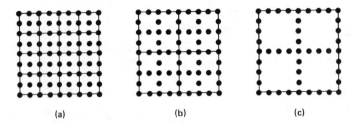

(a)   (b)   (c)

Fig. 6.14.   Sequence of superelements for recursive static condensation: (a) $r = 1$, (b) $r = 2$, (c) $r = 3$. During the rth stage the unknowns corresponding to the interior nodes of the superelements at that stage are eliminated from the Ritz–Galerkin system.

by this procedure. The total computational labor is dominated by that required to compute the superelement stiffness matrices that arise during the recursion plus that required to factorize the final one. Now, the typical superelement stiffness matrix $\hat{K}$ satisfies a relation of the form

$$\hat{K} = K_{22} - K_{21}K_{11}^{-1}K_{21}^{T}$$

[analogous to (6.24)], where the dimensions of the matrices are

$$\hat{K}, K_{22}: \quad (p_r - q_r) \times (p_r - q_r),$$

$$K_{11}: \quad q_r \times q_r,$$

$$K_{21}: \quad (p_r - q_r) \times q_r.$$

Taking advantage of symmetry but ignoring sparsity within submatrices, we find that the computational labor, measured in flops, for determining the typical matrix $\hat{K}$ is as follows:

factorization of $K_{11} = \tilde{L}_{11}\tilde{L}_{11}^{T}$: $\frac{1}{6}q_r^3 \simeq \frac{4}{3} \cdot 2^{3r}$,

computation of $X \equiv \tilde{L}_{11}^{-1}K_{21}^{T}$: $\frac{1}{2}q_r^2(p_r - q_r) \simeq 8 \cdot 2^{3r}$,

computation of $Y \equiv X^{T}X$: $\frac{1}{2}q_r(p_r - q_r)^2 \simeq 16 \cdot 2^{3r}$,

computation of $\hat{K} = K_{22} - Y$: $O((p_r - q_r)^2) = O(2^{2r})$,

or (ignoring the last step) about $C \cdot 2^{3r}$ flops in all, where $C = 76/3$. An estimate of the computational labor required to find all superelement matrices $\hat{K}$ is thus

$$\sum_{r=1}^{t} b_r C2^{3r} = 4^t C \sum_{r=1}^{t} 2^r = 4^t C(2^{t+1} - 2) \simeq (152/3)(2^{3t}).$$

The final superelement matrix is of order $p_t - q_t$ and is factorized in about $\frac{1}{6}(p_t - q_t)^3 \simeq (32/3)(2^{3t})$ flops. The estimate for the entire process is thus roughly $61n^3$ flops.

If all of the b_r superelement matrices at the rth stage are identical, then the estimate is reduced to

$$\sum_{r=1}^{t} C2^{3r} + \tfrac{1}{6}(p_t - q_t)^3 \simeq (608/21)(2^{3t}) + (32/3)(2^{3t}),$$

or about $40n^3$ flops.

These estimates are pessimistic because they ignore zeros within the sub-matrices. In the analysis of nested dissection in George (1973), it is shown that by avoiding operations on zeros one can perform the calculation in about $10n^3$ flops (ignoring lower-order terms). This estimate does not assume that superelement matrices at the rth stage are identical.

Regarding the storage requirement, the number of matrix entries that must be stored does not exceed

$$\sum_{r=1}^{t} \tfrac{1}{2}b_r p_r^2 \simeq 18n^2 \log_2 n$$

in the case of distinct superelement matrices at the rth stage and

$$\sum_{r=1}^{t} \tfrac{1}{2}p_r^2 \simeq 24n^2$$

in the case of identical superelements.

To appreciate these results we must compare them with the computational labor and storage required to factorize the fully assembled $N \times N$ stiffness matrix K when the mesh nodes are ordered to minimize the bandwidth. The minimal half-bandwidth $n + 2$ is achieved by a row-wise (or column-wise) ordering of the mesh nodes. We have seen that the computational labor, measured in flops, for factorizing a symmetric band matrix is roughly half of the order of the matrix times the square of the half-bandwidth, or in this case, about $\tfrac{1}{2}n^4$ flops. For sufficiently large values of n, this is much more work than that required by the recursive static condensation process.

It might be supposed that the estimate of $\tfrac{1}{2}n^4$ flops for factorizing the banded K is unduly pessimistic, since

(1) the band of K is largely populated by zero entries,
(2) the factorization algorithm (whether Gauss or Cholesky) can be programmed so that the basic floating-point calculation, which is of the form $x := x - y \times z$, is omitted if $y = 0$ or $z = 0$.

However, as mentioned earlier it is typical of orderings that minimize the bandwidth that the lower half-band of L or $\tilde{L}$ (where $K = LDL^T = \tilde{L}\tilde{L}^T$) is very dense, and the computational labor required by the factorization is not significantly reduced by avoiding operations on zeros.

Regarding storage, the requirement for the minimum bandwidth method is about n^3 in contrast to the $O(n^2 \log_2 n)$ estimate for the recursive static condensation process. Thus, the recursive static condensation process is asymptotically superior in this respect also.

Nested Dissection Orderings

We shall now introduce an ordering of the mesh nodes based on the way we have formed superelements in the recursive process. Let $S_l^{(r)}$, where $l = 1, 2, \ldots, b_r$, denote the sets of interior nodes of the superelements in the rth stage of the recursion, and let S_B denote the set of nodes on the outer boundary. Clearly, every node in the mesh belongs to one and only one of these sets. Let the nodes be ordered so that

(1)   nodes within a set are ordered consecutively,
(2)   sets at stage r are ordered after those at stage $r - 1$,
(3) S_B is ordered last.

Let K denote the $N \times N$ stiffness matrix produced by this ordering. It can be shown that, provided operations on zeros are avoided, the computational labor of factorizing K is essentially that of the recursive static condensation process, i.e., $O(n^3)$. Further, the number of entries in L (or $\tilde{L}$) is $O(n^2 \log_2 n)$.

Orderings of this type are examples of *nested dissection orderings* (George 1973). Much effort has been devoted to the problem of developing computer subroutines that, given a mesh (or, equivalently, the associated matrix graph), can determine a nested dissection ordering and the location of fill-in produced by that ordering. [See, e.g., George and Liu (1981) and Lipton, Rose, and Tarjan (1979).] With this information, a storage scheme can be established for all entries in the lower triangle of K that are either nonzero or that will be replaced by fill-in during the factorization. The row-ordered list illustrated in Fig. 1.8 can be used here. It is a straightforward programming exercise to rewrite the code of Fig. 6.9 for this storage scheme. The storage schemes of Section 6.1 are definitely not appropriate, since a nested dissection ordering typically leads to a very large band and envelope (Exercise 6.17).

Defining the *fill factor* to be the ratio of fill-ins to the original number of nonzero entries of K, we see that the fill-factor for a nested dissection ordering is $O(\log_2 n)$. It is natural to inquire whether any other mesh ordering can lead to a fill factor asymptotically less than $O(\log_2 n)$ or computational labor asymptotically less than $O(n^3)$. The answer is negative (Hoffman, Martin, and Rose, 1973), and nested dissection orderings are thus asymptotically optimal.

Nested dissection orderings can be extended to a finite element mesh of n^3 cubes. Computational labor and storage are $O(n^6)$ and $O(n^4)$, respectively (Exercise 6.18).

The Frontal Method

During the application of Gaussian elimination to the Ritz–Galerkin system $K\alpha = G$, the operations in position (i, j) of the matrix are

$$k_{ij}^{(r+1)} = k_{ij}^{(r)} - k_{ir}^{(r)} k_{rj}^{(r)} / k_{rr}^{(r)}, \qquad (6.31)$$

where $r = 1, 2, \ldots, \min(i - 1, j - 1)$ and $k_{ij}^{(1)} = k_{ij}$ [see (6.1)]. Similar operations occur in the ith position of the right-hand side vector. Now k_{ij} is the sum of certain entries in the element matrices associated with elements containing the ith node, and it is clear from (6.31) that the assembly of k_{ij} (and G_i) need not be completed prior to the elimination but may take place simultaneously with it. The only requirement is that the ith row be completely assembled before it becomes "pivotal", i.e., before it is used to eliminate α_i in subsequent rows.

This fact is exploited to the full in the *frontal method* (Irons, 1970; Irons and Ahmad, 1980). In the frontal method one proceeds through the mesh, element by element, computing the element matrices and vectors and combining the tasks of assembly and elimination. Each new element introduces new nodes and their associated unknowns, which are called *active*, until they are eliminated. The set of active nodes at any stage of the computation constitutes the *front*. The progress of the front through the mesh as the computation proceeds is determined by the way the elements (not the nodes!) have been ordered.

The process is illustrated in Fig. 6.15 for a mesh for piecewise linear basis functions. In the first step, element e_1 introduces nodes 1, 2, and 4 into the computation. The element matrix and vector $K^{(1)}$ and $G^{(1)}$ are computed and used to initiate the assembly of the Ritz–Galerkin equations associated with these nodes. Since node 1 belongs to no other element, its equation is completely assembled and can be used to eliminate the unknown α_1 from the partially assembled equations associated with nodes 2 and 4, essentially as described in the discussion of static condensation. When this has been done, nodes 2 and 4 are the only active nodes, and these form the front at this point of the computation (see Fig. 6.15a). The next element, e_2, introduces

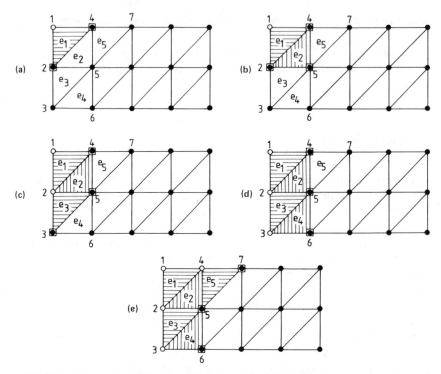

Fig. 6.15.   Progression of the front through a mesh of triangular elements: •, unprocessed node; ◼ frontal node; ○ eliminated node.

node 5, and after $K^{(2)}$ and $\mathbf{G}^{(2)}$ have been computed, the assembly of the equations associated with nodes 2, 4, and 5 can be updated. No elimination can be carried out at this point since none of these equations are completely assembled. Thus, the set of active nodes when the processing of e_2 is completed is 2, 4, and 5 (Fig. 6.15b).

Figure 6.16 depicts the state of assembly and elimination as the computation proceeds. These matrices correspond to the matrices $K^{(1)}$, $K^{(2)}$, ... that arise in the application of Gaussian elimination to the fully assembled stiffness matrix. The active unknowns determine a square block containing all partially assembled entries (and possibly some fully assembled ones as well), and this block moves down the main diagonal as the computation proceeds. The rows above the block are identical to the corresponding rows of $K^{(r)}$.

In the computer implementation of the frontal method, it is possible to transfer the pivotal row to peripheral storage (for later back substitution) as soon as it has been used to eliminate the associated unknown. If u is the

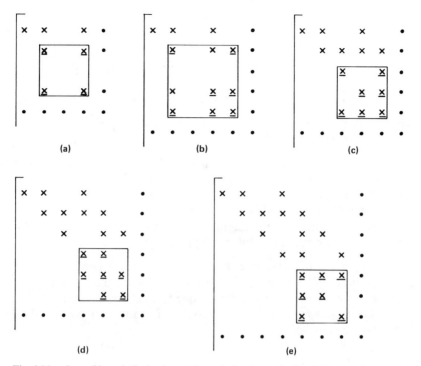

Fig. 6.16. Assembly and elimination at the end of each step in Fig. 6.15: $\times$, fully assembled entry; $\underline{\times}$ partially assembled entry.

largest number of active unknowns at any stage of the computation, then the amount of core storage required for the partially assembled equations never exceeds about $\frac{1}{2}u(u + 3)$. The goal in choosing an ordering of the elements is to make u as small as possible. This is often easier than choosing a node ordering to minimize the band or envelope.

Remark. It will probably be clear that the task of writing computer routines to implement direct methods for solving sparse positive definite systems of equations is far from trivial. (The easiest case is that in which the matrix is stored in band or variable band form, which explains much of the popularity of this method.) It is therefore relevant to mention the existence of available software employing some of the techniques described in this chapter as well as others. Important contributions are SPARSPAK (George, Liu, and Ng, 1980), the Yale Sparse Matrix Package (Eisenstat *et al.*, 1982), and the sparse matrix subroutines in the Harwell Subroutine Library. Most major mathematical libraries have routines for at least the band case. For detailed information on available software see Duff (1982, 1983) and Heath (1982).

6.4   Error Analysis

Any practical procedure for constructing and solving the Ritz–Galerkin equations

$$K\alpha = G, \tag{6.32}$$

where K is an $(N \times N)$ symmetric positive definite matrix, entails some or all of the following types of errors:

(1)   errors in the input data due to finite precision of measurements and/or rounding to the computer's floating-point precision,
(2)   rounding errors and numerical integration errors in the computation of the element matrices and element vectors,
(3)   rounding errors in the assembly of K and G,
(4)   rounding errors incurred in the process of solving (6.32).

The main purpose of this section is to investigate the influence of these errors on the accuracy of the final *computed* solution of (6.32) and to mention a few remedies for difficult problems. We assume throughout that either the symmetric Gauss factorization or the Cholesky factorization, as described in Section 6.2, is used to solve (6.32).

Perturbation Properties of (6.32)

An important part of the analysis is the determination of the perturbation properties of (6.32), i.e., the effect of a small change in G or K on α. We consider first a perturbation of G. Writing

$$K(\alpha + \delta\alpha) = G + \delta G$$

and using (6.32), we immediately obtain

$$\delta\alpha = K^{-1}\delta G$$

and the norm inequality

$$\|\delta\alpha\| \le \|K^{-1}\| \cdot \|\delta G\|. \tag{6.33}$$

The sharpness of this upper bound depends on the direction of δG in relation to the eigenvectors of K and on the eigenvalues. Thus, consider the expansion

$$\delta G = \sum_{i=1}^{N} \varepsilon_i v_i, \tag{6.34}$$

where $K\mathbf{v}_i = \lambda_i \mathbf{v}_i$, $i = 1, 2, \ldots, N$. We assume without loss of generality that $\mathbf{v}_i^T \mathbf{v}_j = \delta_{ij}$ for $i, j = 1, 2, \ldots, N$ and that $0 < \lambda_1 \le \lambda_2 \le \cdots \le \lambda_N$. Since $\delta\boldsymbol{\alpha} = K^{-1}\,\delta\mathbf{G}$ and $K^{-1}\mathbf{v}_i = \lambda_i^{-1}\mathbf{v}_i$, we have

$$\delta\boldsymbol{\alpha} = \sum_{i=1}^{N} \varepsilon_i \lambda_i^{-1} \mathbf{v}_i,$$

and hence

$$\|\delta\boldsymbol{\alpha}\|^2 / \|\delta\mathbf{G}\|^2 = \delta\boldsymbol{\alpha}^T\,\delta\boldsymbol{\alpha} / \delta\mathbf{G}^T\,\delta\mathbf{G} = \sum_{i=1}^{N} \varepsilon_i^2 \lambda_i^{-2} \bigg/ \sum_{i=1}^{N} \varepsilon_i^2.$$

From this and the relations $\|K\| = \lambda_N$, $\|K^{-1}\| = \lambda_1^{-1}$, we obtain the bounds

$$\|K\|^{-1}\cdot\|\delta\mathbf{G}\| \le \|\delta\boldsymbol{\alpha}\| \le \|K^{-1}\|\cdot\|\delta\mathbf{G}\|, \tag{6.35}$$

with equality on the left when $\delta\mathbf{G} = \pm\|\delta\mathbf{G}\|\mathbf{v}_N$ and on the right when $\delta\mathbf{G} = \pm\|\delta\mathbf{G}\|\mathbf{v}_1$.

Often it is the relative error $\|\delta\boldsymbol{\alpha}\|/\|\boldsymbol{\alpha}\|$ that is of interest. To determine it we derive from (6.32) the inequality $\|\mathbf{G}\| \le \|K\|\cdot\|\boldsymbol{\alpha}\|$ and combine this with (6.33) to obtain

$$\|\delta\boldsymbol{\alpha}\|/\|\boldsymbol{\alpha}\| \le \kappa(K)\|\delta\mathbf{G}\|/\|\mathbf{G}\|, \tag{6.36}$$

where $\kappa(K) = \|K\|\cdot\|K^{-1}\| = \lambda_N/\lambda_1$ is the usual spectral condition number of K. Again, we can get a more detailed description by considering the eigenvectors of K. Writing

$$\mathbf{G} = \sum_{i=1}^{N} \beta_i \mathbf{v}_i$$

and using (6.34), it is straightforward to show that

$$\kappa(K)^{-1}\|\delta\mathbf{G}\|/\|\mathbf{G}\| \le \|\delta\boldsymbol{\alpha}\|/\|\boldsymbol{\alpha}\| \le \kappa(K)\|\delta\mathbf{G}\|/\|\mathbf{G}\|, \tag{6.37}$$

with equality on the left when $\mathbf{G} = \pm\|\mathbf{G}\|\mathbf{v}_1$, $\delta\mathbf{G} = \pm\|\delta\mathbf{G}\|\mathbf{v}_N$ and on the right when $\mathbf{G} = \pm\|\mathbf{G}\|\mathbf{v}_N$, $\delta\mathbf{G} = \pm\|\delta\mathbf{G}\|\mathbf{v}_1$ (Exercise 6.19).

In the case of the stiffness matrices encountered in finite element problems, it is common that the components of $\mathbf{v}_1$ have the same sign, whereas the components of $\mathbf{v}_i$, $i > 1$ oscillate with respect to sign, the oscillations tending to be more rapid as i increases. Thus, the relative error $\|\delta\boldsymbol{\alpha}\|/\|\boldsymbol{\alpha}\|$ tends to be nearer the lower bound of (6.37) when $\mathbf{G}$ is "smooth" and $\delta\mathbf{G}$ is "rough." This is a welcome property since in many problems $\mathbf{G}$ is in fact smooth.

We shall now consider how the solution of (6.32) is affected by a perturbation of K. From the relation $(K + \delta K)(\boldsymbol{\alpha} + \delta\boldsymbol{\alpha}) = \mathbf{G}$ and (6.32) we obtain

$$\delta\boldsymbol{\alpha} = -(K + \delta K)^{-1}\,\delta K\,\boldsymbol{\alpha},$$

provided that $(K + \delta K)$ is nonsingular. It is left as an exercise to show that if

$$\|K^{-1}\,\delta K\| < 1, \tag{6.38a}$$

then

$$\|\delta\alpha\|/\|\alpha\| \le a_1/(1 - a_1), \qquad a_1 \equiv \|K^{-1}\,\delta K\|. \tag{6.38b}$$

(See Exercise 6.20.) If

$$\|\delta K\| < \|K^{-1}\|^{-1} \tag{6.39a}$$

[implying (6.38a)], then

$$\|\delta\alpha\|/\|\alpha\| \le a/(1 - a), \qquad a \equiv \kappa(K)\|\delta K\|/\|K\|. \tag{6.39b}$$

This bound is never less than that in (6.38b), but its form makes it more useful. Note that it diverges as equality is approached in (6.39a), reflecting the fact that $(K + \delta K)$ may be singular if $\|\delta K\| = \|K^{-1}\|^{-1}$.

Finally, in the case of simultaneous perturbations in G and K, where we have

$$(K + \delta K)(\alpha + \delta\alpha) = G + \delta G,$$

the relative change in the solution vector can be shown to satisfy

$$\frac{\|\delta\alpha\|}{\|\alpha\|} \le \frac{\kappa(K)}{1 - a}\left(\frac{\|\delta K\|}{\|K\|} + \frac{\|\delta G\|}{\|G\|}\right), \tag{6.40}$$

with "a" as previously defined.

The foregoing analysis shows that the influence of perturbations in data on the solution of the system can be significant if and only if the spectral condition number $\kappa(K)$ is large. Since the perturbations we are concerned with are always some kind of error, we would obviously like $\kappa(K)$ to be small, i.e., we would like K to be *well-conditioned*.

Stability of Gaussian Elimination

We have seen that in solving the system $K\alpha = G$ by Gaussian elimination, as defined by (6.1) and (6.3), we are effectively performing the factorization $K = LU$ and solving triangular systems whose coefficient matrices are L and U. Because of rounding errors caused by the finite precision of the computer, however, the factors actually obtained—we denote them $\hat{L}$ and $\hat{U}$—are not identical to L and U. We introduce as a measure of precision the parameter ε_M, which we define to be the smallest of the floating-point numbers x of the computer such that the computed value of $1 + x$ is greater than 1. The value of ε_M is about β^{1-t}, where β is the base of the floating-point number representation of the computer and t is the number of digits in the mantissa. (The precise value of ε_M depends upon details of hardware such as whether the computer "rounds" or "chops.")

According to the modification in Reid (1971) of a rounding error analysis in Wilkinson (1965), the matrix $F^{(1)}$ defined by $K = \hat{L}\hat{U} + F^{(1)}$ has entries bounded by

$$|f_{ij}^{(1)}| \leq \begin{cases} c_{ij}(i-1) & \text{for } j \geq i, \\ c_{ij}j & \text{for } j < i, \end{cases} \tag{6.41}$$

where

$$c_{ij} = 3.01\varepsilon_M \max_r |k_{ij}^{(r)}|,$$

$k_{ij}^{(r)}$ being defined in (6.1).

Introducing the "growth factor"

$$q \equiv \max_{i,j,r} |k_{ij}^{(r)}| / \max_{ij} |k_{ij}| \geq 1, \tag{6.42}$$

we have

$$c_{ij} \leq 3.01\varepsilon_M q \max_{ij} |k_{ij}|,$$

and a simple calculation establishes that

$$\|F^{(1)}\|_\infty \leq 3.01(\tfrac{1}{2}N + 1)(N - 1)\varepsilon_M q \max_{ij} |k_{ij}|.$$

It turns out in practice that even for nonsparse matrices this rigorous bound is very pessimistic, a more realistic bound being

$$\|F^{(1)}\|_\infty \lesssim N\varepsilon_M q \max_{ij} |k_{ij}|. \tag{6.43}$$

Regarding sparse matrices, note that $f_{ij}^{(1)} = 0$ if $k_{ij} = 0$ and if no fill-in occurs in position (i, j).

The purpose of pivoting in Gaussian elimination is to control the size of q. When K is positive definite, however, then $q = 1$ (Exercise 6.8) and pivoting for this purpose is unnecessary.

It can be established that the computed solution $\hat{\alpha}$ of the system $K\alpha = G$ is the exact solution of $(K + F)\hat{\alpha} = G$, where $F = F^{(1)} + F^{(2)}$, $F^{(2)}$ expressing the rounding errors that arise in solving the two triangular systems of equations. $\|F^{(2)}\|_\infty$ is typically very small, and the bound in (6.43) is usually also valid for $\|F\|_\infty$. For positive definite systems we can thus expect

$$\|F\|_\infty \lesssim N\varepsilon_M \max_{ij} |k_{ij}| \quad \text{and} \quad \|F\| \lesssim N\varepsilon_M \max_{ij} |k_{ij}|,$$

the latter result following from the inequality $\|F\| \leq \|F\|_\infty$.

It is customary in numerical linear algebra to call a computational method *numerically stable*, or simply *stable*, if the computed solution is the exact solution of a small perturbation of the given problem. By this definition the stability of Gaussian elimination depends on the size of F in relation to K. For finite element problems in two space dimensions we have, by Section 5.5,

$$N = O(h^{-2}), \qquad \max_{ij} |k_{ij}| = O(h^0),$$

where h is the greatest element edge length, yielding

$$\|F\| = O(h^{-2}\varepsilon_M).$$

This result is unduly pessimistic since it is based on (6.43), which does not take sparsity into account. Numerical experiments with finite element matrices point to a smaller bound, namely,

$$\|F\| = O(h^{-1}\varepsilon_M).$$

[see, e.g., Jankowski and Wozniakowski (1977) and Axelsson and Gustafsson (1981).] We see even from this improved bound, however, that despite the optimal growth factor $q = 1$, Gaussian elimination tends to become less stable as the mesh is refined. (The assertion of the stability of incomplete factorization in Theorem 1.15, being based exclusively on the growth factor, must correspondingly be accepted with reservation.)

Effects of the Various Errors

We can now assess the influence of the four types of errors mentioned at the beginning of this section. The system of equations given to the equation solver is not actually $K\alpha = G$, but

$$(K + E)\tilde{\alpha} = G + H, \qquad (6.44)$$

where E and H are the accumulated errors of the first three types. Errors of the fourth type, the rounding errors incurred in the process of solving (6.44), have the effect that the final computed solution $\hat{\alpha}$ satisfies exactly a system of the form

$$(K + E + F)\hat{\alpha} = G + H. \qquad (6.45)$$

Since (6.45) is a perturbation of $K\alpha = G$, we can apply (6.40) to obtain

$$\frac{\|\hat{\alpha} - \alpha\|}{\|\alpha\|} \leq \frac{\kappa(K)}{1 - a}\left\{\frac{\|E + F\|}{\|K\|} + \frac{\|H\|}{\|G\|}\right\}, \qquad (6.46)$$

provided that

$$a \equiv \kappa(K) \frac{\|E + F\|}{\|K\|} < 1.$$

It must be stressed that this is a "worst-case" result and that the actual value of $\|\hat{\alpha} - \alpha\|/\|\alpha\|$ can be very much less than this bound. [Note that in (6.37) $\|\delta\alpha\|/\|\alpha\|$ *could* attain the lower bound, which is proportional to $\kappa(K)^{-1}$.]

We now consider a finite element problem in two space dimensions. Errors in data frequently dominate E, and typically

$$\max_{ij} |e_{ij}| = O(1), \qquad h \to 0.$$

Since we then have

$$\max_{ij} |k_{ij} + e_{ij}| = O(1), \qquad h \to 0,$$

the previous discussion of stability in Gaussian elimination indicates that $\|F\| = O(h^{-1})$. Finally, the analysis of Section 5.5 has established that $\|K\| = O(1)$ and $\kappa(K) = O(h^{-2})$, and combining all of these results we obtain $a = O(h^{-3})$.

Thus, we can easily have $a \geq 1$, in which case there is no guaranteed accuracy at all in $\hat{\alpha}$. This situation can arise even without rounding errors in the equation solver. If, for example, errors in data make $\|E\|/\|K\| = 10^{-3}$ and if $\kappa(K) = 2000$, then $a = 2$. Despite the fact that (6.46) is often a very pessimistic bound, there is an obvious danger of significant error in the computed vector $\hat{\alpha}$ when h is small.

Causes of a Large Spectral Condition Number

Each of the following factors tends to make the value of $\kappa(K)$ large:

(1)   a fine mesh,
(2)   lack of smoothness in the data of the original boundary value problem (from discontinuous material coefficients, for example),
(3)   an irregular mesh geometry in the sense of a sharp variation in the lengths of element edges.

The first has already been considered. The reason for refining the mesh is to reduce the discretization error. However, since refining the mesh increases the influence of the four types of errors mentioned at the beginning of this section, there is a point at which further mesh refinement is useless.

To illustrate the effect of lack of smoothness in the data, we consider the simple problem

$$-[p(x)u']' = g(x), \qquad 0 < x < 1, \quad u'(0) = u(1) = 0, \qquad (6.47)$$

where, for some $\varepsilon > 0$, $p(x)$ is the step function

$$p(x) = \begin{cases} 1/2 & \text{for} \quad 0 \le x \le 1/2, \\ \varepsilon/2 & \text{for} \quad 1/2 < x \le 1. \end{cases}$$

The solution $\hat{u}$ of (6.47) is the unique function in V that satisfies $a(\hat{u}, v) = G(v) \; \forall v \in V$, where

$$V = \{u \in H^1(0, 1); u(1) = 0\},$$

$$a(u, v) = \int_0^1 p(x)u'v' \, dx, \qquad G(v) = \int_0^1 g(x)v \, dx.$$

Introducing the piecewise linear basis functions, we find by a simple calculation that if $p(x)$ is constant in an element e_l of length h, then the corresponding element matrix is

$$K^{(l)} = h^{-1}p \begin{bmatrix} 1 & -1 \\ -1 & 1 \end{bmatrix}.$$

For a mesh consisting of just the two elements $e_1 = [0, \frac{1}{2}]$ and $e_2 = [\frac{1}{2}, 1]$, we have

$$K^{(1)} = \begin{bmatrix} 1 & -1 \\ -1 & 1 \end{bmatrix}, \qquad K^{(2)} = \begin{bmatrix} \varepsilon & -\varepsilon \\ -\varepsilon & \varepsilon \end{bmatrix},$$

and the assembly of K yields

$$K = \begin{bmatrix} 1 & -1 \\ -1 & 1 + \varepsilon \end{bmatrix}. \qquad (6.48)$$

(Note that because of the boundary condition $u(1) = 0$, we have been able to reduce the order of K from 3 to 2.) If $\varepsilon = 0$ then K is obviously singular. A simple computation establishes that

$$\kappa(K) = (1/\varepsilon)[1 + \tfrac{1}{2}\varepsilon + \sqrt{1 + (\tfrac{1}{2}\varepsilon)^2}]^2 \simeq 4/\varepsilon, \qquad 0 < \varepsilon \ll 1.$$

Thus, depending on the physical parameter ε, the condition number can be arbitrarily large.

We have here a simple illustration of the importance of ε_M, the floating-point precision of the computer. If $\varepsilon < \varepsilon_M$ then the computed value of $1 + \varepsilon$ is 1, making the stiffness matrix singular. All information regarding $p(x)$ in the subinterval $[\frac{1}{2}, 1]$ has been lost due to finite precision.

Regarding the influence of an irregular mesh geometry, consider the application of piecewise linear basis functions to the problem

$$-u'' = g(x), \qquad 0 < x < 1, \quad u'(0) = u(1) = 0,$$

with the elements $e_1 = [0, h]$ and $e_2 = [h, 1]$. The element matrices are

$$K^{(1)} = h^{-1} \begin{bmatrix} 1 & -1 \\ -1 & 1 \end{bmatrix}, \qquad K^{(2)} = (1 - h)^{-1} \begin{bmatrix} 1 & -1 \\ -1 & 1 \end{bmatrix},$$

and the assembled stiffness matrix is

$$K = \begin{bmatrix} h^{-1} & -h^{-1} \\ -h^{-1} & h^{-1} + (1 - h)^{-1} \end{bmatrix} = h^{-1} \begin{bmatrix} 1 & -1 \\ -1 & 1 + \rho \end{bmatrix},$$

where $\rho = h/(1 - h)$. The spectral condition number, which is the same as that for (6.48), is unbounded for $\rho \to 0$ and $\rho \to \infty$. Hence, the choice of element dimensions can make the condition number arbitrarily large.

Precautions and Remedies

(1)   A good rule is to avoid unnecessarily irregular mesh geometries. This means avoiding very large and small angles (triangular elements) and large and small edge ratios (rectangular elements).

(2)   In Fried (1971) it is observed that although the condition number $\kappa(K)$ increases as a power of N, it is relatively insensitive to the degree of the polynomial basis functions. This suggests the use of high-degree polynomials on a fairly coarse mesh.

(3)   Double-precision computation naturally yields greater accuracy, but at the expense of a considerable increase in storage and computing time.

(4)   Accuracy can often be improved by the technique of *iterative refinement* defined in the case of the Cholesky factorization by

$$\mathbf{r}^k = K\boldsymbol{\alpha}^k - \mathbf{G}, \tag{6.49a}$$

$$(\tilde{L}_0 \tilde{L}_0^{\mathrm{T}})\mathbf{d}^k = -\mathbf{r}^k, \tag{6.49b}$$

$$\boldsymbol{\alpha}^{k+1} = \boldsymbol{\alpha}^k + \mathbf{d}^k, \tag{6.49c}$$

for $k = 0, 1, \ldots$, where $\tilde{L}_0$ and $\boldsymbol{\alpha}^0$ denote the computed Cholesky factor and computed solution, respectively, obtained using single-precision arithmetic. The ability of iterative refinement to produce a more accurate solution vector depends crucially on how the computation of the *residual vector* $\mathbf{r}^k$ in step

(6.49a) is implemented. Methods for performing this step are described in Section 7.4. See, in particular, (7.53) and (7.54). (These formulas are applicable since the gradient and residual vectors are identical.) Because K and $\tilde{L}_0$ must be stored simultaneously, extra storage space is required for K. (Note, however, that K can be stored more economically than $\tilde{L}_0$ since it does not contain fill-in. The row-ordered list of Fig. 1.8 is suitable for K.) Regarding computational labor, we note that step (6.49b) involves the solution of two triangular systems of equations. Normally only a few iterations are necessary, and the total work is dominated by the initial single-precision factorization of K. It is important to mention that iterative refinement, with proper computation of the residual vector, is able to reduce the influence of even errors in K and $\mathbf{G}$. See Section 7.4 for further discussion of this point. Although the analysis there is in the context of the conjugate gradient method, it applies equally to iterative refinement.

The Cholesky factorization can of course be replaced by the Gauss factorization. Further, in an effort to reduce storage at the expense of a larger number of iterations one can replace either of these factorizations by an "incomplete" version. One approach to this—illustrated in Section 1.4—is to limit fill-in to prescribed positions in the matrix. Another is to limit fill-in according to value, i.e., a fill-in is accepted (regardless of its position) if its absolute value exceeds a prescribed value. [See Zlatev and Nielsen (1977a,b); in Axelsson and Munksgaard (1979) this technique is used to obtain a preconditioning matrix for the conjugate gradient method.] In the absence of rounding errors, iterative refinement produces the solution of the system of equations provided that the spectral radius of $(I - C^{-1}K)$ is less than unity, C denoting the product of the approximate factors.

Remarks

1. Let K be an $(N \times N)$ positive definite matrix, and let S be the set of all $(N \times N)$ real diagonal matrices. We define the *minimum condition number* of K to be

$$\overset{*}{\kappa}(K) = \min_{D \in S} \kappa(DKD).$$

Suppose that we wish to solve a system of equations $K\alpha = \mathbf{G}$, where $\overset{*}{\kappa}(K)$ is considerably less than $\kappa(K)$, and suppose we know a diagonal matrix D such that

$$\overset{*}{\kappa}(K) \leq \kappa(DKD) < \kappa(K).$$

[The matrix $D \equiv \mathrm{diag}(k_{11}^{-1/2}, \ldots, k_{NN}^{-1/2})$ often has this property.] Since

$$K\alpha = \mathbf{G} \quad \Leftrightarrow \quad K_1\alpha_1 = \mathbf{G}_1,$$

where $K_1 = DKD$, $\alpha_1 = D^{-1}\alpha$, and $\mathbf{G}_1 = D\mathbf{G}$, we could proceed by computing K_1 and $\mathbf{G}_1$, applying the symmetric Gauss or Cholesky method to $K_1\alpha_1 = \mathbf{G}_1$, and then computing $\alpha = D\alpha_1$. The transformation from the original system to the new one, known as diagonal scaling, would seem sensible in view of the importance we have attached to a small condition number. Numerical experience indicates, however, that diagonal scaling in the context of finite element problems has little effect on rounding errors in the computed value of α. In fact, in the case of Gaussian elimination without pivoting as defined by (6.1), (6.3), it has no effect whatever when the entries $d_{11}, \ldots, d_{NN}$ are powers of β, the floating-point base (Bauer, 1963; Forsythe and Moler, 1967).

2. Criteria are suggested in Irons (1968) for assessing the seriousness of rounding errors during the computation.

3. A rough approximation to the condition number $\kappa(K) \equiv \lambda_N/\lambda_1$ can be computed without excessive extra labor once K has been factorized. λ_N is often well approximated by $\|K\|_\infty$, and λ_1 can be found by *inverse iteration*, which in the case of the Cholesky factorization $K = \tilde{L}\tilde{L}^T$ is performed as follows: choose an initial vector $\mathbf{v}^0$ and for $k = 1, 2, 3, \ldots$

(1) solve $\tilde{L}\mathbf{u}^k = \mathbf{v}^{k-1}$,
(2) solve $\tilde{L}^T\mathbf{w}^k = \mathbf{u}^k$,
(3) compute $\xi^{(k)} = \|\mathbf{w}^k\|$,
(4) compute $\mathbf{v}^k = \mathbf{w}^k/\xi^{(k)}$.

It is easy to show that $\xi^{(k)} \to \lambda_1^{-1}$ and $\mathbf{v}^k \to \mathbf{v}_1$ for $k \to \infty$. After a few iterations, $\xi^{(k)-1}$ is often a good approximation to λ_1.

The smallest eigenvalue of the operator $\mathscr{L}$ in the original differential equation $\mathscr{L}u = f$ may have a known lower bound that is a good approximation to λ_1.

4. The "natural factor formulation" approach described in Argyris and Brønlund (1975) for solving the system $K\alpha = \mathbf{G}$ effectively involves a condition number of only $\kappa(K)^{1/2}$. See the reference for details.

5. For further reading on errors in solving finite element equations see Argyris et al. (1976), Martin and Harrold (1976), and Roy (1971, 1972).

Exercises

6.1. Write a segment of program code that computes the product $\mathbf{y} \equiv K\mathbf{x}$, where K is an $N \times N$ symmetric matrix stored in variable bandwidth form. Use single-indexed arrays of N words each for $\mathbf{x}$ and $\mathbf{y}$.

6.2. Draw the matrix graphs associated with the finite element meshes (a)–(d) shown in the accompanying illustrations.

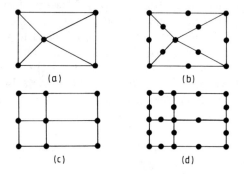

CHECK: The number of graph edges is 8, 48, 20, and 100, respectively. In Exercises 6.3–6.6 we employ the following terminology:

$$\text{OCM ordering,} \quad \text{"ordinary" Cuthill–McKee ordering;}$$

$$\text{RCM ordering,} \quad \text{reverse Cuthill–McKee ordering.}$$

6.3. One of the node orderings (a)–(c) shown in the accompanying illustration is an OCM ordering. Which one? How many other OCM orderings have the same initial node?

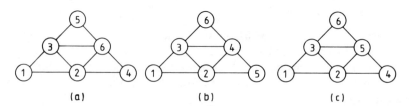

6.4. The graph shown in the accompanying illustration has an OCM ordering. Derive directly from the graph the values of the half-bandwidth $w(K)$ and the envelope parameter $e(K)$. Then write down the matrix, indicating nonzero entries by $\times$.

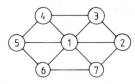

By reversing this ordering we obtain an RCM ordering. Repeat the exercise for this new ordering. Is every RCM ordering also an OCM ordering?

6.5. The application of piecewise linear basis functions on isosceles right-triangular elements to Poisson's equation $-\Delta u = g(x, y)$ on an L-shaped domain can lead to the accompanying graph. Starting at A, determine an RCM ordering of nodes and from this derive the associated values of $w(K)$ and $e(K)$. Write down the matrix and partition it by level sets, as illustrated in Fig. 6.6.

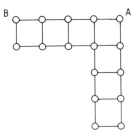

Repeat this procedure for B.

6.6. The graph of an $N \times N$ symmetric matrix K can be conveniently stored in the form of a row-ordered list as shown in the accompanying illustration for graph (a) of Exercise 6.3.†

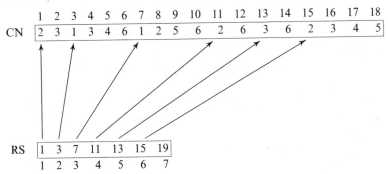

The nodes connected to node I are $CN(K_1)$, $CN(K_1 + 1)$, $CN(K_1 + 2)$, ..., $CN(K_2)$, where $K_1 = RS(I)$ and $K_2 = RS(I + 1) - 1$. (Compare with Fig. 1.8 in Section 1.4 and note that if we store all nonzero entries above and below the main diagonal of K in a row-ordered list and then remove the array of entry values, we are left with the above storage scheme for the graph of K.)

(i) Write a piece of program code that, for a given graph and a given node number, determines the level structure rooted at that node. The level structure can be stored in two arrays analogous to CN and RS, one containing all node numbers in order of increasing level number and the other containing "pointers" to the beginning of each level.

(ii) Extend the code of (i) to determine first an OCM ordering based on the given node and then the corresponding RCM ordering. A possible storage scheme for any new ordering of nodes is an array P where $P(I)$ is the original node number of the node labeled I in the new ordering.

† For reading on the computer analysis of matrix graphs see George and Liu (1981).

6.7. An alternative definition of the concept "envelope" is shown in the accompanying illustration. What property of Gaussian elimination makes this definition useless for our purpose?

6.8. Let K be an $N \times N$ positive definite matrix. One step of Gaussian elimination produces the matrix

$$K^{(2)} = \begin{bmatrix} k_{11} & k_{12} & \cdots & k_{1N} \\ \hline 0 & & & \\ \vdots & & \tilde{K}^{(2)} & \\ 0 & & & \end{bmatrix},$$

where the entries of $\tilde{K}^{(2)}$ are

$$k_{ij}^{(2)} \equiv k_{ij} - \frac{k_{i1}k_{1j}}{k_{11}}, \qquad i, j = 2, 3, \ldots, N.$$

(i) By considering the inequality $\mathbf{x}^T K \mathbf{x} > 0$ for suitable vectors $\mathbf{x}$, establish that $k_{ii} > 0$, $k_{ij}^2 \leq k_{ii}k_{jj}$ for $i, j = 1, 2, \ldots, N$, and hence that $\max_{ij}|k_{ij}| = \max_i k_{ii}$.

(ii) Show that $k_{ii}^{(2)} \leq k_{ii}$ for $i = 2, 3, \ldots, N$.

(iii) By considering the matrix RKR^T, where

$$r_{ij} = \begin{cases} 1 & \text{for} \quad i = j, \\ -k_{i1}/k_{11} & \text{for} \quad j = 1, \quad i = 2, 3, \ldots, N, \\ 0 & \text{otherwise}, \end{cases}$$

show that $\tilde{K}^{(2)}$ is positive definite.

(iv) Deduce the following equality for the entire Gaussian elimination process:

$$\max_{i,j,r} |k_{ij}^{(r)}| = \max_i k_{ii}.$$

(v) Show that if $\tilde{K} = PKP^T$, where P is any permutation matrix, then

$$\max_{i,j,r} |\tilde{k}_{ij}^{(r)}| = \max_i k_{ii}$$

and

$$\kappa(\tilde{K}) = \kappa(K).$$

Because of these properties, symmetric pivoting is unnecessary when K is a positive definite matrix.

6.9. Derive from the Cholesky factorization $K = \tilde{L}\tilde{L}^{\mathrm{T}}$ the relations

$$\|\tilde{L}\| = \|\tilde{L}^{\mathrm{T}}\| = \|K\|^{1/2}, \qquad \|\tilde{L}^{-1}\| = \|\tilde{L}^{-\mathrm{T}}\| = \|K^{-1}\|^{1/2}$$

and hence

$$\kappa(\tilde{L}) = \kappa(\tilde{L}^{\mathrm{T}}) = \kappa(K)^{1/2}.$$

6.10. Let K be a symmetric positive definite band matrix stored as shown in Fig. 6.2.

(i) The code of Fig. 6.9 performs the factorization $K = LDL^{\mathrm{T}}$ when K is stored in an $N \times N$ array. Rewrite the code for the given storage scheme.

(ii) Write a piece of code that solves the system $(LDL^{\mathrm{T}})\alpha = G$.

6.11. Repeat the preceding exercise for the case when K is stored as a variable bandwidth matrix (see Fig. 6.3).

6.12. Let K be an $N \times N$ nonsingular matrix all of whose principal minors are non-zero, and consider the system of equations $K\alpha = G$ in the partitioned form

$$\begin{array}{c} p \\ N-p \end{array} \updownarrow \begin{array}{c} \overset{p}{\longleftrightarrow} \quad \overset{N-p}{\longleftrightarrow} \\ \begin{bmatrix} K_{11} & K_{12} \\ K_{21} & K_{22} \end{bmatrix} \end{array} \begin{bmatrix} \alpha_1 \\ \alpha_2 \end{bmatrix} = \begin{bmatrix} G_1 \\ G_2 \end{bmatrix}.$$

By the process of "block" Gaussian elimination, we can eliminate α_1 to obtain the reduced system

$$\hat{K}_{22}\alpha_2 = \hat{G}_2, \qquad \hat{K}_{22} \equiv K_{22} - K_{21}K_{11}^{-1}K_{12}, \qquad \hat{G}_2 \equiv G_2 - K_{21}K_{11}^{-1}G_1.$$

On the other hand, p steps of "ordinary" Gaussian elimination produce a reduced system that we denote $\tilde{K}_{22}\alpha_2 = \tilde{G}_2$. Prove that $\hat{K}_{22} = \tilde{K}_{22}$ and $\hat{G}_2 = \tilde{G}_2$.

HINT: Use the partitioned form of the factorization $K = LU$ to derive the relation $\hat{K}_{22} = K_{22} - L_{21}U_{12}$. Derive from (6.1), by recursion, the relation $\tilde{K}_{22} = K_{22} - L_{21}U_{12}$.

6.13. We consider the finite element mesh shown in the accompanying illustration.

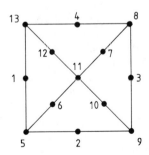

Let K denote the associated stiffness matrix. By analyzing the Gaussian elimination process applied to K, show that the lower triangular factor L in the factorization

$K = LDL^T$ has the following format ("$\otimes$" denotes a fill-in):

$$
\begin{array}{c}
\quad\quad\quad\; 1\;\; 2\;\; 3\;\; 4\;\; 5\;\; 6\;\; 7\;\; 8\;\; 9\;\; 10\; 11\; 12\; 13 \\
\begin{array}{c}
1 \\ 2 \\ 3 \\ 4 \\ 5 \\ 6 \\ 7 \\ 8 \\ 9 \\ 10 \\ 11 \\ 12 \\ 13
\end{array}
\left[
\begin{array}{ccccccccccccc}
\times & & & & & & & & & & & & \\
 & \times & & & & & & & & & & & \\
 & & \times & & & & & & & & & & \\
 & & & \times & & & & & & & & & \\
\times & \times & & & \times & & & & & & & & \\
\times & \times & & & \times & \times & & & & & & & \\
 & & \times & \times & & & \times & & & & & & \\
 & & \times & \times & & & \times & \times & & & & & \\
 & \times & \times & & \times & \times & \times & \times & \times & & & & \\
 & \times & \times & & \times & \times & \times & \times & \times & \times & & & \\
\times & \times & \times & \times & \times & \times & \times & \times & \times & \times & \times & & \\
\times & & & & \times & \times & \times & \times & \times & \times & \otimes & \otimes & \times & \times \\
\times & & & & \times & \times & \times & \times & \times & \times & \otimes & \otimes & \times & \times & \times
\end{array}
\right]
\end{array}
$$

6.14. A connected matrix graph without loops is called a *tree*.

(i) Given a symmetric positive definite matrix K of the form

$$
K =
\begin{bmatrix}
\times & & & & & \times \\
 & \times & & & & \times \\
 & & \times & & & \times \\
 & & & \times & & \times \\
 & & & & \times & \times \\
\times & \times & \times & \times & \times & \times
\end{bmatrix},
$$

show that
(a)   the graph of K is a tree,
(b)   there is no fill-in when Gaussian elimination is applied to K,
(c)   if the nodes of the graph are reordered and Gaussian elimination is applied to the new matrix, then fill-in usually occurs.

(ii) Construct examples to verify the fact that if the graph of a positive definite matrix K is a tree and if the nodes of the graph are suitably ordered, then Gaussian elimination produces no fill-in and

$$l_{ij} = k_{ij}/(l_{jj}d_{jj}), \qquad i > j,$$

where $K = LDL^T$ (Parter, 1961; George and Liu, 1981).

Note that (6.28b) expresses this relation in terms of the Cholesky factorization at the submatrix level.

6.15. Extend the computational procedure given following (6.29b) to include the details for solving $\tilde{L}^T \boldsymbol{\alpha} = \boldsymbol{\beta}$.

6.16. Suggest how the concept of a level structure can be applied to the problem of determining a one-way dissection ordering.

6.17. We consider the finite element mesh shown in Fig. 6.14. If the boundary condition is of the Dirichlet type, then we can work with a stiffness matrix K of order only 49. A nested dissection ordering of the associated graph is shown in the accompanying illustration. An alternative ordering is the row-wise one illustrated in Fig. 6.5c.

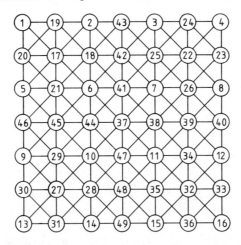

(i)   Compute $w(K)$ and $e(K)$ for each of these orderings. Are either of the storage schemes for band matrices described in Section 6.1 practical in the case of the nested dissection ordering?

(ii)   For each of the orderings determine where fill-in occurs when Gaussian elimination is applied to K.

6.18. Show that the computational labor and storage associated with nested dissection orderings of a finite element mesh of n^3 cubes are $O(n^6)$ and $O(n^4)$, respectively.

6.19. Use the eigensolutions of K to derive the inequalities (6.37).

6.20. We consider the relations

$$K\alpha = G, \qquad (K + \delta K)(\alpha + \delta\alpha) = G,$$

where K is a nonsingular matrix.

(i)   A well-known theorem of linear algebra states that if B is any matrix with the property $\|B\| < 1$, then $(I - B)$ is nonsingular and $\|(I - B)^{-1}\| \le (1 - \|B\|)^{-1}$. Use this theorem to show that if (6.38a) holds, then $(K + \delta K)$ is nonsingular. Note that (6.39a) implies (6.38a).

(ii)   Show by an example that $(K + \delta K)$ may be singular if $\|\delta K\| = \|K^{-1}\|^{-1}$.

(iii)   Use the relation $\delta\alpha = -(K + \delta K)^{-1} \delta K \, \alpha$ and the above theorem to derive (6.39b).

(iv)   Derive the inequality $\|\delta\alpha\|/\|\alpha + \delta\alpha\| \le \kappa(K)\|\delta K\|/\|K\|$.

6.21. Derive (6.40).

6.22. We consider the boundary value problem

$$-(pu')' = g, \qquad 0 < x < 1,$$

$$u(0) = u_0, \qquad u'(1) = 0.$$

Using piecewise linear basis functions defined on a mesh with elements $e_1 = [0, 1 - h]$, $e_2 = [1 - h, 1]$, we obtain the system

$$(c_1 + c_2)\alpha_1 - c_2\alpha_2 = G_1 + c_1 u_0, \qquad -c_2\alpha_1 + c_2\alpha_2 = G_2,$$

where

$$c_1 = (1 - h)^{-2} \int_0^{1-h} p \, dx, \qquad c_2 = h^{-2} \int_{1-h}^1 p \, dx,$$

$$G_1 = (1 - h)^{-1} \int_0^{1-h} gx \, dx + h^{-1} \int_{1-h}^1 g(1 - x) \, dx,$$

$$G_2 = h^{-1} \int_{1-h}^1 g(x - 1 + h) \, dx.$$

Since $c_1 = O(1)$, $c_2 = O(h^{-1})$, $G_1 = O(1)$, $G_2 = O(h)$, and $h \to 0$, the exact solution of the system satisfies

$$\alpha_1 = u_0 + c_1^{-1}(G_1 + G_2) = u_0 + O(1),$$

$$\alpha_2 = \alpha_1 + c_2^{-1}G_2 = \alpha_1 + O(h^2).$$

We assume in the following that c_1, c_2, G_1, and G_2 are calculated by numerical integration with relative errors $O(h^2)$.

(i)   Show that the associated matrix

$$K = \begin{bmatrix} (c_1 + c_2) & -c_2 \\ -c_2 & c_2 \end{bmatrix}$$

has a spectral condition number $O(h^{-1})$ and hence, in general, the relative error due to error in data using, for instance, Gaussian elimination is not better than $O(h)$ (even if all numerical calculations are done exactly).

(ii)   Now use iterative refinement (6.49). Assume that the initial approximations $\alpha_1^{(0)}$, $\alpha_2^{(0)}$ are correct up to errors $O(h)$. Show that the residual will then in general have absolute errors $O(h)$ and hence, by (6.35), the corrected solution has errors $O(h)$ due to errors in data. [Note that $\|K^{-1}\| = O(1)$.] Hence, we did not improve upon the result of (i).

(iii)   Now use the following way of calculating the residual:

$$K\alpha^0 \qquad G = \begin{bmatrix} c_2(\alpha_1^{(0)} - \alpha_2^{(0)}) + c_1(\alpha_1^{(0)} - u_0) - G_1 \\ c_2(\alpha_2^{(0)} - \alpha_1^{(0)}) - G_2 \end{bmatrix}.$$

Show that the absolute errors (due to errors in data) in the residual are now $O(h^2)$ and hence, by (6.35), that the solution corrected by one step of iterative refinement has errors $O(h^2)$.

REMARK: Note that in (iii) we have avoided the cancellation when calculating $(c_1 + c_2)\alpha_1^{(0)} - c_2\alpha_2^{(0)}$ that occurs in (ii).

References

Argyris, J. H., and Brønlund, O. E. (1975). The natural factor formulation of the stiffness for the matrix displacement method. *Comput. Methods Appl. Mech. Engrg.* **5,** 97–119.

Argyris, J. H., Johnson, T. L., Rosanoff, R. A., and Roy, J. R. (1976). On numerical error in the finite element method. *Comput. Methods Appl. Mech. Engrg.* **7,** 261–282.

Axelsson, O., and Gustafsson, I. (1981). A preconditioned conjugate gradient method for finite element equations which is stable for rounding errors. *In* "Information Processing 80" (S. H. Lavington, ed.), pp. 723–728. North-Holland Publ., Amsterdam.

Axelsson, O., and Munksgaard, N. (1979). A class of preconditioned conjugate gradient methods for the solution of a mixed finite element discretization of the biharmonic operator. *Internat. J. Numer. Methods Engrg.* **14,** 1001–1019.

Bathe, K.-J., and Wilson, E. L. (1976). "Numerical Methods in Finite Element Analysis." Prentice-Hall, Englewood Cliffs, New Jersey.

Bauer, F. L. (1963). Optimal scaling and the importance of minimal condition. *In* "Information Processing 1962" (C. M. Poppelwell, ed.), pp. 198–200. North-Holland Publ., Amsterdam.

Cuthill, E., and McKee, J. (1969). Reducing the bandwidth of sparse symmetric matrices. ACM Proceedings of the 24th National Conference, New York.

Dodds, R. H., and Lopez, L. A. (1980). Substructuring in linear and nonlinear analysis. *Internat. J. Numer. Methods Engrg.* **15,** 583–597.

Duff, I. S. (1982). Sparse matrix software for elliptic pde's. *In* "Multigrid Methods" (W. Hackbusch and U. Trottenberg, eds.), LNiM vol. 960, pp. 410–426. Springer-Verlag, Berlin and New York.

Duff, I. S. (1983). A survey of sparse matrix software. *In* "Sources and Development of Mathematical Software" (W. R. Cowell, ed.), pp. 64–98. Prentice-Hall, Englewood Cliffs, New Jersey.

Eisenstat, S. C., Gursky, M. C., Schultz, M. H., and Sherman, A. H. (1982). Yale sparse matrix package I: the symmetric codes. *Internat. J. Numer. Methods Engrg.* **18,** 1145–1151.

Forsythe, G. E., and Moler, C. B. (1967). "Computer Solution of Linear Algebraic Systems." Prentice-Hall, Englewood Cliffs, New Jersey.

Fried, I. (1971). Discretization and computational errors in high-order finite elements. *AIAA J.* **9,** 2071–2073.

George, A. (1973). Nested dissection of a regular finite element mesh. *SIAM J. Numer. Anal.* **10,** 345–363.

George, A. (1977a). Solution of linear systems of equations: direct methods for finite element problems. *In* "Sparse Matrix Techniques" (V. A. Barker, ed.), LNiM vol. 572, pp. 52–101. Springer-Verlag, Berlin and New York.

George, A. (1977b). Numerical experiments using dissection methods to solve $n \times n$ grid problems. *SIAM J. Numer. Anal.* **14,** 161–179.

George, A., and Liu, J. W. (1979). An implementation of a pseudo-peripheral node finder. *ACM Trans. Math. Software* **5,** 286–295.

George, A., and Liu, J. W. (1981). "Computer Solution of Large Sparse Positive Definite Systems." Prentice-Hall, Englewood Cliffs, New Jersey.

George, A., Liu, J. W., and Ng, E. (1980). User guide for SPARSPAK: Waterloo sparse linear equation package. Report CS-78-30 (revised Jan. 1980), Department of Computer Science, University of Waterloo, Waterloo, Canada.

Gibbs, N. E., Poole, W. G., and Stockmeyer, P. K. (1976). An algorithm for reducing the bandwidth and profile of a sparse matrix. *SIAM J. Numer. Anal.* **13**, 236–250.

Heath, M. T., ed. (1982). "Sparse Matrix Software Catalog." Mathematics and Statistics Research Department, Oak Ridge National Laboratory, Oak Ridge, Tennessee.

Hoffman, A. J., Martin, M. S., and Rose, D. J. (1973). Complexity bounds for regular finite difference and finite element grids. *SIAM J. Numer. Anal.* **10**, 364–369.

Irons, B. M. (1968). Roundoff criteria in direct stiffness solutions. *AIAA J.* **6**, 1308–1312.

Irons, B. M. (1970). A frontal solution program for finite element analysis. *Internat. J. Numer. Methods Engrg.* **2**, 5–32.

Irons, B. M., and Ahmad, S. (1980). "Techniques of Finite Elements." Ellis Horwood Ltd., Chichester, England.

Jankowski, M., and Wozniakowski, H. (1977). Iterative refinement implies numerical stability. *BIT* **17**, 303–311.

Jennings, A. (1977). "Matrix Computation for Engineers and Scientists." Wiley, New York.

Lipton, R. J., Rose, D. J., and Tarjan, R. E. (1979). Generalized nested dissection. *SIAM J. Numer. Anal.* **16**, 346–358.

Martin, C. W., and Harrold, A. J. (1976). Removal of truncation error in finite element analysis. *In* "The Mathematics of Finite Elements and Applications II" (J. R. Whiteman, ed.), pp. 525–533. Academic Press, New York.

Martin, R. S., Peters, G., and Wilkinson, J. H. (1965). Symmetric decomposition of a positive definite matrix. *Numer. Math.* **7**, 362–383.

Noor, A. K., Kamel, H. A., and Fulton, R. E. (1977). Substructuring techniques: status and projections. *Comput. and Structures* **8**, 621–632.

Parter, S. V. (1961). The use of linear graphs in Gaussian elimination. *SIAM Rev.* **3**, 119–130.

Reid, J. K. (1971). A note on the stability of Gaussian elimination. *J. Inst. Math. Appl.* **8**, 374–375.

Roy, J. R. (1971). Numerical error in structural solutions. *J. Struct. Div. ASCE* **97** (ST4), 1039–1054.

Roy, J. R. (1972). Numerical error in structural solutions (closure). *J. Struct. Div. ASCE* **98** (ST7), 1663–1665.

Strang, G. (1976). "Linear Algebra and Its Applications." Academic Press, New York.

Wilkinson, J. H. (1965). "The Algebraic Eigenvalue Problem." Oxford Univ. Press, London and New York.

Zlatev, Z., and Nielsen, H. B. (1977a). Preservation of sparsity in connection with iterative refinement. Report NI-77-12, Institute for Numerical Analysis, Technical University of Denmark. Lyngby, Denmark.

Zlatev, Z., and Nielsen, H. B. (1977b). SIRSM: A package for the solution of sparse systems by iterative refinement. Report NI-77-13, Institute for Numerical Analysis, Technical University of Denmark, Lyngby, Denmark.

CHAPTER 7

Iterative Solution
of Finite Element Equations

Introduction

In Chapter 1 we analyzed the conjugate gradient method for solving a positive definite system of equations, giving special attention to preconditioning by SSOR and incomplete factorization. In the present chapter we shall return to these topics, considering now the case in which the matrix of the system arises from the finite element treatment of a boundary value problem.

Section 7.1 is devoted to an analysis of the spectral condition number $\kappa(\tilde{K})$ associated with SSOR preconditioning, the quantity that determines the rate of convergence of the iterations. We find that for boundary value problems with smooth coefficients and a Dirichlet boundary condition, the use of piecewise linear or bilinear basis functions makes $\kappa(\tilde{K}) = O(h^{-1})$, where h is the greatest element edge length in the mesh. This is a great improvement (asymptotically) over $\kappa(K) = O(h^{-2})$, which determines the rate of convergence of the unpreconditioned conjugate gradient method. The same result cannot be established, however, for boundary value problems not having these properties.

Section 7.2 introduces a new variant of incomplete factorization and examines its use for preconditioning. It is found that $\kappa(\tilde{K}) = O(h^{-1})$ for a range of problems that includes discontinuous coefficients and a Neumann boundary condition, still under the assumption, however, that the basis functions are linear or bilinear. In Section 7.3 we show how the computation can be extended to the case of higher-degree basis functions without loss (with respect to the power of h) of rate of convergence.

Section 7.4 deals with the residual (or gradient) vector in the context of computational labor and numerical stability. Methods for computing this vector are given that, by exploiting special properties of the system of equations, are able to reduce the influence of both rounding errors and errors in data.

In Section 7.5 we compare the performance of iterative and direct methods for solving finite element systems of equations.

Section 7.6 gives a concise account of multigrid methods for solving finite element problems.

7.1   SSOR Preconditioning

Review and Extension of Results from Chapter 1

We saw in Chapter 1 that the rate of convergence of the simple conjugate gradient method applied to the system $K\alpha = \mathbf{G}$, where K is an $N \times N$ symmetric positive definite matrix, is described by

$$p(\varepsilon) \leq \tfrac{1}{2}\sqrt{\kappa(K)}\ln(2/\varepsilon) + 1,$$

$p(\varepsilon)$ being the smallest integer k for which

$$\|\alpha^k - \alpha\|_K \leq \varepsilon \|\alpha^0 - \alpha\|_K \qquad \forall \alpha^0 \in R^N.$$

It was further established that with optimal SSOR preconditioning (optimal with respect to the choice of ω) the rate of convergence becomes

$$p(\varepsilon) \leq \tfrac{1}{2}\sqrt{\kappa(\tilde{K})}\ln(2/\varepsilon) + 1$$

where, by (1.73c),

$$\kappa(\tilde{K}) \leq \sqrt{(\tfrac{1}{2} + \delta)\kappa(K)} + \tfrac{1}{2}. \tag{7.1}$$

The parameter δ is defined by

$$\delta = \max_{\mathbf{x} \neq \mathbf{0}} \mathbf{x}^{\mathrm{T}}(LD^{-1}L^{\mathrm{T}} - \tfrac{1}{4}D)\mathbf{x}/\mathbf{x}^{\mathrm{T}}K\mathbf{x},$$

D and L being the diagonal and strictly lower triangular parts of K, respectively. It was shown in Theorem 1.13 that $\delta \geq -\tfrac{1}{4}$, and that if

$$\|\tilde{L}\|_\infty \leq \tfrac{1}{2}, \qquad \|\tilde{L}^{\mathrm{T}}\|_\infty \leq \tfrac{1}{2}, \tag{7.2}$$

where

$$\tilde{L} = D^{-1/2}LD^{-1/2},$$

then $\delta \leq 0$.

A more detailed analysis of δ reveals that

$$\rho(\tilde{L}\tilde{L}^{\mathsf{T}}) \leq \tfrac{1}{4} \quad \Leftrightarrow \quad -\tfrac{1}{4} \leq \delta \leq 0,$$

$$\rho(\tilde{L}\tilde{L}^{\mathsf{T}}) > \tfrac{1}{4} \quad \Rightarrow \quad 0 < \delta \leq [\rho(\tilde{L}\tilde{L}^{\mathsf{T}}) - \tfrac{1}{4}]\kappa(K),$$

where $\rho(\tilde{L}\tilde{L}^{\mathsf{T}})$ is the spectral radius (i.e., largest eigenvalue) of $\tilde{L}\tilde{L}^{\mathsf{T}}$. (See the proof of Theorem 1.13 and Exercise 7.1.) Hence, if $\rho(\tilde{L}\tilde{L}^{\mathsf{T}}) \leq \tfrac{1}{4}$ then

$$\kappa(\tilde{K}) \leq \sqrt{\tfrac{1}{2}\kappa(K)} + \tfrac{1}{2}, \tag{7.3a}$$

whereas if $\rho(\tilde{L}\tilde{L}^{\mathsf{T}}) > \tfrac{1}{4}$ then,

$$\kappa(\tilde{K}) \leq \kappa(K)\sqrt{\rho(\tilde{L}\tilde{L}^{\mathsf{T}}) - \tfrac{1}{4} + \tfrac{1}{2}\kappa(K)^{-1}} + \tfrac{1}{2},$$

$$\simeq \kappa(K)\sqrt{\rho(\tilde{L}\tilde{L}^{\mathsf{T}}) - \tfrac{1}{4}}, \qquad \kappa(K) \gg 1. \tag{7.3b}$$

The inequalities

$$\rho(\tilde{L}\tilde{L}^{\mathsf{T}}) \leq \|\tilde{L}\tilde{L}^{\mathsf{T}}\|_{\infty} \leq \|\tilde{L}\|_{\infty} \cdot \|\tilde{L}^{\mathsf{T}}\|_{\infty} \tag{7.4}$$

are useful here since $\|\tilde{L}\|_{\infty}$, $\|\tilde{L}^{\mathsf{T}}\|_{\infty}$, and even $\|\tilde{L}\tilde{L}^{\mathsf{T}}\|_{\infty}$ can often be determined fairly easily, whereas to find $\rho(\tilde{L}\tilde{L}^{\mathsf{T}})$ one would have to employ a numerical method for eigenvalue computation (the "power method," for example). In particular, we can use the estimate

$$\kappa(\tilde{K}) \lesssim \kappa(K)\sqrt{\|\tilde{L}\tilde{L}^{\mathsf{T}}\|_{\infty} - \tfrac{1}{4}}. \tag{7.5}$$

In considering when it can pay to precondition one must take into account the computational labor per iteration as well as the rate of convergence. Thus, let

$$\xi = F_1/F_2, \tag{7.6}$$

where F_1 and F_2 are the number of flops per iteration required by the simple and SSOR-preconditioned conjugate gradient methods, respectively. The estimates of $p(\varepsilon)$ at the beginning of this section indicate that SSOR preconditioning is advantageous when

$$\kappa(\tilde{K}) < \xi^2\kappa(K).$$

Assuming $\kappa(K)$ is large (which is the case of interest), we see from (7.3a) that preconditioning is very effective indeed when $\rho(\tilde{L}\tilde{L}^{\mathsf{T}}) \leq \tfrac{1}{4}$. If $\rho(\tilde{L}\tilde{L}^{\mathsf{T}}) > \tfrac{1}{4}$, then (7.3b) indicates that preconditioning is justified if

$$\sqrt{\rho(\tilde{L}\tilde{L}^{\mathsf{T}}) - \tfrac{1}{4}} < \xi^2. \tag{7.7}$$

The value of ξ depends on details of the computer implementation of the two methods. For the implementations described in Section 1.4, we have

$$\xi = (r_K + 5)/(2r_K + 6) \qquad \text{and} \qquad \xi = (r_K + 5)/(r_K + 7),$$

corresponding to SSOR preconditioning by (1.92) and (1.100), respectively, where r_K is the average number of nonzero entries per row of K. [See (1.94a), (1.94b), and (1.101a).]

In deriving criterion (7.7) we have used the inequality

$$\delta \le [\rho(\tilde{L}\tilde{L}^T) - \tfrac{1}{4}]\kappa(K).$$

In many cases δ is considerably less than this bound, and SSOR preconditioning is often advantageous even if (7.7) is not satisfied.

Finite Element Matrices

We now suppose that K arises from the application of the finite element method to a second-order boundary value problem in n space dimensions. For an infinite family of meshes satisfying the uniformity conditions (5.102) in Section 5.5, we know that

$$\kappa(K) = O(N^{2/n}) = O(h^{-2}).$$

Since high accuracy tends to require a fine mesh, it is common that $\kappa(K)$ is large.

The success of SSOR preconditioning depends on the size of $\rho(\tilde{L}\tilde{L}^T)$, and we would like estimates of this quantity when K is a finite element matrix. In the following examples we determine the bounds in (7.4) for a few simple problems, thus gaining insight into some of the factors that influence $\rho(\tilde{L}\tilde{L}^T)$. Note that when $\rho(\tilde{L}\tilde{L}^T) \le \tfrac{1}{4}$, then

$$\kappa(\tilde{K}) \le \sqrt{\tfrac{1}{2}\kappa(K)} + \tfrac{1}{2} = O(h^{-1}).$$

Example 7.1. Consider the boundary value problem

$$-p(u_{xx} + u_{yy}) = g(x, y), \qquad (x, y) \in \Omega,$$

$$u = \gamma(x, y), \qquad (x, y) \in \Gamma,$$

where $\bar{\Omega}$ is an axiparallel square and p is a positive constant. We apply piecewise linear basis functions (Example 5.1) over a uniform mesh of $2S^2$ isosceles right triangles. A section of the mesh is shown in Fig. 7.1.

A row-wise global node ordering progressing downward has been selected.

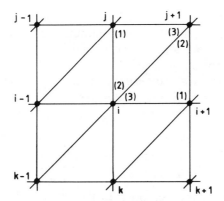

Fig. 7.1. Section of the finite element mesh of Example 7.1: $j < i < k$.

With the local node ordering shown in Fig. 7.1, all elements have the same element matrix, namely,

$$\frac{p}{2}\begin{bmatrix} 2 & -1 & -1 \\ -1 & 1 & 0 \\ -1 & 0 & 1 \end{bmatrix}.$$

The stiffness matrix K has order $N = (S - 1)^2$. Carrying out the assembly process, we find that the nonzero entries in the ith row of K are as follows:

(j)	$(i-1)$	(i)	$(i+1)$	(k)
$-p$	$-p$	$4p$	$-p$	$-p$

(When node i is adjacent to the boundary, then either one or two of the off-diagonal entries in the ith row disappear because of the Dirichlet boundary condition.) Using the relation $\tilde{l}_{ij} = l_{ij}/(d_{ii}d_{jj})^{1/2}$, we find that the ith rows of $\tilde{L}$ and $\tilde{L}^{\mathrm{T}}$ are as follows:

Matrix	(j)	$(i-1)$	$(i+1)$	(k)
$\tilde{L}$	$-1/4$	$-1/4$	—	—
$\tilde{L}^{\mathrm{T}}$	—	—	$-1/4$	$-1/4$

Thus $\|\tilde{L}\|_\infty = \|\tilde{L}^{\mathrm{T}}\|_\infty = \frac{1}{2}$, and it follows that $\rho(\tilde{L}\tilde{L}^{\mathrm{T}}) \le \frac{1}{4}$ and $\kappa(\tilde{K}) = O(h^{-1})$.

Example 7.2. Consider the previous example, assuming now that the co-efficient p is a step function with discontinuity across a vertical line Γ_0 as indicated in Fig. 7.2. We assume that p_0 and p_1 are positive constants and that $p_1 > p_0$. It turns out to be advantageous to replace the row-wise node ordering with a column-wise ordering beginning at the right, so that nodes in the part of Ω where p is greatest are ordered first.

The element matrix is now either

$$\frac{p_0}{2}\begin{bmatrix} 2 & -1 & -1 \\ -1 & 1 & 0 \\ -1 & 0 & 1 \end{bmatrix} \quad \text{or} \quad \frac{p_1}{2}\begin{bmatrix} 2 & -1 & -1 \\ -1 & 1 & 0 \\ -1 & 0 & 1 \end{bmatrix}$$

according to whether the element is to the left or right of Γ_0. For node i situated on Γ_0 as illustrated in Fig. 7.2, we find that the ith row of K is as follows:

(j)	$(i-1)$	(i)	$(i+1)$	(k)
$-p_1$	$-(p_0 + p_1)/2$	$2(p_0 + p_1)$	$-(p_0 + p_1)/2$	$-p_0$

(7.8)

For a node not on Γ_0 the corresponding row in the stiffness matrix is as shown in Example 7.1, p being replaced by p_0 or p_1. A simple computation

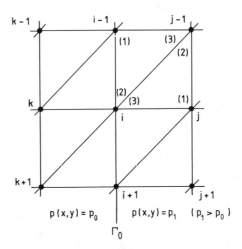

Fig. 7.2. Section of the finite element mesh of Example 7.2: $j < i < k$. The function $p(x, y)$ assumes the values p_0 and p_1 to the left and right of Γ_0, respectively.

shows that (7.8) leads to rows

Matrix	(j)	$(i-1)$	$(i+1)$	(k)
$\tilde{L}$	$-\gamma/4$	$-1/4$	—	—
$\tilde{L}^{\mathrm{T}}$	—	—	$-1/4$	$-\beta/4$

in $\tilde{L}$ and $\tilde{L}^{\mathrm{T}}$, respectively, where

$$\beta = \sqrt{2p_0/(p_0 + p_1)} < 1, \qquad \gamma = \sqrt{2p_1/(p_0 + p_1)} > 1.$$

Hence $\| \tilde{L} \|_\infty \geq \frac{1}{4}(\gamma + 1) > \frac{1}{2}$, and (7.2) is not satisfied.

We shall now consider the problem more closely. If N denotes the order of $\tilde{L}$, then $M \equiv \sqrt{N}$ is an integer. We assume for convenience that the vertical line Γ_0 bisects the square region, and it follows that M is odd. We leave it to the reader to verify that $\tilde{L}$ has the block lower bidiagonal form

$$\tilde{L} = \frac{1}{4}
\begin{bmatrix}
\tilde{D} & & & & & & & \\
-I & \tilde{D} & & & & & & \\
 & \ddots & \ddots & & & & & \\
 & & -I & \tilde{D} & & & & \\
 & & & -\gamma I & \tilde{D} & & & \\
 & & & & -\beta I & \tilde{D} & & \\
 & & & & & -I & \tilde{D} & \\
 & & & & & & \ddots & \ddots \\
 & & & & & & & -I & \tilde{D}
\end{bmatrix}
\begin{array}{l}
1 \\ 2 \\ \vdots \\ \\ \frac{M+1}{2} \\ \\ \\ \vdots \\ M
\end{array},$$

where I is the identity matrix of order M and

$$\tilde{D} =
\begin{bmatrix}
0 & & & & \\
-1 & 0 & & & \\
 & -1 & 0 & & \\
 & & \ddots & \ddots & \\
 & & & -1 & 0 \\
 & & & & -1 & 0
\end{bmatrix}
\begin{array}{l}
1 \\ 2 \\ \vdots \\ \\ M
\end{array}$$

A straightforward calculation yields

$$\tilde{L}\tilde{L}^{\mathrm{T}} = \frac{1}{16} \begin{bmatrix} E & -\tilde{D} \\ -\tilde{D}^{\mathrm{T}} & (I+E) & -\tilde{D} \\ & \ddots & \ddots & \ddots \\ & & -\tilde{D}^{\mathrm{T}} & (I+E) & -\tilde{D} \\ & & & -\tilde{D}^{\mathrm{T}} & (I+E) & -\gamma\tilde{D} \\ & & & & -\gamma\tilde{D}^{\mathrm{T}} & (\gamma^2 I+E) & -\beta\tilde{D} \\ & & & & & -\beta\tilde{D}^{\mathrm{T}} & (\beta^2 I+E) & -\tilde{D} \\ & & & & & & -\tilde{D}^{\mathrm{T}} & (I+E) & -\tilde{D} \\ & & & & & & & \ddots & \ddots & \ddots \\ & & & & & & & & -\tilde{D}^{\mathrm{T}} & (I+E) & -\tilde{D} \\ & & & & & & & & & -\tilde{D}^{\mathrm{T}} & (I+E) \end{bmatrix},$$

where

$$E = \tilde{D}\tilde{D}^{\mathrm{T}} = \begin{bmatrix} 0 \\ & 1 \\ & & 1 \\ & & & \ddots \\ & & & & 1 \\ & & & & & 1 \end{bmatrix}.$$

The relevant range of γ is $1 < \gamma < \sqrt{2}$. An examination of these matrices shows that

$$\|\tilde{L}\|_\infty \cdot \|\tilde{L}^{\mathrm{T}}\|_\infty = \|\tilde{L}\|_\infty^2 = \tfrac{1}{16}(\gamma + 1)^2,$$

$$\|\tilde{L}\tilde{L}^{\mathrm{T}}\|_\infty = \tfrac{1}{16}(\gamma^2 + \gamma + 1 + \beta)$$

$$= \tfrac{1}{16}(\gamma^2 + \gamma + 1 + \sqrt{2 - \gamma^2}) < \|\tilde{L}\|_\infty \cdot \|\tilde{L}^{\mathrm{T}}\|_\infty.$$

Thus,

$$\sqrt{\rho(\tilde{L}\tilde{L}^{\mathrm{T}}) - \tfrac{1}{4}} \le \sqrt{\|\tilde{L}\tilde{L}^{\mathrm{T}}\|_\infty - \tfrac{1}{4}}$$

$$= \tfrac{1}{4}\sqrt{\gamma^2 + \gamma - 3 + \sqrt{2 - \gamma^2}}, \qquad 1 < \gamma < \sqrt{2}.$$

Since this bound vanishes for $\gamma = 1$, there is clearly an interval $1 < \gamma < \gamma_1$ for which (7.7) is satisfied.

Example 7.3. In Example 7.1 let $p = 1$ and let the boundary condition on the left edge of the domain be changed to the Neumann condition $u_v = \xi(x, y)$.

Using the column-wise node ordering of the preceding example, we obtain the stiffness matrix

$$K = \begin{bmatrix} \tilde{K} & -I & & & \\ -I & \tilde{K} & -I & & \\ & \ddots & \ddots & \ddots & \\ & & -I & \tilde{K} & -I \\ & & & -I & \frac{1}{2}\tilde{K} \end{bmatrix},$$

where

$$\tilde{K} = \begin{bmatrix} 4 & -1 & & & \\ -1 & 4 & -1 & & \\ & \ddots & \ddots & \ddots & \\ & & -1 & 4 & -1 \\ & & & -1 & 4 \end{bmatrix}.$$

Then

$$\tilde{L} = \frac{1}{4} \begin{bmatrix} \tilde{D} & & & & \\ -I & \tilde{D} & & & \\ & \ddots & \ddots & & \\ & & -I & \tilde{D} & \\ & & & -\sqrt{2}I & \tilde{D} \end{bmatrix},$$

and

$$\tilde{L}\tilde{L}^{\mathrm{T}} = \frac{1}{16} \begin{bmatrix} E & -\tilde{D} & & & \\ -\tilde{D}^{\mathrm{T}} & (I+E) & -\tilde{D} & & \\ & \ddots & \ddots & \ddots & \\ & & -\tilde{D}^{\mathrm{T}} & (I+E) & -\sqrt{2}\tilde{D} \\ & & & -\sqrt{2}\tilde{D}^{\mathrm{T}} & (2I+E) \end{bmatrix},$$

where $\tilde{D}$ and E are defined as in the preceding example.

We see easily that

$$\|\tilde{L}\|_{\infty} \cdot \|\tilde{L}^{\mathrm{T}}\|_{\infty} = \|\tilde{L}\|_{\infty}^{2} = \tfrac{1}{16}(1+\sqrt{2})^{2},$$

$$\|\tilde{L}\tilde{L}^{\mathrm{T}}\|_{\infty} = \tfrac{1}{16}(3+\sqrt{2}) < \|\tilde{L}\|_{\infty} \cdot \|\tilde{L}^{\mathrm{T}}\|_{\infty},$$

and hence

$$\sqrt{\rho(\tilde{L}\tilde{L}^{\mathrm{T}})} - \tfrac{1}{4} \le \sqrt{\|\tilde{L}\tilde{L}^{\mathrm{T}}\|_\infty} - \tfrac{1}{4} = \tfrac{1}{4}\sqrt{\sqrt{2}-1} \simeq 0.161.$$

Inequality (7.7) is satisfied for each of the values of ξ shown subsequently. Note that this bound is identical to that of the limiting case $p_1/p_0 = \infty$ of Example 7.2.

Certain other simple node orderings lead to a greater bound (see Exercise 7.3).

Example 7.4. We return to the problem of Example 7.1 once again, now choosing a global node ordering of the "checkerboard" type. This means that we consider the nodes to be colored red and black as on a checkerboard and order all of the nodes of one color before ordering those of the other. This gives rise to a stiffness matrix of the form

$$K = \begin{bmatrix} 4I & E^{\mathrm{T}} \\ E & 4I \end{bmatrix},$$

the typical row of E and E^{T} having four "-1" entries. (We are assuming for simplicity that the number of nodes in the interior of the domain is even.) Then,

$$\tilde{L} = \tfrac{1}{4}\begin{bmatrix} 0 & 0 \\ E & 0 \end{bmatrix}, \qquad \tilde{L}\tilde{L}^{\mathrm{T}} = \tfrac{1}{16}\begin{bmatrix} 0 & 0 \\ 0 & EE^{\mathrm{T}} \end{bmatrix},$$

and $\|\tilde{L}\tilde{L}^{\mathrm{T}}\|_\infty = \tfrac{1}{16}\|EE^{\mathrm{T}}\|_\infty$. For a fine mesh we usually have $\|EE^{\mathrm{T}}\|_\infty = 16$ and hence

$$\sqrt{\rho(\tilde{L}\tilde{L}^{\mathrm{T}})} - \tfrac{1}{4} \le \sqrt{\|\tilde{L}\tilde{L}^{\mathrm{T}}\|_\infty} - \tfrac{1}{4} = \sqrt{3}/2 \simeq 0.866.$$

This is much inferior to the result obtained for the row-wise node ordering of Example 7.1.

Discussion

Only in the first of these examples was it possible to establish that $\rho(\tilde{L}\tilde{L}^{\mathrm{T}}) \le \tfrac{1}{4}$ and hence $\delta \le 0$. Both theoretical investigations of simple problems (see Exercise 7.4) and numerical evidence indicate that δ does indeed grow as $h \to 0$ if there is a discontinuous coefficient, a Neumann boundary condition, or an unfavorable node ordering. From the inequality

$$\delta \le [\rho(\tilde{L}\tilde{L}^{\mathrm{T}}) - \tfrac{1}{4}]\kappa(K)$$

and the fact that in general $\rho(\tilde{L}\tilde{L}^{\mathrm{T}}) = O(h^0)$, we see that δ cannot grow faster than $\kappa(K)$, which we know to be $O(h^{-2})$. Note that if δ does not grow this rapidly, then (7.3b) is a very pessimistic bound on $\kappa(\tilde{K})$ and SSOR preconditioning is worthwhile for sufficiently small values of h regardless of whether (7.7) is satisfied.

Until now we have considered only the use of piecewise linear basis functions. These have the important property of making the stiffness matrix K diagonally dominant provided that there are no obtuse element angles. Note that diagonal dominance in K tends to limit the size of the entries of $\tilde{L}$ and hence the size of $\rho(\tilde{L}\tilde{L}^T)$, the critical parameter for SSOR preconditioning. Indeed, with the exception of the piecewise bilinear basis functions, which also make K diagonally dominant, the use of other types of finite element basis functions usually makes $\rho(\tilde{L}\tilde{L}^T) > \frac{1}{4}$ for any boundary value problem.

In summation, the estimate

$$\kappa(\tilde{K}) \le \sqrt{\tfrac{1}{2}\kappa(K)} + \tfrac{1}{2} = O(h^{-1})$$

for SSOR preconditioning is restricted to problems with smooth coefficients and Dirichlet boundary conditions and to the use of piecewise linear or bilinear basis functions with a favorable (row-wise or column-wise, for example) node ordering.

Since this estimate is based on the ω value

$$\omega^* = 2/[1 + (2/\sqrt{\mu})\sqrt{\tfrac{1}{2} + \delta}]$$

given in (1.73b), one wants to know how to compute an approximate value of ω^*. From the inequalities $-\frac{1}{4} \le \delta \le 0$ and $0 < ch^{-2} \le \mu \le dh^{-2}$ (see the end of Section 5.5), we see that the function $\eta^*(h)$ defined implicitly by $\omega^* = 2/(1 + h\eta^*(h))$ satisfies an inequality of the form $0 < \tilde{c} \le \eta^*(h) \le \tilde{d}$. It is left as an exercise to show that if η is an arbitrary positive constant and if $\omega = 2/(1 + h\eta)$, then $\kappa(\tilde{K})(\omega) = O(h^{-1})$. (See Exercise 7.5.) Thus, for the special problems under consideration it is easy to choose ω so as to obtain the optimal asymptotic behavior of $\kappa(\tilde{K})$.

It is developed in the exercises that so-called *block-SSOR preconditioning* can be more effective than ordinary SSOR preconditioning. See Exercises 7.6–7.8 for details.

7.2   Preconditioning by Modified Incomplete Factorization: Part I

Introduction

We saw in Section 1.4 that the application of incomplete factorization to an $N \times N$ symmetric positive definite, diagonally dominant $\hat{M}$ matrix K

having at least one positive row sum gives rise to a splitting $K = C + R$, where C and R are positive definite and semidefinite, respectively. We recall that the algorithm does not determine C explicitly but rather the matrices L and U(or L and D, depending on the implementation) in the Gaussian factorization $C = LU = LDL^T$. Now in general finite element stiffness matrices are $\hat{M}$ matrices only when the basis functions are piecewise linear or bilinear and the mesh is sufficiently uniform. For the time being, then, we make the assumption that the basis functions are of these types. In the following section we shall see how stiffness matrices arising from other types of basis functions can be handled.

Regarding the use of C as a preconditioning matrix, it turns out that the associated spectral condition number $\kappa(\tilde{K})$ can be reduced if appropriate values are added to the main diagonal of K during the incomplete factorization. We describe this "modified" form of incomplete factorization and establish that for an infinite family of finite element meshes we have

$$\kappa(\tilde{K}) = O(\kappa(K)^{1/2}), \qquad N \to \infty \qquad (7.9)$$

for a range of problems that includes discontinuities in the coefficients of the equation and Neumann boundary conditions. This is an improvement over the results obtained for SSOR preconditioning in the preceding section, where we were able to establish (7.9) only for problems with smooth coefficients and Dirichlet boundary conditions.

The main steps in the analysis to follow are:

(1) the definition of the spectral equivalence of two sets of matrices;
(2) an example of spectral equivalence (Theorem 7.1 and following discussion);
(3) the analysis of modified incomplete factorization (including Theorem 7.2) and the relevance of Theorem 7.1 to this process;
(4) the derivation of an upper bound on $\kappa(\tilde{K})$ [Theorems 7.3, 7.4, and the analysis leading to (7.33)];
(5) discussion and examples.

Spectral Equivalence

We consider two infinite sets of symmetric, positive definite or positive semidefinite matrices $\{K_1(h)\}$ and $\{K_2(h)\}$, where h is a parameter that tends to zero. For the same value of h, matrices $K_1(h)$ and $K_2(h)$ are assumed to have the same order, $N = N(h)$.

Definition 7.1. The sets $\{K_1(h)\}$ and $\{K_2(h)\}$ are *spectrally equivalent* if there exist positive constants α and β, independent of h, such that

$$\alpha \mathbf{x}^T K_1(h)\mathbf{x} \leq \mathbf{x}^T K_2(h)\mathbf{x} \leq \beta \mathbf{x}^T K_1(h)\mathbf{x} \qquad \forall \mathbf{x} \in R^N, \quad \forall h.$$

Note that if the matrices are positive definite, then the ratio of the extreme eigenvalues of $K_1(h)^{-1}K_2(h)$ is bounded by β/α for all h. We call β/α a *spectral equivalence bound* for the sets $\{K_1(h)\}$ and $\{K_2(h)\}$. In our application of the spectral equivalence concept in this section, $K_1(h)$ will be a finite element stiffness matrix and $K_2(h)$ will be a matrix obtained from $K_1(h)$ by the addition of positive values to the main diagonal.

The proof of Theorem 7.1 to follow makes use of a matrix graph concept, namely that of a *set of paths* $\{P(i); i \in \mathcal{N}_1\}$ *based on a node set* $\mathcal{N}_1$. Let there be given an $N \times N$ symmetric matrix K and let $\mathcal{N}_1$ denote any subset of the integers $\{1, 2, ..., N\}$. For every $i \in \mathcal{N}_1$ let there be a directed path

$$P(i) = \{j_0(i) = i, j_1(i), j_2(i), ..., j_{Q(i)}(i)\}$$

in the graph of K (Section 6.1) that begins at node i and passes consecutively through nodes $j_1(i), j_2(i), ...,$ terminating at node $j_{Q(i)}(i)$. The parameter $Q(i)$ is the *length of* $P(i)$. We define

$$Q = \min_{i \in \mathcal{N}_1} Q(i). \tag{7.10}$$

We make the assumptions that no node appears twice in the same path (i.e., a path may not have a loop) and that no node appears in more than one path (i.e., two paths may not cross). It is not assumed that every node belongs to some path. Thus, we have the inequalities

$$\sum_{i \in \mathcal{N}_1} (Q(i) + 1) \leq N \qquad \text{and} \qquad N_1 \leq N/(Q + 1),$$

where N_1 denotes the number of integers in the set $\mathcal{N}_1$.

There are usually many ways to choose a set of paths based on a given node set $\mathcal{N}_1$. In Fig. 7.3 we show a few of the sets of paths based on $\mathcal{N}_1 = \{7, 8, 9\}$ for the matrix graph of Fig. 6.5b.

Definition 7.2. An $N \times N$ matrix K is an L *matrix* if

(1) $k_{ii} > 0, i = 1, 2, ..., N.$

(2) $k_{ij} \leq 0, i, j = 1, 2, ..., N, i \neq j.$

The L-matrix concept differs from that of an $\hat{M}$ matrix (see Definition 1.11) in that the requirement that there be a nonzero entry to the right of the main diagonal in each of the first $N - 1$ rows is replaced by the requirement that $k_{NN} > 0$. Since we are interested in finite element stiffness matrices and these invariably have nonzero diagonal entries, the L-matrix concept is less restrictive. Note that conditions (5.57a) and (5.57b) on meshes for piecewise

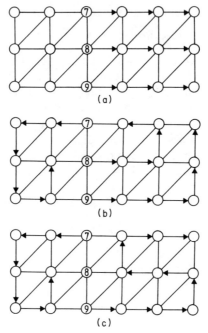

Fig. 7.3. Some sets of paths based on the nodes $\mathcal{N}_1 = \{7, 8, 9\}$ in the graph of Fig. 6.5B:
(a) $Q(7) = Q(8) = Q(9) = Q = 3$; (b) $Q(7) = 6$, $Q(8) = Q = 4$, $Q(9) = 5$; (c) $Q(7) = 6$,
$Q(8) = Q = 0$, $Q(9) = 9$.

linear and bilinear basis functions, respectively, guarantee that the stiffness
matrix for such functions is an L matrix but not necessarily an $\hat{M}$ matrix.

Theorem 7.1. Let K be an $N \times N$ symmetric positive definite, diagonally
dominant L matrix. Let

$$\hat{K} = K + (\xi_1 v)^2 D + \xi_2 v D', \tag{7.11}$$

where ξ_1 and ξ_2 are nonnegative values,

$$v = \mu^{-1/2}, \qquad \mu = \max_{\mathbf{x} \neq \mathbf{0}}(\mathbf{x}^T D \mathbf{x}/\mathbf{x}^T K \mathbf{x}), \qquad D = \mathrm{diag}(k_{11}, k_{22}, \ldots, k_{NN}),$$

and where for some $\mathcal{N}_1 \subseteq \{1, 2, \ldots, N\}$,

$$D' = \mathrm{diag}(d'_1, d'_2, \ldots, d'_N), \qquad d'_i = \begin{cases} k_{ii}, & i \in \mathcal{N}_1, \\ 0, & i \notin \mathcal{N}_1. \end{cases}$$

Let $\{P(i); i \in \mathcal{N}_1\}$ be any set of paths based on $\mathcal{N}_1$, and let Q be defined
by (7.10).
Then

$$1 \leq \frac{\mathbf{x}^T \hat{K} \mathbf{x}}{\mathbf{x}^T K \mathbf{x}} \leq 1 + \xi_1^2 + \xi_2 \left(\frac{2a_0}{vQ} + \frac{vQ}{a_1} \right), \tag{7.12}$$

where

$$a_0 = \max_{i \in \mathcal{N}_1} \max_{0 \le r \le Q-1} k_{ii}/k_{j_r(i),j_r(i)},$$

$$a_1 = \min_{i \in \mathcal{N}_1} \min_{0 \le r \le Q-1} |k_{j_r(i),j_{r+1}(i)}|/k_{ii}.$$

PROOF: Relation (7.11) implies the identity

$$\frac{\mathbf{x}^T \hat{K} \mathbf{x}}{\mathbf{x}^T K \mathbf{x}} = 1 + (\xi_1 v)^2 \frac{\mathbf{x}^T D \mathbf{x}}{\mathbf{x}^T K \mathbf{x}} + (\xi_2 v) \frac{\mathbf{x}^T D' \mathbf{x}}{\mathbf{x}^T K \mathbf{x}},$$

and the left-hand inequality in (7.12) is obviously true. Further, by the definition of μ and v we have

$$\mathbf{x}^T D \mathbf{x}/\mathbf{x}^T K \mathbf{x} \le \mu = v^{-2}$$

so that

$$\mathbf{x}^T \hat{K} \mathbf{x}/\mathbf{x}^T K \mathbf{x} \le 1 + \xi_1^2 + (\xi_2 v)(\mathbf{x}^T D' \mathbf{x}/\mathbf{x}^T K \mathbf{x}).$$

Hence, it remains to show that

$$\mathbf{x}^T D' \mathbf{x}/\mathbf{x}^T K \mathbf{x} \le 2a_0/(v^2 Q) + Q/a_1 \qquad \forall \mathbf{x} \in R^N. \tag{7.13}$$

The proof of (7.13) is carried out in the following steps.

(1)   For any symmetric matrix K we have the identity

$$\mathbf{x}^T K \mathbf{x} = \sum_{i=1}^{N} \left[\left(k_{ii} + \sum_{j \ne i} k_{ij} \right) x_i^2 + \sum_{j > i} (-k_{ij})(x_i - x_j)^2 \right].$$

(The verification of this identity is left to Exercise 7.9.) Since we are assuming that K is a diagonally dominant L matrix, all of the row sums of K are nonnegative and hence

$$\mathbf{x}^T K \mathbf{x} \ge \sum_{i=1}^{N} \sum_{j > i} -k_{ij}(x_i - x_j)^2.$$

Now there is a one-to-one correspondence between the nonzero entries above the main diagonal of K and the edges in the graph of K. Since by assumption no graph edge appears in more than one path, we see that

$$\mathbf{x}^T K \mathbf{x} \ge \sum_{i \in \mathcal{N}_1} \sum_{r=0}^{Q(i)-1} (-k_{j_r(i),j_{r+1}(i)})(x_{j_r(i)} - x_{j_{r+1}(i)})^2.$$

Note that the symmetry of K makes it irrelevant that some of the entries of K in this latter summation may be below the main diagonal. From the definition of Q and a_1 we then obtain

$$\mathbf{x}^T K \mathbf{x} \ge a_1 \sum_{i \in \mathcal{N}_1} k_{ii} \sum_{r=0}^{Q-1} (x_{j_r(i)} - x_{j_{r+1}(i)})^2. \tag{7.14}$$

(2)　The relation

$$x_i^2 - x_{j_r(i)}^2 = \sum_{s=0}^{r-1} (x_{j_s(i)}^2 - x_{j_{s+1}(i)}^2)$$

and the Cauchy–Schwarz inequality for vectors imply

$$\left| x_i^2 - x_{j_r(i)}^2 \right| \le \sum_{s=0}^{r-1} \left| x_{j_s(i)} - x_{j_{s+1}(i)} \right| \cdot \left| x_{j_s(i)} + x_{j_{s+1}(i)} \right|$$

$$\le \left\{ \sum_{s=0}^{r-1} (x_{j_s(i)} - x_{j_{s+1}(i)})^2 \right\}^{1/2} \left\{ \sum_{s=0}^{r-1} (x_{j_s(i)} + x_{j_{s+1}(i)})^2 \right\}^{1/2}.$$

Multiplying by k_{ii}, summing with respect to i, and using the Cauchy–Schwarz inequality again, we obtain

$$\left| \sum_{i \in \mathcal{N}_1} k_{ii}(x_i^2 - x_{j_r(i)}^2) \right| \le \left\{ \sum_{i \in \mathcal{N}_1} k_{ii} \sum_{s=0}^{r-1} (x_{j_s(i)} - x_{j_{s+1}(i)})^2 \right\}^{1/2}$$

$$\times \left\{ \sum_{i \in \mathcal{N}_1} k_{ii} \sum_{s=0}^{r-1} (x_{j_s(i)} + x_{j_{s+1}(i)})^2 \right\}^{1/2}. \quad (7.15)$$

Now for $r = 1, 2, \ldots, Q$ we have, using (7.14),

$$\sum_{i \in \mathcal{N}_1} k_{ii} \sum_{s=0}^{r-1} (x_{j_s(i)} - x_{j_{s+1}(i)})^2 \le \sum_{i \in \mathcal{N}_1} k_{ii} \sum_{s=0}^{Q-1} (x_{j_s(i)} - x_{j_{s+1}(i)})^2$$

$$\le a_1^{-1} \mathbf{x}^T K \mathbf{x}.$$

For the same values of r we find, using the inequality $(a + b)^2 \le 2(a^2 + b^2)$, that

$$\sum_{i \in \mathcal{N}_1} k_{ii} \sum_{s=0}^{r-1} (x_{j_s(i)} + x_{j_{s+1}(i)})^2 \le 2 \sum_{i \in \mathcal{N}_1} k_{ii} \sum_{s=0}^{Q-1} (x_{j_s(i)}^2 + x_{j_{s+1}(i)}^2)$$

$$\le 4 \sum_{i \in \mathcal{N}_1} k_{ii} \sum_{s=0}^{Q} x_{j_s(i)}^2$$

$$\le 4a_0 \sum_{i \in \mathcal{N}_1} \sum_{s=0}^{Q} k_{j_s(i), j_s(i)} x_{j_s(i)}^2$$

$$\le 4a_0 \mathbf{x}^T D \mathbf{x}.$$

Hence (7.15) implies

$$\left| \sum_{i \in \mathcal{N}_1} k_{ii}(x_i^2 - x_{j_r(i)}^2) \right| \le \{ a_1^{-1} \mathbf{x}^T K \mathbf{x} \}^{1/2} \{ 4a_0 \mathbf{x}^T D \mathbf{x} \}^{1/2} \quad (7.16)$$

for $r = 1, 2, \ldots, Q$.

(3)   Since $x_i^2 = x_{j_r(i)}^2 + (x_i^2 - x_{j_r(i)}^2)$, we have

$$\sum_{r=1}^{Q} \sum_{i \in \mathcal{N}_1} k_{ii} x_i^2 = \sum_{r=1}^{Q} \sum_{i \in \mathcal{N}_1} k_{ii} x_{j_r(i)}^2 + \sum_{r=1}^{Q} \sum_{i \in \mathcal{N}_1} k_{ii}(x_i^2 - x_{j_r(i)}^2).$$

Now,

$$\sum_{r=1}^{Q} \sum_{i \in \mathcal{N}_1} k_{ii} x_i^2 = Q \mathbf{x}^T D' \mathbf{x}$$

and

$$\sum_{r=1}^{Q} \sum_{i \in \mathcal{N}_1} k_{ii} x_{j_r(i)}^2 \le a_0 \sum_{i \in \mathcal{N}_1} \sum_{r=0}^{Q} k_{j_r(i), j_r(i)} x_{j_r(i)}^2$$

$$\le a_0 \mathbf{x}^T D \mathbf{x}.$$

Combining these results with (7.16) yields

$$Q \mathbf{x}^T D' \mathbf{x} \le a_0 \mathbf{x}^T D \mathbf{x} + \sum_{r=1}^{Q} \{a_1^{-1} \mathbf{x}^T K \mathbf{x}\}^{1/2} \cdot \{4 a_0 \mathbf{x}^T D \mathbf{x}\}^{1/2}$$

$$= a_0 \mathbf{x}^T D \mathbf{x} + 2\{Q^2 a_1^{-1} \mathbf{x}^T K \mathbf{x}\}^{1/2} \{a_0 \mathbf{x}^T D \mathbf{x}\}^{1/2} = \alpha^2 + 2\alpha\beta,$$

where $\alpha = \{a_0 \mathbf{x}^T D \mathbf{x}\}^{1/2}$ and $\beta = \{Q^2 a_1^{-1} \mathbf{x}^T K \mathbf{x}\}^{1/2}$. Using the inequality $a^2 + 2ab \le 2a^2 + b^2$, we find that

$$Q \mathbf{x}^T D' \mathbf{x} \le 2 a_0 \mathbf{x}^T D \mathbf{x} + Q^2 a_1^{-1} \mathbf{x}^T K \mathbf{x},$$

and (7.13) follows.   ■

It is important to observe that $\hat{K}$, although dependent on $\mathcal{N}_1$ through D', is independent of which set of paths we associate with $\mathcal{N}_1$. As mentioned previously, there are many ways of choosing a set of paths, and each choice determines a value of Q. The bound in (7.12) is valid for all such values of Q.

We shall now consider an infinite set of symmetric positive definite, diagonally dominant L matrices $\{K(h)\}$. For each $K(h)$ let there be a corresponding matrix $\hat{K}(h)$ satisfying (7.11), where ξ_1 and ξ_2 are nonnegative values independent of h. Then (7.12) is valid for each pair $K(h)$ and $\hat{K}(h)$, the parameters a_0, a_1, Q, and v now being functions of h. We observe that if these parameters satisfy inequalities of the form

$$c_1 \le a_1, \qquad a_0 \le d_1 \qquad \forall h, \tag{7.17a}$$

$$c_2 v^{-1} \le Q \le d_2 v^{-1} \qquad \forall h, \tag{7.17b}$$

where $c_i, d_i, i = 1, 2$ are positive constants, then the sets $\{K(h)\}$ and $\{\hat{K}(h)\}$ are spectrally equivalent.

When $\{K(h)\}$ is a set of finite element stiffness matrices associated with a second-order boundary value problem in n space dimensions, and if the meshes satisfy the uniformity conditions in (5.102), then typically (7.17a) is satisfied and v obeys an inequality of the form $\tilde{c}h \leq v \leq \tilde{d}h$. (See the bounds on μ at the end of Section 5.5 and recall that $v = \mu^{-1/2}$.) Thus, (7.17b) is equivalent to an inequality of the form

$$ch^{-1} \leq Q \leq dh^{-1}, \tag{7.17c}$$

and if this is satisfied then the sets $\{K(h)\}$ and $\{\hat{K}(h)\}$ are spectrally equivalent.

Example 7.5. The application of piecewise linear basis functions to a boundary value problem over a rectangular domain often leads to a matrix K whose graph has a structure of the type shown in Fig. 7.3. Let $\mathcal{N}_1$ be the set of nodes in some chosen vertical column of the graph, and let M denote the total number of columns. Then, we can easily find a set of parallel, horizontal paths based on $\mathcal{N}_1$ with the property $(M-1)/2 \leq Q \leq M-1$. Clearly, Q satisfies an inequality of type (7.17c).

Note that this conclusion remains valid if we take as $\mathcal{N}_1$ the nodes in any fixed (i.e., independent of h) number of columns of the graph of K, provided these are distributed in a regular way. By "regular" we mean that the number of columns separating any pair of columns in $\mathcal{N}_1$ must grow like h^{-1}. This is the case, for example, when the columns of $\mathcal{N}_1$ correspond to fixed vertical lines in the domain of the boundary value problem, a fact that will be important later.

Modified Incomplete Factorization

The following algorithm defines *modified incomplete factorization* applied to an $N \times N$ matrix K. Here, as in the "unmodified" version (1.80), J denotes the set of indices (i, j) where fill-ins are permitted. For $r = 1, 2, \ldots, N-1$:

$$\hat{k}_{rr}^{(r)} = \begin{cases} k_{rr}^{(r)}, & \text{if } s_r^{(r)} > \alpha k_{rr}^{(r)}, \\ k_{rr}^{(r)} + \delta_r, & \text{if } s_r^{(r)} < \alpha k_{rr}^{(r)}, \end{cases}$$

$$l_{ir} = k_{ir}^{(r)}/\hat{k}_{rr}^{(r)}, \tag{7.18}$$

$$k_{ij}^{(r+1)} = \begin{cases} k_{ij}^{(r)} - l_{ir}k_{rj}^{(r)}, & (r+1 \leq j \leq N) \wedge \left[(i,j) \in J\right] \wedge (j \neq i), \\ 0, & (r+1 \leq j \leq N) \wedge \left[(i,j) \notin J\right], \\ k_{ii}^{(r)} - l_{ir}k_{ri}^{(r)} + \displaystyle\sum_{\substack{p=r+1 \\ (i,p)\notin J}}^{N} (k_{ip}^{(r)} - l_{ir}k_{rp}^{(r)}), & j = i, \end{cases}$$

for $i = r + 1, ..., N$, where α is some chosen value satisfying $0 < \alpha < 1$,

$$s_r^{(r)} = \sum_{j=r}^{N} k_{rj}^{(r)},$$

$$\delta_r = \frac{\alpha^2}{1 - \alpha} k_{rr}^{(r)} + \frac{\alpha}{1 - \alpha} \max\{t_r^{(1)} - t_r^{(0)}, 0\},$$

$$t_r^{(0)} = \sum_{i=1}^{r-1} (-k_{ir}^{(i)}), \qquad t_r^{(1)} = \sum_{j=r+1}^{N} (-k_{rj}^{(r)}).$$

We shall see later that in the case of an infinite family of symmetric positive definite, diagonally dominant L matrices $\{K(h)\}$ (not necessarily finite element matrices) such that $h \to 0 \Rightarrow v \to 0$, where v is defined under (7.11), then an appropriate value of α is of the form $\alpha = \zeta v$, where ζ is any positive constant satisfying $\zeta < [\max(v)]^{-1}$. In the case of finite element matrices, where h denotes the maximum element edge length, we have seen that $\tilde{c}h \le v \le \tilde{d}h$ for certain positive constants $\tilde{c}$ and $\tilde{d}$ independent of h. For such matrices, then, it is appropriate to put $\alpha = \zeta_1 h$, where ζ_1 is any positive constant satisfying $\zeta_1 < [\max(h)]^{-1}$.

A frequent choice of J is the set

$$J = S_K = \{(i, j); k_{ij} \ne 0\}.$$

We shall always assume that $J \supseteq S_K$, allowing us to write

$$k_{ii}^{(r+1)} = k_{ii}^{(r)} - l_{ir} k_{ri}^{(r)} - \sum_{\substack{p=r+1 \\ (i,p) \notin J}}^{N} l_{ir} k_{rp}^{(r)}, \qquad r = 1, 2, ..., N - 1. \quad (7.19)$$

Comparing (7.18) with (1.80), we see that the only difference in the two processes is that in the modified version there is the possible addition of the values $\delta_1, \delta_2, ..., \delta_{N-1}$ to the main diagonal. Note that it would be superfluous to terminate (7.18) with

$$\hat{k}_{NN}^{(N)} = \begin{cases} k_{NN}^{(N)}, & s_N^{(N)} \ge \alpha k_{NN}^{(N)}, \\ k_{NN}^{(N)} + \delta_N, & s_N^{(N)} < \alpha k_{NN}^{(N)}, \end{cases}$$

since the relation $s_N^{(N)} = k_{NN}^{(N)}$ and the assumption $0 < \alpha < 1$ guarantee that $s_N^{(N)} \ge \alpha k_{NN}^{(N)}$ and hence $\hat{k}_{NN}^{(N)} = k_{NN}^{(N)}$.

The reader is urged to modify the code in Fig. 1.7 to make it accord with (7.18). Regarding the computation of $t_r^{(0)}$ and $t_r^{(1)}$, note that the nonzero values of $k_{ir}^{(i)}$ and $k_{rj}^{(r)}$ will be found in positions (i, r) and (r, j), respectively, of the array when needed. As soon as it is computed, the entry $\hat{k}_{rr}^{(r)}$ can be written over $k_{rr}^{(r)}$ in position (r, r).

An analysis of (7.18) reveals that the application of modified incomplete factorization to a matrix K is equivalent to the application of unmodified incomplete factorization to the matrix

$$\hat{K} \equiv K + \mathrm{diag}(\sigma_1\delta_1, \sigma_2\delta_2, ..., \sigma_{N-1}\delta_{N-1}, 0), \qquad (7.20)$$

where

$$\sigma_r = \begin{cases} 1, & s_r^{(r)} < \alpha k_{rr}^{(r)}, \\ 0, & s_r^{(r)} \geq \alpha k_{rr}^{(r)}. \end{cases}$$

By "equivalent" we mean that if the code of Fig. 1.7 is applied to $\hat{K}$ and if the corresponding code for (7.18) is applied to K, then the final contents of the array in each case is the same. Although this observation is irrelevant for computation (the quantities $\sigma_r\delta_r$, $r = 1, 2, ..., N - 1$ are of course not known a priori), it will be basic for our analysis of modified incomplete factorization as a preconditioning technique.

For $r = 1, 2, ..., N - 1$ we define an $N \times N$ matrix $\hat{K}^{(r+1)}$ by

$$\hat{k}_{ij}^{(r+1)} = \begin{cases} \hat{k}_{ii}^{(i)}, & i = 1, 2, ..., r, \\ k_{ij}^{(i)}, & i = 1, 2, ..., r; \quad j = i + 1, i + 2, ..., N, \\ k_{ij}^{(r+1)}, & i, j = r + 1, r + 2, ..., N, \\ 0, & \text{otherwise.} \end{cases}$$

The entries of $\hat{K}^{(r+1)}$ of the first three types are found in the corresponding positions of the array at the completion of the rth step of (7.18), the remaining positions containing the values l_{ij} for $j = 1, 2, ..., r$, $i = j + 1, j + 2, ..., N$.

Theorem 7.2. Let (7.18) be applied to an $N \times N$ diagonally dominant L matrix K, and let there be defined the row sums

$$s_i^{(r)} = \sum_{j=r}^{N} k_{ij}^{(r)}, \qquad i = r, r + 1, ..., N, \quad r = 1, 2, ..., N.$$

Then the following holds for $r = 1, 2, ..., N - 1$:

(1) $k_{ij}^{(r+1)} \leq k_{ij}^{(r)} \leq 0$, $\qquad i, j = r + 1, r + 2, ..., N$, $\quad i \neq j$.

(2) $s_i^{(r+1)} \geq s_i^{(r)} \geq 0$, $\qquad i = r + 1, r + 2, ..., N$.

(3) $0 < k_{ii}^{(r+1)} \leq k_{ii}^{(r)}$, $\qquad i = r + 1, r + 2, ..., N$.

Further, $\hat{K}^{(2)}, \hat{K}^{(3)}, ..., \hat{K}^{(N)}$ are diagonally dominant L matrices, and $\hat{K}^{(N)}$ is nonsingular.

PROOF: The proof, which proceeds by induction, is similar to that of Theorem 1.14. Thus, consider the rth step of (7.18). We see that

$$\hat{k}_{rr}^{(r)} = k_{rr}^{(r)} + \delta_r,$$

where

$$\delta_r = 0, \qquad s_r^{(r)} \geq \alpha k_{rr}^{(r)},$$

$$\delta_r > 0, \qquad s_r^{(r)} < \alpha k_{rr}^{(r)}.$$

For an off-diagonal entry $k_{ij}^{(r+1)}$ we have

$$k_{ij}^{(r+1)} = k_{ij}^{(r)} - \frac{k_{ir}^{(r)} k_{rj}^{(r)}}{\hat{k}_{rr}^{(r)}} \leq k_{ij}^{(r)}, \qquad (i,j) \in J,$$

$$k_{ij}^{(r+1)} = 0 = k_{ij}^{(r)}, \qquad (i,j) \notin J,$$

so (1) is established.

To investigate row sums we proceed as in the derivation of (1.85) and find that

$$s_i^{(r+1)} = (s_i^{(r)} - k_{ir}^{(r)}) - (k_{ir}^{(r)}/\hat{k}_{rr}^{(r)})(s_r^{(r)} - k_{rr}^{(r)})$$

or

$$s_i^{(r+1)} = s_i^{(r)} - (k_{ir}^{(r)} s_r^{(r)}/\hat{k}_{rr}^{(r)}) - k_{ir}^{(r)}(1 - k_{rr}^{(r)}/\hat{k}_{rr}^{(r)}).$$

Each of the last two terms is nonnegative, so (2) holds. Further, if $k_{ir}^{(r)} \neq 0$, then $s_i^{(r+1)} = s_i^{(r)}$ if and only if $s_r^{(r)} = 0$ and $\delta_r = 0$. But these two conditions are mutually exclusive (why?), so

$$s_i^{(r+1)} = s_i^{(r)} \quad \Leftrightarrow \quad k_{ir}^{(r)} = 0,$$

a fact that will be important immediately below.

Regarding the diagonal entries $k_{ii}^{(r+1)}$, $i = r + 1, ..., N$, we note by consideration of signs in (7.19) that $k_{ii}^{(r+1)} \leq k_{ii}^{(r)}$, and it remains to show that $k_{ii}^{(r+1)} > 0$. Since $s_i^{(r+1)} \geq 0$ and off-diagonal entries are nonpositive, it is obvious that $k_{ii}^{(r+1)} \geq 0$ and that if $s_i^{(r+1)} > 0$, then $k_{ii}^{(r+1)} > 0$. If $s_i^{(r+1)} = 0$, then it follows from (2) that $s_i^{(r+1)} = s_i^{(r)}$ and hence that $k_{ir}^{(r)} = 0$, implying $l_{ir} = 0$. Then, by (7.19), $k_{ii}^{(r+1)} = k_{ii}^{(r)} > 0$, and (3) is established.

Since $\hat{k}_{rr}^{(r)} \geq k_{rr}^{(r)} > 0, r = 1, 2, ..., N - 1$, it is obvious from the preceding results that $\hat{K}^{(2)}, \hat{K}^{(3)}, ..., \hat{K}^{(N)}$ are diagonally dominant L matrices. Finally, $\hat{K}^{(N)}$ is nonsingular because it is an upper triangular matrix with positive diagonal entries. ∎

Application of Theorem 7.1
to Modified Incomplete Factorization

The matrix $\hat{K}$ defined by (7.20) is bounded by a matrix of form (7.11) if K is a diagonally dominant L matrix. To see this we observe first that $k_{rr}^{(r)} \leq k_{rr}$, $r = 1, 2, ..., N$ (this follows from Theorem 7.2), and that

$$\left| t_r^{(1)} - t_r^{(0)} \right| \leq t_r^{(1)} = k_{rr}^{(r)} - s_r^{(r)} \leq k_{rr}.$$

Using these inequalities we easily find that

$$\hat{K} \leq K + [\alpha^2/(1 - \alpha)]D + [\alpha/(1 - \alpha)]D',$$

where D and D' are defined as in Theorem 7.1, the node set $\mathscr{N}_1$ now being

$$\mathscr{N}_1 = \{r; (s_r^{(r)} < \alpha k_{rr}^{(r)}) \wedge (t_r^{(1)} > t_r^{(0)})\}. \tag{7.21}$$

Suppose that in addition to being a diagonally dominant L matrix K is also symmetric positive definite, and let v be defined as in Theorem 7.1. Suppose, further, that $\alpha \leq \frac{1}{2}$ and let $\zeta = \alpha/v$. Then,

$$\hat{K} \leq K + 2(\zeta v)^2 D + 2\zeta v D' = K + (\xi_1 v)^2 D + \xi_2 v D' = K^*, \text{ say,}$$

where we have introduced $\xi_1 = \sqrt{2}\zeta, \xi_2 = 2\zeta$. Since

$$1 \leq \mathbf{x}^T \hat{K}\mathbf{x}/\mathbf{x}^T K\mathbf{x} \leq \mathbf{x}^T K^*\mathbf{x}/\mathbf{x}^T K\mathbf{x} \qquad \forall \mathbf{x} \in R^N, \quad \mathbf{x} \neq \mathbf{0},$$

we can deduce from the application of Theorem 7.1 to K^* that

$$1 \leq \mathbf{x}^T \hat{K}\mathbf{x}/\mathbf{x}^T K\mathbf{x} \leq 1 + 2\zeta^2 + 2\zeta[2a_0/(vQ) + vQ/a_1]. \tag{7.22}$$

The parameters a_0 and a_1 are defined following (7.12). We recall that Q is the minimum path length for any given set of paths based on $\mathscr{N}_1$.[†]

Consider now the application of modified incomplete factorization to an infinite set of symmetric positive definite, diagonally dominant L matrices $\{K(h)\}$, with the property that $h \to 0 \Rightarrow v \to 0$. For any positive constant ζ, let $\alpha = \zeta v$ for each matrix $K(h)$. Then (7.22) holds for values of h small enough to make $\alpha \leq \frac{1}{2}$, the parameters a_0, a_1, and Q (in addition to v) now being functions of h. We conclude from our discussion preceding Example 7.5 that the sets $\{K(h)\}$ and $\{\hat{K}(h)\}$ are spectrally equivalent if conditions (7.17a) and (7.17b) hold. As we shall see, the spectral equivalence property is important for preconditioning by modified incomplete factorization.

In the case of finite element stiffness matrices, we have seen that the conditions for spectral equivalence essentially reduce to (7.17c),

$$ch^{-1} \leq Q \leq dh^{-1}.$$

† Clearly, if $\mathscr{N}_1$ is empty then the last term in (7.22) does not appear.

Now Q is determined by the node set $\mathcal{N}_1$ defined by (7.21). Thus, given a particular problem, we would like to obtain precise information on $\mathcal{N}_1$ with the hope of establishing inequality (7.17c). This task, in general a difficult one, is carried out for some simple problems at the end of this section.

Preconditioning by Modified Incomplete Factorization

In applying (7.18) to a symmetric positive definite, diagonally dominant L matrix K, we are determining a lower triangular matrix $\hat{L}$ and an upper triangular matrix $\hat{U}$ defined by

$$\hat{l}_{ir} = \begin{cases} l_{ir}, & i > r, \\ 1, & i = r, \\ 0, & i < r, \end{cases}$$

and $\hat{U} \equiv \hat{K}^{(N)}$, respectively. Our goal now is to examine the use of $\hat{C} \equiv \hat{L}\hat{U}$ as a preconditioning matrix for the conjugate gradient solution of the system $K\alpha = \mathbf{G}$.

Symmetry considerations allow us to write

$$\hat{C} = \hat{L}\hat{D}\hat{L}^{\mathrm{T}}, \tag{7.23}$$

where

$$\hat{D} = \mathrm{diag}(\hat{k}_{11}^{(1)}, \hat{k}_{22}^{(2)}, \ldots, \hat{k}_{N-1,N-1}^{(N-1)}, k_{NN}^{(N)}).$$

In our discussion of (7.18) it was useful to think of the storage of L and U in the lower and upper triangular parts, respectively, of an $N \times N$ array, analogous to the implementation of unmodified incomplete factorization by the code of Fig. 1.7. As in the unmodified case, (7.18) can be reformulated so as to produce $\hat{L}$ and $\hat{D}$ alone and implemented so as to roughly halve storage and computational labor. Our concern here, however, is to examine the rate of convergence of the process, i.e., to estimate the spectral condition number

$$\kappa(\tilde{K}) = \tilde{\lambda}_N/\tilde{\lambda}_1,$$

where $\tilde{\lambda}_1$ and $\tilde{\lambda}_N$ are the smallest and largest eigenvalues of $\hat{C}^{-1}K$, respectively. Since

$$\tilde{\lambda}_1 = \min_{\mathbf{x} \in R^N, \mathbf{x} \neq \mathbf{0}} \mathbf{x}^{\mathrm{T}}K\mathbf{x}/\mathbf{x}^{\mathrm{T}}\hat{C}\mathbf{x}, \qquad \tilde{\lambda}_N = \max_{\mathbf{x} \in R^N, \mathbf{x} \neq \mathbf{0}} \mathbf{x}^{\mathrm{T}}K\mathbf{x}/\mathbf{x}^{\mathrm{T}}\hat{C}\mathbf{x}$$

and

$$\mathbf{x}^{\mathrm{T}}K\mathbf{x}/\mathbf{x}^{\mathrm{T}}\hat{C}\mathbf{x} = (\mathbf{x}^{\mathrm{T}}K\mathbf{x}/\mathbf{x}^{\mathrm{T}}\hat{K}\mathbf{x})\cdot(\mathbf{x}^{\mathrm{T}}\hat{K}\mathbf{x}/\mathbf{x}^{\mathrm{T}}\hat{C}\mathbf{x}), \tag{7.24}$$

it suffices to find upper and lower bounds for each of the factors on the right-hand side of (7.24). Now (7.22) gives us bounds for the first factor, so the task at hand is to investigate the second. This is done in the next two theorems.

Theorem 7.3. Let (7.18) be applied to a symmetric, diagonally dominant L matrix K. Then,

$$\hat{s}_r^{(r)} \geq \alpha \hat{k}_{rr}^{(r)}, \qquad r = 1, 2, \ldots, N,$$

where

$$\hat{s}_r^{(r)} = \hat{k}_{rr}^{(r)} + \sum_{j=r+1}^{N} k_{rj}^{(r)}$$

and $\hat{k}_{NN}^{(N)} = k_{NN}^{(N)}$.

PROOF: We shall need the inequality

$$s_r^{(r)} \geq \sum_{i=1}^{r-1} (-l_{ri}) \hat{s}_i^{(i)}, \tag{7.25}$$

the proof of which is left to Exercise 7.13.

We proceed by induction. Thus, suppose that

$$\hat{s}_i^{(i)} \geq \alpha \hat{k}_{ii}^{(i)}, \qquad i = 1, 2, \ldots, r - 1. \tag{7.26}$$

If $s_r^{(r)} \geq \alpha k_{rr}^{(r)}$ then, by (7.18), $\hat{k}_{rr}^{(r)} = k_{rr}^{(r)}$ and it follows that $\hat{s}_r^{(r)} = s_r^{(r)}$. Hence $\hat{s}_r^{(r)} \geq \alpha \hat{k}_{rr}^{(r)}$, which is what we want to prove.

If $s_r^{(r)} < \alpha k_{rr}^{(r)}$, then

$$\hat{k}_{rr}^{(r)} = k_{rr}^{(r)} + \frac{\alpha^2}{1-\alpha} k_{rr}^{(r)} + \frac{\alpha}{1-\alpha} \delta_r',$$

where

$$\delta_r' = \max\{t_r^{(1)} - t_r^{(0)}, 0\}.$$

Then,

$$\hat{s}_r^{(r)} - \alpha \hat{k}_{rr}^{(r)} = s_r^{(r)} + \frac{\alpha^2}{1-\alpha} k_{rr}^{(r)} + \frac{\alpha}{1-\alpha} \delta_r' - \alpha \left[k_{rr}^{(r)} + \frac{\alpha^2}{1-\alpha} k_{rr}^{(r)} + \frac{\alpha}{1-\alpha} \delta_r' \right]$$

$$= s_r^{(r)} - \alpha(1-\alpha) k_{rr}^{(r)} + \alpha \delta_r'$$

$$\geq \sum_{i=1}^{r-1} \left(-\frac{k_{ri}^{(i)}}{\hat{k}_{ii}^{(i)}} \right) \hat{s}_i^{(i)} - \alpha(1-\alpha) k_{rr}^{(r)} + \alpha \delta_r'$$

$$\geq \sum_{i=1}^{r-1} \left(-\frac{k_{ir}^{(i)}}{\hat{k}_{ii}^{(i)}} \right) \alpha \hat{k}_{ii}^{(i)} - \alpha(1-\alpha) k_{rr}^{(r)} + \alpha \delta_r'$$

$$= \alpha t_r^{(0)} - \alpha(1-\alpha) k_{rr}^{(r)} + \alpha \delta_r',$$

where we have used (7.25), (7.26) and the fact that $k_{ri}^{(i)} = k_{ir}^{(i)}$. But, the relation $s_r^{(r)} = k_{rr}^{(r)} - t_r^{(1)}$ together with the assumption $s_r^{(r)} < \alpha k_{rr}^{(r)}$ implies

$$k_{rr}^{(r)} \leq \frac{1}{1-\alpha} t_r^{(1)}.$$

Hence,

$$\hat{s}_r^{(r)} - \alpha \hat{k}_{rr}^{(r)} \geq \alpha(t_r^{(0)} - t_r^{(1)} + \delta_r') \geq 0. \qquad \blacksquare$$

Theorem 7.4. Let (7.18) be applied to a symmetric, diagonally dominant L matrix K. If condition (7.29) below is satisfied, then

$$1 \leq x^T \hat{K} x / x^T \hat{C} x \leq 1/\alpha \qquad \forall x \in R^N, \quad x \neq 0, \qquad (7.27)$$

where $\hat{K}$ and $\hat{C}$ are given by (7.20) and (7.23), respectively.

PROOF: In addition to applying (7.18) to K, we shall apply the unmodified algorithm (1.80), with the same set J, to

$$\overset{\circ}{K} \equiv K - \mathrm{diag}(s_1^{(1)}, s_2^{(1)}, ..., s_N^{(1)}),$$

$s_i^{(1)}$ denoting the ith row sum of K. The matrix $\overset{\circ}{K}$ is symmetric and diagonally dominant, possessing nonpositive off-diagonal entries, nonnegative diagonal entries, and row sums

$$\overset{\circ}{s}_i^{(1)} = 0, \qquad i = 1, 2, ..., N.$$

$\overset{\circ}{K}$ is not necessarily an $\hat{M}$ matrix, however, so we cannot exclude the possibility that $\overset{\circ}{k}_{rr}^{(r)} = 0$ for some $r < N$, causing (1.80) to break down. For the time being we make the simplifying assumption that this condition does not occur, leaving an examination of the contrary case until later.

It is easy to deduce from the identity (1.85) that $\overset{\circ}{s}_r^{(r)} = 0$, giving us the relation

$$\overset{\circ}{t}_r^{(1)} \equiv \sum_{j=r+1}^{N} (-\overset{\circ}{k}_{rj}^{(r)}) = \overset{\circ}{k}_{rr}^{(r)}, \qquad (7.28a)$$

which will be needed later. We leave it to the reader to establish that

$$|k_{ij}^{(r)}| \leq |\overset{\circ}{k}_{ij}^{(r)}|, \qquad (i,j) \in J, \quad i \neq j, \qquad (7.28b)$$

which will also be needed later.

Let $b_{ij}^{(r)}$ and $\overset{\circ}{b}_{ij}^{(r)}$, where $(i,j) \notin J$, denote the typical "fill-ins" that arise during the two factorization processes, i.e.,

$$b_{ij}^{(r)} = -k_{ir}^{(r)} k_{rj}^{(r)} / k_{rr}^{(r)}, \qquad \overset{\circ}{b}_{ij}^{(r)} = -\overset{\circ}{k}_{ir}^{(r)} \overset{\circ}{k}_{rj}^{(r)} / \overset{\circ}{k}_{rr}^{(r)}.$$

Theorem 7.3 states that $\hat{s}_r^{(r)} \geq \alpha \hat{k}_{rr}^{(r)}$, and it follows from the identity $\hat{s}_r^{(r)} = \hat{k}_{rr}^{(r)} - t_r^{(1)}$ that $1/(1 - \alpha) \leq \hat{k}_{rr}^{(r)}/t_r^{(1)}$. Hence,

$$\frac{|b_{ij}^{(r)}|}{1 - \alpha} \leq \frac{k_{ir}^{(r)}k_{rj}^{(r)}}{\hat{k}_{rr}^{(r)}} \frac{\hat{k}_{rr}^{(r)}}{t_r^{(1)}} = \frac{k_{ir}^{(r)}k_{rj}^{(r)}}{t_r^{(1)}} = \frac{k_{ri}^{(r)}k_{rj}^{(r)}}{t_r^{(1)}}.$$

Now,

$$\frac{t_r^{(1)}}{k_{ri}^{(r)}k_{rj}^{(r)}} = \frac{1}{k_{ri}^{(r)}k_{rj}^{(r)}} \sum_{\substack{p=r+1 \\ p \neq i,j}}^{N} (-k_{rp}^{(r)}) + \frac{1}{|k_{ri}^{(r)}|} + \frac{1}{|k_{rj}^{(r)}|}$$

$$\geq \frac{1}{k_{ri}^{(r)}k_{rj}^{(r)}} \sum_{\substack{p=r+1 \\ p \neq i,j}}^{N} (-k_{rp}^{(r)}) + \frac{1}{|\mathring{k}_{ri}^{(r)}|} + \frac{1}{|\mathring{k}_{rj}^{(r)}|},$$

where we have used (7.28b). Thus, if

$$\frac{1}{k_{ri}^{(r)}k_{rj}^{(r)}} \sum_{\substack{p=r+1 \\ p \neq i,j}}^{N} (-k_{rp}^{(r)}) \geq \frac{1}{\mathring{k}_{ri}^{(r)}\mathring{k}_{rj}^{(r)}} \sum_{\substack{p=r+1 \\ p \neq i,j}}^{N} (-\mathring{k}_{rp}^{(r)}), \tag{7.29}$$

then by the preceding analysis and (7.28a),

$$t_r^{(1)}/k_{ri}^{(r)}k_{rj}^{(r)} \geq \mathring{t}_r^{(1)}/\mathring{k}_{ri}^{(r)}\mathring{k}_{rj}^{(r)} = \mathring{k}_{rr}^{(r)}/\mathring{k}_{ir}^{(r)}\mathring{k}_{rj}^{(r)}.$$

Hence

$$|b_{ij}^{(r)}|/(1 - \alpha) \leq \mathring{k}_{ir}^{(r)}\mathring{k}_{rj}^{(r)}/\mathring{k}_{rr}^{(r)} = |\mathring{b}_{ij}^{(r)}|. \tag{7.30}$$

Since modified incomplete factorization applied to K is equivalent to unmodified incomplete factorization applied to $\hat{K}$, we have the relation $\hat{K} = \hat{C} + \hat{R}$, where, by Theorem 1.16, $\hat{R}$ is the sum of positive semidefinite matrices of the form

$$|b_{ij}^{(r)}| \begin{bmatrix} & | & & | & \\ & | & & | & \\ \rule{1cm}{0.4pt} & 1 & \rule{1cm}{0.4pt} & -1 & \rule{1cm}{0.4pt} \\ & | & & | & \\ & | & & | & \\ \rule{1cm}{0.4pt} & -1 & \rule{1cm}{0.4pt} & 1 & \rule{1cm}{0.4pt} \\ & | & & | & \end{bmatrix}. \tag{7.31}$$

Let the analogous splitting of $\hat{K}$ be denoted $\hat{K} = \hat{C} + \hat{R}$. For every matrix of type (7.31) in the decomposition of $\hat{R}$, there is a corresponding matrix

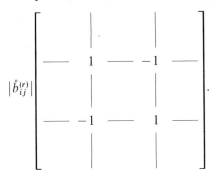

in the decomposition of $\mathring{R}$. By a straightforward computation and the use of (7.30), we find that

$$\mathbf{x}^T\hat{R}\mathbf{x} \le (1 - \alpha)\mathbf{x}^T\mathring{R}\mathbf{x} \le (1 - \alpha)\mathbf{x}^T\mathring{K}\mathbf{x}$$

$$\le (1 - \alpha)\mathbf{x}^T K\mathbf{x} \le (1 - \alpha)\mathbf{x}^T\hat{K}\mathbf{x} \qquad \forall \mathbf{x} \in R^N.$$

Hence,

$$\mathbf{x}^T\hat{C}\mathbf{x} = \mathbf{x}^T\hat{K}\mathbf{x} - \mathbf{x}^T\hat{R}\mathbf{x}$$

$$\ge \mathbf{x}^T\hat{K}\mathbf{x} - (1 - \alpha)\mathbf{x}^T\hat{K}\mathbf{x} \qquad \forall \mathbf{x} \in R^N,$$

and the right-hand inequality of (7.27) follows. The left-hand inequality is trivial.

It remains to examine the case when some $\mathring{k}_{rr}^{(r)} = 0$. Suppose, then, that $\mathring{k}_{rr}^{(r)} \ne 0$, $r = 1, 2, ..., p$, and $\mathring{k}_{p+1,p+1}^{(p+1)} = 0$. Putting $r = p + 1$ in (7.28a) and considering signs, we deduce that

$$\mathring{k}_{p+1,j}^{(p+1)} = 0, \qquad j = p + 2, p + 3, ..., N,$$

and symmetry implies that

$$\mathring{k}_{j,p+1}^{(p+1)} = 0, \qquad j = p + 2, p + 3, ..., N.$$

Then by (7.28b),

$$k_{p+1,j}^{(p+1)} = k_{j,p+1}^{(p+1)} = 0, \qquad j = p + 2, p + 3, ..., N.$$

In this situation the $(p + 1)$st step of (7.18) applied to K does nothing, and we have

$$k_{ij}^{(p+2)} = k_{ij}^{(p+1)}, \qquad i, j = p + 2, p + 3, ..., N.$$

Thus, we can skip over the $(p + 1)$st step of (1.80) applied to $\overset{\circ}{K}$, putting

$$\overset{\circ}{k}_{ij}^{(p+2)} = \overset{\circ}{k}_{ij}^{(p+1)}, \qquad i, j = p + 2, p + 3, ..., N. \qquad \blacksquare$$

Estimate of $\kappa(\tilde{K})$

Let $\{K(h)\}$ be an infinite set of symmetric positive definite, diagonally dominant L matrices. We assume as before that in applying (7.18) to the typical matrix $K = K(h)$, we put $\alpha = \zeta v$, where v is defined in Theorem 7.1 and ζ is a positive constant independent of h. Combining (7.24) with (7.22) and (7.27), we obtain

$$\left\{1 + 2\zeta^2 + 2\zeta\left(\frac{2a_0}{vQ} + \frac{vQ}{a_1}\right)\right\}^{-1} \leq \frac{x^T Kx}{x^T \hat{C}x} \leq (\zeta v)^{-1}.$$

Thus, the spectral condition number $\kappa(\tilde{K})$ associated with preconditioning by modified incomplete factorization has the bound

$$\kappa(\tilde{K}) \leq v^{-1}[\zeta^{-1} + 2\zeta + 2(2a_0/(vQ) + vQ/a_1)]. \qquad (7.32)$$

If (7.17a) and (7.17b) are satisfied, then

$$\kappa(\tilde{K}) = O(v^{-1}), \qquad v \to 0.$$

When $\{K(h)\}$ is a set of finite element matrices, in which case we have an inequality of the form $\tilde{c}h \leq v \leq \tilde{d}h$, and when $\alpha = \zeta_1 h$ for some positive constant ζ_1, then

$$\kappa(\tilde{K}) \leq h^{-1}[e_1 + e_2(a_0/(hQ) + hQ/a_1)]$$

for certain positive constants e_1 and e_2. Equivalently, we can write an inequality of the form

$$\kappa(\tilde{K}) \leq \kappa(K)^{1/2}[\tilde{e}_1 + \tilde{e}_2(a_0/(hQ) + hQ/a_1)]. \qquad (7.33)$$

These bounds, of course, depend on the assumption made in the proof of Theorem 7.4 that

(1)   condition (7.29) holds.   (7.34a)

If, in addition, a_0, a_1, and Q satisfy inequalities of the form

(2) $c_1 \leq a_1, \qquad a_0 \leq d_1, \quad \forall h$ (7.34b)

(3) $ch^{-1} \leq Q \leq dh^{-1}, \quad \forall h$ (7.34c)

then

$$\kappa(\tilde{K}) = O[\kappa(K)^{1/2}] = O(h^{-1}), \qquad h \to 0.$$

Discussion

We consider (7.29) first, expressing it as $F_{ij}^{(r)} \geq \mathring{F}_{ij}^{(r)}$. Defining

$$\beta_i^{(r)} = k_{ri}^{(r)}/\mathring{k}_{ri}^{(r)},$$

we have

$$F_{ij}^{(r)} = [1/(\beta_i^{(r)}\beta_j^{(r)}\mathring{k}_{ri}^{(r)}\mathring{k}_{rj}^{(r)})] \sum_{\substack{p=r+1 \\ p \neq i,j}}^{N} \beta_p^{(r)}(-\mathring{k}_{rp}^{(r)}),$$

whereas

$$\mathring{F}_{ij}^{(r)} = [1/(\mathring{k}_{ri}^{(r)}\mathring{k}_{rj}^{(r)})] \sum_{\substack{p=r+1 \\ p \neq i,j}}^{N} (-\mathring{k}_{rp}^{(r)}).$$

An examination of the incomplete factorization processes that have been applied to K and $\mathring{K}$ shows that $0 \leq \beta_i^{(r)} \leq 1$. Because the power of the β parameters in the denominator of $F_{ij}^{(r)}$ is greater than that in the numerator, we would expect (7.29) to hold in most cases. One case when it always holds is that when $J = S_K$ and when the structure of K is such that the off-diagonal entries of K (and hence those of $\mathring{K}$) are unchanged during the factorization, as illustrated in the following examples. Then $\beta_i^{(r)} = 1$ and $F_{ij}^{(r)} = \mathring{F}_{ij}^{(r)}$. (Another case is discussed in Exercise 7.24.)

Regarding now the second condition (7.34b), we note from the definition of a_0 and a_1 that

$$a_0 \leq \hat{a}, \qquad a_1 \geq \hat{a}^{-1}, \qquad \hat{a} \equiv \max_{i,j}(k_{ii}/k_{jj}) \geq 1.$$

The uniformity conditions (5.102), which we assume to be satisfied by the family of finite element meshes, guarantees that $\hat{a}$ is bounded above by a constant for all meshes. Hence (7.34b) is satisfied.

We turn our attention finally to (7.34c). Whether this condition holds depends on the node set $\mathcal{N}_1$ defined by (7.21). It is instructive here to reconsider the examples of Section 7.1.

Example 7.6. The stiffness matrix from Example 7.1, with $N = 25$, begins as follows:

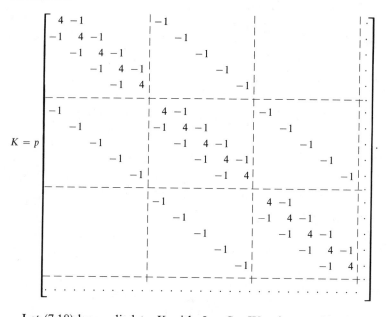

Let (7.18) be applied to K with $J = S_K$. We observe that for this matrix off-diagonal entries are unaffected, i.e.,

$$k_{ij}^{(r)} = k_{ij}, \qquad i,j = r, r+1, \ldots, N, \quad i \neq j. \tag{7.35}$$

The node set to be considered is

$$\mathscr{N}_1 = \{r; (s_r^{(r)} < \alpha k_{rr}^{(r)}) \wedge (t_r^{(1)} > t_r^{(0)})\}.$$

Relation (7.35) and the symmetry of K imply that

$$t_r^{(0)} = \sum_{j=1}^{r-1} (-k_{rj}), \qquad t_r^{(1)} = \sum_{j=r+1}^{N} (-k_{rj}). \tag{7.36}$$

We wish to determine which values of r belong to $\mathscr{N}_1$. Inspection of K and the mesh from which it arises shows that if the rth node in the mesh is not adjacent to the boundary, then

$$t_r^{(1)} - t_r^{(0)} = 2p - 2p = 0,$$

implying $r \notin \mathscr{N}_1$.

Suppose now that the rth node is adjacent to the boundary, making $s_r \geq p$, where $s_r = \sum_{j=1}^{N} k_{rj}$. Theorem 7.2 yields the inequalities

$$k_{rr}^{(r)} \leq k_{rr} = 4p, \qquad s_r^{(r)} \geq s_r \geq p,$$

and hence

$$s_r^{(r)}/k_{rr}^{(r)} \geq s_r/k_{rr} \geq \tfrac{1}{4}.$$

But since

$$r \in \mathcal{N}_1 \quad \Rightarrow \quad s_r^{(r)}/k_{rr}^{(r)} < \alpha,$$

it follows that $\alpha \leq \tfrac{1}{4} \Rightarrow r \notin \mathcal{N}_1$.

Now let the mesh be refined, with $\alpha = \zeta_1 h$, where ζ_1 is a constant. For sufficiently small values of h, we find that $\mathcal{N}_1$ is empty. In this situation the parameter Q is irrelevant since now $D' = 0$ in the bound on $\hat{K}$ given under (7.21), causing (7.33) to reduce to

$$\kappa(\tilde{K}) \leq \tilde{e}_1 \kappa(K)^{1/2}.$$

Example 7.7. In Example 7.2 let the vertical line Γ_0 bisect the domain. For convenience we denote the constants p_0 and p_1 by p and q, respectively, and define $\xi = \tfrac{1}{2}(p + q)$. We assume that $p < q$.

With the column-wise node ordering described in Example 7.2, K has the same sparsity pattern (i.e., distribution of zero entries) as in Example 7.6. The nonzero entries in a typical row are now

$$
\begin{array}{ccccc c}
-q & -q & 4q & -q & -q & \text{Case 1,} \\
-q & -\xi & 4\xi & -\xi & -p & \text{Case 2,} \\
-p & -p & 4p & -p & -p & \text{Case 3,}
\end{array}
$$

according to whether the row corresponds to a node to the right of, on, or to the left of Γ_0, respectively. When a node is adjacent to the boundary, then one (or two) of the nonzero off-diagonal entries vanishes.

Applying (7.18) with $J = S_K$, we find again that off-diagonal entries are unaffected and (7.36) holds. For a node r adjacent to the boundary we obtain, reasoning as before,

$$s_r^{(r)}/k_{rr}^{(r)} \geq s_r/k_{rr} \geq \tfrac{1}{4}, \qquad \alpha \leq \tfrac{1}{4} \quad \Rightarrow \quad r \notin \mathcal{N}_1.$$

For a node r not adjacent to the boundary we have, corresponding to the three cases given previously,

$$t_r^{(1)} - t_r^{(0)} = \sum_{j=r+1}^{N} (-k_{rj}) - \sum_{j=1}^{r-1} (-k_{rj}) = \begin{cases} 0, & \text{for Case 1,} \\ p - q < 0, & \text{for Case 2,} \\ 0, & \text{for Case 3.} \end{cases}$$

In each case $t_r^{(1)} - t_r^{(0)} \leq 0$, and it follows that $r \notin \mathcal{N}_1$. We conclude that when $\alpha \leq \tfrac{1}{4}$, then $\mathcal{N}_1$ is empty and

$$\kappa(\tilde{K}) \leq \tilde{e}_1 \kappa(K)^{1/2}.$$

Suppose now that the node ordering proceeds column-wise from left to right. Corresponding to a node on Γ_0, we now have

$$t_r^{(1)} - t_r^{(0)} = q - p > 0,$$

and it can happen that $r \in \mathcal{N}_1$. Example 7.5 shows, however, that condition (7.34c) is satisfied, so we still have $\kappa(\tilde{K}) = O[\kappa(K)^{1/2}]$.

Example 7.8. We return to the problem of Example 7.3, where a Neumann boundary condition is given on the left boundary. With the column-wise ordering given in that example, the Neumann boundary condition affects only the bottom of the matrix, where we find rows with nonzero entries

$$-1, \quad -\tfrac{1}{2}, \quad 2, \quad -\tfrac{1}{2},$$

one with

$$-1, \quad 2, \quad -\tfrac{1}{2},$$

and one with

$$-1, \quad -\tfrac{1}{2}, \quad 2.$$

In all cases $t_r^{(1)} - t_r^{(0)} < 0$, so $r \notin \mathcal{N}_1$. Since the rest of the matrix is as shown in Example 7.6, we conclude that

$$\kappa(\tilde{K}) \le \tilde{e}_1 \kappa(K)^{1/2}$$

for sufficiently fine meshes.

A comparison of Examples 7.6–7.8 with 7.1–7.3 indicates that for certain problems preconditioning by modified incomplete factorization is asymptotically (for $h \to 0$) superior to SSOR preconditioning. We note that for problems in which (7.18) does not affect off-diagonal entries and every row of K satisfies at least one of the conditions

$$s_r/k_{rr} \ge c > 0, \qquad \sum_{j=r+1}^{N} (-k_{rj}) \le \sum_{j=1}^{r-1} (-k_{rj}), \qquad (7.37)$$

where c is a constant independent of the mesh, then $\mathcal{N}_1$ is empty and $\kappa(\tilde{K}) = O[\kappa(K)^{1/2}]$. As illustrated by the second node ordering of Example 7.7, even if $\mathcal{N}_1$ is not empty it may be possible to establish that $\kappa(\tilde{K}) = O[\kappa(K)^{1/2}]$ by showing that (7.34c) is satisfied.

When $\mathcal{N}_1$ is empty, (7.32) reduces to

$$\kappa(\tilde{K}) \le v^{-1}(\zeta^{-1} + 2\zeta).$$

This bound can be improved even further by avoiding the inequality

$$\alpha^2/(1 - \alpha) \le 2\alpha^2, \qquad 0 \le \alpha \le \tfrac{1}{2},$$

which was introduced following (7.21). A more precise analysis yields

$$\kappa(\tilde{K}) \le v^{-1}[\zeta^{-1} + \zeta/(1 - \zeta v)]$$
$$\lesssim v^{-1}(\zeta^{-1} + \zeta), \qquad v \to 0,$$
$$= 2\sqrt{\mu}, \qquad \qquad \mu \to \infty,$$

where we have put $\zeta = 1$ and used the relation $v = \mu^{-1/2}$ [see (7.11)].

This holds in particular for Example 7.6, and it is interesting to compare it with the bound for SSOR preconditioning for the same problem. Example 7.1 establishes (7.3a) for SSOR, but a better bound is obtained from (1.73a) in Section 1.4, namely $\kappa(\tilde{K}) \lesssim (1/\sqrt{2})\sqrt{\mu}$.

On the basis of these upper bounds one would expect $\kappa(\tilde{K})$ to be smaller for SSOR preconditioning than for preconditioning by modified incomplete factorization. Actual computation, however, indicates that the opposite is true, even when the set J used in (7.18) is minimal, i.e., $J = S_K$. This is an appropriate place to point out that the bounds given by (7.32) and (7.33) are independent of J. Expanding J tends to decrease $\kappa(\tilde{K})$, but at the same time increase the computational labor per iteration. Numerical evidence indicates that the optimal J is not much larger than S_K.

HISTORICAL NOTE: Types of incomplete factorization leading to $\kappa(\tilde{K}) = O[\kappa(K)^{1/2}]$ for five-point difference equations for second-order boundary value problems with smooth coefficients on rectangular domains were considered in Dupont, Kendall, and Rachford (1968) and for more general problems in Axelsson (1972). The choice of J in these papers was S_K. More general types of incomplete factorization were developed in Bracha-Barak and Saylor (1973) and in Gustafsson (1979, 1983), in which applications to the finite element method were discussed.

For problems with a discontinuous coefficient on a line in the domain (as in Example 7.7), Gustafsson adds values of order of magnitude $O(h)$ to all rows corresponding to nodes on the line of discontinuity prior to making the incomplete factorization.† Our method (7.18) is dynamic in that additions to the main diagonal [beyond those that also occur in (1.80)] are made during the factorization and are subject to conditions. For some problems these additions may not take place.

For an alternative presentation of some of the results of this section see Beauwens (1979, 1984).

---

† For similar modifications applied to matrices that are not necessarily diagonally dominant, see Kershaw (1978) and Manteuffel (1980).

7.3   Preconditioning by Modified Incomplete Factorization: Part II

Preliminaries

In Section 7.2 we examined preconditioning by modified incomplete factorization under the assumption that the stiffness matrix K is an L matrix, and this amounts to the assumption that the basis functions are the piecewise linear or bilinear types. Although numerical evidence indicates that this preconditioning process works quite well for basis functions of higher degree, the analysis of Section 7.2 is of course inapplicable to such cases. In this section we shall present a preconditioning technique designed specifically for higher-degree basis functions and show by an example that the corresponding spectral condition number $\kappa(\tilde{K})$ is essentially as good as for the case when K is an L matrix.

The main ideas are as follows. Given a boundary value problem, let

$$K\boldsymbol{\alpha} = \mathbf{G} \tag{7.38}$$

denote the Ritz–Galerkin equations corresponding to some choice of higher-degree basis functions defined on a mesh $\mathcal{M}$. Let $\overset{*}{K}$ denote the stiffness matrix obtained from the same boundary value problem and the use of linear or bilinear basis functions on a mesh $\overset{*}{\mathcal{M}}$ having the same nodes as $\mathcal{M}$. The two stiffness matrices have the same order, and $\overset{*}{K}$ is usually an L matrix. Let the modified incomplete factorization algorithm (7.18) be applied to $\overset{*}{K}$, producing (in factored form) a matrix $\hat{C}$. We propose the use of $\hat{C}$ as a preconditioning matrix for the conjugate gradient solution of (7.38).

The spectral condition number $\kappa(\tilde{K})$ associated with this process is $\tilde{\lambda}_N/\tilde{\lambda}_1$, where

$$\tilde{\lambda}_1 = \min_{\mathbf{x} \neq \mathbf{0}}(\mathbf{x}^T K\mathbf{x}/\mathbf{x}^T\hat{C}\mathbf{x}), \qquad \tilde{\lambda}_N = \max_{\mathbf{x} \neq \mathbf{0}}(\mathbf{x}^T K\mathbf{x}/\mathbf{x}^T\hat{C}\mathbf{x}).$$

Since

$$\mathbf{x}^T K\mathbf{x}/\mathbf{x}^T\hat{C}\mathbf{x} = (\mathbf{x}^T K\mathbf{x}/\mathbf{x}^T\overset{*}{K}\mathbf{x})\cdot(\mathbf{x}^T\overset{*}{K}\mathbf{x}/\mathbf{x}^T\hat{C}\mathbf{x}),$$

we have

$$\kappa(\tilde{K}) \leq \frac{\max_{\mathbf{x} \neq \mathbf{0}}(\mathbf{x}^T K\mathbf{x}/\mathbf{x}^T\overset{*}{K}\mathbf{x})}{\min_{\mathbf{x} \neq \mathbf{0}}(\mathbf{x}^T K\mathbf{x}/\mathbf{x}^T\overset{*}{K}\mathbf{x})}\cdot\frac{\max_{\mathbf{x} \neq \mathbf{0}}(\mathbf{x}^T\overset{*}{K}\mathbf{x}/\mathbf{x}^T\hat{C}\mathbf{x})}{\min_{\mathbf{x} \neq \mathbf{0}}(\mathbf{x}^T\overset{*}{K}\mathbf{x}/\mathbf{x}^T\hat{C}\mathbf{x})}.$$

Now, (7.33) shows that the second factor is bounded by

$$\kappa(\overset{*}{K})^{1/2}\{\tilde{e}_1 + \tilde{e}_2(a_0/hQ + hQ/a_1)\}.$$

Hence, if there are positive constants d_1 and d_2 such that

$$d_1 \mathbf{x}^T \overset{*}{K} \mathbf{x} \leq \mathbf{x}^T K \mathbf{x} \leq d_2 \mathbf{x}^T \overset{*}{K} \mathbf{x} \qquad \forall \mathbf{x} \in R^N, \tag{7.39}$$

then

$$\kappa(\tilde{K}) \leq (d_2/d_1)\kappa(\overset{*}{K})^{1/2}\{\tilde{e}_1 + \tilde{e}_2(a_0/hQ + hQ/a_1)\}. \tag{7.40}$$

Consider now two infinite sets of meshes, the typical members being $\mathscr{M}$ and $\overset{*}{\mathscr{M}}$, and suppose that the two corresponding sets of stiffness matrices are spectrally equivalent. Then, d_2/d_1 can be assumed to be constant for all meshes. Since the remaining part of the bound in (7.40) is the bound that applies when $\hat{C}$ is used to precondition a system of equations with coefficient matrix $\overset{*}{K}$, we have justified our assertion (under the above assumption of spectral equivalence) that $\kappa(\tilde{K})$ is essentially as good as in the case when K is an L matrix. In particular, if $\overset{*}{K}$ satisfies the conditions in (7.34), then

$$\kappa(\tilde{K}) = O[\kappa(\overset{*}{K})^{1/2}] = O[\kappa(K)^{1/2}] = O(h^{-1})$$

for second-order boundary value problems.

Determination of Spectral Equivalence

Our task now is to explain how mesh $\overset{*}{\mathscr{M}}$ can be derived from $\mathscr{M}$ and to investigate the question of spectral equivalence. It is helpful to have a specific boundary value problem in mind and we shall use (5.23), (5.24), assuming for simplicity that $\sigma = 0$ in (5.24b). Figures 7.4a and 7.4b illustrate the construction of $\overset{*}{\mathscr{M}}$ for two examples of higher-degree basis functions. In each figure e_l is the typical element of $\mathscr{M}$, the original mesh. By connecting nodes in the manner shown we form new elements $e_{l,p}$, $p = 1, 2, 3, 4$, which are suited to piecewise linear (Fig. 7.4a) or bilinear (Fig. 7.4b) basis functions. We define $\overset{*}{\mathscr{M}}$ to be the mesh consisting of these new elements.

The higher-degree basis functions of Figs. 7.4a and 7.4b are generalized in Exercises 5.6 and 5.9, respectively. The construction of $\overset{*}{\mathscr{M}}$ is obvious for all of the basis functions in these exercises.

Let T denote the number of nodes in e_l, and let $e_{l,p}$, $p = 1, 2, ..., P$ be the new elements formed by the subdivision of e_l. Let $\phi_i(x, y)$ be the global higher-degree basis function associated with node (x_i, y_i), and let $\theta_i(x, y)$ be the global linear or bilinear basis function associated with the same node. Writing the bilinear form of the boundary value problem as

$$a(u, v) = \iint_\Omega F(u, v)\, dx\, dy$$

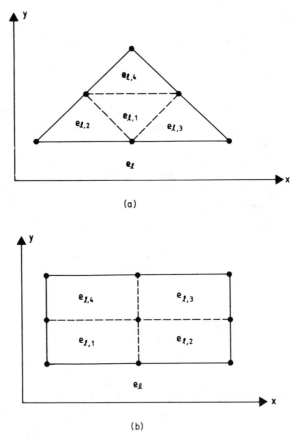

Fig. 7.4.   (a) e_l is a single element in a mesh $\mathcal{M}$ for the quadratic basis functions of Example 5.2. The dashed lines form four elements suited to the linear basis functions of Example 5.1. (b) e_l is a single element in a mesh $\mathcal{M}$ for biquadratic basis functions (Exercise 5.7). The dashed lines form four elements suited to the bilinear basis functions of Example 5.3.

[the assumption that $\sigma = 0$ in (5.24b) implies that there is no line integral in the bilinear form], we define matrices $K^{(l)}$ and $\overset{*}{K}{}^{(l)}$ of order T by

$$k_{rs}^{(l)} = \iint_{e_l} F(\phi_i, \phi_j)\, dx\, dy,$$

$$\overset{*}{k}{}_{rs}^{(l)} = \iint_{e_l} F(\theta_i, \theta_j)\, dx\, dy,$$

for $r, s = 1, 2, ..., T$, where, in terms of the usual node number convention, $i = i_r^{(l)}$ and $j = i_s^{(l)}$. The number of nodes in element $e_{l,p}$ is 3 or 4, depending on whether $e_{l,p}$ is a triangle or a rectangle. Denoting this number by $\overset{*}{T}$, we define a matrix $K^{(l,p)}$ of order $\overset{*}{T}$ by

$$k_{rs}^{(l,p)} = \iint_{e_{l,p}} F(\theta_i, \theta_j)\, dx\, dy, \qquad r, s = 1, 2, \ldots, \overset{*}{T}.$$

Observations

1. $K^{(l)}$ and $K^{(l,p)}$ are the element matrices for e_l and $e_{l,p}$, respectively.
2. K can be assembled from $K^{(l)}$, $l = 1, 2, \ldots, L$, where L is the number of elements in $\mathcal{M}$.
3. $\overset{*}{K}{}^{(l)}$ can be assembled from $K^{(l,p)}$, $p = 1, 2, \ldots, P$.
4. $\overset{*}{K}$ can be assembled from $\overset{*}{K}{}^{(l)}$, $l = 1, 2, \ldots, L$.

Theorem 7.5. Suppose that there are positive constants d_1 and d_2, independent of l, such that

$$d_1 \mathbf{x}^T \overset{*}{K}{}^{(l)} \mathbf{x} \leq \mathbf{x}^T K^{(l)} \mathbf{x} \leq d_2 \mathbf{x}^T \overset{*}{K}{}^{(l)} \mathbf{x} \qquad \forall \mathbf{x} \in R^T, \qquad l = 1, 2, \ldots, L. \quad (7.41)$$

Then (7.39) holds.

PROOF: For any set of vectors $\mathbf{x}^{(1)}, \mathbf{x}^{(2)}, \ldots, \mathbf{x}^{(L)}$ in R^T we obviously have

$$d_1 \sum_{l=1}^{L} \mathbf{x}^{(l)T} \overset{*}{K}{}^{(l)} \mathbf{x}^{(l)} \leq \sum_{l=1}^{L} \mathbf{x}^{(l)T} K^{(l)} \mathbf{x}^{(l)} \leq d_2 \sum_{l=1}^{L} \mathbf{x}^{(l)T} \overset{*}{K}{}^{(l)} \mathbf{x}^{(l)}.$$

For an arbitrary $\mathbf{x} \in R^N$, let $\mathbf{x}^{(l)} \in R^T$ be determined from $\mathbf{x}$ in the same way $\boldsymbol{\alpha}^{(l)}$ was determined from $\boldsymbol{\alpha}$ following (5.99). Then by analogy to (5.99) we have the identities

$$\mathbf{x}^T K \mathbf{x} = \sum_{l=1}^{L} \mathbf{x}^{(l)T} K^{(l)} \mathbf{x}^{(l)}, \qquad \mathbf{x}^T \overset{*}{K} \mathbf{x} = \sum_{l=1}^{L} \mathbf{x}^{(l)T} \overset{*}{K}{}^{(l)} \mathbf{x}^{(l)}.$$

Combining these with the preceding inequalities we obtain (7.39). ∎

It follows from this theorem that if for an infinite family of meshes there exist positive constants d_1 and d_2 independent of the mesh parameter h as well as l, such that (7.41) is satisfied, then the two sets of stiffness matrices $\{K(h)\}$ and $\{\overset{*}{K}(h)\}$ are spectrally equivalent. This is a very practical result since it permits us to restrict our attention henceforth to the low-order matrices $K^{(l)}$ and $\overset{*}{K}{}^{(l)}$.

Example 7.9. We now consider Poisson's equation with a Dirichlet boundary condition,

$$-u_{xx} - u_{yy} = g(x, y) \qquad \text{in } \Omega,$$

$$u = \gamma(x, y) \qquad \text{on } \Gamma,$$

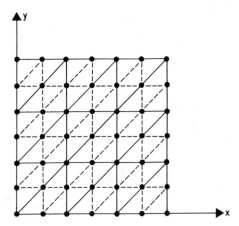

Fig. 7.5. Meshes for the application of quadratic and linear basis functions to the problem of Example 7.9.

where $\bar{\Omega}$ is a square. Let piecewise quadratic basis functions be used on a uniform mesh of six-node isosceles right triangles as illustrated in Fig. 7.5. The dashed lines form a mesh of smaller three-node elements for the use of piecewise linear basis functions.

Let the local node ordering for an element e_l in the coarse mesh be as shown for the standard element in Example 5.2, starting with the vertex at the right angle. The element matrix $K^{(l)}$ is then

$$K^{(l)} = \frac{1}{6} \begin{bmatrix} 6 & 1 & 1 & 0 & -4 & -4 \\ 1 & 3 & 0 & 0 & 0 & -4 \\ 1 & 0 & 3 & 0 & -4 & 0 \\ 0 & 0 & 0 & 16 & -8 & -8 \\ -4 & 0 & -4 & -8 & 16 & 0 \\ -4 & -4 & 0 & -8 & 0 & 16 \end{bmatrix}.$$

(See Exercise 5.15.)

If the local ordering of nodes in an element $e_{l,p}$ in the fine mesh also starts at the vertex of the right angle, then the corresponding element matrix is

$$K^{(l,p)} = \frac{1}{2} \begin{bmatrix} 2 & -1 & -1 \\ -1 & 1 & 0 \\ -1 & 0 & 1 \end{bmatrix}.$$

The assembly of $\overset{*}{K}{}^{(l)}$ from $K^{(l,p)}$, $p = 1, 2, 3, 4$ is carried out in exactly the same way as the assembly of K from $K^{(l)}$, $l = 1, 2, \ldots, L$, the local ordering

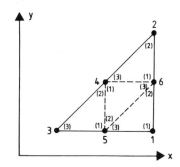

Fig. 7.6. Node orderings for the assembly of $\overset{*}{K}{}^{(l)}$.

of e_l now acting as a global ordering (see Fig. 7.6). A straightforward calculation yields

$$\overset{*}{K}{}^{(l)} = \frac{1}{2}\begin{bmatrix} 2 & 0 & 0 & 0 & -1 & -1 \\ 0 & 1 & 0 & 0 & 0 & -1 \\ 0 & 0 & 1 & 0 & -1 & 0 \\ 0 & 0 & 0 & 4 & -2 & -2 \\ -1 & 0 & -1 & -2 & 4 & 0 \\ -1 & -1 & 0 & -2 & 0 & 4 \end{bmatrix}.$$

Having found $K^{(l)}$ and $\overset{*}{K}{}^{(l)}$, the next step is to establish (7.41), and a way to do this is to examine the *generalized eigenvalue problem*

$$K^{(l)}\mathbf{x} = \lambda\overset{*}{K}{}^{(l)}\mathbf{x}. \tag{7.42}$$

The eigensolutions are shown in Table 7.1. See Exercise 7.17 for details of the computation.

$\mathbf{x}_1$ is special in that

$$K^{(l)}\mathbf{x}_1 = \overset{*}{K}{}^{(l)}\mathbf{x}_1 = \mathbf{0}, \tag{7.43}$$

Table 7.1
The Eigensolutions of (7.42)

i	λ_i	$\mathbf{x}_i$
1	λ	$[1, 1, 1, 1, 1, 1]^T$
2	$\frac{2}{3}$	$[0, 2, 2, 1, 1, 1]^T$
3	$\frac{8}{9}$	$[4, 0, 8, 4\ 5, 3]^T$
4	$\frac{4}{3}$	$[0, 0, 0, 1, 0, 0]^T$
5	$\frac{4}{3}$	$[0, 0, 0, 1, 2, 0]^T$
6	$\frac{4}{3}$	$[0, 0, 0, 2, 1, 3]^T$

so any number λ is a corresponding eigenvalue. We leave it to the reader to verify that

$$\mathbf{x}_i^{\mathrm{T}} \overset{*}{K}{}^{(l)} \mathbf{x}_j = 0, \qquad i \neq j. \tag{7.44}$$

Any $\mathbf{x} \in R^6$ can be expanded in the form $\mathbf{x} = \sum_{i=1}^{6} c_i \mathbf{x}_i$, and using (7.43) and (7.44) we find that

$$\mathbf{x}^{\mathrm{T}} K^{(l)} \mathbf{x} = \sum_{i,j=1}^{6} c_i c_j \mathbf{x}_i^{\mathrm{T}} K^{(l)} \mathbf{x}_j = \sum_{i,j=2}^{6} c_i c_j \mathbf{x}_i^{\mathrm{T}} K^{(l)} \mathbf{x}_j$$

$$= \sum_{i,j=2}^{6} c_i c_j \lambda_j \mathbf{x}_i^{\mathrm{T}} \overset{*}{K}{}^{(l)} \mathbf{x}_j = \sum_{i=2}^{6} c_i^2 \lambda_i \mathbf{x}_i^{\mathrm{T}} \overset{*}{K}{}^{(l)} \mathbf{x}_i$$

and similarly that

$$\mathbf{x}^{\mathrm{T}} \overset{*}{K}{}^{(l)} \mathbf{x} = \sum_{i=2}^{6} c_i^2 \mathbf{x}_i^{\mathrm{T}} \overset{*}{K}{}^{(l)} \mathbf{x}_i.$$

Then,

$$\lambda_2 \mathbf{x}^{\mathrm{T}} \overset{*}{K}{}^{(l)} \mathbf{x} \leq \mathbf{x}^{\mathrm{T}} K^{(l)} \mathbf{x} \leq \lambda_6 \mathbf{x}^{\mathrm{T}} \overset{*}{K}{}^{(l)} \mathbf{x} \qquad \forall \mathbf{x} \in R^6,$$

and (7.41) is established with $d_1 = \lambda_2$ and $d_2 = \lambda_6$. Since these constants are independent of the size of the elements, we have from Theorem 7.5 the spectral equivalence bound $d_2/d_1 = 2$ for the sets of stiffness matrices $\{K(h)\}$ and $\{\overset{*}{K}(h)\}$.

The number of iterations required by the preconditioned conjugate gradient method is proportional to $\kappa(\tilde{K})^{1/2}$, and we see from (7.40) and the subsequent remark that at most 41% more iterations (this is probably a very pessimistic estimate) are needed to solve $K\boldsymbol{\alpha} = \mathbf{G}$ than $\overset{*}{K}\boldsymbol{\alpha} = \overset{*}{\mathbf{G}}$ (the Ritz–Galerkin system for $\mathscr{M}$) when $\hat{C}$ is used to precondition each system. This result is independent of the fineness of the mesh.

We continue Example 7.9 to illustrate an alternative technique for obtaining a spectral equivalence bound, based on separate examinations of the matrices $K^{(l)}$ and $\overset{*}{K}{}^{(l)}$. Thus, let the eigenvalues of these matrices be denoted

$$0 = \mu_1 < \mu_2 \leq \cdots \leq \mu_6 \qquad \text{and} \qquad 0 - \overset{*}{\mu}_1 < \overset{*}{\mu}_2 \leq \cdots \leq \overset{*}{\mu}_6,$$

respectively. These orderings reflect the fact that $K^{(l)}$ and $\overset{*}{K}{}^{(l)}$ are positive semidefinite and that the smallest eigenvalue of each is simple. Further,

$$\mathbf{x}^{\mathrm{T}} K^{(l)} \mathbf{x} = 0 \quad \Leftrightarrow \quad \mathbf{x}^{\mathrm{T}} \overset{*}{K}{}^{(l)} \mathbf{x} = 0 \quad \Leftrightarrow \quad \mathbf{x} = c \begin{bmatrix} 1 \\ 1 \\ 1 \\ 1 \\ 1 \\ 1 \end{bmatrix}.$$

Let $\tilde{R}^6$ denote the set of vectors obtained from R^6 by removing all vectors of this type. It is easy to show that

$$0 < \mu_2 \mathbf{x}^T \mathbf{x} \leq \mathbf{x}^T K^{(l)} \mathbf{x} \leq \mu_6 \mathbf{x}^T \mathbf{x},$$

$$0 < \overset{*}{\mu}_2 \mathbf{x}^T \mathbf{x} \leq \mathbf{x}^T \overset{*}{K}{}^{(l)} \mathbf{x} \leq \overset{*}{\mu}_6 \mathbf{x}^T \mathbf{x},$$

$\forall \mathbf{x} \in \tilde{R}^6$, implying

$$(\mu_2/\overset{*}{\mu}_6) \mathbf{x}^T \overset{*}{K}{}^{(l)} \mathbf{x} \leq \mathbf{x}^T K^{(l)} \mathbf{x} \leq (\mu_6/\overset{*}{\mu}_2) \mathbf{x}^T \overset{*}{K}{}^{(l)} \mathbf{x} \qquad \forall \mathbf{x} \in R^6.$$

Thus (7.41) is established, with

$$d_1 = \mu_2/\overset{*}{\mu}_6, \qquad d_2 = \mu_6/\overset{*}{\mu}_2. \tag{7.45}$$

It is left to the reader (Exercise 7.20) to verify that $d_2/d_1 \simeq 155$, a much larger bound than that obtained from our analysis of (7.42).

That the second technique in Example 7.9 could not give a better bound than the first follows immediately from a well-known property of (7.42), namely,

$$\lambda_2 = \min_{\mathbf{x} \in \tilde{R}^6} (\mathbf{x}^T K^{(l)} \mathbf{x} / \mathbf{x}^T \overset{*}{K}{}^{(l)} \mathbf{x}), \qquad \lambda_6 = \max_{\mathbf{x} \in \tilde{R}^6} (\mathbf{x}^T K^{(l)} \mathbf{x} / \mathbf{x}^T \overset{*}{K}{}^{(l)} \mathbf{x}).$$

Nevertheless, the second technique is sometimes more convenient for the proof of spectral equivalence in more difficult cases.

We shall now extend the analysis of the boundary value problem in Example 7.9 to more general basis functions and a class of nonuniform meshes. It was described in Section 5.1 how an infinite family of meshes of triangular elements can be systematically generated by repeated refinement of an original coarse mesh. At each step of the refinement process new vertex nodes are created at the mid-edge points of the old element edges and joined so as to divide every old element into four new elements (see Fig. 5.3). The same procedure can be applied to rectangular elements. Clearly, every element of every mesh is geometrically similar to at least one of the elements of the original mesh. (Two triangles are similar if they have the same angles; two rectangles are similar if they have the same edge ratio.) We call any mesh refinement process with this property *strictly uniform*.

Let $\mathcal{M}$ denote the original coarse mesh and let L be the number of elements in $\mathcal{M}$. We assume that the nodes of $\mathcal{M}$ correspond to the use of higher degree basis functions. Let $\overset{*}{\mathcal{M}}$ be the mesh derived from $\mathcal{M}$ for the use of linear or bilinear basis functions, as described earlier. We denote the eigenvalues of $K^{(l)}$ and $\overset{*}{K}{}^{(l)}$ by

$$0 = \mu_1^{(l)} < \mu_2^{(l)} \leq \cdots \leq \mu_T^{(l)} \qquad \text{and} \qquad 0 = \overset{*}{\mu}_1^{(l)} < \overset{*}{\mu}_2^{(l)} \leq \cdots \leq \overset{*}{\mu}_T^{(l)},$$

respectively.

Let a strictly uniform mesh refinement take place. An analysis, which we omit, shows that the eigenvalues of any element matrix $K^{(l)}$ associated with any mesh are identical to those of one of the element matrices of the original mesh. In fact, if consistent local node orderings are used, then the two matrices are identical, as illustrated in Example 7.9. Similar remarks apply to $\overset{*}{K}{}^{(l)}$. Applying the second technique of Example 7.9 to the present problem, we see that (7.41) is valid with

$$d_1 = \min_{1 \le l \le L} (\mu_2^{(l)}/\overset{*}{\mu}_T^{(l)}), \qquad d_2 = \max_{1 \le l \le L} (\mu_T^{(l)}/\overset{*}{\mu}_2^{(l)}).$$

Since d_1 and d_2 are independent of the level of the mesh refinement, d_2/d_1 is a spectral equivalence bound for the sets $\{K(h)\}$ and $\{\overset{*}{K}(h)\}$.

In the case of Poisson's equation in n dimensions, the eigenvalues of an element matrix $K^{(l)}$ associated with the typical mesh $\mathcal{M}(h)$ are proportional by a factor ch^{n-2} to those of one of the original element matrices. This obviously does not affect the values of d_1 and d_2 defined previously. Further, the analysis can be extended to problems with variable coefficients. In certain cases $K^{(l)}$ and $\overset{*}{K}{}^{(l)}$ are definite rather than semidefinite (see Theorem 5.1), in which case $\mu_2^{(l)}$ and $\overset{*}{\mu}_2^{(l)}$ in the expressions for d_1 and d_2 must be replaced by $\mu_1^{(l)}$ and $\overset{*}{\mu}_1^{(l)}$, respectively.

Let $\mathcal{M}(h_q) \to \mathcal{M}(h_{q+1})$ denote the typical step in the mesh refinement process. This may—but need not—be identical to the step $\mathcal{M}(h_q) \to \overset{*}{\mathcal{M}}(h_q)$. Figures 5.3 and 7.4a illustrate the case in which the two coincide.

7.4   Calculation of Residuals:
Computational Labor and Stability

Introduction

This section is devoted to two topics connected with the application of iterative methods, namely, computational labor and stability. Although much of the material is relevant to iterative methods in general, we naturally emphasize the preconditioned conjugate gradient method.

At the heart of almost any iterative method for solving the system $K\alpha = G$ is the determination (implicit or explicit) of the *residual vector*

$$\mathbf{r}^k = K\alpha^k - \mathbf{G}.$$

For example, the stationary iterative method defined by

$$C\alpha^{k+1} = -R\alpha^k + \mathbf{G}, \qquad k = 0, 1, 2, \ldots, \qquad \text{(version 1)}$$

based on the splitting

$$K = C + R,$$

has the equivalent "iterative refinement" formulation

$$\boldsymbol{\alpha}^{k+1} = \boldsymbol{\alpha}^k - C^{-1}\mathbf{r}^k, \qquad k = 0, 1, 2, \ldots, \qquad \text{(version 2)}.$$

[See (1.61), (1.74), and (6.49).]

In the simple conjugate gradient method (1.45) the residual (or, gradient, as we have called it in this context) is computed explicitly by a recursive formula. The same is true of the untransformed preconditioned conjugate gradient method (1.56). In the transformed preconditioned conjugate gradient method (1.98) the vector $\overset{*}{\mathbf{g}}^k$ satisfies (with obvious changes of notation)

$$\overset{*}{\mathbf{g}}^k = \overset{*}{K}\mathbf{z}^k - \overset{*}{\mathbf{G}} = (F^{-1}KF^{-\mathrm{T}})(F^{\mathrm{T}}\boldsymbol{\alpha}^k) - F^{-1}\mathbf{G} = F^{-1}\mathbf{r}^k;$$

i.e., we are here computing a *transformed* residual.

The computational labor of an iterative method, the first topic of this section, is largely determined by how the residual is formulated. In the following discussion we are primarily interested in comparing (1.98) (transformed residual), as implemented by (1.100), with (1.56) (untransformed residual), as implemented by (1.92). We saw in Section 1.4 that the former is generally superior in the case of preconditioning by SSOR. It will be demonstrated by an example that for finite element problems this superiority often carries over to preconditioning by modified incomplete factorization.

The second topic is the numerical stability of an iterative method. The more stable the method, the lesser the influence of rounding errors and errors in data on the computed solution. Stability is intimately related to details of the computation of the residual vector. Some special techniques for computing the untransformed residual $\mathbf{r}^k$ when the system of equations arises from a finite element problem will be presented. (They need only be used in the final iterations.) We shall see how such techniques can also be applied to methods such as (1.98) that involve a transformed residual.

Computational Labor

Although the first version of the stationary iterative method mentioned previously was not explicitly expressed in terms of the residual vector, it corresponds very closely with regard to computational labor and storage to the iterations

$$\boldsymbol{\alpha}^{k+1} = \boldsymbol{\alpha}^k - C^{-1}\mathbf{r}^k, \qquad k = 0, 1, 2, \ldots,$$

where $C^{-1}\mathbf{r}^k$ is computed from the identity

$$C^{-1}\mathbf{r}^k = C^{-1}[(C + R)\boldsymbol{\alpha}^k - \mathbf{G}] = \boldsymbol{\alpha}^k + C^{-1}(R\boldsymbol{\alpha}^k - \mathbf{G}).$$

In the second version $C^{-1}\mathbf{r}^k$ is computed from

$$C^{-1}\mathbf{r}^k = C^{-1}(K\boldsymbol{\alpha}^k - \mathbf{G}).$$

Thus, although the two versions are mathematically equivalent their computer implementations are not, the first requiring R instead of K. If R is sparser than K, the first version is more efficient. We shall see that in finite element problems R may well be the sparser matrix. With preconditioning by incomplete factorization the relation between the conjugate gradient algorithms (1.98) and (1.56) is very similar, the first requiring R instead of K.

We turn our attention now to (1.100), the computer implementation of (1.98). Our first task is to update (1.100) to cover the case of preconditioning by *modified* incomplete factorization. We recall that it was the exploitation of the relation $H = LDL^T + R$ that led to the version of (1.100) for unmodified incomplete factorization [see (1.99)]. With modified incomplete factorization, as defined by (7.18), we have

$$\hat{K} = K + \hat{E} = \hat{L}\hat{D}\hat{L}^T + \hat{R},$$

where K is the given matrix, $\hat{E}$ is defined by

$$\hat{E} = \text{diag}(\sigma_1\delta_1, \sigma_2\delta_2, \ldots, \sigma_{N-1}\delta_{N-1}, 0)$$

[see (7.20)], and $\hat{L}$ and $\hat{D}$ are the computed factors. Hence

$$K = \hat{L}\hat{D}\hat{L}^T + \hat{R}_1,$$

where

$$\hat{R}_1 = \hat{R} - \hat{E}, \tag{7.46}$$

and in (1.100) we must now put

$$F = \hat{L}, \qquad G = \hat{D}^{-1}, \qquad R = \hat{R}_1.$$

Further, the statement $\mathbf{g} := F^{-1}(H\mathbf{x} - \mathbf{g})$ must be replaced by either

$$\mathbf{g} := \hat{L}^{-1}(K\mathbf{x} - \mathbf{g}) \qquad \text{or} \qquad \mathbf{g} := \hat{L}^{-1}[(\hat{L}\hat{D}\hat{L}^T + \hat{R}_1)\mathbf{x} - \mathbf{g}].$$

The latter has the important advantage that it eliminates the need for K, i.e., it permits an implementation of (7.18) in which $\hat{L}$ and $\hat{D}$ are written over K, saving storage.

The implementation of (7.18) must of course now include the computation and storage of $\hat{R}_1$. This can be done by assembling the nonzero entries of the "fill-in" matrices (7.31) together with the nonzero diagonal entries of $-\hat{E}$. All of these numbers are available during the computation, and the complexity of the programming of this assembly process depends mainly on whether the sparsity pattern of $\hat{R}_1$ has been determined a priori, making possible a preassigned data structure for $\hat{R}_1$. In principle, the sparsity pattern of $\hat{R}_1$ can be deduced directly from the finite element mesh. As we shall see, this is often a straightforward process when $J = S_K$.

When $\hat{R}_1$ is sparser than K, then (1.100), updated as described, is more efficient than the use of (1.92) with $C = \hat{L}\hat{D}\hat{L}^T$. (The two methods are of course mathematically equivalent.) The following example shows that $\hat{R}_1$ may indeed be the sparser matrix.

Example 7.10. We consider the boundary value problem

$$-[p(x, y)u_x]_x - [p(x, y)u_y]_y + q(x, y)u = g(x, y) \qquad \text{in } \Omega,$$

$$u = \gamma(x, y) \qquad \text{on } \Gamma,$$

where $\bar{\Omega}$ is a rectangle, and the use of piecewise linear basis functions on a mesh of isosceles right triangles. Let the interior nodes be ordered first, row-wise as illustrated in Fig. 7.7. The parameter M is the number of interior nodes on a horizontal line of the mesh.

We show in Fig. 7.8 the upper left corner of the stiffness matrix K when $M = 6$, denoting its nonzero entries by " $\times$," together with the nonzero off-diagonal entries of $\hat{R}_1$ (which are also those of $\hat{R}$), denoted $-c_3, -c_4, \ldots$. We have put $J = S_K$ in the factorization process (7.18). It is left to the reader to verify that the rth step of (7.18), where $r = 1, 2, \ldots, N - 1$, produces

$$c_{r+1} = \begin{cases} 0, & r = 1, 2, M + 1, M + 2, 2M + 1, 2M + 2, \ldots, \\ (k^{(r)}_{r+M-1,r})^2/\hat{k}^{(r)}_{rr}, & \text{otherwise}. \end{cases}$$

Defining $c_i = 0$ for $i < 2$ and $i > N$, we can write the ith row of $\hat{R}$ as follows:

$(i + 2 - M)$	(i)	$(i - 2 + M)$
$-c_{i+2-M}$	$(c_{i+2-M} + c_i)$	$-c_i$

Hence, for any vector $\mathbf{x}$ we have

$$(\hat{R}_1\mathbf{x})_i = -c_{i+2-M}x_{i+2-M} + d_ix_i - c_ix_{i-2+M}, \qquad (7.47a)$$

where $d_i = c_{i+2-M} + c_i - \sigma_i\delta_i$.

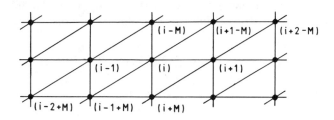

Fig. 7.7.   A section of the mesh of Example 7.10.

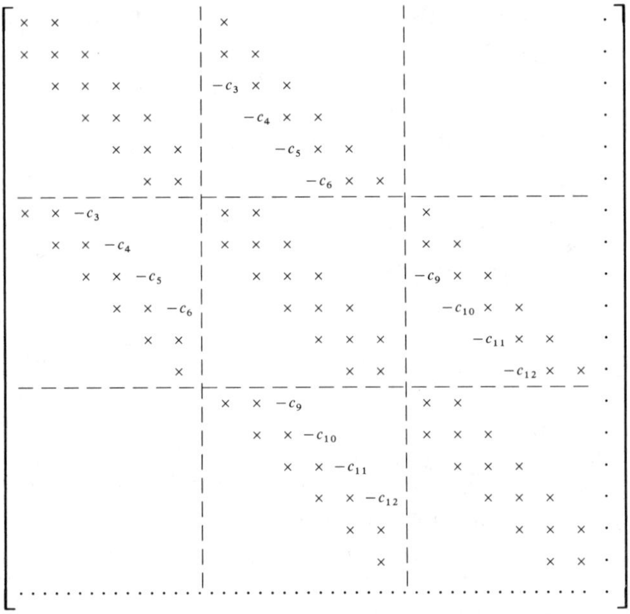

Fig. 7.8. Nonzero entries of the stiffness matrix K of Example 7.10 ($\times$) and nonzero off-diagonal entries of the associated matrix $\hat{R}_1(-c_3, -c_4, \ldots)$.

Thus, the program that implements (7.18) can store the value $\{c_i\}$ and $\{d_i\}$ in two single-indexed arrays for later reference whenever a product of the form $\hat{R}_1 \mathbf{x}$ is required by the program that implements (1.100). Alternatively, (7.47a) can be expressed as

$$(\hat{R}_1 \mathbf{x})_i = c_{i+2-M}(x_i - x_{i+2-M}) + c_i(x_i - x_{i-2+M}) - \sigma_i \delta_i x_i, \quad (7.47b)$$

and we can store the values of $\{c_i\}$ and $\{\sigma_i \delta_i\}$.

The use of (1.92) instead of (1.100) would require the storage of K and the computation of products of the form $K\mathbf{x}$ instead of the storage of $\hat{R}_1$ and the computation of $\hat{R}_1\mathbf{x}$. Since K and $\hat{R}_1$ have seven and three nonzero diagonals, respectively, we are saving $2N$ words of storage by using (1.100). Further, from (1.94c) and (1.101b) we find that the number of flops per iteration is about

$$(r_K + r_K^{(J)} + 5)N = (7 + 7 + 5)N = 19N$$

and

$$(r_K^{(J)} + r_{\hat{R}_1} + 6)N = (7 + 3 + 6)N = 16N$$

for (1.92) and (1.100), respectively.

We shall see shortly that (7.47b) is preferable to (7.47a) with regard to rounding errors.

Since the complete factorization of a band matrix tends to produce fill-in in the entire band, it may seem strange that the fill-in matrix $\hat{R}$ in the preceding example is not dense in the second and third diagonals above and below the main diagonal. The explanation is that in the case of complete factorization fill-in produces more fill-in, whereas with incomplete factorization fill-in (outside of the index set J) is removed before this can happen.

For the same reason, it is easier to determine directly from the finite element mesh the positions of the nonzero entries of $\hat{R}$ than it is to determine the positions of fill-in in the case of complete factorization. We leave it to the reader to verify that if $J = S_K$, then $(\hat{R})_{ij} \neq 0$, $i \neq j$ only if

(1) mesh nodes N_i and N_j do not belong to a common element,
(2) there is a node N_k, where $k < i$ and $k < j$, such that N_k and N_i belong to a common element and N_k and N_j belong to a common element.

For i as shown in Fig. 7.7, for example, there are only two nonzero entries in the ith row of $\hat{R}$, and these have column numbers $j = i + 2 - M$ ($k = i + 1 - M$) and $j = i - 2 + M$ ($k = i - 1$).

It should be mentioned that if $\hat{L}\hat{D}\hat{L}^T$ is a modified (or unmodified) incomplete factorization of a stiffness matrix $\overset{*}{K}$ based on linear or bilinear basis functions to be used to precondition a matrix K based on higher-degree basis functions, as described in Section 7.3, then (1.100) is not applicable.

Numerical Stability: Introduction

Let $K\alpha = G^*$ be the Ritz–Galerkin system derived from the finite element treatment of a boundary value problem with solution $u(x, y)$. [Regarding the notation for the right-hand side vector, it is convenient in this section to adhere to the convention of Section 5.2 [see (5.29)], according to which G and G^* denote the vector before and after, respectively, the imposition of a Dirichlet boundary condition.] Suppose that $u \in H^{k+1}(\Omega)$, where k is the usual accuracy parameter of the basis functions. The Aubin–Nitsche method (Section 5.4) establishes that if the boundary value problem has elliptic regularity, then

$$\| u - u_N \| = O(h^{k+1}).$$

Defining $u_i = u(N_i)$ and using the relation

$$u_i - \alpha_i = u(N_i) - u_N(N_i),$$

it is straightfoward to show that

$$\|\mathbf{u} - \boldsymbol{\alpha}\|/\|\mathbf{u}\| \simeq \|u - u_N\|/\|u\| = O(h^{k+1}).$$

Let $\tilde{\alpha}_i$ denote the *computed* value of α_i produced by some equation solver on a computer with machine precision ε_M. (See Section 6.4 for the definition of this parameter.) Because of rounding errors, there is typically a value $s \geq 0$, dependent on the details of the computation, for which

$$\|\boldsymbol{\alpha} - \tilde{\boldsymbol{\alpha}}\|/\|\boldsymbol{\alpha}\| = O(\varepsilon_M h^{-s}).$$

Since $\|\boldsymbol{\alpha}\| \simeq \|\mathbf{u}\|$ we have

$$\|\mathbf{u} - \tilde{\boldsymbol{\alpha}}\|/\|\mathbf{u}\| \lesssim \|\mathbf{u} - \boldsymbol{\alpha}\|/\|\mathbf{u}\| + \|\boldsymbol{\alpha} - \tilde{\boldsymbol{\alpha}}\|/\|\boldsymbol{\alpha}\|$$
$$= O(h^{k+1}) + O(\varepsilon_M h^{-s}).$$

We call the three terms in this inequality the *total relative error*, the *relative discretization error*, and the *relative rounding error*, respectively. They are illustrated in Fig. 7.9. Obviously, there is a point at which further mesh refinement is useless. The value of h at this point and the corresponding value of the total error depend on ε_M.

In making these remarks we have implicitly assumed that the only source of error is the rounding error incurred in the process of solving the given system of equations. In addition to this there may be errors in some or all of the entries of K and $\mathbf{G}^*$. If these errors are roughly of size ε, where ε is independent of the mesh parameter h and satisfies $\varepsilon > \varepsilon_M$, then the behavior of the total relative error typically behaves like $O(h^{k+1}) + O(\varepsilon h^{-s})$ for the same value of s. Data errors of this type include measurement errors and rounding errors in numerical integration and in the assembly of K.

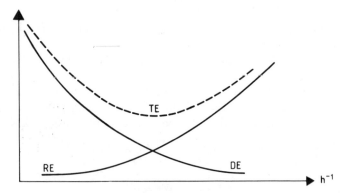

Fig. 7.9. Typical behavior of relative discretization error (DE), relative rounding error (RE), and total relative error (TE) as a function of h^{-1}.

As mentioned in Section 6.4, with the use of a direct method to solve the system of equations, we typically have $s = 3$. Our interest here, however, is the influence of errors in the context of the preconditioned conjugate gradient method as defined by versions (1.56) and (1.98). To keep the material within bounds, we confine our attention to the computation of the gradient vector alone, since this turns out to be the crucial step. After showing that the straightforward calculation of the gradient in (1.56) can be expected to make $s = 2$, we present two methods for computing the gradient with less error. Both methods replace the recursive calculation

$$g^{k+1} = g^k + \tau_k K d^k \tag{7.48a}$$

by implementations of the direct formulation

$$g^{k+1} = K\alpha^{k+1} - G^* \tag{7.48b}$$

that exploit the finite element origin of the system of equations. Since the direct computation of the gradient roughly doubles the computational labor per iteration, it should only be used for the final iterations.

In version (1.98) of the conjugate gradient method, we have

$$\overset{*}{g}{}^{k+1} = \overset{*}{g}{}^k + \overset{*}{\tau}_k \overset{*}{K} \overset{*}{d}{}^k.$$

Replacing this by the mathematically equivalent formulation

$$\alpha^{k+1} = F^{-T} z^{k+1}, \qquad g^{k+1} = K\alpha^{k+1} - G^*, \qquad \overset{*}{g}{}^{k+1} = F^{-1} g^{k+1},$$

we can exploit the methods to be described for the accurate computation of (7.48b). Again, this need be done only in the final iterations.

Preliminary Analysis

We assume for the time being that there are no errors in K and G^*. If there were no rounding errors in the execution of algorithm (1.56), then the gradient g^{k+1} would satisfy

$$g^{k+1} = g^k + \tau_k K d^k = K\alpha^{k+1} - G^*. \tag{7.49a}$$

Suppose, however, that in this iteration g^{k+1} is computed from (7.48a) in finite-precision floating-point arithmetic. If

$$\tilde{g}^{k+1} \equiv \mathrm{fl}(g^k + \tau_k K d^k) \tag{7.49b}$$

denotes the computed value of g^{k+1}, then the corresponding rounding error is

$$\varepsilon^{k+1} = g^{k+1} - \tilde{g}^{k+1}.$$

Obviously,

$$\tilde{g}^{k+1} = K\alpha^{k+1} - (G^* + \varepsilon^{k+1}),$$

showing that $\tilde{g}^{k+1}$ is the exact gradient produced by α^{k+1} for a perturbed system of equations, which we can write in the form

$$K(\alpha + \delta^{k+1}) = G^* + \varepsilon^{k+1}.$$

This relation, which implicitly defines δ^{k+1}, suggests that we cannot expect the rounding error in the computed solution of $K\alpha = G^*$ to be less than δ^{k+1}. From the foregoing we see that $K\delta^{k+1} = \varepsilon^{k+1}$, so

$$\| \delta^{k+1} \| \le \| K^{-1} \| \cdot \| \varepsilon^{k+1} \|.$$

For ease of presentation we shall assume that the system $K\alpha = G^*$ has been normalized by diagonal scaling as indicated by the operations $K := D^{-1/2}KD^{-1/2}$ and $G^* := D^{-1/2}G^*$, where D is the diagonal part of the original stiffness matrix. The entries of the scaled matrix then satisfy $k_{ij} = O(1), h \to 0$. (This assumption can be dropped in the case of a second-order boundary value problem in two space dimensions, since even without scaling the entries of K have this order of magnitude.) For a series of mesh refinements satisfying (5.102), the number of nonzero entries in the ith row of K is bounded by a constant independent of i and h. Hence $\| K \|_\infty = O(1), h \to 0$, and from the inequality $\| K \| \le \| K \|_\infty$ (valid for any symmetric matrix K) and the result $\kappa(K) = O(h^{-2})$ from Section 5.5, it follows that $\| K^{-1} \| = O(h^{-2})$. Thus,

$$\| \delta^{k+1} \| = O(h^{-2}) \cdot \| \varepsilon^{k+1} \|. \tag{7.50}$$

An analysis of (7.49b), which we omit, establishes that

$$|\varepsilon_i^{(k+1)}| = \varepsilon_M \cdot O(1), \qquad h \to 0.$$

Then,

$$\| \varepsilon^{k+1} \| = N^{1/2}\varepsilon_M O(1) = \| \alpha \| \varepsilon_M O(1), \qquad h \to 0$$

[since $\| \alpha \| = O(N^{1/2})$], and it follows from (7.50) that the relative rounding error satisfies

$$\| \delta^{k+1} \| / \| \alpha \| = O(\varepsilon_M h^{-2}).$$

Hence, we are led to the value $s = 2$ for the parameter introduced at the beginning of this discussion.

We shall now consider the case in which there are errors in data bounded by some value ε. That is, the system given to the equation solver has the data

$K + \Delta K$ and $\mathbf{G}^* + \Delta \mathbf{G}^*$, where

$$|(\Delta K)_{ij}| \leq \varepsilon, \qquad |(\Delta \mathbf{G}^*)_i| \leq \varepsilon, \qquad i, j = 1, 2, \ldots, N.$$

Naturally, it can be assumed that

$$k_{ij} = 0 \quad \Rightarrow \quad (\Delta K)_{ij} = 0.$$

With no errors in data and no rounding errors in the execution of (1.56), the gradient $\mathbf{g}^{k+1}$ would again satisfy (7.49a). Suppose, however, that in this iteration the data errors in K and $\mathbf{G}^*$ are introduced. Ignoring rounding errors for simplicity, we see that the computed gradient is

$$\tilde{\mathbf{g}}^{k+1} \equiv (K + \Delta K)\alpha^{k+1} - (\mathbf{G}^* + \Delta \mathbf{G}^*) = K\alpha^{k+1} - (\mathbf{G}^* + \varepsilon^{k+1}),$$

where

$$\varepsilon^{k+1} \equiv \mathbf{g}^{k+1} - \tilde{\mathbf{g}}^{k+1} = \Delta \mathbf{G}^* - (\Delta K)\alpha^{k+1}.$$

Thus, once again the computed gradient $\tilde{\mathbf{g}}^{k+1}$ is the exact gradient produced by α^{k+1} for a perturbed system of the form

$$K(\alpha + \delta^{k+1}) = \mathbf{G}^* + \varepsilon^{k+1}.$$

It is easy to see that

$$|\varepsilon_i^{(k+1)}| = \varepsilon \cdot O(1), \qquad h \to 0,$$

and proceeding as before we arrive at the bound

$$\| \delta^{k+1} \| / \| \alpha \| = O(\varepsilon h^{-2}). \tag{7.51}$$

This analysis supports the assertion made earlier that the influence of errors in data is essentially the same as that of rounding errors. The combined influence of both types of error is described by (7.51), where ε is understood to be replaced by ε_M if ε_M exceeds the error in data.

Among the possible attempts to improve accuracy are the following.

(1) In (1.56) replace (7.48a) by a straightforward implementation of (7.48b). An analysis of this procedure shows that we still have $s = 2$.

(2) Carry out all calculations in double precision. This doubles storage and increases computing time considerably. Further, it cannot substantially reduce the influence of those data errors that are independent of machine precision.

(3) In (1.56) replace (7.48a) by an implementation of (7.48b) based on double-precision inner product accumulation, otherwise retaining single-precision accuracy. This technique, which costs very little, is effective when the level of error in data is less than the single-precision value of ε_M.

A common feature of all of these techniques is that in each case $s = 2$, the improved accuracy obtained from (2) and (3) being essentially due to a reduction of ε_M. The remainder of this section is devoted to two alternative methods that achieve a lower value of s and thereby reduce the influence of even machine-independent data errors.

Method 1: Summation of First-Order Differences

This technique will be illustrated for the case of the finite element treatment of boundary value problem (5.23), (5.24) described in Section 5.2. To simplify the discussion slightly we assume that $\sigma = \xi = 0$ in the boundary condition on Γ_1. Thus, at the end of the fourth step of the assembly process [see (5.31)] arrays K and G contain the values

$$k_{ij} = \iint_\Omega \left[p(\phi_i)_x(\phi_j)_x + p(\phi_i)_y(\phi_j)_y + q\phi_i\phi_j \right] dx\, dy,$$

$$G_i = \iint_\Omega g\phi_i\, dx\, dy.$$

The "condensed" $N \times N$ Ritz–Galerkin system is

$$\sum_{j \in J} k_{ij}\alpha_j = G_i^* \equiv G_i - \sum_{j \in J_0} k_{ij}\gamma(N_j) \qquad \forall i \in J. \tag{7.52}$$

If α^{k+1} is some approximation to α, the components of the corresponding gradient are

$$g_i^{(k+1)} = \sum_{j \in J} k_{ij}\alpha_j^{(k+1)} - \left[G_i - \sum_{j \in J_0} k_{ij}\gamma(N_j) \right]$$

$$= \sum_{j=1}^{M} k_{ij}\alpha_j^{(k+1)} - G_i, \qquad i \in J,$$

where we have defined

$$\alpha_j^{(k+1)} = \gamma(N_j), \qquad j \in J_0,$$

and where M denotes the total number of nodes in the mesh. Introducing the parameter $\sigma_i = \sum_{j=1}^{M} k_{ij}$, we can write

$$g_i^{(k+1)} = \sum_{j=1}^{M} k_{ij}\alpha_j^{(k+1)} - G_i + \alpha_i^{(k+1)}\left(\sigma_i - \sum_{j=1}^{M} k_{ij} \right)$$

$$= \sum_{j=1,\, j \neq i}^{M} k_{ij}(\alpha_j^{(k+1)} - \alpha_i^{(k+1)}) - G_i + \alpha_i^{(k+1)}\sigma_i, \qquad i \in J. \tag{7.53a}$$

This is the *method of first-order differences* for computing the gradient vector. Since it requires all of the nonzero entries k_{ij}, including those that correspond to a coupling between an internal node and a node on Γ_0, the fifth step of the assembly process (5.31e) must be modified to save the latter entries.

This method can be implemented at *element level* provided the element matrices $\{K^{(l)}\}_{l=1}^L$ and element vectors $\{G^{(l)}\}_{l=1}^L$ have been saved. The computation is described by

$$g_i^{(k+1)} = \sum_{l \in S_i} \left\{ \sum_{s=1, s \neq r}^T k_{rs}^{(l)}(\alpha_j^{(k+1)} - \alpha_i^{(k+1)}) - G_r^{(l)} + \alpha_i^{(k+1)}\sigma_r^{(l)} \right\}. \quad (7.53b)$$

S_i is the set of element numbers of elements containing node N_i, T is the number of nodes in an element, i and j are related to r and s, respectively, by $i = i_r^{(l)}$ and $j = i_s^{(l)}$ (this node number convention is described in Section 5.1), and $\sigma_r^{(l)} = \sum_{s=1}^T k_{rs}^{(l)}$.

Generally speaking, (7.53b) is preferable to (7.53a) when element matrix entries of greatly varying orders of magnitude are combined during the assembly of K, leading to significant rounding errors.

The following example illustrates (7.53a) and (7.53b) in a simple case.

Example 7.11. We consider the application of piecewise linear basis functions to a second-order boundary value problem in one space dimension (for simplicity), a typical section of the mesh being as follows.

$$\begin{array}{ccccccc} |\ (1) & e_i & (2)\ | \ (1) & e_{i+1} & (2)\ | \\ x_{i-1} & & x_i & & x_{i+1} \end{array}$$

The Ritz–Galerkin equation corresponding to node i can be written

$$k_{i,i-1}\alpha_{i-1} + k_{ii}\alpha_i + k_{i,i+1}\alpha_{i+1} = G_i,$$

where

$$k_{i,i-1} = k_{21}^{(i)}, \qquad\qquad k_{i,i+1} = k_{12}^{(i+1)}$$
$$k_{ii} = k_{22}^{(i)} + k_{11}^{(i+1)}, \qquad G_i = G_2^{(i)} + G_1^{(i+1)}.$$

Equations (7.53a) and (7.53b) become

$$g_i^{(k+1)} = k_{i,i-1}(\alpha_{i-1}^{(k+1)} - \alpha_i^{(k+1)}) + k_{i,i+1}(\alpha_{i+1}^{(k+1)} - \alpha_i^{(k+1)})$$
$$- G_i + \alpha_i^{(k+1)}\sigma_i$$

and

$$g_i^{(k+1)} = \{k_{21}^{(i)}(\alpha_{i-1}^{(k+1)} - \alpha_i^{(k+1)}) - G_2^{(i)} + \alpha_i^{(k+1)}\sigma_2^{(i)}\}$$
$$+ \{k_{12}^{(i+1)}(\alpha_{i+1}^{(k+1)} - \alpha_i^{(k+1)}) - G_1^{(i+1)} + \alpha_i^{(k+1)}\sigma_1^{(i+1)}\},$$

respectively, where

$$\sigma_i = k_{i,i-1} + k_{ii} + k_{i,i+1},$$

$$\sigma_r^{(l)} = k_{r1}^{(l)} + k_{r2}^{(l)}, \qquad (l,r) = (i,2),(i+1,1).$$

Method 2: Summation of Second-Order Differences

Consider again the problem mentioned at the beginning of Method 1, assuming now that $\bar{\Omega}$ is an axiparallel rectangle. Figure 7.10 shows a section of a uniform mesh for the use of piecewise linear basis functions. With σ_i defined as in Method 1, we have

$$g_i^{(k+1)} = \sum_{j=1}^{M} (k_{ij}\alpha_j^{(k+1)}) - G_i$$

$$= \sum_{r=0}^{6} (k_{i,i_r}\alpha_{i_r}^{(k+1)}) - G_i + \alpha_i^{(k+1)}\left(\sigma_i - \sum_{r=0}^{6} k_{i,i_r}\right)$$

$$= \sum_{r=1}^{3} \{k_{i,i_r}[(\alpha_{i_{r+3}}^{(k+1)} - \alpha_i^{(k+1)}) - (\alpha_i^{(k+1)} - \alpha_{i_r}^{(k+1)})]$$

$$+ (k_{i,i_r} - k_{i,i_{r+3}})(\alpha_i^{(k+1)} - \alpha_{i_{r+3}}^{(k+1)})\}$$

$$- G_i + \alpha_i^{(k+1)}\sigma_i, \qquad i \in J. \tag{7.54}$$

This is the *method of second-order differences* for computing the gradient in the case of piecewise linear basis functions. It can also be formulated for basis functions of higher degree. Further, the uniformity of the mesh can be relaxed in the sense that corresponding edges in neighboring triangles need only satisfy the relation $h_1/h_2 = 1 + O(h)$. Such a mesh can be constructed in the interior of an arbitrary domain $\bar{\Omega}$ and often everywhere in $\bar{\Omega}$ if there exists a smooth mapping of $\bar{\Omega}$ onto a union of rectangels. See Gordon and

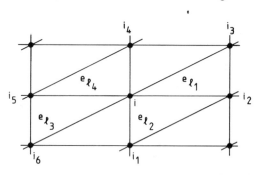

Fig. 7.10.   Section of mesh for piecewise linear basis functions.

Hall (1973) and Axelsson and Nävert (1977) for further information on this point.

Analysis of Methods 1 and 2

The accuracy with which $g_i^{(k+1)}$ can be computed from (7.53) or (7.54) with finite precision is closely related to the order of magnitude of the various quantities appearing in these formulas. Under the previous assumption of diagonal scaling (which is unnecessary if $n = 2$), one finds that in the absence of rounding errors,

$$k_{ij} = O(1), \qquad k_{rs}^{(l)} = O(1),$$
$$G_i = O(h^2), \qquad G_r^{(l)} = O(h^2),$$
$$\sigma_i = O(h^2), \qquad \sigma_r^{(l)} = O(h^2).$$

Further, in the case of a uniform or "almost" uniform mesh, as described for Method 2, we have

$$k_{i,i_r} - k_{i,i_{r+3}} = O(h).$$

Finally, if $u \in C^1(\bar{\Omega})$ then

$$u(N_i) - u(N_j) = O(h) \qquad \text{if} \quad k_{ij} \neq 0$$

and if $u \in C^2(\bar{\Omega})$, then

$$u(N_{i_{r+3}}) - 2u(N_i) + u(N_{i_r}) = O(h^2),$$

where N_{i_r} and $N_{i_{r+3}}$ $(r = 1, 2, 3)$ are as shown in Fig. 7.10.

We denote by $\tilde{\mathbf{g}}^{k+1}$ the computed value of $\mathbf{g}^{k+1}$ obtained from (7.53) (either version) or (7.54), assuming finite precision accuracy ε_M and errors in data of level $\varepsilon \geq \varepsilon_M$. If $\varepsilon < \varepsilon_M$ then ε should be replaced by ε_M in the following estimates. An analysis of these formulas using the given relations establishes that the vector

$$\boldsymbol{\varepsilon}^{k+1} = \mathbf{g}^{k+1} - \tilde{\mathbf{g}}^{k+1}$$

satisfies

$$\frac{\|\boldsymbol{\varepsilon}^{k+1}\|}{\|\boldsymbol{\alpha}\|} = \begin{cases} O(\varepsilon h) & \text{for} \quad (7.53\text{a,b}), \\ O(\varepsilon h^2) & \text{for} \quad (7.54). \end{cases} \qquad \begin{matrix} (7.55\text{a}) \\ (7.55\text{b}) \end{matrix}$$

Substituting in (7.50), we obtain

$$\frac{\|\boldsymbol{\delta}^{k+1}\|}{\|\boldsymbol{\alpha}\|} = \begin{cases} O(\varepsilon h^{-1}) & \text{for} \quad (7.53\text{a,b}), \\ O(\varepsilon) & \text{for} \quad (7.54), \end{cases}$$

and observe that $s = 1$ and 0, respectively.

An important fact, however, is that the derivation of (7.55b) requires the assumptions that no rounding errors appear in the floating-point calculation of $(\alpha_{i_{r+3}}^{(k+1)} - \alpha_i^{(k+1)}) - (\alpha_{i_r}^{(k+1)} - \alpha_i^{(k+1)})$ and that the *relative* error in the calculation of $k_{i,i_r} - k_{i,i_{r+3}}$ is $O(\varepsilon_M)$. The first of these is satisfied because this expression involves differences between almost equal numbers, implying that no digit is lost by rounding in most cases. The second condition can be satisfied if we calculate matrix entries k_{i,i_r} and the differences $k_{i,i_r} - k_{i,i_{r+3}}$ in double precision and then store them in single precision.

Alternatively, assuming there is no double-precision facility we can compute this difference to within the required accuracy by rewriting the integration for the individual terms as an integration for the difference. We illustrate the procedure for the mesh shown in Fig. 7.10 taking $r = 2$. Thus

$$k_{i,i_2} - k_{i,i_5} = I_1 + I_2,$$

where

$$I_1 = \int_{e_{l_1} \cup e_{l_2}} p(\nabla \phi_i)^{\mathrm{T}} \nabla \phi_{i_2}\, dx - \int_{e_{l_3} \cup e_{l_4}} p(\nabla \phi_i)^{\mathrm{T}} \nabla \phi_{i_5}\, dx,$$

$$I_2 = \int_{e_{l_1} \cup e_{l_2}} q \phi_i \phi_{i_2}\, dx - \int_{e_{l_3} \cup e_{l_4}} q \phi_i \phi_{i_5}\, dx.$$

Now,

$$I_1 = \int_{e_{l_1}} \left[p(\mathbf{x})\big|_{\mathbf{x} \in e_{l_1}} - p(\mathbf{x})\big|_{\mathbf{x} \in e_{l_3}} \right] (\nabla \phi_i)^{\mathrm{T}} \nabla \phi_{i_2}\, dx$$

$$+ \int_{e_{l_2}} \left[p(\mathbf{x})\big|_{\mathbf{x} \in e_{l_2}} - p(\mathbf{x})\big|_{\mathbf{x} \in e_{l_4}} \right] (\nabla \phi_i)^{\mathrm{T}} \nabla \phi_{i_2}\, dx,$$

where $p(\mathbf{x})\big|_{\mathbf{x} \in e_{l_1}}$ and $p(\mathbf{x})\big|_{\mathbf{x} \in e_{l_3}}$ denote values of p at points in e_{l_1} and e_{l_3}, respectively, located "symmetrically" with respect to $\mathbf{x}_i$. Hence,

$$I_1 - \int_{e_{l_1}} \left[p(\mathbf{x}_i \mid \mathbf{x} \quad \mathbf{x}_i) - p(\mathbf{x}_i - \mathbf{x} + \mathbf{x}_i) \right] (\nabla \phi_i)^{\mathrm{T}} \nabla \phi_{i_2}\, dx$$

$$+ \int_{e_{l_2}} \left[p(\mathbf{x}_i + \mathbf{x} - \mathbf{x}_i) - p(\mathbf{x}_i - \mathbf{x} + \mathbf{x}_i) \right] (\nabla \phi_i)^{\mathrm{T}} \nabla \phi_{i_2}\, dx$$

$$= 2 \int_{e_{l_1} \cup e_{l_2}} \left[(\nabla p(\mathbf{x}_i))^{\mathrm{T}} (\mathbf{x} - \mathbf{x}_i) \right] \left[(\nabla \phi_i)^{\mathrm{T}} \nabla \phi_{i_2} \right] dx + O(h^3),$$

where we have made straightforward use of Taylor expansions. The integral I_2 can be determined analogously:

$$I_2 = 2 \int_{e_{i_1} \cup e_{i_2}} [(\nabla q(\mathbf{x}_i))^{\mathrm{T}}(\mathbf{x} - \mathbf{x}_i)] \phi_i \phi_{i_2} \, d\mathbf{x} + O(h^3).$$

With the use of these relations the difference $k_{i,i_2} - k_{i,i_5}$ can be computed sufficiently accurately in single precision.

For an account of numerical experiments with the techniques described, see Axelsson and Gustafsson (1981), where also an extension of Method 2 to the case of discontinuous coefficients p can be found. An analysis of rounding errors due to the conjugate gradient algorithm itself, i.e., one that is not restricted to the computation of the gradient vectors, may be found in Wozniakowski (1978). [See also Bollen (1980).] His analysis indicates a somewhat greater growth of rounding errors than our results do when the number of iterations is extremely large. In most practical finite element calculations with preconditioned algorithms this condition does not arise.

7.5 Comparison of Iterative and Direct Methods

Generalities

In this section we shall compare the computational labor and storage required by the iterative and direct methods of Chapters 1 and 6, respectively, when these are applied to a system of equations

$$K\alpha = G, \tag{7.56}$$

where K is an $N \times N$ symmetric positive definite matrix. We are particularly interested in the case when (7.56) are the Ritz–Galerkin equations associated with the finite element treatment of a boundary value problem.

Table 7.2 summarizes the results for the iterative methods. We recall that $r_K, r_K^{(J)}$, and r_R are the average number of nonzero entries per row of K, $(D + L + L^{\mathrm{T}})$, and R, respectively.

Table 7.2 does not show the extra computational labor required to compute the factors in the $IC–CG$ case. For finite element problems this task typically requires $O(N)$ flops and hence becomes insignificant as $N \to \infty$ in comparison to the $O[N\sqrt{\kappa(\tilde{K})}]$ flops required by the iterations.

Table 7.2

Computational Labor and Storage Required by the Simple Conjugate Gradient Method (CG),
the SSOR–Preconditioned Conjugate Gradient Method (SSOR–CG), and the Conjugate
Gradient Method Preconditioned by Incomplete Factorization (IC–CG)

Method	Implementation	Computational labor (flops)	Storage
CG	(1.46)	$\frac{1}{2}(r_K + 5)N\sqrt{\kappa(K)}\ln(2/\varepsilon)$	$\frac{1}{2}(r_K + 9)N$
SSOR–CG	(1.92)	$\frac{1}{2}(2r_K + 6)N\sqrt{\kappa(\tilde{K})}\ln(2/\varepsilon)$	$\frac{1}{2}(r_K + 9)N$
SSOR–CG	(1.100)	$\frac{1}{2}(r_K + 7)N\sqrt{\kappa(\tilde{K})}\ln(2/\varepsilon)$	$\frac{1}{2}(r_K + 11)N$
IC–CG	(1.92)	$\frac{1}{2}(r_K + r_K^{(J)} + 5)N\sqrt{\kappa(\tilde{K})}\ln(2/\varepsilon)$	$\frac{1}{2}(r_K + r_K^{(J)} + 10)N$
IC–CG	(1.100)	$\frac{1}{2}(r_R + r_K^{(J)} + 6)N\sqrt{\kappa(\tilde{K})}\ln(2/\varepsilon)$	$\frac{1}{2}(r_R + r_K^{(J)} + 12)N$

Regarding storage, the table shows only "primary" storage, i.e., the storage required for floating-point arrays. With the simple conjugate gradient method, for example, this consists of $4N$ words for the four arrays in (1.46) plus $(r_K + 1)(N/2)$ words for the nonzero entries in the lower triangle of K. Additional storage is usually required for integer arrays used in the data structure for K (e.g., arrays CN and RS in Fig. 1.8). For cases in which K has a very regular structure and few distinct nonzero entries (as in Example 7.1), it may be possible to dispense with a data structure for K entirely (see Exercise 1.25).

Let k denote the number of iterations performed, and let

$$\varepsilon = \|\boldsymbol{\alpha}^k - \boldsymbol{\alpha}\|_K / \|\boldsymbol{\alpha}^0 - \boldsymbol{\alpha}\|_K. \tag{7.57}$$

The convergence theory for the conjugate gradient method states that in the absence of rounding errors,

$$k \lesssim \begin{cases} \frac{1}{2}\sqrt{\kappa(K)}\ln(2/\varepsilon) & \text{without preconditioning,} \\ \frac{1}{2}\sqrt{\kappa(\tilde{K})}\ln(2/\varepsilon) & \text{with preconditioning,} \end{cases}$$

and it is these bounds that have been used to derive the estimates of computational labor in Table 7.2. Let γ be defined by the relation

$$\varepsilon = 10^{-\gamma}(\|\boldsymbol{\alpha}\|_K / \|\boldsymbol{\alpha}^0 - \boldsymbol{\alpha}\|_K). \tag{7.58a}$$

Then,

$$\|\boldsymbol{\alpha}^k - \boldsymbol{\alpha}\|_K / \|\boldsymbol{\alpha}\|_K = 10^{-\gamma}, \tag{7.58b}$$

and hence γ gives a rough indication of the number of correct decimal digits in the components of $\boldsymbol{\alpha}^k$. Naturally, in the presence of rounding errors $10^{-\gamma}$ cannot fall below a certain value determined by machine precision ε_M.

Turning now to the direct methods, we show in Table 7.3 the data for Gaussian elimination when K is a band matrix. The table gives only the

Table 7.3
Computational Labor and Storage Required
by Gaussian Elimination When K is a Band Matrix
with Half-Bandwidth $w(K)$,
Stored as Shown in Fig. 6.2[a]

Task	Computational labor (flops)	Storage
Factorize	$\frac{1}{2}Nw(K)^2$	$Nw(K)$
Solve	$2Nw(K)$	$Nw(K)$

[a] "Factorize" is the task of computing L and D in the factorization $K = LDL^T$. "Solve" is the task of solving (7.56) when L and D are known.

"leading term" in the expressions for computational labor and storage under the assumption that $1 \ll w(K) \ll N$. The total storage is only $Nw(K)$ since L and D can be written over K. Table 7.3 applies equally to the Cholesky method.

When one is faced with the problem of solving a single system, the total computational labor is dominated by the factorization. When there are many systems to be solved, all with the same matrix, then the factorization tends to become insignificant since it is done only once. (Note, however, that there must be as many as about $\frac{1}{4}w(K)$ systems before the factorization ceases to dominate the total computational labor.) This situation often arises in solving time-dependent problems with time-independent coefficients using a constant step length Δt. Since there are typically very many systems, the computational labor of a direct method can be estimated on the basis of the "solve" operation alone. On the other hand, we note that an iterative method has the advantage here that the solution at the previous time step usually provides an excellent initial vector for the iterations at the new time step. Moreover, this holds even for the case of time-dependent coefficients and variable step length, where a direct method would require repeated factorizations.

Similarly, when solving a boundary value problem on a sequence of meshes by an iterative method, one can use the solution on the previous mesh to derive a good initial vector for the calculation of the solution on the new mesh.

Finite Element Case

Suppose now that (7.56) arises from the application of the finite element method to a boundary value problem in n space dimensions, where $n = 2$

or 3. Regarding first the iterative methods, we have in general

$$\kappa(K) = O(h^{-2}) = O(N^{2/n}),$$

and in the case of preconditioning we make the favorable assumption that

$$\kappa(\tilde{K}) = O(h^{-1}) = O(N^{1/n}).$$

The conditions under which this property holds were examined extensively in Sections 7.1–7.3.

Let the initial vector α^0 be determined by some guess $v(x, y)$ at the solution $u(x, y)$ of the boundary value problem, i.e., $\alpha_i^{(0)} = v(N_i)$. We assume that v is independent of the mesh. Straightforward calculations establish that

$$\|\alpha\|_K / \|\alpha^0 - \alpha\|_K = \|u_N\|_{\mathscr{L}} / \|v_1 - u_N\|_{\mathscr{L}},$$

where v_1 is the interpolant of v in the span of the basis functions, u_N the Ritz–Galerkin approximation to u, and $\|\cdot\|_{\mathscr{L}}$ the energy norm. [We recall that $\|\cdot\|_{\mathscr{L}} = a(\cdot, \cdot)^{1/2}$, where $a(\cdot, \cdot)$ is the bilinear form of the boundary value problem.] Hence,

$$\|\alpha\|_K / \|\alpha^0 - \alpha\|_K \to \|u\|_{\mathscr{L}} / \|v - u\|_{\mathscr{L}}, \qquad N \to \infty,$$

and we see from (7.58a) that

$$\varepsilon \simeq 10^{-\gamma} (\|u\|_{\mathscr{L}} / \|v - u\|_{\mathscr{L}}) \tag{7.59}$$

for sufficiently large values of N.

If we require the accuracy parameter γ to be constant for all meshes, then it follows that ε must be constant. Alternatively, we can let γ depend on N in such a way that the Ritz–Galerkin discretization error is balanced by the error due to the finite termination of the iterations. Thus, let $u_N^{(k)}$ denote the unique function in the span of the basis functions with the property $u_N^{(k)}(N_i) = \alpha_i^{(k)}$ at all nodes N_i. Then,

$$\|u - u_N^{(k)}\|_{\mathscr{L}} \le \|u - u_N\|_{\mathscr{L}} + \|u_N - u_N^{(k)}\|_{\mathscr{L}},$$

and the two types of error are balanced in the energy norm when k is such that

$$\|u_N - u_N^{(k)}\|_{\mathscr{L}} \simeq \|u - u_N\|_{\mathscr{L}}. \tag{7.60a}$$

Now, using (7.57) we obtain

$$\|u_N - u_N^{(k)}\|_{\mathscr{L}} = \varepsilon \|v_1 - u_N\|_{\mathscr{L}} \simeq \varepsilon \|v - u\|_{\mathscr{L}}, \qquad N \gg 1, \tag{7.60b}$$

and we know from Section 5.4 that $\|u - u_N\|_{\mathscr{L}} = O(h^p)$ if the span of the basis functions contains all polynomials of degree p and if u is sufficiently regular. Hence, since $\|v - u\|_{\mathscr{L}} = O(1)$, (7.60) suggests that we make

$\varepsilon = O(h^p)$. It then follows from (7.59) that

$$\gamma = O[\ln(h^{-1})] = O[\ln(N)]$$

and that the computational labor is as shown in Table 7.2, where

$$\ln(2/\varepsilon) = O[\ln(N)].$$

This relation holds only for a limited range of N, however. The finite precision of the computer puts an upper bound on γ, and because of (7.59) a corresponding lower bound ε_0 on ε, and

$$\ln(2/\varepsilon) \leq \ln(2/\varepsilon_0) = O(1), \qquad N \to \infty.$$

In fact, because of rounding errors there is usually a point at which γ actually begins to decrease as N increases, as illustrated in Fig. 7.9. We have seen that this behavior is sensitive to details of the computer implementation of the method.

We mentioned previously that iterative methods are well suited to solving the systems of equations that arise in time-dependent problems, in that the solution at the previous time step provides a good choice of α^0. When $\Delta t = O(h)$, which is not unusual, then

$$\| \alpha^0 - \alpha \|_K = O(h),$$

and (7.58a) together with the relation

$$\| \alpha \|_K = \| u_N \|_{\mathscr{L}} \simeq \| u \|_{\mathscr{L}}, \qquad N \gg 1$$

yields

$$\varepsilon = 10^{-\gamma} O(h^{-1}).$$

We note that if $\gamma = O[\ln(h^{-1})]$, then $\varepsilon = O(1)$, i.e., ε is essentially independent of the mesh.

Regarding the direct methods, we shall include the case when the ordering of nodes is of the nested-dissection type, even though we did not describe in Chapter 6 how such orderings can be efficiently determined. Our reason for presenting this case here is that it represents the limit of what can be achieved by the use of Gaussian elimination (or the Cholesky method), and hence is a suitable benchmark for measuring the performance of the iterative methods.

Table 7.4 gives data for the various iterative and direct methods in terms of order of magnitude with respect to N. We have used the relations

$$w(K) = O(N^{1-(1/n)}), \qquad r_K = O(1),$$

where n is the number of space dimensions. Naturally 1.33 indicates $\frac{4}{3}$, etc. In the case of the iterative methods, we have assumed that ε is independent of N.

Table 7.4

Computational Labor and Storage to Solve a Finite Element Problem
in n Space Dimensions by the Simple Conjugate Gradient Method (CG),
the Preconditioned Conjugate Gradient Method (PC–CG), Gaussian Elimination
With a Band-Minimizing Ordering of Nodes (Band–Gauss), and Gaussian Elimination
With a Nested-Dissection Ordering of Nodes (ND–Gauss)

| | $n = 2$ | | $n = 3$ | |
| | Computational labor | Storage | Computational labor | Storage |
Method				
CG	$O(N^{1.5})$	$O(N)$	$O(N^{1.33})$	$O(N)$
PC–CG	$O(N^{1.25})$	$O(N)$	$O(N^{1.17})$	$O(N)$
Band–Gauss (factorize)	$O(N^2)$	$O(N^{1.5})$	$O(N^{2.33})$	$O(N^{1.67})$
Band–Gauss (solve)	$O(N^{1.5})$	$O(N^{1.5})$	$O(N^{1.67})$	$O(N^{1.67})$
ND–Gauss (factorize)	$O(N^{1.5})$	$O(N \ln N)$	$O(N^2)$	$O(N^{1.33})$
ND–Gauss (solve)	$O(N \ln N)$	$O(N \ln N)$	$O(N^{1.33})$	$O(N^{1.33})$

The table indicates a general superiority of the iterative methods for large values of N, especially in the case of three-dimensional problems, where we note that the power of N in the estimates of computational labor for the iterative methods is actually less than in the two-dimensional case. The value of N is generally much greater for three dimensions than for two, however, if the discretization errors are comparable, since discretization error depends on h alone and $N = O(h^{-n})$.

A Model Problem

The statement that one method is superior to another for a sufficiently large value of N gives only partial information; we would like to know how large "sufficiently large" is. Thus, it is instructive to consider the model problem

$$-\Delta u = g(x, y), \qquad (x, y) \in \Omega,$$

$$u = 0, \qquad (x, y) \in \Gamma,$$

where Ω is the unit square, and the application of piecewise linear basis functions on a uniform mesh of isosceles right triangles. For the corresponding stiffness matrix K we have

$$r_K \simeq 5, \qquad w(K) \simeq N^{1/2},$$

and it can be shown that the extreme eigenvalues of K are $\lambda_1 \simeq 2\pi^2/N$ and $\lambda_N \simeq 8$. Hence, $\kappa(K) \simeq 4N/\pi^2$.

With regard to SSOR preconditioning, we note from (7.1) that

$$\kappa(\tilde{K}) \lesssim \sqrt{(\tfrac{1}{2} + \delta)\kappa(K)} \leq \sqrt{\tfrac{1}{2}\kappa(K)},$$

since Example 7.1 establishes that $\delta \leq 0$ for this problem. We can obtain a smaller bound, however, by going back to the analysis preceding (1.73c) in Section 1.4:

$$\kappa(\tilde{K}) \lesssim \sqrt{(\tfrac{1}{2} + \delta)\mu} \leq \sqrt{d/2\lambda_1},$$

where d is the largest entry on the main diagonal of K. For this problem we have $d = 4$, so $\kappa(\tilde{K}) \lesssim \sqrt{N}/\pi$.

The assessment of computational labor for the iterative methods requires an assumption about the accuracy of the initial vector, and ours is

$$\|\alpha^0 - \alpha\|_K / \|\alpha\|_K = \tfrac{1}{2}.$$

This is not unrealistic, since one usually has some idea of what the solution of the problem looks like. (With no idea at all one can always put $\alpha^0 = 0$, making this quotient unity.) Hence, by (7.58a),

$$\ln(2/\varepsilon) = \ln(10^\gamma) \simeq 2.3\gamma.$$

Using these assumptions and Table 7.2, we obtain the results shown for the first two methods in Table 7.5. The estimate for Gaussian elimination in the Band–Gauss case is based on a more refined computation of the cost of factorization than that given in Table 7.3 and also includes the "solve" operation. Both this estimate and that for the nested-dissection ordering are derived from George and Liu (1981).

Ignoring the $O(N)$ term, we see that the crossover point between CG and Band–Gauss is $N \simeq 213(\gamma - 0.44)^2$. For $\gamma = 3$, for example, we obtain $N \simeq 1400$. This is actually only an upper bound on the crossover point, since the estimate of the number of iterations required by the conjugate gradient method, which we used in obtaining the computational labor for this method in Table 7.2, is itself an upper bound.

Table 7.5

Computational Labor and Storage for a Model Finite Element
Problem [SSOR–CG is Implemented by (1.100)]

Method	Computational labor (flops)	Storage
CG	$7.3\gamma N^{1.5}$	$7N$
SSOR–CG	$7.8\gamma N^{1.25}$	$8N$
Band–Gauss	$(0.5N^2 + 3.2N^{1.5}) + O(N)$	$N^{1.5}$
ND–Gauss	$9.9N^{1.5} + O(N \ln N)$	$O(N \ln N)$

For $\gamma = 3$ one finds that the crossover point between SSOR–CG and Band–Gauss is $N \simeq 83$, a very much smaller value. Further, it is easy to see that an upper bound on the crossover point for any γ is $N \simeq 39\gamma^{4/3}$, a slowly increasing function of γ.

Ignoring the term $O[N \ln(N)]$, we find that the crossover point between SSOR–CG and ND–Gauss for large values of γ is about $N \simeq 0.39\gamma^4$ and hence very sensitive to γ.

Regarding storage, CG and SSOR–CG are more economical than Band–Gauss for $N \gtrsim 49$ and $N \gtrsim 64$, respectively. (For this simple problem one could actually eliminate the storage of K for the two iterative methods, as indicated in Exercise 1.25, saving $3N$ words of storage in each case.)

It was shown earlier that if the iterations are terminated according to the criterion

$$\| u_N - u_N^{(k)} \|_{\mathscr{L}} \simeq \| u - u_N \|_{\mathscr{L}},$$

then $\gamma = O[\ln(N)]$. We shall now examine this function more closely for the model problem at hand.

Combining the basic error result (5.87b) with the elliptic regularity property (5.92), which is valid for the present problem, we obtain a bound of the form

$$|u - u_N|_1 \le ch \| g \|,$$

where c is a constant. Let

$$c^* = |u - u_N|_1/(h \| g \|).$$

c^* is a function of both g and the mesh. Numerical studies reported in Barnhill *et al.* (1977) [see also Arbenz (1982)] show, however, that c^* varies remarkably little, the inequalities $0.170 \le c^* \le 0.344$ holding for all test cases. Using the identity $|\cdot|_1 = \| \cdot \|_{\mathscr{L}}$, introducing the parameter $\lambda = \| g \|^2 / \| u \|^2_{\mathscr{L}}$, and observing from the mesh that $h \simeq N^{-1/2}$, we can write

$$\| u - u_N \|_{\mathscr{L}} \simeq c^* \sqrt{\lambda} N^{-1/2} \| u \|_{\mathscr{L}}. \tag{7.61}$$

To investigate λ we note from the variational formulation of the problem

$$a(u, v) \equiv \iint_\Omega (u_x v_x + u_y v_y)\, dx\, dy = \iint_\Omega gv\, dx\, dy \qquad \forall v \subset \mathring{H}^1(\Omega)$$

that

$$\lambda = (g, g)/a(u, u) = (g, g)/(g, u).$$

Expanding g in terms of the eigenfunctions of the operator $\mathscr{L} = -\Delta$, one can deduce from the last expression that λ is a weighted average of the eigenvalues of $\mathscr{L}$. These are known to be

$$(p^2 + q^2)\pi^2, \qquad p, q = 1, 2, 3, \dots .$$

We want to balance the discretization error $\| u - u_N \|_{\mathscr{L}}$ against the error $\| u_N - u_N^{(k)} \|_{\mathscr{L}}$ due to the finite termination of the iterations. Since

$$\| u_N - u_N^{(k)} \|_{\mathscr{L}} = \| \boldsymbol{\alpha} - \boldsymbol{\alpha}^k \|_K = (\| \boldsymbol{\alpha} - \boldsymbol{\alpha}^k \|_K / \| \boldsymbol{\alpha} \|_K) \| u_N \|_{\mathscr{L}}$$

$$\simeq (\| \boldsymbol{\alpha} - \boldsymbol{\alpha}^k \|_K / \| \boldsymbol{\alpha} \|_K) \| u \|_{\mathscr{L}}, \qquad N \gg 1,$$

we find from (7.58b) that

$$\| u_N - u_N^{(k)} \|_{\mathscr{L}} \simeq 10^{-\gamma} \| u \|_{\mathscr{L}}.$$

Hence, the condition for balance is $10^{-\gamma} \simeq c^* \sqrt{\lambda} \, N^{-1/2}$, or

$$\gamma \simeq \tfrac{1}{2} \log_{10}(N) - \log_{10}(c^* \sqrt{\lambda})$$

$$\simeq \tfrac{1}{2} \log_{10}(N), \qquad N \gg 1.$$

This number is not very large even for very large values of N (for $N = 10^4$ we obtain $\gamma = 2$). We note from (7.61) that

$$N \simeq \lambda (c^* \| u \|_{\mathscr{L}})^2 | u - u_N |_1^{-2},$$

showing that N may have to be quite large if the gradient error $| u - u_N |_1$ is to be small.

It is important to point out, however, that the given value of γ may not make the iteration error in the Euclidean vector norm $\| \boldsymbol{\alpha} - \boldsymbol{\alpha}^k \|$ as small as desired. Suppose, then, that to increase the number of iterations we double γ, making $\gamma = \log_{10}(N)$. For this choice of γ we find the crossover point between CG and Band–Gauss to be $N \simeq 1650$, but there does not exist any crossover point between SSOR–CG and ND–Gauss; i.e., the former is superior for all N. (More precisely, for all sufficiently large values of N, since our analysis has ignored lower-order terms. Small values of N have, of course, little practical interest.)

Numerical Stability

A comparison of methods must take into account the influence of rounding errors and errors in data. This amounts to comparing the values of the parameter s in Section 7.4 for the different methods. Regarding the direct methods, we have mentioned that typically $s = 3$. Regarding iterative refinement (Section 6.4) and the iterative methods of Chapter 1, we have $s = 2, 1,$ or 0 according to whether the residuals (or gradients) are computed (1) "normally," (2) by (7.53a) or (7.53b), or (3) by (7.54), respectively. These results indicate that the direct methods, without iterative refinement, are less accurate than the iterative methods. We recall that iterative refinement increases the storage requirement of a direct method substantially.

The Case of Many Right-Hand Side Vectors

If there are r right-hand side vectors, $r > 1$, then the efficiency of a direct method is improved, since the factorization is performed only once. As an extreme case let $r = \frac{1}{4}w(K)$, and consider the use of Band–Gauss. This value of r makes the computational labor for the factorization the same as that for the r solve operations (see Table 7.3), the average labor per system being $4Nw(K)$ For the model problem discussed previously, we have $w(K) \simeq N^{1/2}$, and the average labor per system is thus $4N^{1.5}$. Comparing this with SSOR–CG in Table 7.5, we find that Band–Gauss is more efficient for values of N up to about $14.5\gamma^4$.

Remark. A final word of warning regarding the foregoing comparison of the iterative and direct methods is in order. The computational labor required by an iterative method depends on $\kappa(K)$ or $\kappa(\tilde{K})$, and these values depend in turn on the particular boundary value problem. For certain problems (e.g., problems with discontinuous coefficients) these spectral condition numbers are much greater than for "model" problems such as the one previously analyzed. On the other hand, the computational labor of a direct method is in a sense independent of the boundary value problem. Thus, the crossover point at which an iterative method becomes faster than a direct method tends to increase as the problem "worsens."

This apparent point in favor of the direct methods is often offset, however, by a greater loss of accuracy. An increase in $\kappa(K)$ leads to an increase in the effect of rounding and other types of errors in the computed solution. The greater numerical stability of the iterative methods (which can be improved even further by using the special techniques of Section 7.4) makes the iterative methods more immune to errors.

7.6   Multigrid Methods

In this section we shall provide an introductory account of some of the so-called *multigrid methods* that have arisen in recent years and that are still the subject of much research. [See Hackbusch and Trottenberg (1982), one of the first books on the subject.] A convenient point of departure is the variational problem

$$a(u, v) = (g, v) \qquad \forall v \in H_0^1(\Omega),$$

where

$$a(u, v) = \int_\Omega p \, \nabla u \cdot \nabla v \, d\Omega.$$

We assume that $\Omega \subset R^2$ is a simply connected polygonal domain and that the solution $\hat{u} \in H_\gamma^1(\Omega)$ is sufficiently smooth. We construct a sequence of triangular meshes $\{\Omega_h^{(1)}\}$, $\{\Omega_h^{(2)}\} \subset \Omega$ as described in Section 7.3. In particular we shall consider meshes for linear $\{\lambda_i(h)\}_{i=1}^{N(h)}$ and quadratic $\{\phi_i(h)\}_{i=1}^{N(h)}$ basis functions (see Section 7.3). Note that the nodes in the two meshes coincide for every h, and hence the order of the corresponding finite element matrices is equal. We get finite element matrices $K_h^{(i)}$, $i = 1, 2$, for which the solutions $\hat{u}_h^{(i)}$ of

$$K_h^{(1)} \hat{u}_h^{(1)} = f_h^{(1)}, \qquad f_{h,i}^{(1)} = (g, \lambda_i), \tag{7.62a}$$

$$K_h^{(2)} \hat{u}_h^{(2)} = f_h^{(2)}, \qquad f_{h,i}^{(2)} = (g, \phi_i), \tag{7.62b}$$

satisfy

$$\|\hat{u} - \hat{u}_h^{(1)}\|_1 = O(h^p), \qquad \|\hat{u} - \hat{u}_h^{(2)}\|_1 = O(h^q),$$

where $q > p$.

To solve the higher-order-of-accuracy problem (7.62b), we consider the use of the lower-order-of-accuracy operator $K_h^{(1)}$, because it has a simpler structure and in general it may be easier to solve (7.62a) than (7.62b).

Defect-Correction Method. The defect-correction method proceeds as follows. Solve for an initial approximation

$$K_h^{(1)} u_h^{(0)} = f_h^{(1)} \qquad \text{(i.e., } u_h^{(0)} = \hat{u}_h^{(1)}\text{)}.$$

Then, calculate a correction $\delta_h^{(1)}$ from

$$K_h^{(1)} \delta_h^{(1)} = -r_h^{(2)},$$

where the residual $r_h^{(2)}$ satisfies

$$r_h^{(2)} = K_h^{(2)} u_h^{(0)} - f_h^{(2)}.$$

Finally, let

$$u_h^{(1)} = u_h^{(0)} + \delta_h^{(1)}$$

be the corrected solution. We would now like to estimate the error $\|u_h^{(1)} - \hat{u}\|_1$. [By $u_h^{(1)}$ we mean a function spanned by the basis functions $\{\phi_i\}$, assuming the values $u_h^{(1)}(N_i) = (\mathbf{u}_h^{(1)})_i$ at the nodes.] We shall now illustrate this in the case $p = 1$ and $q = 2$ (linear–quadratic case). We have

$$K_h^{(1)}(\mathbf{u}_h^{(1)} - \hat{\mathbf{u}}_h^{(2)}) = K_h^{(1)}(\mathbf{u}_h^{(1)} - \mathbf{u}_h^{(0)}) + K_h^{(1)}(\mathbf{u}_h^{(0)} - \hat{\mathbf{u}}_h^{(2)})$$

$$= (K_h^{(1)} - K_h^{(2)})(\mathbf{u}_h^{(0)} - \hat{\mathbf{u}}_h^{(2)}). \tag{7.63}$$

Since the solution is smooth, we have

$$\hat{u}_h^{(1)} - \hat{u} = h^2 e^{(1)} + O(h^3), \qquad h \to 0,$$

and

$$\hat{u}_h^{(2)} - \hat{u} = h^3 e^{(2)} + o(h^3), \qquad h \to 0,$$

in the sense that

$$\left\| \hat{u}_h^{(1)} - \hat{u} - h^2 e^{(1)} \right\|_1 = O(h^3), \qquad \text{etc.}$$

Here $e^{(i)}$ are smooth functions in $H^1(\Omega)$, independent of h. Since

$$u_h^{(0)} - \hat{u}_h^{(2)} = \hat{u}_h^{(1)} - \hat{u} - (\hat{u}_h^{(2)} - \hat{u}) = h^2 e^{(1)} + O(h^3)$$

and since a calculation shows that

$$K_h^{(1)^{-1}}(K_h^{(1)} - K_h^{(2)})e^{(1)} = O(h), \tag{7.64}$$

it follows from (7.63) that

$$\left\| \mathbf{u}_h^{(1)} - \hat{\mathbf{u}}_h^{(2)} \right\| = O(h^3).$$

[For (7.64) to be true, the function $e^{(1)}$ must be smooth in the sense that it is represented by a linear combination of the lower-order eigenfunctions— sometimes called the "first harmonics"—of the corresponding differential operator.]

Hence,

$$\left\| u_h^{(1)} - \hat{u} \right\|_1 \le \left\| u_h^{(1)} - \hat{u}_h^{(2)} \right\|_1 + \left\| \hat{u}_h^{(2)} - \hat{u} \right\|_1$$

$$= O(h^{\min(2p, q)}) = O(h^2).$$

Therefore, after *two* solutions of systems with matrix $K_h^{(1)}$ we get the full order of accuracy of the quadratic problem. Similarly, if $p = 1$ and $q = 3$, we get $\left\| u_h^{(2)} - \hat{u} \right\|_1 = O(h^3)$ after *three* solutions of $K_h^{(1)}$, etc.

At this point we note that if we intend to solve the linear systems with matrix $K_h^{(1)}$ by iteration, it is more efficient to use the method in Section 7.3 based on spectral equivalence, because then in practice the computational labor corresponds essentially to the solution of only one system with matrix $K_h^{(1)}$. Furthermore, this method works well independently of the smoothness of $\hat{u}$. The reason why we have discussed the defect-correction method here is that it serves as a convenient introduction to multigrid methods.

Multigrid Methods of the Classical Type

We consider two meshes $\Omega_{h_2} \subset \Omega_{h_1}$, $h_1 < h_2$ in the sequence of meshes $\{\Omega_h\}$. In the multigrid method we distinguish between two phases, *smoothing* and *correction*.

Phase 1: Smoothing. On the fine mesh Ω_{h_1} we first perform a number of smoothing iteration steps (i.e., by Gauss–Seidel relaxation or by Chebyshev iteration with parameters chosen to damp out the highly oscillatory components of the residual, but essentially leave the smoother components). It is well known that the Gauss–Seidel and similar relaxation methods damp mainly the higher-order components of the residual. This smoothing results in an approximation $\mathbf{u}_{h_1}^{(0)}$ and residual $\mathbf{r}_{h_1}^{(0)} = K_{h_1}\mathbf{u}_{h_1}^{(0)} - \mathbf{f}_{h_1}$ on Ω_{h_1}. Now, we want to calculate a correction $\boldsymbol{\delta}_{h_1}^{(1)}$ satisfying

$$K_{h_1}\boldsymbol{\delta}_{h_1}^{(1)} = -\mathbf{r}_{h_1}^{(0)} \tag{7.65}$$

and then set

$$\mathbf{u}_{h_1}^{(1)} = \mathbf{u}_{h_1}^{(0)} + \boldsymbol{\delta}_{h_1}^{(1)}.$$

However, the cost of solving (7.65) exactly is presumed to be prohibitive (otherwise we might as well have solved the original problem $K_{h_1}\hat{\mathbf{u}}_{h_1} = \mathbf{f}_{h_1}$ exactly). To solve this we use the defect correction method, but performed on the coarse grid Ω_{h_2}, where the cost is (much) smaller.

We note that the resulting approximation on the coarse grid should be reasonable in as much as the residual has mainly smooth components, which clearly can also be reasonably well approximated on the coarser grid.

To formulate the defect correction process, we first introduce the restriction and extension operators to be used in connection with finite element multigrid methods.

The restriction operator is defined as follows. For any u defined on Ω_{h_1}, let $I_{h_1}^{h_2}u$ be a function defined on Ω_{h_2} satisfying

$$I_{h_1}^{h_2}u(N_j) = u(N_j), \qquad N_j \in \Omega_{h_2}$$

and defined by interpolation on Ω_{h_2} in interior points. It may also be defined by taking a weighted average of values at neighboring points. For an extension operator we simply choose the interpolation operator: for any u defined on Ω_{h_2} let $I_{h_2}^{h_1}u$ be a function on Ω_{h_1} satisfying

$$I_{h_2}^{h_1}u(N_j) = u(N_j), \qquad N_j \in \Omega_{h_1}$$

(and defined by interpolation in the interior points). We note that in the context of finite elements there is a natural definition of the restriction and interpolation operators that is based on the global nature of the approximating functions, all being functions in one and the same Sobolev space, such as $H^1(\Omega)$.

Phase 2: Multigrid Defect Correction. Solve on Ω_2:

$$K_{h_2}\,\delta_{h_2}^{(0)} = -I_{h_1}^{h_2}\mathbf{r}_{h_1}^{(0)} \tag{7.66a}$$

and possibly also

$$K_{h_2}(\delta_{h_2}^{(1)} - \delta_{h_2}^{(0)}) = -I_{h_1}^{h_2}(K_{h_1}I_{h_2}^{h_1}\,\delta_{h_2}^{(0)} - \mathbf{r}_{h_1}^{(0)}). \tag{7.66b}$$

Then, let

$$\mathbf{u}_{h_1}^{(1)} = \mathbf{u}_{h_1}^{(0)} + I_{h_2}^{h_1}\,\delta_{h_2}^{(1)}$$

be the resulting corrected approximation on Ω_{h_1}.

If we perform only one correction step (7.66a) [and hence not (7.66b)], we get

$$u_{h_1}^{(1)} = u_{h_1}^{(0)} - I_{h_2}^{h_1}K_{h_2}^{-1}I_{h_1}^{h_2}\mathbf{r}_{h_1}^{(0)}.$$

Thus,

$$\mathbf{r}_{h_1}^{(1)} = (I_{h_1}^{h_1} - K_{h_1}I_{h_2}^{h_1}K_{h_2}^{-1}I_{h_1}^{h_2})\mathbf{r}_{h_1}^{(0)}$$

(here $I_{h_1}^{h_1}$ is, of course, the identity operator on Ω_{h_1}) and the rate of convergence depends on the size of the right-hand side. Since for smoothed residuals $\mathbf{r}_h^{(0)}$ contains mainly smooth components, this size depends mainly on approximation properties, i.e.,

$$I_{h_1}^{h_1} - K_{h_1}I_{h_2}^{h_1}K_{h_2}^{-1}I_{h_1}^{h_2} = K_{h_1}(K_{h_1}^{-1}I_{h_1}^{h_1} - I_{h_2}^{h_1}K_{h_2}^{-1}I_{h_1}^{h_2})$$

should be $o(h_1)$ as $h_1, h_2 \to 0$. Note the similarity of this expression with the corresponding one (7.64) for the defect-correction method. If this is not accurate enough we have to repeat the whole process, i.e., first smooth the resulting residual and then correct. This is repeated until eventually the residual on Ω_{h_1} is small enough.

So far we have described only the *basic two-level grid step* of the multigrid method. The complete multigrid method now utilizes the whole sequence of grids in the following way. When in (7.66) we solve a finite element system of equations on grid Ω_{h_2}, we may use the basic two-level grid step but now on grids $\Omega_{h_2} \to \Omega_{h_3}$, $h_3 > h_2$. Similarly, when in this latter process we solve equations of type (7.66) on Ω_{h_3}, we may again use the basic step and this can be repeated recursively until we reach a coarse enough grid on which it is most efficient to solve the systems of equations by a direct method. This means that we perform a (usually fixed) number of smoothing steps on each mesh level except on the coarsest level, e.g., $h = h_m$. The resulting approximation on this level now defines the correction on the nearest finer level

Fig. 7.11.   The W-cycle and V-cycle multigrid methods for mesh levels h_1, h_2, and h_3. Before taking the restriction (↘) of a vector and sometimes before taking the interpolant (↗), we perform a number of smoothing operations on the current level.

where $h = h_{m-1}$. Here we have a choice. We can either smooth and correct once more or we can go directly to the next finer level, possibly after some smoothing steps on level h_{m-1}. On level h_{m-2} we have the same choice, etc. In the first case we get a so-called W-multigrid cycle, and in the latter case a V-multigrid cycle. The two methods are illustrated in Fig. 7.11, where $m = 3$. Note that the computational cost of the smoothing steps on a level h is $O(N_h)$, where N_h is the number of unknowns at this level.

One can now prove that the overall computational complexity is $O(N \log N)$ [See Bank and Dupont (1981), Hackbusch (1980), Hemker (1980), McCormick and Ruge (1982), and Nicolaides (1977).]

There are many versions of this method in which the number of smoothing steps, the actually chosen smoothing method, etc. may differ. It is not yet clear how critical the actual smoothness of the solution is to the performance of the method. For example, corner singularities (Section 5.6) can slow the rate of convergence too much to make the method a practical one for general problems. For recent results on robust multigrid methods, see Dendy (1982) and Hemker *et al.* (1983).

A more recent version of multigrid type methods will now be presented. Here the method works well even if the solution is not smooth, although its actual performance on a particular problem may be better if the solution is smooth. Hence, it seems as if this new method may be more robust than the classical multigrid methods.

Multigrid Methods of the Two-Level Type

We first define a fundamental parameter for this type of method. Given a Hilbert space V and a symmetric, nonnegative, bounded bilinear form $a(\cdot, \cdot)$ on $V \times V$, let $(u, v)_a = a(u, v)$ define a (semi-) inner product and let $\|u\|_a = \{(u, u)_a\}^{1/2}$ be the associated (semi-) norm. From the Cauchy–Schwarz inequality we have

$$|(u, v)_a| \le \|u\|_a \|v\|_a \qquad \forall u, v \in V.$$

Let V_1 and V_2 be two nontrivial finite-dimensional subspaces of V with only the zero element in common, i.e., $V_1 \cap V_2 = \{0\}$. Let

$$\mathscr{N}_0 = \{u_0; a(u_0, v) = 0 \ \forall v \in V\}$$

and let $\mathscr{N}_0 \subset V_1$. Hence $V_2 \cap \mathscr{N}_0 = \{0\}$. Then,

$$\gamma = \sup_{\substack{u \in V_1 \backslash \mathscr{N}_0 \\ v \in V_2}} \frac{a(u, v)}{\|u\|_a \|v\|_a} < 1.$$

(γ is the cosine of the abstract angle between the two subspaces.) Now consider the bilinear form

$$a(u, v) = \int_\Omega p \, \nabla u \cdot \nabla v \, d\Omega, \qquad u, v \in V = \mathring{H}^1(\Omega).$$

Here $\mathscr{N}_0 = \{u_0; u_0 = C$, constant on $\Omega\}$. We shall also consider

$$a_l(u, v) = \int_{e_l} p \, \nabla u \cdot \nabla v \, d\Omega,$$

where e_l is an arbitrary element in a (regular) finite element mesh on Ω. As subspaces V_1, V_2 we shall use a special choice of finite element spaces.

Consider at first a triangulation of $\Omega \subset R^2$ with nodes chosen as in Section 5.1. On each triangle e_l let $V_1 = \text{SPAN}\{\lambda_i^{(l)}\}_{i=1}^3$, where $\lambda_i^{(l)}$ are the linear basis functions at the vertex nodes $N_i^{(l)}$, $i = 1, 2, 3$, of e_l and let $V_2 = \text{SPAN}\{\phi_i^{(l)}\}_{i=1}^q$, where $\phi_i^{(l)}$ are the basis functions in the remaining nodes on e_l. V_1 contains the monomials 1, x, y, and $\phi_i^{(l)}$ are chosen so that $V_1 \cup V_2$ contains all monomials up to a given order. Hence if, for instance, $V_1 \cup V_2$ spans all quadratic polynomials, then $q = 3$ and, if $V_1 \cup V_2$ spans all cubics, then $q = 7$, etc. The linear–quadratic case is illustrated in Fig. 7.12.

We choose for ϕ_i the Lagrange basis functions, i.e., $\phi_i(N_j) = \delta_{ij}$, $i = 1, 2, \ldots, q$, $j = 1, 2, \ldots, q + 3$, but clearly λ_i is nonzero at some of the other nodes. The set $V_1 \cup V_2$ spans the same polynomial space as if we had chosen Lagrange-type basis functions (i.e., quadratic in Fig. 7.12) also at the vertex points.

An important fact for the following analysis is that the constant function on e_l is not contained in V_2. Let

$$\gamma_l = \sup_{\substack{u \in V_1 \backslash \mathscr{N}_0 \\ v \in V_2}} \frac{a_l(u, v)}{a_l(u, u) a_l(v, v)}.$$

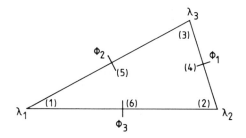

Fig. 7.12.   Choice of nodes and basis functions for the linear–quadratic case.

It is easy to see that there exists $\gamma^* < 1$ independent of h such that $\gamma_l \leq \gamma^*$. Clearly,

$$|a_l(u, v)| \leq \gamma_l\{a_l(u, u)a_l(v, v)\}^{1/2} \leq \tfrac{1}{2}\gamma_l[a_l(u, u) + a_l(v, v)],$$

and because

$$a_l(u + v, u + v) = a_l(u, u) + a_l(v, v) + 2a_l(u, v),$$

we get

$$(1 - \gamma_l)[a_l(u, u) + a_l(v, v)] \leq a_l(u + v, u + v)$$
$$\leq (1 + \gamma_l)[a_l(u, u) + a_l(v, v)] \qquad \forall u \in V_1, \quad v \in V_2.$$

Hence, by summation over l we get

$$(1 - \gamma)[a(u, u) + a(v, v)] \leq a(u + v, u + v)$$
$$\leq (1 + \gamma)[a(u, u) + a(v, v)] \qquad \forall u \in V_1, \quad v \in V_2, \qquad (7.67)$$

where $\gamma = \max_l \gamma_l$.

We now give an indication of the actual values assumed by γ by considering the following example. Let the basis functions be linear at the vertices and quadratic at the midedge points of isosceles right triangles, and let

$$a(u, v) = \int_\Omega \nabla u \cdot \nabla v \, d\Omega, \qquad \Omega = (0, 1)^2.$$

Then,

$$V_1 = \{u; u = \alpha_0 + \alpha_1 x + \alpha_2 y\}, \qquad V_2 = \left\{v; v = \sum_{j=1}^{3} \beta_j \phi_j\right\},$$

where $\phi_1 = 4\lambda_2\lambda_3$, $\phi_2 = 4\lambda_1\lambda_3$, $\phi_3 = 4\lambda_1\lambda_2$, and λ_1, λ_2, λ_3 are the usual barycentric coordinates. Then, for the corresponding unit standard element,

$$a(u, u) = \tfrac{1}{2}(\alpha_1^2 + \alpha_2^2),$$

$$a(v, v) = \tfrac{8}{3}(\beta_1^2 + \beta_2^2 + \beta_3^2 - \beta_1\beta_2 - \beta_1\beta_3),$$

and

$$a(u, v) = \tfrac{2}{3}[\alpha_1(\beta_1 - \beta_2) + \alpha_2(\beta_1 - \beta_3)].$$

By the symmetry with respect to x and y we realize that $\alpha_1 = \alpha_2$ at the extreme points. Now, an easy calculation shows that

$$\frac{a(u, v)^2}{a(u, u)a(v, v)} = \frac{2}{3}\left(1 - \frac{\beta_2^2 + \beta_3^2}{\frac{1}{3}(2\beta_1 - \beta_2 - \beta_3)^2 + \beta_2^2 + \beta_3^2}\right)$$

and the upper bound $\tfrac{2}{3}$ is taken if and only if $\beta_2 = \beta_3 = 0$, $\beta_1 \neq 0$. Hence $\gamma = (2/3)^{1/2}$. In this case the spectral condition number $(1 + \gamma)/(1 - \gamma)$ derived below is about 9.9. For further information on how γ depends on the geometry of the mesh, see Maitre and Mush (1982).

We now define matrices $A^{(l)}$, $B^{(l)}$, $C^{(l)}$ by

$$A^{(l)} = [a_l(\lambda_j^{(l)}, \lambda_i^{(l)})]_{i,j=1}^3, \qquad B^{(l)} = [a_l(\phi_j^{(l)}, \phi_i^{(l)})]_{i,j=1}^q$$

$$C^{(l)} = [a_l(\lambda_j^{(l)}, \phi_i^{(l)})], \qquad i = 1, 2, ..., q, \quad j = 1, 2, 3.$$

Then,

$$\mathscr{A}^{(l)} = \begin{bmatrix} B^{(l)} & C^{(l)} \\ C^{(l)\mathrm{T}} & A^{(l)} \end{bmatrix}$$

is the finite element matrix associated with e_l. Note that the basis functions, and hence these matrices, depend on the mesh length parameter, i.e., $B^{(l)} = B_h^{(l)}$, etc. In the usual way, by assembly we get global finite element matrices with the same structure,

$$\mathscr{A}_h = \begin{bmatrix} B_h & C_h \\ C_h^{\mathrm{T}} & A_h \end{bmatrix}$$

if we choose a global node ordering in which the nonvertex nodes appear first.

We note that B_h is positive definite (irrespective of the boundary conditions on Γ) and has a spectral condition number $O(1)$, $h \to 0$. This follows because $B_h^{(l)}$ has extreme eigenvalues $\mu_l^{(1)}$, $\mu_l^{(0)}$, where the smallest $\mu_l^{(1)}$ is positive, since $1 \notin V_2$. Hence, both are bounded (below and above, respectively) by positive numbers, independent of h, because the entries of $B_h^{(l)}$ are bounded in this way. Therefore,

$$0 < \min_l(\mu_l^{(1)})p_1\alpha^{\mathrm{T}}\alpha \leq \alpha^{\mathrm{T}}B_h\alpha \leq \max_l(\mu_l^{(0)})p_2\alpha^{\mathrm{T}}\alpha, \qquad (7.68)$$

where p_1, p_2 are the smallest and largest numbers, respectively, of triangles having a nonvertex node in common (clearly $p_2 = 2$). The spectral condition number of A_h is of course $O(h^{-2})$ (see Section 5.5), because A_h is the usual piecewise linear finite element matrix. It is also easy to prove that

$$\begin{bmatrix} B_h & 0 \\ 0 & A_h \end{bmatrix} \quad \text{and} \quad \mathscr{A}_h = \begin{bmatrix} B_h & C_h \\ C_h^T & A_h \end{bmatrix}$$

are spectrally equivalent. For the proof we just use (7.67), noting that

$$\boldsymbol{\alpha}^T A_h \boldsymbol{\alpha} = a(u, u), \qquad u = \sum \alpha_i \lambda_i,$$
$$\boldsymbol{\beta}^T B_h \boldsymbol{\beta} = a(v, v), \qquad v = \sum \beta_i \phi_i,$$

etc. It follows that we may use

$$\begin{bmatrix} B_h & 0 \\ 0 & A_h \end{bmatrix}$$

as a preconditioning matrix for $\mathscr{A}_h$. The number of iterations will then essentially be independent of h (as long as the relative accuracy parameter ε does not depend on h), because γ, and hence the spectral condition number $(1 + \gamma)/(1 - \gamma)$, is essentially independent of h.

At each step of the iteration method we must then solve for the systems with matrices B_h and A_h. The former matrix has a condition number $O(1)$, which is independent of h and may therefore be solved in an optimal order of computational complexity equal to $O[N(B_h)]$, where $N(B_h)$ is the order of B_h. For A_h we can use an incomplete factorization preconditioned method. The cost of calculating this quite accurately is not very prohibitive, because the order of A_h is much smaller than that of $\mathscr{A}_h$. Typically we have $N(A_h) \simeq \frac{1}{4} N(\mathscr{A}_h)$. (It is also advisable with respect to B_h to use some preconditioning, at least by the diagonal of B_h.)

For A_h we may also use a classical multigrid method. Methods similar to those described are discussed in Bank and Dupont (1980) and Axelsson and Gustafsson (1983).

In one particular and important case, B_h takes such a simple form that linear systems with B_h may be solved with little labor by a direct method. To see this, consider again the bilinear form

$$a(u, v) = \int_\Omega \nabla u \cdot \nabla v \, d\Omega,$$

where $\Omega = (0, 1)^2$ (or consisting of a union of axiparallel rectangles). We now use regular rectangular elements with the usual bilinear basis functions at the vertices and quadratic basis functions at the mid-edge nodes (see

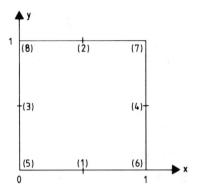

Fig. 7.13.   The standard element.

Fig. 7.13). (Note that there is no interior node present as in the case of the "biquadratic" element.)

Let

$$\lambda_1 = 1 - x, \qquad \lambda_2 = 1 - \lambda_1, \qquad \mu_1 = 1 - y, \qquad \mu_2 = 1 - \mu_1.$$

The quadratic basis functions are then

$$\phi_1 = 4\lambda_1\lambda_2\mu_1, \qquad \phi_2 = 4\lambda_1\lambda_2\mu_2,$$

$$\phi_3 = 4\lambda_1\mu_1\mu_2, \qquad \phi_4 = 4\lambda_2\mu_1\mu_2,$$

and the bilinear basis functions are

$$\phi_5 = \lambda_1\mu_1, \qquad \phi_6 = \lambda_2\mu_1, \qquad \phi_7 = \lambda_2\mu_2, \qquad \phi_8 = \lambda_1\mu_2.$$

One now finds that

$$b_{1,3} = a(\phi_1, \phi_3) = 0, \qquad b_{1,4} = a(\phi_1, \phi_4) = 0, \qquad \text{etc.,}$$

$$b_{2,3} = b_{2,4} = 0.$$

This means that $B_h^{(l)}$ has the nonzero structure

$$B_h^{(l)} = \begin{bmatrix} \begin{matrix} \times\ \times \\ \times\ \times \end{matrix} & 0 \\ 0 & \begin{matrix} \times\ \times \\ \times\ \times \end{matrix} \end{bmatrix}.$$

The nodes and basis functions at nodes 1–4 in Fig. 7.13 are of the "Serendipity" type [see Zienkiewicz (1977) and Exercise 5.8]. It follows that if we use a node ordering as indicated in Fig. 7.14 (for an L-shaped domain), the global matrix takes the form (I).

Hence, since B_h is tridiagonal, we can solve systems with B_h at a cost of

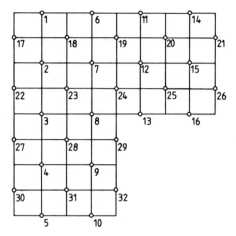

Fig. 7.14. Global node orderings of mid-edge nodes. The vertex nodes can be ordered arbitrarily.

$$\mathscr{A}_h = \begin{bmatrix} \begin{array}{cccccccccccc} \times & \times & & & & & & & & & \\ \times & \times & \times & & & & & & & & \\ & \times & \times & \times & & & & & & & \\ & & \times & \times & \times & & & & & & \\ & & & \times & \times & & & & & & \\ & & & & & \times & \times & & & & \\ & & & & & \times & \times & \times & & & \\ & & & & & & \times & \times & \times & & \\ & & & & & & & \times & \times & \times & \\ & & & & & & & & \times & \times & \\ \end{array} & \vline & \Large C_h \\ \hline & \vline & \\ \Large C_h^{\mathrm{T}} & \vline & \Large A_h \end{bmatrix} \begin{array}{l} \left. \rule{0pt}{40pt}\right\} \dfrac{2N}{3} \\[20pt] \left. \rule{0pt}{20pt}\right\} \dfrac{N}{3} \end{array} \qquad \textbf{(I)}$$

about $2N$ flops (the factorization, which is done once, costs about $\frac{10}{3}N$), and hence in the preconditioned method it remains only to solve for the matrix A_h. Again, it is clear that it will be better now than in the methods described in Section 7.3 to calculate a more accurate incomplete factorization, i.e., to let the index set J be quite larger than S_K.

An alternative procedure is actually to eliminate $\boldsymbol{\beta}_h$ in

$$\mathscr{A}_h \begin{bmatrix} \boldsymbol{\beta}_h \\ \boldsymbol{\alpha}_h \end{bmatrix} = \begin{bmatrix} B_h & C_h \\ C_h^{\mathrm{T}} & A_h \end{bmatrix} \begin{bmatrix} \boldsymbol{\beta}_h \\ \boldsymbol{\alpha}_h \end{bmatrix} = \begin{bmatrix} \mathbf{g}_2 \\ \mathbf{g}_1 \end{bmatrix}, \qquad (7.69)$$

which leads to

$$(A_h - C_h^T B_h^{-1} C_h)\alpha_h = \mathbf{g}_1 - C_h^T B_h^{-1} \mathbf{g}_2. \tag{7.70}$$

(Naturally B_h^{-1} is not calculated explicitly.)

Now one can prove that A_h is spectrally equivalent to $A_h - C_h^T B_h^{-1} C_h$ with condition number $1/(1 - \gamma^2)$ [see Axelsson (1982).] Hence A_h, or a preconditioning of A_h, can be used for preconditioning when solving (7.70). One finds that the value of γ for the element mentioned previously is $\gamma = \sqrt{5/11}$. This means that the spectral condition numbers are

$$(1 + \gamma)/(1 - \gamma) \simeq 5.1 \qquad \text{and} \qquad 1/(1 - \gamma^2) = 11/6,$$

remarkably small values.

Methods of this type are discussed in Axelsson (1982).

The Linear–Linear Combination of Basis Functions

As we have seen in (7.70), the crucial step in deriving an optimal order process [of computational complexity $O(N)$] is the ability to solve equations with matrix A_h, corresponding to piecewise linear basis functions, by an optimal order process. Therefore we shall consider the combination of linear basis functions $\lambda_j^{(h_0)}$ at the vertex nodes (indicated by o in Fig. 7.15) of mesh Ω_{h_0}, with linear basis functions $\lambda_i^{(h_1)}$ at the midedge points (indicated by × in Fig. 7.15) of this mesh, but with support on the smaller sized elements. For isosceles triangles and for the previously given bilinear form one finds that the corresponding value of γ is $\sqrt{1/2}$.

We shall now present an alternative method of solving (7.70), particularly suited for this combination. We shall then calculate an approximation of its solution by the following two basic steps. (It is easily seen that together they form nothing but a block overrelaxation step.)

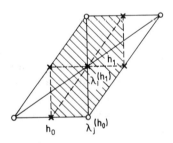

Fig. 7.15. Support of $\lambda_i^{(h_1)}$.

Initial Step. Assume that we have an initial approximation $\alpha_h^{(0)}$ of α_h. This may be calculated by solving [i.e., by letting $\beta_h^{(0)} = 0$ in (7.69)] $A_h\alpha_h^{(0)} = \mathbf{g}_1$. However, we shall primarily consider the case in which we work on a sequence of meshes upwards from coarse to fine. Then we already have an approximation of this vector, namely, the solution (or approximation thereof) on the previous mesh.

First Step. Solve

$$B_h\beta_h^{(1)} = \mathbf{g}_2 - C_h\alpha_h^{(0)}. \tag{7.71}$$

Second Step. Solve

$$A_h\alpha_h^{(1)} = (1 - \omega)A_h\alpha_h^{(0)} + \omega(\mathbf{g}_1 - C_h^T\beta_h^{(1)}), \tag{7.72}$$

where ω is a relaxation parameter, the choice of which is discussed later. Let

$$\mathbf{e}_h^{(i)} = \alpha_h - \alpha_h^{(i)}, \qquad i = 0, 1.$$

It follows from (7.69) and (7.71) that

$$B_h(\beta_h - \beta_h^{(1)}) = -C_h\mathbf{e}_h^{(0)}$$

and from (7.69) and (7.72) that

$$A_h\mathbf{e}_h^{(1)} = (1 - \omega)A_h\mathbf{e}_h^{(0)} - \omega C_h^T(\beta_h - \beta_h^{(1)})$$

or

$$A_h\mathbf{e}_h^{(1)} = [(1 - \omega)A_h + \omega C_h^T B_h^{-1} C_h]\mathbf{e}_h^{(0)}.$$

By the preceding spectral equivalence result we see that the eigenvalues λ of $A_h^{-1}C_h^T B_h^{-1} C_h$, which are nonnegative, are all bounded by γ^2. Hence, the eigenvalues μ of

$$A_h^{-1}[(1 - \omega)A_h + \omega C_h^T B_h^{-1} C_h]$$

satisfy

$$\mu = 1 - \omega + \omega\lambda, \qquad 0 \leq \lambda \leq \gamma^2.$$

To minimize $\max_{0 \leq \lambda \leq \gamma^2} |\mu|$ we choose $\omega = 2/(2 - \gamma^2)$ and then find

$$\|\mathbf{e}_h^{(1)}\| \leq \max |\mu| \cdot \|\mathbf{e}_h^{(0)}\| = [\gamma^2/(2 - \gamma^2)]\|\mathbf{e}_h^{(0)}\|. \tag{7.73}$$

Relaxation process steps 1 and 2 can be repeated, and because $\gamma^2/(2 - \gamma^2) < 1$ we have convergence. For $\gamma^2 = \frac{1}{2}$ the reduction factor at each step is $\gamma^2/(2 - \gamma^2) = \frac{1}{3}$.

Consider now the case in which, for mesh Ω_{2h}, we have an approximate solution α_{2h} with error $\sim C(2h)^2$. By linear interpolation we can then calculate $\alpha_h^{(0)}$ on mesh Ω_h, and the error is then also $\sim C(2h)^2$.

We now want to calculate an approximation of α_h with an error not greater than $\sim Ch^2$. In this way the errors of the actually calculated solution at each mesh Ω_h, $h = h_0, h_0/2, \ldots$ will remain on the order of the discretization error $O(h^2)$, assuming that $u \in H^2(\Omega)$. Clearly, from (7.73) it follows that this would be achieved by at most v relaxation steps if $\gamma^2 \leq 2/(1 + \sqrt[\nu]{4})$ and if we were able to solve (7.71) and (7.72) exactly or with negligible errors.

However, since we are aiming at an optimal order process, we cannot spend too much computational labor on this calculation. For simplicity we assume that (7.71) is solved with an error that can be neglected and with an optimal order method [compare with (7.68)]. For (7.72) we use multigrid recursion of the two-level grid type, i.e., we rewrite the linear equations on each mesh Ω_{2h}, Ω_{4h}, $\ldots$ in the two-by-two block form by use of the linear–linear combination of basis functions. On each mesh we perform v relaxation steps ($1 \leq v \leq 3$), and at every step the corresponding equation (7.72) is again solved by this recursive method onto coarser and coarser meshes until we eventually reach such a coarse mesh that the system can be solved by a direct method with negligible cost.

The computational complexity of this process is easily calculated. Assume that the cost of solving (7.71) and the cost of calculating the right-hand side of (7.72) once is $\sim Kh^{-n}$ in a problem in n space dimensions. Let $Q(h)$ be the total cost at mesh Ω_h. Then,

$$Q(h) = vKh^{-2} + vQ(2h) = v[Kh^{-2} + vK(2h)^{-2} + vQ(4h)]$$

$$\leq vKh^{-2}\left[1 + \frac{v}{4} + \left(\frac{v}{4}\right)^2 + \cdots\right] = [4v/(4 - v)]Kh^{-2}$$

for a two-dimensional problem, and similarly

$$Q(h) \leq [8v/(8 - v)]Kh^{-3}$$

for a three-dimensional problem. Hence, for $v = 2$ the total cost is not larger than 4 and $\frac{8}{3}$ times the cost Kh^{-n}, $n = 2, 3$, respectively, and we have an optimal order process for $1 \leq v \leq 2^n - 1$.

We leave it to the reader to establish that the errors due to applying relaxation only v times at each level are small enough so that the total errors remain $O(h^2)$ if γ is small enough.

Finally, let us mention that all iterative methods converge very much faster when we work on a sequence of meshes that proceed gradually from the coarsest to the finest. We then start with the solution on the coarsest mesh Ω_{h_0} (the solution may simply be calculated by a direct method) and let the interpolation of the corresponding solution onto the next grid Ω_{h_1} be the initial approximation for the iterations on Ω_{h_1}. Here we make a few iterations to get, by interpolation, an initial approximation on Ω_{h_2} and so on, until we eventually reach the finest grid Ω_{h_k}.

The explanation, which we do not consider in detail here, is that the upper bounds for the number of iterations in, for instance, the conjugate gradient method have been derived assuming the worst possible case. But when we work on a sequence of meshes in the described manner, we always work on fairly "smooth" functions, i.e., we can restrict the analysis when we derive condition numbers and so forth to subspaces of smooth functions.

In this chapter we have analyzed iterative methods only for positive definite symmetric matrices. It should be mentioned that for the iterative solution of unsymmetric systems of linear equations there is currently much research going on [see, e.g., Axelsson (1979, 1980), Eisenstat *et al.* (1983), Hageman and Young (1981), Saad (1981), and Young and Jea (1980).]

For recent developments on incomplete factorization methods for matrices partitioned into block form, see Axelsson *et al.* (1984), Axelsson (1983), and Concus *et al.* (1982).

Exercises

7.1.

(i) Use the proof of Theorem 1.13 to show that

$$\delta \le 0 \quad \Leftrightarrow \quad \rho(\tilde{L}\tilde{L}^{\mathrm{T}}) \le \tfrac{1}{4}.$$

(ii) Use the identity

$$\mathbf{x}^{\mathrm{T}}LD^{-1}L^{\mathrm{T}}\mathbf{x}/\mathbf{x}^{\mathrm{T}}D\mathbf{x} = \mathbf{y}^{\mathrm{T}}\tilde{L}\tilde{L}^{\mathrm{T}}\mathbf{y}/\mathbf{y}^{\mathrm{T}}\mathbf{y}, \qquad \mathbf{y} \equiv D^{1/2}\mathbf{x}$$

and the analysis preceding (1.73c) to show that

$$\delta \le [\rho(\tilde{L}\tilde{L}^{\mathrm{T}}) - \tfrac{1}{4}]\kappa(K).$$

7.2. Show that if in Example 7.2 the node ordering is changed to either the row-wise ordering of Example 7.1 or a column-wise ordering starting at the left column, then

$$\|\tilde{L}\tilde{L}^{\mathrm{T}}\|_\infty = (\gamma^2 + \gamma + 2)/16.$$

Compare this with the corresponding result of Example 7.2.

7.3. Show that if in Example 7.3 the node ordering is changed to either of the orderings of the preceding exercise, then

$$\|\tilde{L}\tilde{L}^{\mathrm{T}}\|_\infty = (4 + \sqrt{2})/16, \qquad \sqrt{\rho(\tilde{L}\tilde{L}^{\mathrm{T}}) - \tfrac{1}{4}} < 0.298.$$

Compare this with the corresponding result of Example 7.3.

7.4. The purpose of this exercise is to demonstrate by a simple example that the parameter δ defined following (7.1) can grow without bound as $N \to \infty$. Thus, consider the one-dimensional problem

$$-u'' = f(x), \qquad 0 < x < 1,$$

$$u'(0) = u(1) = 0$$

and the use of piecewise linear basis functions on the uniform mesh

$$x_i = (i-1)h, \qquad i = 1, 2, ..., N+1, \quad h \equiv 1/N.$$

(i) Show that the Nth-order stiffness matrix is

$$K = \frac{1}{h}\begin{bmatrix} 1 & -1 & & & & \\ -1 & 2 & -1 & & & \\ & \cdot & \cdot & \cdot & & \\ & & \cdot & \cdot & \cdot & \\ & & & -1 & 2 & -1 \\ & & & & -1 & 2 \end{bmatrix}.$$

(ii) Establish the identity

$$\mathbf{v}^T(LD^{-1}L^T - \tfrac{1}{4}D)\mathbf{v} = (1/4h)(-v_1^2 + 2v_2^2)$$

and hence deduce that

$$\delta \geq (-v_1^2 + 2v_2^2)/(4h\lambda\mathbf{v}^T D\mathbf{v}) \qquad \forall \mathbf{v} \in R^N, \quad \mathbf{v} \neq \mathbf{0}$$

where λ is the smallest eigenvalue of $D^{-1}K$ and $\mathbf{v}$ the corresponding eigenvector.

(iii) It is known that $\lambda = 1 - \cos(\pi h/2)$ and $\mathbf{v} = [\cos(\tfrac{1}{2}(i-1)\pi h)]_{i=1}^N$. Show that $\delta \gtrsim 2N/\pi^2$.

NOTE: It follows from Exercise 7.7 that block-SSOR preconditioning is applicable here and can make $\delta \leq 0$.

7.5. From the analysis in Section 1.4 of the sensitivity of the rate of convergence of SSOR preconditioning with respect to ω, we can easily obtain the inequality

$$\kappa(\tilde{K})(\omega) \leq \tfrac{1}{2}(\sqrt{\alpha} + 1/\sqrt{\alpha})[\sqrt{(\tfrac{1}{2} + \delta)\kappa(K)} + \tfrac{1}{2}],$$

where

$$\omega = \frac{2}{1 + (2/\sqrt{\tilde{\mu}})\sqrt{\tfrac{1}{2} + \tilde{\delta}}}, \qquad \alpha = \frac{\tilde{\mu}/(\tfrac{1}{2} + \tilde{\delta})}{\mu/(\tfrac{1}{2} + \delta)}.$$

$\tilde{\mu}$ and $\tilde{\delta}$ are arbitrary approximations to the parameters μ and δ defined in Theorem 1.13.

Show that if K is a finite element matrix such that $-\tfrac{1}{4} \leq \delta \leq 0$ and if ω is defined by $\omega = 2/(1 + \eta h)$, where η is a positive constant independent of h, then $\kappa(\tilde{K})(\omega) = O(h^{-1})$.

7.6. Let K be an $N \times N$ symmetric positive definite matrix with the block tri-diagonal form

$$K = \begin{bmatrix} D_1 & L_2^T & & & \\ L_2 & D_2 & L_3^T & & \\ & \cdot & \cdot & \cdot & \\ & & \cdot & \cdot & \cdot \\ & & & L_m & D_m \end{bmatrix}.$$

The block-SSOR preconditioning matrix is defined to be

$$
C = \begin{bmatrix} \dfrac{1}{\omega_1} D_1 & & & \\ L_2 & \dfrac{1}{\omega_2} D_2 & & \\ & \ddots & \ddots & \\ & & L_m & \dfrac{1}{\omega_m} D_m \end{bmatrix} \begin{bmatrix} \left(\dfrac{1}{\omega_1} D_1\right)^{-1} & & & \\ & \left(\dfrac{1}{\omega_2} D_2\right)^{-1} & & \\ & & \ddots & \\ & & & \left(\dfrac{1}{\omega_m} D_m\right)^{-1} \end{bmatrix}
$$

$$
\times \begin{bmatrix} \dfrac{1}{\omega_1} D_1 & L_2^T & & \\ & \dfrac{1}{\omega_2} D_2 & L_3^T & \\ & & \ddots & \ddots \\ & & & \dfrac{1}{\omega_m} D_m \end{bmatrix},
$$

where $0 < \omega_1 < 1; 0 < \omega_i < 2, i = 2, 3, ..., m$.

(i)   Following the proof of Theorem 1.13, show that

$$
(2 - \max_{1 \le i \le m} \omega_i)^{-1} \mathbf{x}^T C \mathbf{x} \ge \mathbf{x}^T (A + V) A^{-1} (A + V)^T \mathbf{x}
$$

$$
\ge \mathbf{x}^T K \mathbf{x} \qquad \forall \mathbf{x} \in R^N, \quad \mathbf{x} = [\mathbf{x}_1^T, ..., \mathbf{x}_m^T]^T
$$

(**x** is partitioned consistently with the blocks of K), where

$$
A = \begin{bmatrix} \left(\dfrac{2}{\omega_1} - 1\right) D_1 & & & \\ & \left(\dfrac{2}{\omega_2} - 1\right) D_2 & & \\ & & \ddots & \\ & & & \left(\dfrac{2}{\omega_m} - 1\right) D_m \end{bmatrix},
$$

$$
V = \begin{bmatrix} \left(1 - \dfrac{1}{\omega_1}\right) D_1 & & & \\ L_2 & \left(1 - \dfrac{1}{\omega_2}\right) D_2 & & \\ & \ddots & \ddots & \\ & & L_m & \left(1 - \dfrac{1}{\omega_m}\right) D_m \end{bmatrix}.
$$

(ii)   Show that $C = K + \tilde{D}$, where

$$\tilde{D} = \text{diag}(\tilde{D}_1, \tilde{D}_2, ..., \tilde{D}_m),$$

$$\tilde{D}_1 = (1/\omega_1 - 1)D_1,$$

$$\tilde{D}_i = \frac{1}{4\omega_i}(2 - \omega_i)^2 D_i + \omega_i\left[L_i\left(\frac{\omega_i}{\omega_{i-1}}D_{i-1}\right)^{-1}L_i^T - \frac{1}{4}D_i\right],$$

$i = 2, 3, ..., m$.

(iii)   Show that the spectral condition number $\kappa(\tilde{K})$ associated with the preconditioning matrix C satisfies

$$\kappa(\tilde{K}) < (2 - \max_{1 \leq i \leq m} \omega_i)^{-1}(1 + \gamma\mu + \delta),$$

where

$$\gamma = \max_{2 \leq i \leq m}[(2 - \omega_i)^2/4\omega_i],$$

$$\mu = \max_{\mathbf{x} \neq \mathbf{0}}\{[\gamma^{-1}(1/\omega_1 - 1)\mathbf{x}_1^T D_1 \mathbf{x}_1 + \mathbf{x}^T D\mathbf{x}]/\mathbf{x}^T K\mathbf{x}\},$$

$$\delta = \max_{\mathbf{x} \neq \mathbf{0}} \frac{\sum_{i=2}^m \omega_i \mathbf{x}_i^T\{L_i[(\omega_i/\omega_{i-1})D_{i-1}]^{-1}L_i^T - \frac{1}{4}D_i\}\mathbf{x}_i}{\mathbf{x}^T K\mathbf{x}},$$

$$D = \text{diag}(D_1, D_2, ..., D_m).$$

7.7.   In Example 7.3 let the nodes be ordered column-wise, starting at the left edge where the Neumann boundary condition is imposed. The stiffness matrix K can be partitioned in the block tridiagonal form shown in the preceding exercise, m being the number of columns. We consider the application of block-SSOR preconditioning, where for some positive constant η independent of h

$$\omega_1 = 1/(1 + \eta h), \qquad \omega_i = 2/(1 + \eta h), \qquad i = 2, 3, ..., m.$$

(It is assumed that $\eta < h^{-1}$ for the coarsest mesh considered.)

Show that $\delta \leq 0$, $\mu = O(h^{-2})$ and hence that

$$\kappa(\tilde{K}) = O(h^{-1}), \qquad h \to 0.$$

[Note that in Exercise 7.4, with $\omega_i = \omega_1$, $i = 2, 3, ..., N$, we find that $\delta \geq O(h^{-1})$.]

HINTS:

(i)   Note with regard to δ that

$$\mathbf{x}_2^T[L_2((\omega_2/\omega_1)D_1)^{-1}L_2^T - \tfrac{1}{4}D_2]\mathbf{x}_2 = \mathbf{x}_2^T[\hat{D}^{-1} - \tfrac{1}{4}\hat{D}]\mathbf{x}_2$$

$$\leq (\xi_1^{-1} - \tfrac{1}{4}\xi_1)\mathbf{x}_2^T\mathbf{x}_2 \qquad \forall \mathbf{x}_2,$$

where

$$\hat{D} = \begin{bmatrix} 4 & -1 & & & \\ -1 & 4 & -1 & & \\ & \cdot & \cdot & \cdot & \\ & & \cdot & \cdot & \cdot \\ & & & -1 & 4 \end{bmatrix}$$

and ξ_1 is the smallest eigenvalue of $\hat{D}$, i.e., $\xi_1 = 2 + [2\sin(\pi h/2)]^2$.

(ii)   For the analysis of μ we let $\alpha_m = 2$ and $\alpha_{i-1} = 2 - \alpha_i^{-1}$ for $i = m, m-1, ..., 2$. [That is, $\alpha_{m-i} = (i+2)/(i+1)$.] Show that with $D_0 = \frac{1}{2}\hat{D}$,

$$\mathbf{x}^T K \mathbf{x} = \sum_{i=1}^{m-1} \{\alpha_{i+1}\mathbf{x}_{i+1}^T D_0 \mathbf{x}_{i+1} - 2\mathbf{x}_i^T \mathbf{x}_{i+1} + (2 - \alpha_i)\mathbf{x}_i^T D_0 \mathbf{x}_i\} + (\alpha_1 - 1)\mathbf{x}_1^T D_0 \mathbf{x}_1.$$

Using the inequality

$$2\mathbf{x}_i^T \mathbf{x}_{i+1} \leq \alpha_{i+1}^{-1}\mathbf{x}_i^T \mathbf{x}_i + \alpha_{i+1}\mathbf{x}_{i+1}^T \mathbf{x}_{i+1}$$

and the positive definite property of $D_0 - I$, show that

$$\mathbf{x}^T K \mathbf{x} \geq (\alpha_i - 1)\mathbf{x}_1^T D_0 \mathbf{x}_1 = m^{-1}\mathbf{x}_1^T D_0 \mathbf{x}_1.$$

Hence, defining

$$c(h) = \gamma^{-1}(\omega_1^{-1} - 1), \qquad \mu_0 = \max_{\mathbf{x} \neq 0}(\mathbf{x}^T D \mathbf{x}/\mathbf{x}^T K \mathbf{x}),$$

show that

$$\mu = \max_{\mathbf{x} \neq 0} \frac{c(h)\mathbf{x}_1^T D_1 \mathbf{x}_1 + \mathbf{x}^T D \mathbf{x}}{\mathbf{x}^T K \mathbf{x}} \leq \max_{\mathbf{x} \neq 0} \frac{c(h)\mathbf{x}_1^T D_1 \mathbf{x}_1 + \mathbf{x}^T D \mathbf{x}}{\frac{1}{2}m^{-1}\mathbf{x}_1^T D_0 \mathbf{x}_1 + \frac{1}{2}\mathbf{x}^T K \mathbf{x}}$$

$$\leq 2\max\{c(h)m, \mu_0\} = O(h^{-2}).$$

7.8. We consider again the block matrices K and C in Exercise 7.6, now letting $1 \leq \omega_i \leq 2, i = 1, 2, ..., m$.

(i)   Show that

(a) $\mathbf{x}^T C \mathbf{x} = \mathbf{x}^T(\hat{D} + L)\hat{D}^{-1}(\hat{D} + L)\mathbf{x} = \mathbf{x}^T K \mathbf{x} + \mathbf{x}^T(\hat{D} - D + L^T\hat{D}^{-1}L)\mathbf{x}$,

where $\hat{D} = \text{diag}\left(\dfrac{1}{\omega_1} D_1, ..., \dfrac{1}{\omega_m} D_m\right)$,

(b) $\mathbf{x}_i^T L_i^T D_{i-1}^{-1} L_i \mathbf{x}_i = \mathbf{y}_i^T \tilde{L}_i^T \tilde{L}_i \mathbf{y}_i \leq \rho_i \mathbf{x}_i^T D_i \mathbf{x}_i$,

where $\mathbf{y}_i = D_i^{1/2}\mathbf{x}_i, \tilde{L}_i = D_{i-1}^{-1/2} L_i D_i^{-1/2}$, and $\rho_i = \rho(\tilde{L}_i^T \tilde{L}_i)$, ρ denoting the spectral radius,

(c) $\mathbf{x}^T(\hat{D} - D + L^T\hat{D}^{-1}L)\mathbf{x}$

$$\leq \left(\frac{1}{\omega_1} - 1\right)\mathbf{x}_1^T D_1 \mathbf{x}_1 + \sum_{i=2}^{m}\left(\frac{1}{\omega_i} - 1 + \omega_{i-1}\rho_i\right)\mathbf{x}_i^T D_i \mathbf{x}_i.$$

(ii)   Prove the following lemma.
Let $0 \leq \varepsilon < 1$ be given and let $\{\rho_i\}$ be a given sequence satisfying

$$\varepsilon < \rho_{i+1} \leq \rho_i \leq \rho_0 \leq [\tfrac{1}{2}(1 + \varepsilon)]^2.$$

Let

$$\omega_1 = 1, \qquad \omega_i^{-1} = 1 + \varepsilon - \rho_i \omega_{i-1}, \qquad i = 2, 3, ...$$

Then,

$$1 \leq \omega_i < \omega_{i+1} < \omega_0 = 2/[1 + \varepsilon + \sqrt{(1 + \varepsilon)^2 - 4\rho_0}], \qquad i = 1, 2, ...$$

HINTS: Note that

$$\omega_2^{-1} = 1 + \varepsilon - \rho_1 < 1 = \omega_1,$$

that is,

$$1 = \omega_i < \omega_{i+1} < 2/(1 + \varepsilon), \qquad i = 1.$$

Prove that this relation holds for any i by showing that $\omega_{i+1}^{-1} - \omega_i^{-1} < 0$ and that

$$\omega_{i+1}^{-1} = 1 + \varepsilon - \rho_i \omega_{i-1} > (1 + \varepsilon)/2.$$

Then prove that $\{\omega_i\}$ converges (monotonically) to ω, where $\omega \le \omega_0$ and ω_0 is the smallest root of $\omega_0^{-1} = 1 + \varepsilon - \rho_0 \omega_0$.

(iii) Let $\{\omega_i\}$ be as in (ii) with $\rho_0 = \frac{1}{4}(1 + \varepsilon)$. Prove that

$$\kappa(\tilde{K}) \le (1 + \varepsilon \mu_0)/(2 - \omega_m), \qquad \mu_0 = \max_{\mathbf{x} \ne \mathbf{0}} (\mathbf{x}^T D \mathbf{x}/\mathbf{x}^T K \mathbf{x})$$

and

$$\kappa(\tilde{K}) \lesssim \tfrac{1}{2}(1/\sqrt{\varepsilon} + \sqrt{\varepsilon \mu_0})\sqrt{1 + \varepsilon},$$

that is,

$$\kappa(\tilde{K}) \lesssim \sqrt{\mu_0} \qquad \text{if} \quad \varepsilon = \mu_0^{-1/2}.$$

(iv) If $D_i = D_0$, $L_i = -I$, then $\rho_i \le \frac{1}{4}$. Prove that with $\varepsilon = 0$, $\omega_i^{-1} = 1 - \omega_{i-1}/4$ [i.e., $\omega_i = 2 - 2/(i + 1)$], then

$$\kappa(\tilde{K}) \le 1/(2 - \omega_m) = (m + 1)/2.$$

7.9. Establish the identity

$$\mathbf{x}^T K \mathbf{x} = \sum_{i=1}^{N} \left[\left(k_{ii} + \sum_{j \ne i} k_{ij} \right) x_i^2 + \sum_{j > i} (-k_{ij})(x_i - x_j)^2 \right],$$

where K is an arbitrary $N \times N$ symmetric matrix.

HINT: $x_i x_j = \frac{1}{2}[x_i^2 + x_j^2 - (x_i - x_j)^2]$.

7.10. Verify that modified incomplete factorization applied to a matrix K is equivalent to unmodified incomplete factorization applied to the matrix $\hat{K}$ in (7.20).

7.11. Extend the pseudocode of Fig. 1.7 to the case of the modified incomplete factorization process (7.18).

7.12. Analyze the problem of extending the program code of Exercise 1.27 to the case of modified incomplete factorization.

7.13. Establish inequality (7.25).

7.14. When the finite element method is applied to a boundary value problem of the type

$$-\Delta u = g, \qquad (x, y) \in \Omega,$$

$$u_v = \xi, \qquad (x, y) \in \Gamma,$$

satisfying the consistency condition

$$\iint_\Omega g \, dx \, dy = -\int_\Gamma \xi \, ds$$

(see Exercise 3.10), the associated Ritz–Galerkin equations $K\alpha = G$ are a consistent, positive semidefinite system. To solve this system consider the use of the simple conjugate gradient method (1.45).

(i)   Show that the component of α^k along the eigenvector of K corresponding to the zero eigenvalue remains the same as for α^0.

(ii)   Show that the rate of convergence is determined by the ratio of the extreme positive eigenvalues of K. In what norm do the gradients $\{g^k\}$ converge monotonically?

(iii)   Suppose the Ritz–Galerkin equations are inconsistent, owing to rounding errors. Investigate again the simple conjugate gradient method, but now with the step $d^0 = -g^0$ replaced by $d^0 = -Kg^0$.

7.15.   The purpose of this exercise is to extend the preconditioned conjugate gradient method to an $N \times N$ nonsingular *unsymmetric* system of equations $K\alpha = G$. We assume that the preconditioning matrix C has been determined in the Gaussian factored form $C = LU$. If K is a diagonally dominant L matrix, then L and U could be determined, for example, by modified incomplete factorization.

(i)   A possible strategy is to choose matrices P and Q such that the system $\tilde{K}\tilde{\alpha} = \tilde{G}$, where $\tilde{K} = PKQ$, $\tilde{\alpha} = Q^{-1}\alpha$, and $\tilde{G} = PG$, is positive definite. The idea is to compute $\tilde{G} = PG$, solve the new system by the simple conjugate gradient method, and then compute $\alpha = Q\tilde{\alpha}$.

Let $F = L^{-1}KU^{-1}$. Find P and Q for each of the following cases.

(a) $\tilde{K} = F^T F$ (Answer: $P = U^{-T}K^T L^{-T}L^{-1}$, $Q = U^{-1}$).
(b) $\tilde{K} = FF^T$ (Answer: $P = L^{-1}$, $Q = U^{-1}U^{-T}K^T L^{-T}$).

(ii)   For either of these choices $\tilde{K}$ show that $\kappa(\tilde{K}) = \kappa(F)^2$ and discuss the computational labor and storage required by procedure (i) for finding α.

Note that if F is symmetric positive definite, then this procedure is much less efficient than others described in this book.

7.16.   We consider again the Ritz–Galerkin system $K\alpha = G$ of Exercise 7.14. Let $C = LL^T$ be a modified incomplete factorization of K. To find α we can apply the preconditioned conjugate gradient method to solve

$$\tilde{K}\alpha = \tilde{G}, \qquad \tilde{K} = K^T C^{-T} C^{-1} K, \qquad \tilde{G} = K^T C^{-T} C^{-1} G,$$

taking as the initial vector $\alpha^0 = C^{-1}G$. Discuss the rate of convergence of this process.

NOTE: For the method to be effective, C should be a good approximation to K; i.e., the index set J should be considerably larger than S_K. Observe that this method is also applicable to unsymmetric systems.

7.17.   The purpose of this exercise is to investigate the eigensolutions of (7.42). Note that $K^{(l)}$ and $\overset{*}{K}^{(l)}$ can be partitioned as

$$K^{(l)} = \frac{1}{6}\begin{bmatrix} A & C^T \\ C & B \end{bmatrix}, \qquad \overset{*}{K}^{(l)} = \frac{1}{8}\begin{bmatrix} \overset{*}{A} & C^T \\ C & B \end{bmatrix},$$

where

$$A = \begin{bmatrix} 6 & 1 & 1 \\ 1 & 3 & 0 \\ 1 & 0 & 3 \end{bmatrix}, \qquad B = \begin{bmatrix} 16 & -8 & -8 \\ -8 & 16 & 0 \\ -8 & 0 & 16 \end{bmatrix},$$

$$C = \begin{bmatrix} 0 & 0 & 0 \\ -4 & 0 & -4 \\ -4 & -4 & 0 \end{bmatrix}, \qquad \overset{*}{A} = \begin{bmatrix} 8 & 0 & 0 \\ 0 & 4 & 0 \\ 0 & 0 & 4 \end{bmatrix}.$$

Let $\mathbf{x} = \begin{bmatrix} \mathbf{y} \\ \mathbf{z} \end{bmatrix}$ be a corresponding partitioning of any vector $\mathbf{x} \in R^6$.

(i) Show that $\lambda = \frac{4}{3}$ is an eigenvalue of (7.42) corresponding to any vector $\mathbf{x}$ such that $(A - \overset{*}{A})\mathbf{y} = \mathbf{0}$, and hence establish that the eigenvector for this eigenvalue can be expressed as

$$\mathbf{x} = \begin{bmatrix} 0 \\ 0 \\ 0 \\ z_1 \\ z_2 \\ z_3 \end{bmatrix} + c \begin{bmatrix} 1 \\ 1 \\ 1 \\ 1 \\ 1 \\ 1 \end{bmatrix} \qquad \forall \mathbf{z} \in R^3, \quad \forall c \in R.$$

(ii) Assuming $\lambda \neq \frac{4}{3}$, show that if $(\mu, \mathbf{y})$ is an eigensolution of the third-order problem

$$(\overset{*}{A} - C^{\mathrm{T}}B^{-1}C)\mathbf{y} = \mu(\overset{*}{A} - A)\mathbf{y},$$

then $(\lambda, \mathbf{x})$ is an eigensolution of (7.42), where

$$\lambda = \tfrac{4}{3}(1 - \mu^{-1}), \qquad \mathbf{x} = \begin{bmatrix} \mathbf{y} \\ -B^{-1}C\mathbf{y} \end{bmatrix}.$$

Solve this third-order problem and show that the following are eigensolutions of (7.42):

$$\lambda = \tfrac{2}{3}, \qquad \mathbf{x} = c \begin{bmatrix} 0 \\ 2 \\ 2 \\ 1 \\ 1 \\ 1 \end{bmatrix} + d \begin{bmatrix} 1 \\ 1 \\ 1 \\ 1 \\ 1 \\ 1 \end{bmatrix} \qquad \forall c, d \in R,$$

$$\lambda = \tfrac{8}{9}, \qquad \mathbf{x} = c \begin{bmatrix} 4 \\ 0 \\ 8 \\ 4 \\ 5 \\ 3 \end{bmatrix} + d \begin{bmatrix} 1 \\ 1 \\ 1 \\ 1 \\ 1 \\ 1 \end{bmatrix} \qquad \forall c, d \in R.$$

7.18. The purpose of this exercise is to extend the analysis of Example 7.9 and the preceding exercise to the case when e_l is the arbitrary triangle shown in the accompanying illustration. Let $\alpha = \cot(\tilde{\alpha})$, $\beta = \cot(\tilde{\beta})$, $\gamma = \cot(\tilde{\gamma})$.

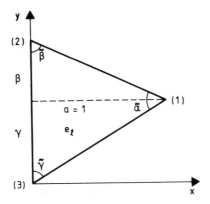

(i) Show that the finite element matrix for linear basis functions is

$$\frac{1}{2}\begin{bmatrix} \beta + \gamma & -\gamma & -\beta \\ -\gamma & \alpha + \gamma & -\alpha \\ -\beta & -\alpha & \alpha + \beta \end{bmatrix}.$$

HINT: Choose the Euclidean coordinate system as indicated. (By a homogeniety argument we can let $a = 1$.)

Let $A = \text{area}(e_l) = \frac{1}{2}(\beta + \gamma)$. The barycentric coordinates are

$$\lambda_1 = x, \qquad \lambda_2 = [1/(2A)](y - \gamma x), \qquad \lambda_3 = 1 - \lambda_1 - \lambda_2.$$

We obtain

$$\int_{e_l} |\nabla\lambda_1|^2 \, dx \, dy = A, \qquad \int_{e_l} \nabla\lambda_1 . \nabla\lambda_2 \, dx \, dy = -\tfrac{1}{2}\gamma, \qquad \int_{e_l} \nabla\lambda_1 . \nabla\lambda_3 \, dx \, dy = -\tfrac{1}{2}\beta.$$

The remaining entries are obtained by permutation: $\alpha \to \beta \to \gamma$.

(ii) Introduce the midpoint nodes ($i = 4, 5, 6$) and the four corresponding subtriangles. Prove that the assembled piecewise linear element matrix is

$$K_1 = \frac{1}{2}\left[\begin{array}{ccc|ccc} \beta + \gamma & 0 & 0 & 0 & -\beta & -\gamma \\ 0 & \alpha + \gamma & 0 & -\alpha & 0 & -\gamma \\ 0 & 0 & \alpha + \beta & -\alpha & -\beta & 0 \\ \hline 0 & -\alpha & -\alpha & 2d & -2\gamma & -2\beta \\ -\beta & 0 & -\beta & -2\gamma & 2d & -2\alpha \\ -\gamma & -\gamma & 0 & -2\beta & -2\alpha & 2d \end{array}\right], \qquad d = \alpha + \beta + \gamma.$$

(iii)   Calculate the corresponding quadratic finite element matrix,

$$K_2 = \frac{1}{3} \left[\begin{array}{ccc|ccc} 3(\beta + \gamma) & \gamma & \beta & 0 & -4\beta & -4\gamma \\ \gamma & 3(\alpha + \gamma) & \alpha & -4\alpha & 0 & -4\gamma \\ \beta & \alpha & 3(\alpha + \beta) & -4\alpha & -4\beta & 0 \\ \hline 0 & -4\alpha & -4\alpha & 8d & -8\gamma & -8\beta \\ -4\beta & 0 & -4\beta & -8\gamma & 8d & -8\alpha \\ -4\gamma & -4\gamma & 0 & -8\beta & -8\alpha & 8d \end{array} \right].$$

HINT: The basis functions are

$$\phi_i = \lambda_i(2\lambda_i - 1), \qquad i = 1, 2, 3,$$

$$\phi_{i+3} = 4\lambda_{\pi(i)}\lambda_{\pi[\pi(i)]}, \qquad i = 1, 2, 3,$$

where the permutation $\pi(i)$ is the cyclic permutation of the set $\{1, 2, 3\}$:

$$\pi(i) \rightarrow \pi[\pi(i)] \rightarrow \pi\{\pi[\pi(i)]\}.$$

We have

$$\mathbf{V}\phi_i = (4\lambda_i - 1) \, \mathbf{V}\lambda_i,$$

$$\mathbf{V}\phi_{i+3} = 4(\lambda_{\pi(i)} \, \mathbf{V}\lambda_{\pi[\pi(i)]} + \lambda_{\pi[\pi(i)]} \, \mathbf{V}\lambda_{\pi(i)}), \qquad i = 1, 2, 3,$$

and

$$\int_{e_l} |\mathbf{V}\phi_1|^2 \, dx \, dy = \beta + \gamma,$$

$$\int_{e_l} \mathbf{V}\phi_1 \cdot \mathbf{V}\phi_2 \, dx \, dy = \tfrac{1}{3}\gamma,$$

and by a symmetry argument

$$\int_{e_l} \mathbf{V}\phi_1 \, \mathbf{V}\phi_3 \, dx \, dy = \tfrac{1}{3}\beta.$$

Further,

$$\int_{e_l} \mathbf{V}\phi_1 \cdot \mathbf{V}\phi_4 \, dx \, dy = -\tfrac{4}{3}\beta,$$

$$\int_{e_l} |\mathbf{V}\phi_4|^2 \, dx \, dy = \tfrac{8}{3}[\beta + \gamma + (1 - \beta\gamma)/(\beta + \gamma)]$$

$$= \tfrac{8}{3}d,$$

[use the trigonometric identity

$$(\alpha + \beta)(\alpha + \beta + \gamma) = \alpha^2 + \beta^2 + \alpha\beta + 1],$$

$$\int_{e_l} \mathbf{V}\phi_4 \cdot \mathbf{V}\phi_5 \, dx \, dy = -\tfrac{8}{3}\gamma.$$

The remaining entries are obtained by permutation and symmetry arguments.

7.19. Repeat the computation of the spectral equivalence bound in Example 7.9 for the case when the typical element e_l of the coarse mesh is a ten-node right triangle for

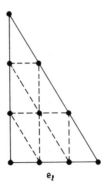

e_l

the use of piecewise cubic basis functions. The nodes of e_l are positioned uniformly as shown in the accompanying illustration.

7.20. The analysis of (7.42) for the matrices $K^{(l)}$ and $\overset{*}{K}{}^{(l)}$ of Example 7.9 established the spectral equivalence bound $\lambda_6/\lambda_2 = 2$. Another bound is given by d_2/d_1, where d_1 and d_2 are defined by (7.45). Show that $d_2/d_1 \simeq 155$.

7.21. Fill in the details of the computation of $\hat{R}$ in Example 7.10.

7.22. Let the mesh elements of Example 7.10 be changed to six-node triangles. By direct inspection of the mesh determine the location of the nonzero entries of $\hat{R}$, assuming $J = S_K$. Compare the computational labor and storage required by (1.92) and (1.100) to solve this problem by preconditioning with modified incomplete factorization.

7.23. Determine the location of the off-diagonal nonzero entries of $\hat{R}$ for the stiffness matrix of Example 7.6.

These entries can be interpreted as "couplings" between certain pairs of mesh nodes. Draw a section of the mesh and show these couplings.

7.24. In the accompanying diagram we show an intermediate stage of modified

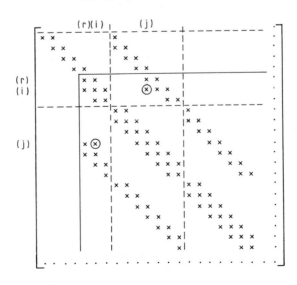

incomplete factorization applied to a matrix with seven (at most) nonzero entries per row. The rth row is the current pivot row; the corresponding fill-ins are denoted by $\otimes$.

Prove that condition (7.29) is satisfied. [Note that entries in one subdiagonal are not affected by the factorization and that these entries do not cause any fill-in, i.e., they do not have any of the index values i, j in (7.29).]

7.25. Justify the assertion that in the case of a fine mesh there is often no rounding error in the floating-point computation of $(\alpha_j^{(k+1)} - \alpha_i^{(k+1)})$ and $[(\alpha_{i_{r+3}}^{(k+1)} - \alpha_i^{(k+1)}) - (\alpha_i^{(k+1)} - \alpha_{i_r}^{(k+1)})]$, $(\alpha_i^{(k+1)} - \alpha_{i_{r+3}}^{(k+1)})$ in (7.53) and (7.54), respectively,

7.26. Consider the boundary value problem

$$-[p(u')]' = g, \qquad 0 < x < 1,$$

$$u(0) = u(1) = 0, \qquad p, g \in C^3[0, 1],$$

with piecewise linear basis functions on a uniform subdivision of $[0, 1]$ in $N + 1$ sub-intervals of length h. We assume that $h > \varepsilon_M$, the machine precision. The Ritz–Galerkin system is

$$-p_{i-1}\alpha_{i-1} + (p_{i-1} + p_i)\alpha_i - p_i\alpha_{i+1} = h^2 G_i, \qquad i = 1, 2, ..., N,$$

where

$$p_i = h^{-1} \int_{x_i}^{x_{i+1}} p(x)\, dx, \qquad G_i = h^{-1} \int_{x_{i-1}}^{x_{i+1}} G(x)\phi_i(x)\, dx, \qquad \alpha_0 = \alpha_{N+1} = 0.$$

(i)   Consider the case in which $p \equiv 1$. Then the system becomes

$$-\alpha_{i-1} + 2\alpha_i - \alpha_{i+1} = h^2 G_i, \qquad i = 1, 2, ..., N.$$

To solve this system consider the use of an iterative method in which the residual at the kth iterative step is calculated by

(a) $$r_i^{(k)} = -\alpha_{i-1}^{(k)} + 2\alpha_i^{(k)} - \alpha_{i+1}^{(k)} - h^2 G_i,$$

(b) $$r_i^{(k)} = (\alpha_i^{(k)} - \alpha_{i-1}^{(k)}) - (\alpha_{i+1}^{(k)} - \alpha_i^{(k)}) - h^2 G_i.$$

Prove that in the first case we generally make rounding errors of $O(\varepsilon_M)$ and that in the second case, when the iterates $\alpha_i^{(k)}$ are close enough to the exact solution, the only rounding error in (b) comes from $h^2 G_i$ and is of order $h^2 \varepsilon_M$. (Exercise 7.25 can be used here.)

Prove that the errors in the calculated approximation of the solution due to these rounding errors are

$$\|e\|/\|\alpha\| = O(\|K_h^{-1}\|)\varepsilon_M = O(h^{-2})\varepsilon_M, \qquad \text{case (a)},$$

and

$$\|e\|/\|\alpha\| = O(1)\varepsilon_M, \qquad \text{case (b)},$$

respectively.

(ii)   Now consider the general case in which p is variable and we only have approximations $\tilde{p}_j$ of p_j with errors $\delta_j = p_j - \tilde{p}_j$ at our disposal. The errors can be numerical integration errors and errors due to rounding to finite precision. Prove that the errors in case (a), where

(a) $$r_i^{(k)} = -p_{i-1}\alpha_{i-1}^{(k)} + (p_{i-1} + p_i)\alpha_i^{(k)} - p_i\alpha_{i+1}^{(k)} - h^2 G_i$$

are $O(\delta_i)$ and hence that the corresponding (maximum) errors in α are $O(h^{-2}) \max|\delta_i|$. In case (b) we write the residual in the form

(b)
$$r_i^{(k)} = \tfrac{1}{2}(p_{i-1} + p_i)[(\alpha_i^{(k)} - \alpha_{i-1}^{(k)}) - (\alpha_{i+1}^{(k)} - \alpha_i^{(k)})]$$
$$+ \tfrac{1}{2}(p_i - p_{i-1})[\alpha_{i-1}^{(k)} - \alpha_{i+1}^{(k)}] - h^2 G_i,$$

where we calculate $p_i - p_{i-1}$ in the following way:

$$p_i - p_{i-1} = h^{-1} \int_{x_{i-1}}^{x_i} [p(x + h) - p(x)] \, dx.$$

We assume that $p(x + h) - p(x)$ can be calculated with errors not larger than $O(h)\varepsilon_M + O(h^3)$. If this is not the case we use the approximation

$$p_i - p_{i-1} = \int_{x_{i-1}}^{x_i} p'\left(x + \frac{h}{2}\right) dx + O(h^3).$$

Prove that the errors in $r_i^{(k)}$ in case (b) are then

$$O(h^2)(\max|\delta_j| + \varepsilon_M) + O(h^4).$$

7.27. Using the data in Table 7.5, determine the crossover point between Band–Gauss and SSOR–CG.

References

Arbenz, P. (1982). Computable finite element error bounds for Poisson's equation. *IMA J. Numer. Anal.* **2**, 475–479.

Axelsson, O. (1972). A generalized SSOR method. *BIT* **13**, 443–467.

Axelsson, O. (1979). A generalized conjugate direction method and its application on a singular perturbation problem. *In* "Numerical Analysis" (G. A. Watson, ed.), LNiM vol. 773, pp. 1–11. Springer-Verlag, Berlin and New York.

Axelsson, O. (1980). Conjugate gradient type methods for unsymmetric and inconsistent systems of linear equations. *Linear Algebra Appl.* **29**, 1–16.

Axelsson, O. (1982). On multigrid methods of two-level type. *In* "Multigrid Methods" (W. Hackbusch and U. Trottenberg, eds.), LNiM vol. 960, pp. 352–367. Springer-Verlag, Berlin and New York.

Axelsson, O. (1983). A general incomplete block-matrix factorization method. Report 8337, Department of Mathematics, University of Nijmegen, Nijmegen, The Netherlands.

Axelsson, O., and Gustafsson, I. (1981). A preconditioned conjugate gradient method for finite element equations which is stable for rounding errors. *In* "Information Processing 80" (S. H. Lavington, ed.), pp. 723–728. North-Holland Publ., Amsterdam.

Axelsson, O., and Gustafsson, I. (1983). Preconditioning and two-level multigrid methods of arbitrary degree of approximation. *Math. Comp.* **40**, 219–242.

Axelsson, O., and Nävert, U. (1977). On a graphical package for nonlinear differential equation problems. *In* "Information Processing 77" (B. Gilchrist, ed.), pp. 103–108. North-Holland, Amsterdam.

Axelsson, O., Brinkkemper, S., and Il'in, V. P. (1984). On some versions of incomplete block-matrix factorization iterative methods. Report 8322, Department of Mathematics, University of Nijmegen, Nijmegen, The Netherlands. (To appear in *Linear Algebra Appl.*)

Bank, R. E., and Dupont, T. F. (1980). Analysis of a two-level scheme for solving finite element equations. Report CNA-159, Center for Numerical Analysis, University of Texas at Austin, Austin, Texas.

Bank, R. E., and Dupont, T. F. (1981). An optimal order process for solving finite element equations. *Math. Comp.* **36**, 35–51.

Barnhill, R. E., Brown, J. H., McQueen, N., and Mitchell, A. R. (1977). Computable finite element error bounds for Poisson's equation. *Internat. J. Numer. Methods Engrg.* **11**, 593–603.

Beauwens, R. (1979). On OBV methods. Report 79-10-NAM-01, Department of Electrical Engineering and Computer Science, Northwestern University, Evanston, Illinois.

Beauwens, R. (1984). Upper eigenvalue bounds for pencils of matrices. (To appear in *Linear Algebra Appl.*)

Bollen, J. (1980). Round-off error analysis of descent methods for solving linear equations. Ph. D. Thesis, Department of Mathematics and Informatics, Technical University, Eindhoven, The Netherlands.

Bracha-Barak, A., and Saylor, P. E. (1973). A symmetric factorization procedure for the solution of elliptic boundary value problems. *SIAM J. Numer. Anal.* **10**, 190–206.

Concus, P., Golub, G. H., and Meurant, G. (1982). Block preconditioning for the conjugate gradient method. Report LBL-14856, Lawrence Berkeley Laboratory, University of California, Berkeley, California.

Dendy, J. E., Jr. (1982). Black box multigrid. *J. Comput. Phys.* **48**, 366–386.

Dupont, T., Kendall, R. P., and Rachford, H. H., Jr. (1968). An approximate factorization procedure for solving self-adjoint elliptic difference equations. *SIAM J. Numer. Anal.* **5**, 559–573.

Eisenstat, S. C., Elman, H. C., and Schultz, M. H. (1983). Variational iterative methods for nonsymmetric systems of linear equations. *SIAM J. Numer. Anal.* **20**, 345–361.

George, A., and Liu, J. W. (1981). "Computer Solution of Large Sparse Positive Definite Systems." Prentice-Hall, Englewood Cliffs, New Jersey.

Gordon, W. J., and Hall, C. H. (1973). Construction of curvilinear co-ordinate systems and applications to mesh generation. *Internat. J. Numer. Methods Engrg.* **7**, 461–477.

Gustafsson, I. (1979). Stability and rate of convergence of modified incomplete Cholesky factorization methods. Report 79.02R (Ph.D. Thesis), Department of Computer Sciences, Chalmers University of Technology, Gothenburg, Sweden.

Gustafsson, I. (1983). Modified incomplete Cholesky (MIC) methods. *In* "Preconditioning Methods, Theory and Applications," (D. J. Evans, ed.), pp. 265–294. Gordon and Breach, New York.

Hackbusch, W. (1980). Survey of convergence proofs for multigrid iteration. *In* "Special Topics in Applied Mathematics" (J. Frehse, D. Pallasche, and U. Trottenberg, eds.), pp. 151–164. North-Holland Publ., Amsterdam.

Hackbush, W., and Trottenberg, U., eds. (1982). "Multigrid Methods," LNiM vol. 960. Springer-Verlag, Berlin and New York.

Hageman, L. A., and Young, D. M. (1981). "Applied Iterative Methods." Academic Press, New York.

Hemker, P. (1980). Introduction to multigrid methods. *In* "MC Syllabus: Colloquium Numerical Solution of Partial Differential Equations" (J. G. Verwer, ed.), pp. 59–97. Mathematisch Centrum, Amsterdam.

Hemker, P. W., Kettler, R., Wesseling, P., and de Zeeuw, P. M. (1983). Multigrid methods: developments of fast solvers. Report 83-05, Department of Mathematics and Informatics, Delft University of Technology, The Netherlands.

Kershaw, D. S. (1978). The incomplete Choleski–conjugate gradient method for the iterative solution of systems of linear equations. *J. Comput. Phys.* **26**, 43–65.

Maitre, J. F., and Musy, F. (1982). The contraction number of a class of two-level methods; an exact evaluation for some finite element subspaces and model problems. *In* "Multigrid Methods" (W. Hackbusch and U. Trottenberg, eds.), LNiM vol. 960, pp. 535–544. Springer-Verlag, Berlin and New York.

Manteuffel, T. A. (1980). An incomplete factorization technique for positive definite linear systems. *Math. Comp.* **34**, 473–497.

McCormick, S. F., and Ruge, J. W. (1982). Multigrid methods for variational problems. *SIAM J. Numer. Anal.* **19**, 924–929.

Nicolaides, R. A. (1977). On the l^2 convergence of an algorithm for solving finite element equations. *Math. Comp.* **31**, 892–906.

Saad, Y. (1981). Krylov subspace methods for solving large unsymmetric linear systems. *Math. Comp.* **37**, 105–126.

Wozniakowski, H. (1978). Round-off error analysis of a new class of conjugate gradient algorithms. Report CMU-CS-78-153, Department of Computer Science, Carnegie-Mellon University, Pittsburg, Pennsylvania.

Young, D. M., and Jea, K. C. (1980). Generalized conjugate gradient acceleration of nonsymmetrizable iterative methods. *Linear Algebra Appl.* **34**, 159–194.

Zienkiewicz, O. C. (1977). "The Finite Element Method," 3rd ed. McGraw-Hill, New York.

APPENDIX A

Chebyshev Polynomials

Chebyshev polynomials have a number of uses in numerical analysis. [See, e.g., Achieser (1956), Davis (1963), Fox and Parker (1968), Lanczos (1957), and Varga (1962).] Our brief discussion of them here is tailored to the needs of Section 1.3, in particular Theorem 1.12.

The function

$$\cos(k\theta), \qquad -\pi \le \theta \le \pi,$$

where k is a nonnegative integer, can be expressed as a polynomial of degree k in terms of $\cos(\theta)$. This is obvious for $k = 0, 1$ and follows for all $k > 1$ from the trigonometric identity

$$\cos[(k + 1)\theta] = 2\cos(\theta)\cos(k\theta) - \cos[(k - 1)\theta].$$

The relation

$$\cos(k\theta) = T_k[\cos(\theta)] \tag{A.1}$$

defines the *Chebyshev polynomial* of degree k.

Making the variable transformation

$$x = \cos(\theta), \qquad -\pi \le \theta \le \pi,$$

we see that

$$T_0(x) = 1, \qquad T_1(x) = x,$$

$$T_{k+1}(x) = 2xT_k(x) - T_{k-1}(x), \qquad k = 2, 3, \dots.$$

The first six Chebyshev polynomials are found to be

$$T_0(x) = 1, \qquad T_1(x) = x, \qquad T_2(x) = 2x^2 - 1,$$

$$T_3(x) = 4x^3 - 3x, \qquad T_4(x) = 8x^4 - 8x^2 + 1,$$

$$T_5(x) = 16x^5 - 20x^3 + 5x.$$

Obviously, the domain of definition of these polynomials can be extended from the interval $-1 \le x \le 1$ to arbitrary values of x.

Consider the function

$$\cosh(k\theta) = \tfrac{1}{2}(e^{k\theta} + e^{-k\theta}), \qquad \theta \ge 0.$$

From the relations

$$\cosh(0) = 1 = T_0[\cosh(\theta)], \qquad \cosh(\theta) = T_1[\cosh(\theta)]$$

and the identity

$$\cosh[(k + 1)\theta] = 2 \cosh(\theta) \cosh(k\theta) - \cosh[(k - 1)\theta],$$

we see that

$$\cosh(k\theta) = T_k[\cosh(\theta)].$$

This, combined with (A.1) and consideration of symmetry, yields the following formulas for $T_k(x)$:

$$T_k(x) = \begin{cases} \cos[k \cos^{-1}(x)] & \text{for } -1 \le x \le 1, \quad \text{(A.2a)} \\ \cosh[k \cosh^{-1}(x)] & \text{for } x \ge 1, \quad \text{(A.2b)} \\ (-1)^k \cosh[k \cosh^{-1}(-x)] & \text{for } x \le -1, \quad \text{(A.2c)} \end{cases}$$

or equivalently,

$$T_k(x) = \tfrac{1}{2}[(x + \sqrt{x^2 - 1})^k + (x - \sqrt{x^2 - 1})^k], \qquad -\infty < x < \infty. \quad \text{(A.2d)}$$

Inspection of (A.2a) shows that

$$\max_{-1 \le x \le 1} |T_k(x)| = 1$$

and that

$$T_k(x_i) = (-1)^i, \qquad i = 0, 1, \ldots, k, \qquad \text{(A.3)}$$

where $x_i = \cos(i\pi/k)$. For $|x| > 1$ the value of $|T_k(x)|$ increases rapidly with $|x|$. The following theorem reflects the fact that in a certain sense the rate of increase is maximal among polynomials of degree k.

Theorem A.1. Let Π_k^1 denote the set of kth-degree polynomials with the property $P_k(0) = 1$, and let $b > a > 0$. Then,

$$\max_{a \le x \le b} |\tilde{P}_k(x)| = \min_{P_k \in \Pi_k^1} \max_{a \le x \le b} |P_k(x)|,$$

where

$$\tilde{P}_k(x) = T_k\left(\frac{b + a - 2x}{b - a}\right) \bigg/ T_k\left(\frac{b + a}{b - a}\right).$$

PROOF: Following Varga (1962), suppose that for some $P_k \in \Pi_k^1$ we have

$$\max_{a \le x \le b} |P_k(x)| < \max_{a \le x \le b} |\tilde{P}_k(x)| \tag{A.4}$$

and let

$$r(x) = \tilde{P}_k(x) - P_k(x).$$

The polynomial $T_k[(b + a - 2x)/(b - a)]$ is the generalization of $T_k(-x)$ to the interval $a \le x \le b$. Its absolute value does not exceed unity in this interval, and from (A.3) we see that it oscillates between 1 and -1 on the set of $k + 1$ points

$$a = \tilde{x}_0 < \tilde{x}_1 < \cdots < \tilde{x}_{k-1} < \tilde{x}_k = b,$$

where $\tilde{x}_i = \frac{1}{2}[b + a - (b - a)x_i]$. It follows then from (A.4) that $r(x)$ attains alternately positive and negative values on this set of points and hence has k zeros in the interval $a < x < b$. Further,

$$r(0) = \tilde{P}_k(0) - P_k(0) = 0.$$

Thus, $r(x)$ is a polynomial of degree $\le k$ possessing at least $k + 1$ zeros. Since this is impossible, the theorem is proved. ∎

Theorem 1.12 in Section 1.3 requires that we determine the smallest integer k such that

$$T_k[(b + a)/(b - a)] > 1/\varepsilon$$

for a given value of ε. Using (A.2d) we find that for any $\alpha > 1$,

$$T_k\left(\frac{\alpha + 1}{\alpha - 1}\right) = \frac{1}{2}\left[\left(\frac{\sqrt{\alpha} + 1}{\sqrt{\alpha} - 1}\right)^k + \left(\frac{\sqrt{\alpha} - 1}{\sqrt{\alpha} + 1}\right)^k\right] > \frac{1}{2}\left(\frac{\sqrt{\alpha} + 1}{\sqrt{\alpha} - 1}\right)^k.$$

Hence,

$$k > \ln\left(\frac{2}{\varepsilon}\right) \bigg/ \ln\left(\frac{\sqrt{\alpha} + 1}{\sqrt{\alpha} - 1}\right) \quad \Rightarrow \quad T_k\left(\frac{\alpha + 1}{\alpha - 1}\right) > \frac{1}{\varepsilon}.$$

Since

$$\ln[(\sqrt{\alpha} + 1)/(\sqrt{\alpha} - 1)] > 2/\sqrt{\alpha}, \qquad \alpha > 1,$$

we obtain, putting $\alpha = b/a$,

$$k > \tfrac{1}{2}\sqrt{b/a}\,\ln(2/\varepsilon) \quad \Rightarrow \quad T_k[(b + a)/(b - a)] > 1/\varepsilon. \tag{A.5}$$

References

Achieser, N. I. (1956). "Theory of Approximation." Ungar, New York.

Davis, P. J. (1963). "Interpolation and Approximation." Ginn (Blaisdell), Boston, Massachusetts.

Fox, L., and Parker, I. B. (1968). "Chebyshev Polynomials in Numerical Analysis." Oxford Univ. Press, London and New York.

Lanczos, C. (1957). "Applied Analysis." Prentice-Hall, Englewood Cliffs, New Jersey.

Varga, R. S. (1962). "Matrix Iterative Analysis." Prentice-Hall, Englewood Cliffs, New Jersey.

Index

427

Computer Science and Applied Mathematics
A SERIES OF MONOGRAPHS AND TEXTBOOKS

Editor
Werner Rheinboldt
University of Pittsburgh

HANS P. KÜNZI, H. G. TZSCHACH, AND C. A. ZEHNDER. Numerical Methods of Mathematical Optimization: With ALGOL and FORTRAN Programs, Corrected and Augmented Edition

AZRIEL ROSENFELD. Picture Processing by Computer

JAMES ORTEGA AND WERNER RHEINBOLDT. Iterative Solution of Nonlinear Equations in Several Variables

AZARIA PAZ. Introduction to Probabilistic Automata

DAVID YOUNG. Iterative Solution of Large Linear Systems

ANN YASUHARA. Recursive Function Theory and Logic

JAMES M. ORTEGA. Numerical Analysis: A Second Course

G. W. STEWART. Introduction to Matrix Computations

CHIN-LIANG CHANG AND RICHARD CHAR-TUNG LEE. Symbolic Logic and Mechanical Theorem Proving

C. C. GOTLIEB AND A. BORODIN. Social Issues in Computing

ERWIN ENGELER. Introduction to the Theory of Computation

F. W. J. OLVER. Asymptotics and Special Functions

DIONYSIOS C. TSICHRITZIS AND PHILIP A. BERNSTEIN. Operating Systems

A. T. BERZTISS. Data Structures: Theory and Practice, Second Edition

N. CHRISTOPHIDES. Graph Theory: An Algorithmic Approach

SAKTI P. GHOSH. Data Base Organization for Data Management

DIONYSIOS C. TSICHRITZIS AND FREDERICK H. LOCHOVSKY. Data Base Management Systems

JAMES L. PETERSON. Computer Organization and Assembly Language Programming

WILLIAM F. AMES. Numerical Methods for Partial Differential Equations, Second Edition

ARNOLD O. ALLEN. Probability, Statistics, and Queueing Theory: With Computer Science Applications

ELLIOTT I. ORGANICK, ALEXANDRA I. FORSYTHE, AND ROBERT P. PLUMMER. Programming Language Structures

NOV 0 4 1991